Life and Death Responsibilities in Jewish Biomedical Ethics

Edited by
Aaron L. Mackler

The Louis Finkelstein Institute
The Jewish Theological Seminary of America
New York 2000

ISBN 0-87334-081-7
Printing and Binding by G & H Soho Inc.

Contents

II. Responsibilities for Fetal Life

III. Responsibilities at the End of Life

Foreword

With characteristic foresight, Dr. Louis Finkelstein, *z"l,* late chancellor of the Jewish Theological Seminary, created the Institute of Social and Religious Studies. It was his response, in 1937, to the growing threat of ideologies of hate that were engulfing Europe and that would trigger the horrors of a world conflagration. His design of an academic institute that would allow scholars and activists of all persuasions to engage in dialogue and study was unique at that time and has set a standard for such endeavors in the ensuing years.

The conferences and meetings, sponsored by the Institute, examined a wide variety of societal issues: government and politics, labor, communications, intergroup relations, and so on. All these issues were examined through the prism of religious or secular ethics. These deliberations set a standard for frank but respectful conversation among thinkers of every orientation. An important part of that process was a publication program. The Institute sponsored a number of volumes that are of value to this day. A rereading of them reveals insights that have contemporary impact from important voices of the past.

Through a generous gift from Mr. Louis Stein, of blessed memory, the Institute of Social and Religious Studies was renamed in honor and in memory of Dr. Finkelstein. In the tradition of Dr. Finkelstein's response to the challenge of his day, the current chancellor of the Seminary, Dr. Ismar Schorsch, has expanded the Finkelstein Institute program to create an in-depth exploration of Judaism's ethical insights into modern advances in medical technology. Bioethics, a relatively new academic discipline that is concerned with the moral implications of this technology, has become a major category of study and response in an astonishingly short amount of time. Ethical issues in medicine are a familiar theme in Judaism. The Jewish people's long association with medical care as a healing art has produced a wealth of ethical-legal responsa. They are valuable tools as we are currently confronted with perplexing issues that involve end-of-life care, reproductive techniques, genetics, health care delivery, caregiving, and so forth.

The Finkelstein Institute is pleased to renew its publication program with a valuable collection of responsa from the Bioethics Subcommittee of the Committee on Jewish Law and Standards. They reflect the insights of scholars of the Conservative movement as they apply the principles of commitment to halakhah coupled with respect for the insights and demands of modern technology and societal concerns. This volume is a major chapter in the storied history of responsa literature as well as a vital guide for rabbis, the Jewish community, and the health care community. Of special value are the introductory essays to the responsa, written by the editor, Rabbi Aaron Mackler. Bridging the technical terms of rabbinics and medicine, they allow members of both communities to study traditional Jewish bioethics as it is applied to modern scientific insights, techniques, and challenges.

This volume indicates the vitality of the Conservative movement as it applies halakhic responses to some of the most perplexing issues of our age. The volume is a welcomed example of the commitment of the Finkelstein Institute to renew and continue its traditional publication sponsorship of ethical guides for the Jewish and general communities.

Rabbi Gerald I. Wolpe
Director
Louis Finkelstein Institute
of the Jewish Theological Seminary

Acknowledgments

This book represents the fruits of collaborative efforts extending back more than a decade. Thanks must go first to the authors of the papers included in this volume, and to the entire membership of the Rabbinical Assembly's Committee on Jewish Law and Standards, which contributed to the development of these works. Special recognition goes to Rabbi Kassel Abelson, chair of the Committee, who originally suggested the idea for this volume; and to Rabbis Elliot Dorff and Avram Reisner, who have been leaders in the Committee's work on bioethics, and whose writings are richly represented in this collection.

The Rabbinical Assembly has graciously offered permission for the publication of these essays and has provided invaluable help in the preparation of this book. Special thanks go to Rabbi Joel Meyers, Executive Vice President; Rabbi Jan Caryl Kaufman, Director of Special Projects; and Rabbi David Fine, Secretary to the Committee.

I appreciate the support of Rabbi Ismar Schorsch, Chancellor of the Jewish Theological Seminary of America, and Rabbi Gerald Wolpe, Director of the Finkelstein Institute, which has made publication of this volume possible. Dr. Alan Cooper, Director of the Jewish Theological Seminary Press, has skillfully managed the publication of this volume. Janice Meyerson as copy editor has contributed to the clarity and elegance of the book, and Rabbi Raymond Scheindlin has supervised the accuracy and consistency of transliterations. It has been a pleasure working with and learning from all of these individuals.

On a personal note, I would like to acknowledge the support and friendship of my colleagues in the Theology Department at Duquesne University. I also would like to thank my children, Hannah, Joel, and Daniel, for their patience and encouragement during my involvement in this project. My wife, Lorraine, has offered many suggestions that have strengthened the material I have written, and has assisted me with legal research. I am immensely grateful for her love and support.

Finally, I am thankful to have the opportunity to acknowledge my debt of gratitude to my parents and teachers, Dr. Hyman and Ruth Mackler. This volume is dedicated in their honor.

Pittsburgh, Pennsylvania A.L.M.
January 2000
Shevat 5760

• • •

All numbered chapters were prepared for the Committee on Jewish Law and Standards of the Rabbinical Assembly and are printed here by permission of the Rabbinical Assembly. Chapters 10–14 have appeared in the *Proceedings of the Committee on Jewish Law and Standards: 1980–85,* ed. Kassel Abelson (New York: Rabbinical Assembly, 1988). Chapters 9, 15–23, and 32 are scheduled to appear in the *Proceedings of the Committee on Jewish Law and Standards: 1986–90,* ed. Kassel Abelson (New York: Rabbinical Assembly, forthcoming). Chapters 1–8, 24–26, and 28–31 are scheduled to appear in forthcoming volumes of the *Proceedings.*

Versions of chapters 1–3 appeared as "Artificial Insemination, Egg Donation, and Adoption," *Conservative Judaism* 49, no. 1 (1996): 3–60, and in Elliot N. Dorff, *Matters of Life and Death: A Jewish Approach to Modern Medical Ethics* (Philadelphia: Jewish Publication Society, 1998), 35–115.

Significant material from chapter 4 has appeared in "An Expanded Partnership with God? In Vitro Fertilization in Jewish Ethics," *Journal of Religious Ethics* 25 (1997): 277–304.

Significant material from chapter 6 has appeared in " 'Through Her I Too Shall Bear a Child': Birth Surrogates in Jewish Law," *Journal of Religious Ethics* 24 (1996): 65–97.

Significant material from chapter 7 has appeared in "Comment on ' "Through Her I Too Shall Bear a Child": Birth Surrogates in Jewish Law,' " *Journal of Religious Ethics* 27 (1999): 361–66.

Chapter 15 has appeared as "Mai Beinaihu?" *Conservative Judaism* 43, no. 3 (1991): 90–91.

A version of chapters 16–17 appeared as "A Halakhic Ethic of Care for the Terminally Ill," *Conservative Judaism* 43, no. 3 (1991): 52–89.

A version of chapters 18–20 appeared as "A Jewish Approach to End-Stage Medical Care," *Conservative Judaism* 43, no. 3 (1991): 3–51. Significant material from these chapters appeared in Dorff, *Matters of Life and Death*, 167–241.

Chapters 21 and 22 have appeared in *Conservative Judaism* 43, no. 3 (1991): 92–94 and 95–96.

Chapter 23 was published by the Rabbinical Assembly in 1994 and is currently available through the United Synagogue Book Service.

Versions of chapter 26 were published as "*Teshuvah* on Assisted Suicide," *Conservative Judaism* 50, no. 4 (1998): 3–24, and in Dorff, *Matters of Life and Death*, 176–98.

A version of chapter 27 appeared in Isaac Klein, *Responsa and Halakhic Studies* (New York: Ktav, 1975), 34–42.

Chapter 29 was published by the Rabbinical Assembly in 1996 and is currently available from the Rabbinical Assembly.

Abbreviations Used in This Volume

B. = Babylonian Talmud
CJLS = the Committee on Jewish Law and Standards
E.H. = *Even Ha'ezer*
Ḥ.M. = *Ḥoshen Mishpat*
J. = Jerusalem (Palestinian) Talmud
M. = Mishnah
M.T. = *Mishneh Torah*
O.Ḥ. = *Oraḥ Ḥayyim*
S.A. = *Shulḥan Arukh*
T. = Tosefta
Y.D. = *Yoreh De'ah*

Introduction

Aaron L. Mackler

When may artificial technologies be used to help create human life? Is abortion ever morally right? When should life-sustaining treatment be stopped? How extensive are my responsibilities to support the health needs of others? Technological and social developments have placed these questions at the center of society's concerns and in the middle of people's lives. Our answers will shape the values and institutions of society and will literally make the difference between life and death for many of its members. The United States and other nations have explored these issues through courts and commissions, through legislative debate and private deliberations of conscience.

In the Jewish tradition, the central means of addressing these concerns is through halakhah, or Jewish law. While the insights of halakhah are central to the lives of many Jews, these perspectives have also been found valuable by persons of other religious traditions and secular outlooks. This volume presents papers on biomedical ethics that integrate the resources of millennia with the most recent developments in medicine and ethical thought. The papers include some of the most thoughtful and important works in Jewish medical ethics on such issues as treatment decisions near the end of life, abortion, and reproductive technologies. Each paper is the product of a particular author, but all have been discussed and authorized by the Rabbinical Assembly's Committee on Jewish Law and Standards, halakhic guide for the Conservative (centrist) movement, as discussed below. The papers appear in the final form as completed by the author and approved by the Committee.

(Headings have been added where appropriate, and some longer papers have been divided into two or three parts.)

The papers are presented in four general divisions, most of which are divided into a number of topical sections. Each section begins with an introduction summarizing the documents and highlighting points of special interest, including conclusions of practical application. The first division is "Responsibilities in the Creation of Life," with sections discussing artificial insemination, in vitro fertilization, and surrogate motherhood. The second division, "Responsibilities for Fetal Life," contains papers on abortion. The longest division is called "Responsibilities at the End of Life," and its sections present extensive discussions of medical care at the end of life, shorter works reflecting on and developing these basic positions, and consideration of physician-assisted suicide and euthanasia. The final division, "Responsibilities for the Health Needs of Others," addresses organ transplantation and autopsy, and new challenges involving genetic engineering, smoking, and responsibilities for providing health care.

This introduction will begin with a discussion of the significance of a halakhic approach to contemporary bioethical issues. Next, attention will be given to developments over the past decades in health care and biology that have posed challenges to the halakhic method and that have suggested anew some strengths of this approach. Consideration will be given as well to special characteristics of approaches to Jewish law and ethics in the Conservative movement, as well as the Rabbinical Assembly's Committee on Jewish Law and Standards. The introduction will conclude with a brief orientation to classical halakhic literature.

1. Jewish ethics and Jewish law. Ethical concerns have always been central to Judaism and have been understood within the broad context of Jewish life. Basic concepts in Judaism include: God; Torah, or "teaching"; and the community of Israel, the Jewish people. For Jews and Jewish thinkers across a wide spectrum of beliefs, individuals as well as the Jewish community as a whole participate in a covenantal relationship with God. Torah is central to this relationship and basic to Jewish life. In its narrowest sense, Torah refers to the first five books of the Bible, Genesis through Deuteronomy, traditionally termed the "Written Torah." More broadly, Torah includes the extensive "Oral Torah," and refers to all Jewish traditional teaching—in fact, all authentic Jewish thought and practice.[1]

Jewish ethics has been understood within this context, not sharply distinguished from other spheres of life. As one example, the mandate to "love your neighbor as yourself" is found within the Holiness Code (*parashat Kedoshim*) of the Book of Leviticus (19:18). The general injunction of this section is: "You shall be holy, for I, the Lord your God, am holy" (Lev. 19:2). This call to holiness provides the basis for responsibilities that we would identify as ethical, such as positive obligations to revere parents, to leave corners of one's field unharvested for the poor to take, and to maintain honest weights for commerce; and prohibitions against stealing and standing idly by as the blood of one's fellow is shed. These are intermixed with injunctions that could be characterized as ritual: to observe the Sabbath; not to worship idols; not to eat meat from sacrifices on the wrong day. Both ethical and ritual perspectives are important in answering the question, "What ought I to do?" For this code, as for the Jewish tradition in general, all aspects of our activities meld together holistically in a life of service to God and our fellow.

Two additional features of the Holiness Code may be noted. First, the passage is introduced by God instructing Moses, "Speak to the whole Israelite community, and say to them . . ." (Lev. 19:2). The call to holiness, and all that follows, are not understood exclusively or even primarily as pertaining to individuals, but to an entire community. Second, the commitment to holiness entails particular behavioral norms that are expected of individuals and the community. Such norms are traditionally termed *mitzvot* (singular, *mitzvah,* "commandment"). A mitzvah is a shared normative practice, expressing what members of the Jewish community may expect from one another. As well, in the words of Abraham Heschel, "a mitzvah is an act which God and man have in common."[2]

Each mitzvah contributes to a system of *halakhah,* a word literally meaning "path" or "way," and signifying Jewish law. Halakhah has been central to Judaism's ethical teachings for a number of reasons. Halakhah's role as a legal system provides for cohesion and a sense of community among Jews worldwide, as well as within local communities. It offers continuity with the past, maintaining cohesion of the covenantal community over time, and affording contemporary individuals the benefit of accumulated wisdom of the past. Halakhah traditionally has been understood to express God's will and God's wise and beneficent counsel. Finally, the very fact of the centrality of halakhah to Jewish ethics over the millennia might be seen as itself carrying normative weight. A halakhically centered approach simply is the Jewish way to do ethics; to use Wittgenstein's image, such are the rules of the language game of Jewish ethics.[3]

Although halakhah has been central to Jewish life and thought, it has never been exclusive. Accompanying halakhah has been *aggadah,* or narrative. This term broadly refers to Jewish theological reflection, lore, articulation of values, expressions of meaning, and cultivation of virtues. Returning to the Holiness Code of Leviticus 19, Moses Naḥmanides (fourteenth century) writes that the opening call to holiness is not merely a classificatory heading, but an injunction in its own right. Without this, a person might observe all rules and yet be "a scoundrel with Torah license."[4] The call to holiness includes, but also goes beyond, the specific norms of halakhah. While there may at times be tension between halakhah and aggadah, between the letter and the spirit of the law, the relation is essentially symbiotic.[5] In Heschel's image, halakhah is like a body, while aggadah is spirit. Halakhah without aggadah, its animating spirit, is like a corpse. Aggadah without halakhah, its worldly concretization, is like a ghost, too ethereal to be realized.[6]

2. *Contemporary challenges and opportunities.* Ideally, rules and values, halakhah and aggadah, accord. The law is a primary source of ethical guidance and helps to determine which ethical values are most authentic and worthy of our commitment. Halakhah reflects our best ethical insights and develops in response to ethical values of aggadah.

At times, though, halakhah and aggadah diverge: our best available understanding of halakhah does not fit our best available understanding of aggadah. In such cases, further reflection on our rules, our values, or both is required. In some cases, the best application or interpretation of halakhah may be uncertain. It may be unclear how to understand or specify ethical values, or how to balance competing ethical considerations. Like all legal systems, halakhah must develop new applications when unprecedented situations arise. New ethical insights may develop over time, leading to reconsideration of previous norms and growth of the tradition.

Contemporary developments in health care and science pose significant challenges for halakhah. With new technologies, new activities are possible, so new questions are confronted. When, if ever, would the use of in vitro fertilization to have a child be warranted? Is it appropriate to alter plants and animals by genetic engineering? A few decades ago, respirators could not prolong the life of dying patients, and little could be done to treat severely disabled newborns. Now that new interventions are technically possible, should they be pursued? New social arrangements may also pose challenges—for example, how should Jewish law and ethics respond to rapid and ongoing changes in the delivery and financing of health care?

Biomedical issues confront halakhic approaches, like all ethical and legal approaches, with the challenge of uncharted territory. Answers that were formulated in a radically different context may no longer be the best answers; minimally, they would need to be understood and applied in new ways. Traditional halakhah, like secular case law, utilizes analogies with precedent cases to decide new cases. With many medical developments, such as organ transplantation and reproductive technologies, precedents may be too remote to offer extensive guidance. Indeed, for these and other reasons, some Jewish thinkers have argued that Jewish ethical approaches in biomedical ethics should not center on halakhah.[7]

At the same time, developments in science and health care offer new grounds for attending to Jewish ethics and to halakhic methodology. While Jewish ethics encounters challenges in responding to new developments, so do all ethical and legal approaches. Much of bioethics touches on our most profound concerns: questions of life and death, of what makes human life valuable, of the place of humanity in the universe. These are the types of questions with which religions such as Judaism have grappled for millennia. In the words of ethicist Daniel Callahan, to ignore religious views in public deliberations on bioethics leaves us "bereft of the accumulated wisdom and knowledge that are the fruit of long-established religious traditions. I do not have to be a Jew to find it profitable and illuminating to see how the great rabbinical teachers have tried to understand moral problems over the centuries."[8]

Especially in the past, some have eschewed an explicitly Jewish ethical stance in favor of what was perceived as a more objective or universalist approach. Developments in philosophy as well as in society have led to increased awareness that all moral reasoning occurs within a particular context and reflects a particular tradition. There is no available neutral stance of "just plain ethics" that can be pursued in a purely objective manner, abstracting from all particular viewpoints such as Judaism. With this awareness has come greater interest on the part of many in listening to perspectives of Jewish ethics, offering distinct contributions within a broader conversation.[9]

Furthermore, while developments in health care have pointed out limitations in the case-reasoning methodology of traditional halakhah, with its attention to precedent and analogy, contemporary experience has revealed problems with other approaches. Relying on intuitions or common sense has a place in ethical decision making but is not sufficient to deal with the complexities and unprecedented challenges of bioethics. A strategy of simply applying general values and principles, while attractive, faces problems as well. Many in philosophical bioethics and clinical ethics have criticized approaches that seek to establish basic principles and to deduce rules and resolve particular cases on the basis of this foundation. "Applied ethics" models that focus on theory and foundational principles have been condemned as making inflated claims regarding their principles, and as producing simplistic and inequitable decisions, or failing to provide guidance for real patients in real cases. A focus on broad and abstract norms fails to provide the sensitive and prudent guidance needed in an individual case and leads instead to speculative irrelevance or overly blunt imposition of generalizations. These concerns have led to arguments for a return to particular cases and casuistical approaches in bioethics, focusing on the details of cases and looking to analogical reasoning and case judgments, strikingly similar to the methodology of traditional halakhah.[10]

3. Conservative approaches to halakhah. Well before the challenges of contemporary biomedical advances, another powerful set of challenges to traditional halakhah arose with the emergence of modernity. Radical changes occurred in the relationships of Jews and non-Jews, and in the social conditions of Jews and Jewish communities. For most of Judaism's history, Jews lived in independent Jewish communities, or semiautonomous communities within a broader corporate state. Since about 1800, large and growing numbers of Jews came to have the status of individual citizens within secular states.[11] The advent of modernity entailed radically new ideas and a radically new life situation. The three largest movements of Judaism in the United States have their roots in responses to modernity in nineteenth-century Germany. Representatives of each movement tend to see their movement as in many ways the most authentic Jewish approach, as well as the path offering the best prospects for the future. Each movement is complex and includes a broad range of stances. The following simplified descriptions are intended only to convey a general sense of tendencies common within each.

Reform Judaism is the most left-wing of the three major movements. This approach originated with a sense that, as Judaism changed radically in the past, radical changes are called for by modern developments. The Written Torah text (Genesis through Deuteronomy) is divinely inspired in some sense but is predominantly the work of human hands. Throughout the history of Reform Judaism, autonomy has been central to the articulation of Jewish ethics. Autonomy has taken various forms: a Kantian sense of the individual following dictates of universal reason; an individual liberty right of choice; a complex Jewish self, authentically making choices that reflect an identity that is largely shaped by community and covenant with God.[12] In recent decades, some Reform thinkers have accepted an increased role for halakhah in offering guidance to individuals, but individual autonomy remains predominant.

Orthodox Judaism, the most right-wing of the major movements, developed as a movement in response to Reform. While modernity may bring benefits, it poses threats to the integrity of Judaism. In response to changes among Jews as well as in the broader world, lines of practice and belief are to be sharpened. Tendencies to emphasize the role of received tradition over reason, halakhah over aggadah, and stringency over flexibility are common in Orthodoxy. Torah in general, and halakhah in particular, are essentially unchanging. Typically, the text of the Written Torah is understood to have been presented by God to Moses, word by word and letter by letter, in a form identical to our printed text.[13] Oral Torah is understood primarily in terms of its articulation in the Talmud (based on material communicated by God to Moses) and received now as tradition from the past. While new situations may call for thoughtful application of past precedents, Orthodox leaders tend to emphasize the need for caution and a desire to minimize change.

The Conservative movement also developed as a traditionalist response to Reform, but of a more centrist sort. Torah (both Written and Oral) is divine in its origin, but is shaped significantly by human reception, transmission, and interpretation.[14] Halakhah plays a definitive role in Jewish life and Jewish ethics. At the same time, halakhah has historically developed over time, through gradual evolution, and by means of textual and judicial interpretation. Such development, by such means, should continue; the model is one of "tradition and change." Moreover, while halakhah is central, significant weight is given to values of aggadah and to each individual's conscientious judgment.

Compared with those of other Jewish movements, Conservative writings on halakhah tend to exhibit certain characteristics. (Many of these are a matter of degree and vary widely among individual authors, so that particular Conservative writings may be virtually indistinguishable from some Orthodox or some Reform works.) Conservative writers characteristically attend to the historical development of halakhah. While Torah is in some sense eternal, it develops in a way that manifests its strength and vitality as a living tradition. Past sources are read diachronically, tracing streams within the tradition and often finding divergent tendencies as well as ongoing development. Development has been, and should continue to be, organic, gradual, and evolutionary.

Conservative halakhic writings also tend to reflect a self-consciousness that halakhic decision making is often a matter of interpretation. Positions generally are not presented monolithically, as simply "the" Jewish position. Each writer presents what he or she judges to be the best interpretation and best halakhic decision. Attention is given to textual sources, tradition, ethical values, theological concepts, contemporary circumstances, and the needs of individuals and the Jewish community. The best way to realize and balance these values is a complex, often disputed matter.[15]

Finally, Conservative writings on issues such as those arising in contemporary health care tend to devote conscious attention to ethical values. The primary source of ethical values in these works is the Jewish tradition, in explicit statements of aggadah and in values implicit in halakhah (and aggadic narrative). At the same time, ethical reflections of non-Jewish thinkers are to be considered as well: those of health care professionals and of thinkers in general bioethics, philosophy, and varied religious traditions. Such sources are not determinative of Jewish ethics, and in some cases contrasts are drawn between Jewish and other views. Still, these sources are acknowledged, discussed, and learned from, in the spirit of Ben Zoma in *Ethics of the Fathers* (*Pirkei Avot*, third century): "Who is wise? One who learns from every person."[16]

4. The Committee on Jewish Law and Standards. The model of halakhic decision making sketched above is one of seeking the best interpretation, given relevant circumstances. One should not expect a simple answer to complex issues. At times, more than one interpretation may be plausible, or different judgments may be appropriate in different sets of circumstances. On the other hand, not every conceivable claim is plausible, and some judgments are better than others. The model is one of pluralism, but not relativism.

This understanding has influenced the approach of the Committee on Jewish Law and Standards, halakhic guide of the Conservative movement. The Committee's membership includes twenty-five rabbis affiliated with the Conservative movement. They are appointed by the president of the Rabbinical Assembly, representing the movement's rabbis; the chancellor of the Jewish Theological Seminary of America, which trains most Conservative rabbis as well as other educators and leaders; and the United Synagogue of Conservative Judaism, representing Conservative congregations. The majority of rabbis on the Committee serve congregations, though a number come from academia or Jewish institutional life. Five lay individuals, as well as one cantor, contribute to the Committee's deliberations as nonvoting members. The Committee's membership comes primarily from North America, but it serves a central role in providing guidance for Conservative Judaism worldwide.

The papers included in this volume, like other papers of the Committee, are written by individual authors, but reflect input from the Committee's entire membership. Typically, an author will write a paper and present it to the Committee for discussion. The author will revise the paper in response to this discussion, utilizing insights raised and responding to concerns presented, according to his or her own judgment. For papers addressing issues in biomedical ethics, this process is preceded by discussion among members of the Subcommittee on Bioethics. The revised paper is presented again to the Committee for further discussion, and for the Committee's decision on whether the paper should be authorized as an approved paper of the Committee. While most papers garner the support of a majority, any paper that receives at least six votes is recognized as an authorized paper of the Committee.

Accordingly, on some issues, more than one paper may be approved by the Committee. In some instances, papers may not essentially disagree, but may offer different nuances or explore differing aspects of a broader issue. The papers on abortion in section D of this volume offer examples. On other complex issues, authors may disagree on the best interpretation and direction of development for Jewish law. Papers on surrogate motherhood in section C reflect this situation. Here, the Committee judged that each position was acceptable as a plausible (or probable) position. Papers on medical care at the end of life in section E represent positions that overlap significantly, but also differ on important points. When more than one paper is authorized, a summary statement is generally adopted (chapters 5, 10, 15).

The positions authorized by the Committee offer important guidance for Conservative Jews and others. Still, each Conservative rabbi has the authority to make halakhic judgments. Each rabbi formulates decisions about numerous issues not discussed explicitly by the Committee, relying on other halakhic sources and his or her own judgment.

For issues the Committee has addressed, each rabbi may choose among various positions endorsed by the Committee, or may even find a different position best mandated by halakhah. On most matters, a congregation's rabbi functions as *mara d'atra,* the halakhic authority for that local community. Furthermore, while halakhah presents important communal guidelines that are seen as normative, a significant component of ethical decision making rests with each individual's conscientious and reflective judgment.

5. *Classical halakhic sources.* All the papers in this volume draw on, and represent the continuation of, a tradition extending back thousands of years.[17] The Written Torah provides the ultimate foundation of the halakhic system. Other books of the Hebrew Bible (termed *Tanakh* in Hebrew and called the Old Testament by some in English) are important for later development of halakhah but do not have the same foundational status. The works of Oral Torah are manifold, representing a variety of forms of literature. The *Mishnah* (meaning "study") was compiled in the early third century by Rabbi Judah Hanasi, presenting material that developed and was transmitted orally over the preceding centuries. The Mishnah consists primarily of a listing of halakhic positions attributed to different halakhic authorities, especially those of the second century, organized topically in a number of *masekhtot* (singular, *masekhet,* "tractate"). The *Tosefta* ("addition") is a supplemental and less authoritative collection of materials from this period, edited later in the fourth or fifth century. A particular section of the Mishnah is referred to as a mishnah; a statement from this period that does not appear in the Mishnah is termed a *baraita* ("outside").

Another type of literature is represented by *midrash* ("search"), offering creative and interpretive commentaries on the Hebrew Bible. Prominent collections of halakhic midrash are the *Mekhilta* (on Exodus), *Sifra* (on Leviticus), and *Sifre* (on Numbers and Deuteronomy); these were compiled in the fourth or fifth century but contain earlier material. Numerous works of aggadic midrash developed over subsequent centuries.

The *Talmud* (like Mishnah, a term meaning "study") is in many ways the central work of the halakhic tradition. It records commentary on and discussion stemming from the Mishnah, developing over succeeding centuries. The Babylonian Talmud, compiled in Babylonia (currently Iraq) in the sixth and seventh centuries, is most authoritative, and is often referred to simply as "the Talmud." The Jerusalem Talmud, also referred to as the "Talmud of the Land of Israel" or "Palestinian Talmud," was compiled in northern Israel in the fifth century.

Three types of post-talmudic literature offer the most significant contributions to the fabric of Jewish law. One genre represents *commentaries* on the Talmud. The best-known and most influential commentary is that of Rashi (Rabbi Shlomo Yitzḥaki, eleventh century). This commentary is printed together with the talmudic text in standard editions of the Talmud. Also appearing in the standard edition are commentaries of Rashi's grandchildren and others known as the *Tosafot* ("additions"). Numerous additional commentaries have been developed over the centuries as well.

A second major genre is that of *responsa,* in Hebrew, *teshuvot* (singular, *teshuvah,* "response"). These are the halakhic decisions of rabbinic authorities, addressing specific issues or cases, and collectively constituting the case law of Judaism. The papers in this volume represent contemporary examples of this genre. Many are structured explicitly in the form of a statement of a question (*she'eilah*) and the development of a response (*teshuvah*).

A third genre is represented by legal codes. Codes are not formally enacted, but come to be recognized as authoritative, similar to the way in which the *Oxford English Dictionary* and the *Encyclopaedia Britannica* have come to be recognized as authoritative. The first major systematic codification was produced by Maimonides (Rambam, Rabbi Moshe ben Maimon) in the twelfth century and is known as the *Mishneh Torah* (*M.T.*) ("repetition of the teaching"). The fourteenth century saw the *Arba'ah Turim* ("four columns") of Rabbi Jacob ben Asher; both the work and its author are often referred to as the "*Tur.*" This work is divided into four major sections: *Oraḥ Ḥayyim* (*O.Ḥ.*), presenting laws on prayer, the Sabbath, and festivals; *Yoreh De'ah* (*Y.D.*), dealing with diverse laws, including those on kosher dietary practices, as well as laws of visiting the sick and providing medical treatment; *Even Ha'ezer* (*E.H.*), addressing marriage and sexuality; and *Ḥoshen Mishpat* (*Ḥ.M.*), presenting laws related to business and legal procedures.

The most authoritative code of law is the *Shulḥan Arukh* (*S.A.*) ("set table"), written by Rabbi Joseph Karo in the sixteenth century. This work follows the organization of the *Tur,* and draws on Karo's monumental commentary (the *Beit Yosef*) on this work. Karo's code reflects Sephardic practices, those of Jews historically associated with

Spain and the Mediterranean. Karo's text is published with interspersed glosses of Rabbi Moses Isserles, termed the *Mappah* ("tablecloth" for the set table), which reflect the customs of Ashkenazic Jews, those historically associated with Germany and Eastern Europe. Karo intended his work as a definitive statement of halakhah, and it has achieved this status to a remarkable extent. At the same time, the *Shulḥan Arukh* itself has spawned numerous commentaries, many of which are printed together with the Karo/Isserles text in the standard edition. Numerous halakhic codes have appeared over the centuries since the *Shulḥan Arukh*. The tradition of commentaries, codes, and responsa continues to develop to this day, as reflected by the papers in this volume.

Notes

1. According to one challenging but rich statement, "even that which a student in the future would teach in the presence of his teacher was already said to Moses at Sinai" (J. *Pe'ah* 17a). See also B. *Menaḥot* 29b.
2. Abraham Joshua Heschel, *God in Search of Man* (New York: Farrar, Straus and Giroux, 1955), 287.
3. For further material on the significance of halakhah in Jewish ethics, see the sources cited in n. 15 below, as well as Elliot Dorff's discussion in chap. 18 of this vol., and Louis E. Newman, "Ethics as Law, Law as Religion: Reflections on the Problem of Law and Ethics in Judaism," in *Contemporary Jewish Ethics and Morality,* ed. Elliot N. Dorff and Louis E. Newman (New York: Oxford University Press, 1995), 79–93.
4. Naḥmanides, commentary to Lev. 19:2, in *Perushei Hatorah Lerabenu Moshe ben Naḥman,* ed. Chaim Dov Chavel (Jerusalem: Mossad Harav Kook, 1960), 2:115.
5. In dealing with *tzedakah* (support for the poor), for example, halakhah prescribes fixed amounts that individuals are obligated to give, while aggadah emphasizes the importance of generosity and compassion.
6. Heschel, 341.
7. David H. Ellenson, "How to Draw Guidance from a Heritage: Jewish Approaches to Mortal Choices," in *A Time to Be Born and a Time to Die: The Ethics of Choice,* ed. Barry S. Kogan (New York: Aldine de Gruyter, 1991), 219–32; reprinted in Dorff and Newman, eds., *Contemporary Jewish Ethics and Morality,* 129–39.
8. Daniel Callahan, "Religion and the Secularization of Bioethics," *Hastings Center Report* 20, no. 3, supp. (1990): 4.
9. See, e.g., Jeffrey Stout, *Ethics After Babel* (Boston: Beacon, 1988); Lisa Sowle Cahill, "Can Theology Have a Role in 'Public' Bioethical Discourse?" *Hastings*

Center Report 20, no. 3, supp. (1990): 10–14; David Novak, "Bioethics and the Contemporary Jewish Community," *Hastings Center Report* 20, no. 3, supp. (1990): 14–17; Louis E. Newman, *Past Imperatives: Studies in the History and Theory of Jewish Ethics* (Albany: State University of New York Press, 1998), 101–15, 205–20; Noam J. Zohar, *Alternatives in Jewish Bioethics* (Albany: State University of New York Press, 1997), 1–16; Laurie Zoloth-Dorfman, "Face to Face, Not Eye to Eye: Further Conversations on Jewish Medical Ethics," *Journal of Clinical Ethics* 6 (1995): 222–31.

10. See, e.g., Albert R. Jonsen and Stephen Toulmin, *The Abuse of Casuistry: A History of Moral Reasoning* (Berkeley: University of California Press, 1988); Baruch A. Brody, *Life and Death Decision Making* (New York: Oxford University Press, 1988); Elliot N. Dorff, "A Methodology for Jewish Medical Ethics," in Dorff and Newman, eds., *Contemporary Jewish Ethics and Morality,* 161–76; and Aaron L. Mackler, "Cases and Principles in Jewish Bioethics: Toward a Holistic Model," in ibid., 177–93.
11. For most of the past two thousand years, Jews were discriminated against to one extent or another, oppressed or at best tolerated by what was experienced as an external non-Jewish world. Jewish ethics accordingly focused on the relation of Jews with other Jews. The tradition includes some discussions of the ethical responsibilities of all persons, understood through a model of God's covenant with "the children of Noah," i.e., with all humanity. This literature was very limited, however, for until recent times, virtually no non-Jews were interested in considering ethical insights emerging from the Jewish tradition. While ethical responsibilities of Jews toward non-Jews are discussed, these tended to fit a model of a responsible but distant ethics of strangers, reflecting the real-life context of the time. Halakhah is not understood as binding on non-Jews. Still, halakhah may be a valuable resource, as Callahan's remarks above suggest.
12. See Eugene B. Borowitz, *Exploring Jewish Ethics* (Detroit: Wayne State University Press, 1990), 22–25, 176–92.
13. See Norman Lamm's statement in *The Condition of Jewish Belief* (New York: Macmillan, 1966), 124–25.
14. See Elliot N. Dorff, *Conservative Judaism: From Our Ancestors to Our Descendants* (New York: United Synagogue of America, 1977); Neil Gillman, *Conservative Judaism* (West Orange, N.J.: Behrman House, 1993), and *Sacred Fragments: Recovering Theology for the Modern Jew* (Philadelphia: Jewish Publication Society, 1990).
15. See, e.g., Seymour Siegel, ed., *Conservative Judaism and Jewish Law* (New York: Rabbinical Assembly, 1977); Dorff, "A Methodology for Jewish Medical Ethics"; Joel Roth, *The Halakhic Process: A Systemic Analysis* (New York: Jewish Theological Seminary of America, 1986); Gordon Tucker, "God, the Good, and Halakhah," *Judaism* 38 (1989): 365–76; Mackler, "Cases and Principles in Jewish Bioethics."

16. M. *Avot* 4:1.
17. For more on classical sources, see David M. Feldman, *Birth Control in Jewish Law,* rev. ed. (Northvale, N.J.: Jason Aronson, 1998), 3–18; *Back to the Sources: Reading the Classic Jewish Texts,* ed. Barry W. Holtz (New York: Summit, 1984); and relevant articles in the *Encyclopaedia Judaica.*

I. RESPONSIBILITIES IN THE CREATION OF LIFE

A. ARTIFICIAL INSEMINATION

Introduction

Judaism values children for their intrinsic worth and for their contribution to their family and community. Having children additionally represents the fulfillment of a mitzvah (commandment). These values can heighten the suffering entailed by infertility, which affects about one in seven married couples in the United States. In many cases, medical treatments can restore the ability to have children. In others, even with medical treatments a couple would be unable to have a child through sexual relations. Assisted reproductive technologies would be required for the couple to have a child.

Among reproductive technologies, artificial insemination is the most common method and, from a medical and technical perspective, the simplest. From an ethical and religious perspective, the matter can be more complicated. Especially weighty concerns are raised if a couple considers using sperm that is not from the husband, but from a donor, in the procedure.

The following three papers, by Rabbi Elliot N. Dorff, originally constituted one lengthy work addressing issues of artificial insemination. They have been divided into three chapters in this volume for the convenience of the reader. In the first paper, "Artificial Insemination:

General Considerations and Insemination Using the Husband's Sperm," Dorff introduces the topic by examining traditional Jewish views on procreation and infertility, as well as the medical range of infertility treatments available today. These interventions are supported by Jewish law. Dorff also surveys traditional sources that discuss nonsexual insemination in contexts that are in some ways surprisingly analogous with, though in others strikingly different from, contemporary artificial insemination. This paper concludes by examining artificial insemination using the husband's sperm, arguing that this procedure is permitted by Jewish law.

In the second paper, "Artificial Insemination: The Use of a Donor's Sperm," Dorff first discusses a number of legal issues that have been raised by halakhic authorities, which include: the claim made by some that donor insemination constitutes adultery, and that children born from such procedures would be illegitimate; a concern for unintentional incest among genetic siblings in the next generation; and determination of the identity of the father, with the related issue of whether such a procedure would constitute fulfillment of the mitzvah of procreation. Dorff then examines moral concerns, which are less strictly legal but still relevant to halakhah. These include the claim by some that donor insemination is licentious. More serious issues are raised by considering the impact of donor insemination on the couple's marriage and on the relationship of the parents with the child born from such procedures. Special attention is given to complications resulting from secrecy, and to the biological "asymmetry" of the child's relation to its mother and to its father when donor sperm is used. Finally, the implications of Jewish demographic concerns and the value of compassion are considered. Dorff concludes that donor insemination is permissible, though by no means required.

The third paper is entitled "Artificial Insemination and Reproductive Technologies: Using Donor Eggs, Donating Sperm and Eggs, and Adoption." Like donor insemination, the use of donor eggs is considered permissible, but not required. Individuals may donate sperm or eggs, "but only after due consideration of the implications of what they are doing and only with due respect and, indeed, awe for the whole procedure." Prospective egg donors must also ascertain that the drugs used to stimulate ovaries before egg donation would not pose excessive medical risk in their case. Finally, infertile couples (among others) should consider adoption, an act of loving-kindness strongly supported by Jewish law and ethics.

CHAPTER 1

Artificial Insemination: General Considerations and Insemination Using the Husband's Sperm*

Elliot N. Dorff

She'eilah (Question):

An infertile Jewish couple has asked the following questions: Which, if any, of the new developments in reproductive technology does Jewish law require us to try? Which may we try? Which, if any, does Jewish law forbid us to try? If we are not able to conceive, how does Jewish law view adoption?

Teshuvah (Response):

These questions can best be treated by dividing those issues that apply to the couple from those that apply to potential donors of sperm or eggs, and by separately delineating the status in Jewish law of the various techniques currently available.

For the couple: May an infertile Jewish couple use any or all of the following methods to procreate? Must they use one of these methods if they cannot procreate through their own sexual intercourse? Which of

*The first three chapters of this volume present material that originally appeared in the form of one longer paper, "Artificial Insemination, Egg Donation and Adoption." The introductory and summary sections of each chapter have been revised to reflect this division. This paper was approved by the Rabbinical Assembly Committee on Jewish Law and Standards, Mar. 1994.

the following methods for becoming parents, if any, fulfill the commandment to procreate? 1) artificial insemination with the husband's sperm; 2) artificial insemination with a donor's sperm; 3) egg donation; 4) adoption.

For the donor: May Jews donate their sperm or eggs so that other people who are infertile can have children? If so, are there any restrictions?

[This chapter will present an overview of issues raised by developments in reproductive technology, and will address the question regarding artificial insemination with the husband's sperm. Chapter 2 will consider the question of artificial insemination using sperm from a donor. The remaining questions will be discussed in chapter 3. The three chapters originally constituted sections of a single responsum.]

The Subcommittee on Bioethics has agreed to divide the many issues on the beginning of life, so those connected with in vitro fertilization (IVF), gamete intrafallopian transfer (GIFT), zygote intrafallopian transfer (ZIFT), and surrogate motherhood, while described here, will be treated in separate responsa [see chapters 4–9 below].

A. Procreation and Infertility

Within Jewish sources, children are seen as one of God's chief blessings. Sarah, Rebecca, Rachel, and Hannah have trouble conceiving and bearing them, but that only adds to the preciousness of the children they ultimately have. God's blessings of the patriarchs promise children as numerous as the stars, and later Deuteronomy and the Psalmist include children prominently in their descriptions of life's chief goods.[1]

Moreover, Jewish law understands propagation not only as a blessing, but a commandment. It is indeed the first of the biblical commandments, and its occurrence in the creation story in the opening chapter of the Torah indicates the centrality of children in the Bible's understanding of human life. While both husband and wife are obviously necessary to procreate, for exegetical and probably economic and physical reasons, the Mishnah later asserts that it is only the man who is subject to the commandment—thus, the reason that Jewish law is more permissive in the use of female contraceptives than male ones—and that to fulfill this biblical demand one must have two children.[2] Here, as usual, the Mishnah is only specifying the minimum needed to fulfill one's obligation under the law. Jewish practice at that time and throughout the centuries since then and later Jewish law itself make it clear that one was supposed to have as many children as one could, for, as Maimonides says, "whoever adds even one Jewish soul is considered as having created an [entire] world."[3]

As the biblical stories indicate, though, couples cannot always have the children that both they and the Jewish tradition would like. Like the biblical characters, modern couples often experience their inability to have children as frustrating and degrading. Somehow, they think, they should be able to do what their bodies were designed to do and what most other people's bodies enable them to do. Especially when all their married friends are having children, an infertile couple often feels not only unlucky and deprived, but embarrassed and defensive as they continually feel the need to explain why they do not have children, too. It even challenges many people's feelings of adequacy as a man or as a woman—and as a mate. Some marriages fall apart because of the tension engendered by continued unsuccessful attempts to have children.

The Jewish emphasis on children can be an additional source of consternation for infertile couples. Couples who cannot have children are no longer obligated to fulfill the commandment to propagate, for commandments make logical and legal sense only when the one commanded has the ability to obey. Still, Jewish couples who seek to abide by Jewish law—and even those who do not—often feel that they are letting down not only each other, but their parents, the Jewish people, and God.

In addition to these legal concerns, there are emotional and theological components of the tradition that add to infertile couples' misery. The tradition, as we have noted, glories in children. So, for example, when the Psalmist wants truly to bless his listener or reader, he says:

> Happy are all who fear the Lord, who follow His ways. . . . Your wife shall be like a fruitful vine within your house; your sons, like olive saplings around your table. So shall the man who fears the Lord be blessed. May the Lord bless you from Zion; may you . . . live to see your children's children. May all be well with Israel![4]

As that passage indicates, such positive feelings about children are, at least in part, due to the tradition's conviction that children are an expression of God's blessing of those who abide by the conditions of God's covenant with Israel. As the Torah says explicitly:

> If you obey these rules and observe them faithfully, the Eternal, your God, will maintain for you the gracious covenant that God made on oath with your forebears. God will love you and bless you and multiply you. . . . There shall be no sterile male or female among you.[5]

While this sounds warm and loving to those who have children, it has a very different ring to those who do not. As one infertile Jewish woman has written, "Fertility, it seems, is an integral component of the covenant. Is barrenness, then, next to godlessness? If you who are fertile have received a sacred blessing, have we who are not received a divine curse?"[6]

The people involved in the biblical stories of infertility include no less than our patriarchs and matriarchs, who are depicted as being in very good graces with God. Indeed, in later sections of the Torah, the merits of those people and the oath God swore to them are the grounds for forgiving the seriously erring Israelites after the molten calf incident and for God's choosing the People Israel in love.[7] The Torah, therefore, is ambivalent about piety producing fertility and about fertility being the mark of piety, and one hopes that should be of some comfort to infertile Jewish couples.

If the biblical stories of infertility raise internal theological problems within the Torah, their prevalence should not surprise us at all. In our own time, one in seven couples in the United States is infertile, where "infertile" denotes a couple who is actively trying to have a child over the period of a year and cannot conceive. Since Jews go to college and graduate school in percentages far exceeding the national norm, they generally do not even try to have children until their late twenties or thirties. That compounds the problem yet further for the Jewish people, for infertility increases with age: 13.9 percent of couples in which the wife is between 30 and 34 are infertile, 24.6 percent in which the wife is between 35 and 39, and 27.2 percent in which the wife is between 40 and 44. As many as 1.2 million patients are treated annually in the United States for infertility problems, with approximately $1 billion spent each year for their care. Even so, for as many as one in five infertile couples, a cause is never found, and as many as half the infertile couples seeking treatment are ultimately unsuccessful, despite trying various avenues of treatment.[8]

In contrast to biblical times, scientific methods now exist to enable the other half of these couples to bear children. This provides new hope to such couples, and we certainly rejoice with them when they succeed in having the children they want. Whenever we can do something new, though, we must ask the moral and legal question of whether we *should* do so, and the new methods of achieving conception come with clear moral, financial, communal, and personal costs that must be acknowledged and balanced against the great good of having children.

B. Traditional Sources on Nonsexual Insemination

Artificial insemination is one method used when a couple cannot conceive through sexual intercourse because of sexual dysfunction, insufficient or abnormal sperm, or less than the required motility of the sperm. There are four sources within the tradition that contemplate insemination of a woman without sexual intercourse. Even though they do not reflect methods of insemination parallel to modern means, they are commonly invoked in contemporary Jewish discussions of artificial insemination.

The first occurs in the Talmud:

> Ben Zoma was asked: "May a high priest [who, according to Lev. 21:13, must marry a virgin] marry a maiden who has become pregnant [yet who claims she is still a virgin]? Do we take into consideration Samuel's statement, for Samuel said: 'I can have repeated sexual connections without [causing] bleeding [i.e., without the woman losing her virginity],' or is the case of Samuel rare?" He replied: "The case of Samuel is rare, but we do consider [the possibility] that she may have conceived in a bath [into which a male has discharged semen, and therefore she may marry a high priest]."[9]

However implausible conception by these means may seem to moderns, this talmudic source clearly contemplates the possibility of conception without sexual intercourse, and its simple meaning is that artificial insemination neither invokes the prohibitions nor leads to the illegitimacy that adultery or incest through sexual relations would. Even some medieval and early modern rabbis, though, had trouble imagining such a situation, let alone using it as a basis for legal decision, and so they interpret the passage metaphorically.[10] Others, however, accept the possibility of such conception and interpret the passage on its face, leading Rabbi Moshe Feinstein, for example, to permit donor insemination.[11]

The second source generally cited is a medieval midrash regarding Ben Sira, the second-century B.C.E. author of a book of the Apocrypha cited several times in the Talmud. This legend, first mentioned by Rabbi Jacob Moellin Segal (1365–1427) in his work *Likutei Maharil,* claims that Ben Sira was conceived without sexual intercourse by the prophet Jeremiah's daughter in a bath, the father having been Jeremiah himself, who, coerced by a group of wicked men, had emitted semen into the water. The midrash is undoubtedly based on the fact that the Hebrew spellings of "Jeremiah" and "Sira" have the same numerical equivalent (271). The legend subsequently appears in many medieval texts as well as most, if not all, of the rabbinic responsa dealing with artificial insemination.[12] The story is denied, however, by Rabbi David Gans, who notes its absence in the Talmud and the classical collections of midrash, and who quotes Rabbi Solomon ibn Verga to the effect that Ben Sira was the son of the daughter of Joshua ben Jehozadak, a high priest mentioned in the Book of Ezra.[13] Be that as it may, this story supports three contentions: that conception without sexual intercourse is possible; that, unlike sexual intercourse, it does not impart the status of illegitimacy (*mamzeir*) as it normally would on a child conceived by a father and daughter; and, since the legend asserts that Ben Sira was the child of Jeremiah, the sperm donor is apparently to be considered the legal, as well as the biological, father of the offspring.

The third source commonly quoted is the comment of Rabbi Peretz ben Elijah of Corbeil in his work *Hagehot Semak,* who states:

> A woman may lie on her husband's sheets but should be careful not to lie on sheets upon which another man slept lest she become impregnated from his sperm. Why are we not afraid that she become pregnant from her husband's sperm and the child will be conceived of a menstruating woman [*niddah*]? The answer is that [we are not concerned about the child being the progeny of a menstruating woman] since there is not forbidden intercourse, [so] the child is completely legitimate [*kasheir*] even from the sperm of another, just as Ben Sira was legitimate. However, we are concerned about the sperm of another man because the child may eventually marry his sister.[14]

Whether a woman can, in fact, be impregnated by sperm on a sheet (presumably, shortly after the man left the bed), Rabbi Peretz clearly assumes that she can, and thus we have another source within the tradition that contemplates insemination without sexual intercourse. As with the legend cited above, Rabbi Peretz assumes that the child so conceived is legitimate, even if the sexual union of the biological parents would have been prohibited—here, because the woman was (or might have been) menstruating. He also mentions a concern that will arise in cases of artificial insemination by a donor (and also in cases of adoption), namely, the worry that the child will later have intercourse with his half-sister or her half-brother, an act that Lev. 18:9 classifies as incest. The people involved would presumably be acting unknowingly, and one then must ask whether the prohibition would apply; but even if it does not, contemporary Jewish law must be concerned with the danger of genetic defects in the children of such a biologically consanguineous relationship.

Finally, Rabbi Moses ben Naḥman (Naḥmanides), in explaining the verse "One may not have intercourse with one's neighbor's wife for seed [or sperm]" (Lev. 18:20), points out that the last two Hebrew words of that verse seem unnecessary. He then raises the possibility that they were included in the text to emphasize one reason for the prohibition of adultery, namely, that society will not know from whom the child is descended. On this basis, Rabbi Yoel Teitelbaum rules that donor insemination is biblically prohibited, for it is like adultery in that the identity of the donor is usually unknown and because donor insemination establishes a genetic relationship between the biological father and the child that, had there been intercourse, would have been categorized as an act of adultery. Rabbi Eliezer Waldenberg goes even further: he uses Naḥmanides' interpretation as forbidding the very act of injecting a donor's semen into a married woman's womb as an act of adultery, regardless of the absence of sexual contact involved.[15]

Note that the first three sources are all ruling after the fact (*be'diavad*) of insemination. Using them for rulings of artificial insemination, whether such rulings be stringent or lenient, will require us to ignore this false analogy. There is another problem in using them. As a matter of general policy, I maintain that we should use the precedents within our tradition to guide us in our own rulings as much as possible, even when they are scant in number and considerably different in context from the questions we are asking, as long as we keep these false analogies in mind in assessing the weight we give the precedents and the conclusions we draw from them.[16] Rabbi Teitelbaum, however, already anticipates a problem in using the commentary of Naḥmanides, for it is not obvious that biblical commentaries were ever intended to be sources of law.[17] Moreover, the first three sources discussed in this section, the ones that explicitly contemplate the possibility of artificial insemination, are so unlike the contemporary conditions in which the question of the permissibility of artificial insemination arises that one wonders whether they can seriously serve as a legal resource for our questions.

C. The Range and Costs of Available Infertility Treatments

The methods of insemination described in the sources above, even if physically possible, are happenstance at best. Modern infertility treatments differ from the first three of the above sources in two significant ways. First, when contemporary techniques are used, all parties involved intend for conception to take place; and second, the probability of that happening is considerably greater than it is in the situations described by these sources.

Specifically, in our time, about 50 percent of infertile couples are ultimately treated successfully, and about 80 percent of those are aided in producing children through conventional medical and surgical therapy. Medical treatment ranges from relatively simple techniques, such as teaching the couple to pinpoint the time of ovulation for maximum potential for conception, to more sophisticated treatments, such as artificial insemination or drug therapy to stimulate the ovaries to ovulate. Surgical treatments also span a wide spectrum of complexity, ranging from ligation of testicular veins for eliminating varicocele to delicate microsurgical repair of reproductive-tract structures in both men and women.

Ovulation induction, surgery, and artificial insemination are the most widespread and the most successful approaches to overcoming infertility. Drug therapy with Clomid for stimulating ovulation and artificial insemination are successful in slightly less than 50 percent of the cases in which they are tried, and they generally cost $300 to $400. (If Pergonal is used instead of Clomid, the cost is considerably greater, amounting to $2,000–$3,000 per cycle.) Corrective surgery is also expensive, but when it is appropriate, it holds out the hope for a permanent solution to the couple's infertility problems.

Three more complicated and more expensive reproductive technologies—in vitro fertilization (IVF), gamete intrafallopian transfer (GIFT), and zygote intrafallopian transfer (ZIFT)—account for the other 20 percent of those couples who are successfully treated.[18] In addition, the couple may enlist the help of another woman through "traditional surrogacy" or gestational surrogacy. Since these procedures are not the subject of this responsum, I will not describe them in detail here. Suffice it to say that these procedures are much more costly ($8,000–$10,000 for each attempt), have a much lower rate of success in producing a baby (approximately 10 percent for each attempt), and raise gnarly legal, moral, and psychological problems.[19]

Even the less costly and morally less complicated methods of correcting infertility have financial, legal, moral, and psychological costs, and couples thinking about using them must recognize these burdens and plan support mechanisms to deal with them before deciding to employ such aids. Sex on schedule does take much of the joy out of making love. It also makes you think of your body as a machine somehow detached from "you." Since that machine is not working as well as you would like, at least in this one area, you may lose a measure of self-confidence and self-respect. Many feel sad and alone; some cannot talk about this even with their spouses. Indeed, some fear losing their spouses altogether because of the trials of reproductive technology; infertility is already a strain on most marriages, but using reproductive technology focuses attention on children and the couple's inability to have them. If repeated attempts are necessary, repeated failures are possible, and the couple will need to deal with ever-renewed hopes and oft-recurring disappointments. After all, only half of the couples with infertility problems are ultimately successful in having children of their own through the techniques now available.[20]

None of this is sufficient reason to ban the use of these techniques by Jews, but the psychological costs of seeking to treat infertility in these technological ways, as well as the economic, legal, and moral costs, must be balanced against the emotional costs of not having children or of having them through adoption. Infertile couples are under no Jewish obligation to use modern technology to have children. If they nevertheless choose to do so, they must recognize and take into account all the factors involved in order to make a reasonable and Jewishly responsible decision.

Let us return to the beginning. Couples having trouble becoming pregnant are normally first advised to time their intercourse to coincide with the woman's most fertile time. Rabbis do not object to this, since it usually comes at the beginning of the time when the couple is permitted by the laws of family purity (*tohorat hamishpaḥah*—or, as Rabbi Susan Grossman has suggested, *kedushat hamishpaḥah*) to have conjugal relations after waiting for the woman's menstrual period to be over.[21]

If timing does not work, physicians commonly do a thorough analysis of both the husband and the wife. If corrective surgery can help either or both of them to become fertile, Jewish law would permit taking the risks of surgery for such a purpose, although it would not require it. The life or health of neither of them is threatened by their inability to have a baby, and so the surgery would not be required on those grounds. Furthermore, even though the man has a duty to procreate under Jewish law, he is under no obligation to undertake the risks of surgery to fulfill that duty—although, again, both he and his wife may do so.

Sometimes drug therapy is required to stimulate the woman's ovaries. Even though there is evidence that such drugs increase to some extent the risk of ovarian cancer, high blood pressure, and strokes, the demonstrated risk is not so great that such therapy must be prohibited because of the overriding Jewish concern of Jewish law to preserve the woman's life and health.[22] On the other hand, because the woman's own health is not threatened by her infertility, and because, in any case, she is not subject to the command to procreate, she is not required by Jewish law to use such drugs. That is an option she has, an option she can choose to act on or refuse with the full endorsement of Jewish law for either choice.

The next most common method of reproductive therapy is artificial insemination, including artificial insemination by the husband (A.I.H.) or by a donor (A.I.D., but to avoid confusion with the AIDS virus, the more common abbreviation is now D.I., for donor insemination, or, in some discussions, S.D.I., for surrogate donor insemination). This responsum [presented in this and the following two chapters] will focus on both these forms of artificial insemination, along with the converse of D.I., egg donation, and the alternative to all such reproductive technologies, adoption. In so doing, one hopes that this discussion will lay the groundwork for other, later responsa that will deal with the yet more complicated issues raised by IVF, GIFT, ZIFT, and surrogacy [see chaps. 4–9 of this volume].

D. Artificial Insemination Using the Husband's Sperm

1. The circumstances in which artificial insemination is used. The practice of artificial insemination has been used and documented in animals since the late eighteenth century, and the first successful case in humans was reported by a Scottish surgeon, Dr. John Hunter, in 1790.[23] This, however, may be long after success with artificial insemination actually occurred, for whereas IVF, GIFT, and ZIFT require surgery and therefore doctors, hospitals, and anesthesia, and whereas artificial insemination is now usually performed in a doctor's office or on an outpatient basis in a clinic or hospital, women may have performed artificial insemination on their own for some time before this, using the "turkey baster" method.

Although artificial insemination is only one method used to treat infertility, the process has a much higher national success rate (57 percent) than other available procedures (estimated at 17 percent at best), and it is less invasive and less dangerous than some of the alternatives. Although many people assume that infertility is almost always rooted in a problem in the female, actually close to half of the time the problem resides in the male.[24] Average sperm counts over the past fifty years have declined by 50 percent for reasons that researchers are now investigating.[25] Whatever the cause, the consequent need for artificial insemination has increased dramatically in the last several decades. Thus, when it becomes clear that a couple is infertile and cannot be made fertile through timing their intercourse for the woman's most fertile period, through pills to aid ovulation, or through surgery to remove blockages in the testes or fallopian tubes, artificial insemination is usually the first technique attempted. Estimates for the number of children born each year in the United States through donor insemination range from 10,000 to more than 30,000, and many more are born through A.I.H. Dr. Fred Rosner estimated in 1970 that by then, some 250,000 Americans were the products of artificial insemination, and the U.S. Government's 1987 survey suggested that some 65,000 children are born each year through artificial insemination, almost half through D.I. and the remainder through A.I.H.[26]

About half of all artificial inseminations are performed to overcome fertility problems in the husband, and the other half serve to circumvent problems in the wife (or in both partners). If the number of sperm in the husband's semen is too small to generate children, or if it is insufficiently motile (that is, if it is not shaped correctly or energized enough to swim up the vaginal cavity), then if it can be made effective if several ejaculates are combined, the husband's semen, thus enhanced, is used for inseminating his wife.[27] This is artificial insemination by the husband (A.I.H.).

If the husband's sperm is not sufficiently numerous or motile, and if attempts to enhance its number or motility fail, the couple can request donor insemination (D.I.). While it is possible that the sperm of a fertile male family member can be used, the more common practice is to use the sperm from a sperm bank of a donor whose medical history and often whose occupation and personal characteristics are known to the couple but whose identity is usually not revealed to them.

Semen has proteins that, if injected directly into the woman's uterus, could produce anaphylactic shock in the woman, collapse, and even death. As a result, in most artificial inseminations, whether using the husband's semen or a donor's, the semen is placed at the opening of the cervix so that the mucous membranes in the cervical canal can remove the antigens in the semen, leaving only sperm that reaches the uterus. This, of course, is exactly what happens in normal intercourse, and this form of artificial insemination is the cheapest and most effective way of assisting generation.

Under some conditions, this relatively easy method cannot be used, and so more developed and more expensive means of reproductive technology must be invoked—assuming that the couple chooses to do so. Specifically, if concentrating several ejaculates does not work to increase the sperm's motility or number, the semen may be "washed" or "spun down" with various tissue culture media to separate viable sperm from the other components of the semen. Since this process removes the semen's accompanying antigens, the sperm thus isolated can be injected directly into the uterus, thus ameliorating problems of motility. Because washing away the other elements of the semen concentrates the sperm, problems of low sperm count can also be overcome through this method.

Artificial insemination is also used to overcome reproductive problems in the female. If, for example, the woman's cervix is damaged, the man's sperm cannot reach the uterus and must be washed and artificially implanted there. Similarly, if the woman's cervix does not produce adequate mucus naturally, or if the drugs she is taking to stimulate her ovaries spoil the effectiveness of her cervical mucus, the sperm must be washed and implanted into her uterus to avoid shock. In such cases, the husband's sperm is used when it can be, and these cases constitute other situations when A.I.H. is used. If the husband's sperm cannot be used and if the woman suffers from any of these problems, a donor's sperm may be implanted in her uterus. This is another set of circumstances in which D.I. is used—in this case, to resolve problems in both the male and the female.

2. Rabbinic responses to A.I.H. When the semen of a man is united artificially with his wife's ovum, most rabbis who have written on the subject have not objected.[28] Because of Judaism's appreciation of medicine as an aid to God, there is no abhorrence of such means merely because they are artificial.

The only issue is the means by which the husband's sperm is obtained. To ensure that there is no "destruction of the seed in vain," some rabbis advocate collecting it from the vaginal cavity after intercourse, but an obstetrician whom I consulted—who has many observant Orthodox and Conservative patients—told me that collecting sperm in that way is simply "unrealistic." Moreover, the vaginal pH kills the sperm, since it is more acidic than cervical mucus. Consequently, rabbis have permitted using a condom to collect the semen for A.I.H. (clearly, one without spermicide). Some of these rabbis insist that the condom have a small hole so that there is still some chance of conception through the couple's intercourse. While I have no particular objection to such stringencies, it does seem to me that they are unnecessary, for producing semen for the specific purpose of procreating cannot plausibly be called wasting it. Indeed, some Orthodox rabbis follow the same line of reasoning and permit a man to masturbate to produce semen for artificial insemination of his wife.[29] We should adopt this latter approach.

In the same spirit, Rabbi Morris Shapiro has argued that where the husband is the donor, he should be credited with fulfilling the mitzvah of procreation, for the mitzvah is to produce two viable children for which both intercourse and artificial insemination are merely preparations.[30] This severs the command to procreate from the method of conception, interpreting the command instead as a matter of the couple's intent to produce children and their success in doing so. Despite this separation of procreation from sexual intercourse and the emotional bonding that commonly accompanies it, I would agree with Rabbi Shapiro for three reasons: 1) The sperm involved is the husband's, in any case, and the child is therefore the husband's, according to all understandings of Jewish law.[31] 2) The husband, by hypothesis, cannot fulfill the commandment in any other way. By virtue of going through the expense and trouble of artificial insemination, though, he has demonstrated clearly that he wants to obey the commandment, and the Talmud says that God attributes the merit of fulfilling a commandment if one tries to do so but cannot.[32] 3) The husband generally goes through considerable humiliation, pain, and perhaps depression in coming to terms with his inability to impregnate his wife through sexual intercourse, and therefore we should do all we can to augment his satisfaction with the whole procedure so that he does not forever associate his new child with his own frustration in the process of conceiving him or her—a result that is as important for the child as it is for the man.

E. Summary

1. *Medical interventions to induce fertility.* When couples cannot have children, Jewish law clearly allows that they take advantage of fertility drugs and other techniques that may help them to have children through their own sexual intercourse—as couples undoubtedly prefer, as well. Then the emotional values of coitus and reproduction can be preserved, and the medical intervention is solely to aid a natural process.

2. *Artificial insemination using the husband's sperm.* When such interventions do not work, artificial insemination is permissible. Use of the husband's sperm, if possible, is preferable to that of a donor. In the case of A.I.H., the semen may be collected in a condom, but masturbation to procure the husband's semen is permissible. Since the husband's semen is being used, he fulfills the commandment to procreate through artificial insemination.

3. *The commandment to procreate.* Couples who cannot produce children through their own sexual intercourse are exempt from the commandment to procreate. They *may* use many of the modern means to assist them in having children, but they are not required to use any of them.

Notes

1. Sarah, Rebecca, Rachel, and Hannah have trouble having children: Gen. 15:2–4; 18:1–15; 25:21; 30:1–8, 22–24; 35:16–20; 1 Sam. 11–20. God's blessings of the patriarchs promise numerous children: Gen. 15:5; 17:3–6, 15–21; 18:18; 28:14;

32:13. Children figure prominently in the descriptions of life's chief goods in Deuteronomy (e.g., 7:13–14; 28:4, 11) and in Psalms (e.g., 128:6).

2. The biblical command to "be fruitful and multiply": Gen. 1:28. The Mishnah's determination that it is only the man who is subject to the commandment: M. *Yevamot* 6:6 (61b), where the ruling is recorded as the majority opinion (that is, without ascription) but without textual support and where Rabbi Yoḥanan ben Beroka immediately objects: "With regard to both of them [i.e., the male and female God first created] the Torah says, 'And God blessed them and said to them, "Be fruitful and multiply." ' " The Talmud (B. *Yevamot* 65b–66a) brings conflicting evidence as to whether a woman is legally responsible for procreation and ultimately does not decide the matter. That is left for the later codes; cf. *M.T., Laws of Marriage* 15:2; *S.A., E.H.* 1:1, 13. The Talmud there also brings conflicting exegetical grounds for the Mishnah's ruling restricting the command to men, basing it alternatively on "Replenish the earth and subdue it" (Gen. 1:28) or on Gen. 35:11, "I am God Almighty, be fruitful and multiply." There are problems in using both texts, however. The traditional pronunciation of the Hebrew verb in the first verse (Gen. 1:28) is in the plural, making propagation a commandment for both the man and the woman; it is only the written form of the text that is in the masculine singular (and even that can apply, according to the rules of Hebrew grammar, to either men alone or to both men and women). The second verse (Gen. 35:11) is indeed in the masculine singular, but that may be only because God is there talking to Jacob; the fact that Jacob is subject to the commandment proves nothing in regard to whether his wives were.

   These problems make it likely that the real reason for limiting the commandment of procreation to men is not exegetical at all, and we have to look elsewhere for what motivated the Rabbis to limit it in that way. I would suggest that that reason is to be found in the economic sphere—specifically, that since men were going to be responsible for supporting their children (although there is some question as to whether they were legally obligated to support their daughters), it was against the man's best economic interests to have children, and so it was precisely the men that had to be commanded. Alternatively, since the man has to offer to have conjugal relations with his wife for procreation to take place, it may be that physical factor that prompted the Rabbis to impose the commandment on men.

   The Mishnah's determination that that command is fulfilled with a minimum of two children is also found in M. *Yevamot* 6:6 (61b). In that mishnah, the School of Shammai say that one has to have two boys and the School of Hillel say that one must have a boy and a girl. The Talmud understands the School of Shammai's position to be based on the fact that Moses had two sons, Gershom and Eliezer (1 Chron. 23:15), while the Mishnah already states that the School of Hillel's ruling is based on Gen. 1:27, according to which God created the human being, "male and female God created them."

   There are several variations on this ruling in the sources. A tosefta (T. *Yevamot* 8:3) included in the Talmud (B. *Yevamot* 62a) asserts that the School of

Judaism 10, no. 2 (Febr. 1990): 17–42. The Dorff, Ellenson, and Newman articles are reprinted as chaps. 11, 9, and 10, respectively, in *Contemporary Jewish Ethics and Morality: A Reader,* ed. Elliot N. Dorff and Louis E. Newman (New York: Oxford University Press, 1995).

17. Teitelbaum, 2 *Divrei Yoel,* 110, 140. He claims that biblical commentaries may nevertheless be considered a source of law if they engender a stringency rather than a leniency. For Rabbi Moshe Feinstein's reply, see *Dibbrot Moshe, Ketubbot* 238–39.
18. The 85–90 percent and 10–15 percent breakdown between conventional treatments and the more technologically sophisticated approaches of IVF, GIFT, and ZIFT is found in the report of the Office of Technology Assessment of the U.S. Congress, *Infertility,* 7.
19. Dr. Brenda Fabe, a gynecologist/obstetrician at Kaiser Permanente Hospital in West Los Angeles, supplied these approximate costs for me. See also Elizabeth Royte, "The Stork Market," *Lear's,* Dec. 1993, 52–55, who reports similar prices.

    Royte also notes that success rates "were widely overreported in the early 1980s, with clinics reporting take-home baby rates of 30 to 35 percent. After an Office of Technology Assessment investigation in 1987, numbers became more realistic, but because the fertility industry isn't yet regulated by law, there are still no reporting standards." As a result, instead of live births, clinics may count pregnancies, and "they may not disclose the number of babies born with congenital diseases or that die within a month of birth." Moreover, "a woman who has triplets may add three births to the clinic's log, though only one mother takes babies home" (all citations from p. 54).

    The American Fertility Society asserts that IVF has a 15.2 percent success rate, and then only counting couples who produce quality eggs, sperm, and embryos (54). That does not count the couples who drop out because they cannot produce such genetic materials. Still, ten years ago [1984], IVF's success rate stood at less than 5 percent; by 1987, it had doubled (p. 55), and by now [1994] it has effectively tripled.
20. U.S. Congress, *Infertility,* 9.
21. Susan Grossman, "Feminism, Midrash, and Mikveh," *Conservative Judaism* 44, no. 2 (winter 1992): 14. Rabbi Grossman has pointed out to me that sometimes one of the manifestations of a woman's infertility problem, particularly in older women, is that she spots during the middle of her cycle, and that could mean, according to the laws of family purity, that she must refrain from conjugal relations with her husband for three days during her time of ovulation to ensure that her menstrual period is indeed over. To make it possible for such women to have conjugal relations during ovulation despite such spotting, traditional women, sometimes with the collusion of Orthodox rabbis, have invented creative ways to circumvent such possibilities, such as wearing dark underwear during that time so that the spots are not noticeable. For those infertile couples

in the Conservative community who observe the laws of family purity, we would heartily endorse such creative solutions to this problem of staining, especially since the time about which we are talking is, at worst, during the women's "clean days," which are only rabbinically enacted, while the commandment to have children incumbent upon her husband is biblical.

22. The general imperative to take steps to maintain our health is, according to Maimonides and Isserles, based on Deut. 4:9 and 4:15, "and you shall guard yourselves." The verses in context speak about guarding ourselves against following other gods, but Maimonides and Isserles applied them to guarding our bodies against illness as well. See *M.T., Laws of Ethics* (*De'ot*), chaps. 3–5; *Laws of Murder* 11:4–5; *S.A., Y.D.* 116:5, gloss. Because they are reading the verses out of context, there is a debate in later sources as to whether by quoting these verses they mean to make the requirement biblical or whether the verses are merely a supporting text (*asmakhta*) and the command is therefore rabbinic; see the *Tumim* (27:1), affirming its biblical nature, and the *Leḥem Mishneh* to *M.T., De'ot* 3:5 and the Meiri, who both consider it to be rabbinic. In any case, saving a life (*pikuaḥ nefesh*), the extreme case of maintaining our health and the issue here, is a well-attested principle in Jewish law, one that the Rabbis deduce from Lev. 18:5, understanding "and you shall live by them [i.e., My commandments]" to mean that you shall not die by them; see B. *Shabbat* 32b, 129a, 132a, 151b; *Yoma* 82a–85b; *M.T., Laws of the Foundations of the Torah* 5:1. The Rabbis also asserted the converse, that we may not unduly put ourselves at risk; see chap. 3, n. 1 of this vol.
23. Fader, *Sperm Banking: A Reproductive Resource* (Los Angeles: California Cryobank, Inc., 1994), 3; Jakobovits, *Jewish Medical Ethics,* 244, claims that the first successful human insemination was in 1866.
24. Fader, ibid., 8, 11.
25. "Health Report," *Time,* 7 June 1993, 20. Two researchers claimed recently that the decline is due to men's increased exposure to estrogen in milk from hormone-dosed cows and water supplies contaminated by chemical spills.
26. The numbers in this paragraph are from Andrews, *New Conceptions,* 160; Lauritzen, "Pursuing Parenthood," 57–58; Fred Rosner, "Artificial Insemination in Jewish Law," *Judaism* (fall 1970) (reprinted in Rosner and Bleich, *Jewish Bioethics,* 105); and Fader, *Sperm Banking,* 12–13. The 1987 U.S. Government report was based on a survey conducted by the Office of Technology Assessment, entitled *Artificial Insemination: Practice in the United States: Summary of a 1987 Survey-Background Paper,* OTA-bp-ba-48 (Washington, D.C.: U.S. Government Printing Office, 1988). That survey reported only a 37 percent success rate for artificial insemination (instead of 57 percent), and thus 65,000 babies from the 172,000 women inseminated each year. Even so, that is still more than double the highest success rate claimed by those using the more complicated methods—and almost four times as high as the actual, 10 percent success rate of those procedures.

27. According to Meredith F. Small ("Sperm Wars," *Discover,* July 1991, 50), "Doctors look for a sperm count of at least 20 million per milliliter of semen, but they are more interested in sperm motility—the speed and swimming direction of individual sperm—because a few fast swimmers are more likely to succeed than millions of sluggards. Reproductive physiologists believe that at least 40 percent of the sperm viewed under the microscope must be vigorous, well-aimed swimmers for a couple to have a good chance at conception." Of the 300 million sperm in a typical human ejaculation, within ten minutes of landing at the cervix only thousands speed toward the fallopian tubes at the far end of the uterus, where the egg lies in wait after drifting down from the ovaries, and only 200 sperm typically make it to the egg. Once one sperm has managed to bore into the egg, the shell of the egg releases enzymes that detach the other sperm. Ibid., 51–52. This article also presents the results of recent research to the effect that sperm counts for ejaculations during intercourse decreased the more time couples spent together and, conversely, increased when the male assumed female infidelity. That is *not* a justification for an infertile couple to try promiscuity as a therapy!
28. See, for example, Jakobovits, *Jewish Medical Ethics,* 264; J. David Bleich, *Judaism and Healing: Halakhic Perspectives* (New York: Ktav, 1981), 83–84. Dr. Rosner lists, in addition, Rabbis Feinstein, Schwadron, Wolkin, and Zevi Pesah Frank as permitting A.I.H., while Rabbis Tanenbaum and Waldenberg "frown upon it, stating it is permissible only in extreme situations"—but that is, by hypothesis, always the case. See Rosner, "Artificial Insemination," 112.
29. Cf. Bleich, ibid., 84 n. 3, for a list of sources on this issue.
30. Rabbi Morris Shapiro, "Artificial Insemination in Jewish Law," prepared in Aug. 1978 for the CJLS, 3.
31. Dr. Rosner cites the following as among those who claim that the donor is considered the father in Jewish law: Rabbis Moses of Brisk, Samuel ben Uri, Judah Rozanes of Constantinople [a commentator on Maimonides' *Mishneh Torah*], Jacob ben Samuel, Israel Ze'ev Mintzberg, Simeon Zemah Duran, and Jacob Ettlinger. Rabbis Jacob Emden and Moses Schick rule that the child is the son of the donor, but the donor has not fulfilled the commandment of procreation because there has been no sexual act involved. Only Rabbis Hadaya and Moses Aryeh Leib Shapiro on Dr. Rosner's list do not consider the child as that of the donor. See Rosner, "Artificial Insemination," 111; specific sources, 117 nn. 30–37.
32. B. *Berakhot* 6a; B. *Kiddushin* 40a; J. *Pe'ah* 1. But according to B. *Kiddushin* 39b, there is one exception to the converse of this rule: in weighing the culpability of a person, God does not ordinarily connect an evil thought to its act (when not fulfilled), but God does so when one thinks of idolatry.

CHAPTER 2

Artificial Insemination: The Use of a Donor's Sperm*

Elliot N. Dorff

She'eilah (Question):

May an infertile Jewish couple use artificial insemination with a donor's sperm to procreate? Must they do so if they cannot procreate otherwise? Would this method fulfill the commandment to procreate?

Teshuvah (Response):

A. Artificial Insemination with a Donor's Sperm: Legal Concerns

When the husband cannot provide sperm capable of impregnating his wife in artificial insemination [as discussed in chapter 1], the matter becomes more complicated. After such infertility is diagnosed, the obligation to procreate ceases to apply to the man, for one cannot be legally obligated to do that which one cannot do. A Jewish couple faced with this situation should pause, seek counseling, and think carefully about whether they want to use donor sperm or engage in costly and often

*The first three chapters of this volume present material that originally appeared in the form of one longer paper, "Artificial Insemination, Egg Donation and Adoption." The introductory and summary sections of each chapter have been revised to reflect this division. This paper was approved by the Rabbinical Assembly Committee on Jewish Law and Standards, Mar. 1994

frustrating attempts to have a child through some of the new reproductive technologies.

There is no Jewish obligation to do any of these things. The Jewish tradition would have all people, fertile or infertile, understand that our ability to procreate is not the source of our ultimate, divine worth; that comes from being created in God's image, which is true of each of us from the moment of birth to the moment of death, whether or not we manage to have children in between. (Note that, in contrast to many religions of the ancient past, God in the Bible and in the Talmud and midrash specifically does not engage in sexual union to create us or anything else, and so imitating God does not require procreation through sexual union.) As Jews, we gain additional divine worth through our covenant with God, which foresees a reward of children "as numerous as the stars above" but which is made with the current generation of Jews just as much as with any past or future one. Moreover, the religious commandment to generate children, which, in any case, traditionally is only incumbent upon the male, ceases to apply to those men who cannot have them, and there is no guilt or shame involved in that. That is just the way God created some of our bodies.

On the other hand, as I shall argue below, the couple may choose to use at least some of the new procedures. Such a choice should be made only when the couple has understood all the factors involved. In addition to the psychological problems that affect the vast majority of couples who have infertility problems [described in the previous chapter], using someone else's sperm (or eggs) engenders some specific problems of its own, which will be described below. The couple must understand the strains that all these factors are likely to impose on their marriage if they go through with these procedures, and they must make plans to get help in dealing with them. Finally, they should investigate alternatives such as adoption before trying such reproductive technology.

If the couple does choose to forge ahead and use donor sperm, may they do so in accordance with Jewish law? Rabbis addressing that question to date have raised several legal and moral objections.

1. *Adultery and illegitimacy.* Some rabbis object to donor insemination as a form of adultery. If artificial insemination is construed as adultery, then its product would be an illegitimate child (*mamzeir*) who himself or herself and whose descendants may not marry a Jew for ten genera-

tions, according to the Torah.[1] Rabbi Eliezer Waldenberg, for example, takes strong exception to artificial insemination on these grounds:

> The very essence of this matter—namely, the placing in the womb of a married woman the seed of another man—is a great abomination of the tent of Jacob, and there is no greater profanation of the family than this in the dwelling places of Israel. This destroys all the sublime concepts of purity and holiness of Jewish family life, for which our people has been so noted since it became a nation.[2]

For me, this misstates our concern with preventing adultery. The Torah, of course, prohibits adultery with no special explanation aside from the general rationales that it gives for all its laws regarding prohibited sexual relations, namely, that we should observe those commandments to make us holy and pure as a people. From the context of the Torah, holiness clearly denotes making us different in moral character and action from the ancient Egyptians and Canaanites, and purity entails avoiding pollution of the Land of Israel through licentious sexual practices;[3] but these terms can include other factors as well, factors intrinsic to what we understand holiness and purity in spousal relations to mean. The question, then, is whether artificial insemination violates our understanding of holiness and purity in a marital relationship.

The crucial part of those concepts involved in the prohibition of adultery, it seems to me, is maintaining the trust between husband and wife; it is that trust that is violated when either spouse has an extramarital affair. In standard cases of artificial insemination by a donor, however, the husband not only knows about the insemination, but deeply wants it so that he and his wife can have children.[4] This is not in and of itself sufficient to make donor insemination acceptable, for even if both partners agreed to each other's adultery, that would not make it permissible. The vast majority of cases of adultery, however, involve a breach of trust, and that is what explains much of our abhorrence of adultery, for such untrustworthiness undermines the honesty and holiness that we want in marriage. While trust is the critical feature that is lacking in most cases of adultery, it is fully present in most, if not all, cases of donor insemination. Contrary to Rabbi Waldenberg, then, I think that artificial insemination by a donor is not an "abomination" or a "profanation" that destroys all Jewish concepts of holiness and purity, but rather is a desperate attempt to have children—an undisputed good in marital relationships for the Jewish tradition—in a context of mutual openness and trust.

On a more technical level, the Talmud, Maimonides, Rabbi David Halevi (the "Taz"), and the majority of recent authorities have already maintained that adultery takes place only when the penis of the man enters the vaginal cavity of the woman.[5] That is clearly not the case when insemination takes place artificially. The lack of contact of the genital organs in donor insemination means that it does not legally constitute adultery, and the child conceived by D.I. (donor insemination) is legitimate and does not suffer from the liabilities of an illegitimate child (*mamzeir*).

Not only is the physical contact missing; the intent to have an illicit relationship is also absent. While lack of intent to commit adultery does not excuse an act of sexual intercourse from the requirement to bring a sin offering, it does excuse the couple from the more serious penalties of extirpation (*kareit*), death at the hands of the court, or lashes.[6] Thus, the intent of the couple is an important legal consideration, and it is even a more important moral consideration. In the case of D.I., the couple's intent is the exact opposite of adultery, for they are going through expensive and emotionally taxing procedures in an effort to express their love for each other through having and raising a child. Thus, D.I. should not be construed as adultery theologically, legally, or morally.

2. Unintentional incest in the next generation. If the donor is anonymous, there is the possibility of unintentional incest in the next generation, for the product of the artificial insemination might happen to marry one of the children whom the donor has with his wife. In that case, the child born through donor insemination would be marrying his or her biological half-brother or half-sister. This issue is resolved in Jewish law if the donor is known and the children avoid his offspring as mates. It is also resolved if it is known that the donor is not Jewish, for Jewish law does not recognize family relationships among non-Jews through the father's line.[7] On that basis, Rabbi Moshe Feinstein permitted D.I. if the donor were not Jewish—although he was later pressured to withdraw his responsum.[8] The pressure notwithstanding, Rabbi Feinstein stood on sound Jewish legal grounds in permitting D.I. from a non-Jewish donor.

Some Orthodox rabbis object to using the sperm of a non-Jewish donor, however, for fear that this will pollute the purity of the Jewish genetic line and will transfer non-Jewish qualities of character (whatever that means) to Jewish offspring. Curiously, physicians report that traditional Jews prefer non-Jewish donors for fear of incest in the next generation, but liberal Jews want Jewish donors. The motivations for that may be many, but undoubtedly for some people, insemination by a non-Jew smacks of intermarriage, and others probably hold an ethnic notion of Jewish identity and want a Jewish donor for reasons not unlike the Orthodox arguments against polluting the Jewish biological line. This line of reasoning is clearly rooted in exclusivist views of Jews and non-Jews, views to which we should not be party. In the case of the Orthodox respondents who hold this view, it is also, as Daniel J. Lasker has shown, the product of kabbalistic affirmations of original sin, a doctrine roundly rejected by the nonmystic sources of Jewish thought—and rightly so.[9]

There is another factor that should prompt us to urge that the identity of the donor, or at least, substantial parts of his medical history, be known. In addition to Jewish law's prohibition of sexual intercourse between Jews and non-Jews, there is an independent commandment in Jewish law to maintain health. We therefore must be concerned to prevent progeny with serious genetic defects or diseases due to the consanguinity of the couple. This is clearly a concern if we know that the donor is Jewish, but in our own day, with rampant intermarriage, it is even a worry if the donor is not Jewish, for a child born through D.I. may someday marry a non-Jew who is his or her natural half-brother or half-sister—or have intercourse with such a person outside of marriage. This concern is all the more worrisome because sperm banks are largely unregulated, and many use the same donors for numerous inseminations.[10] All these factors would argue all the more strongly that a child born through D.I. should know the identity of his or her natural father, whether Jewish or not—or at least enough of his medical history to avoid people with similar medical histories as mates. The same, incidentally, would be true for an adopted child.

In light of much larger numbers of non-Jews than Jews in North America, this concern would not be as great if it were known that the natural father (or, in the case of adoption, the natural parents) were not Jewish, for then the chances of such an unwitting, consanguineous union occurring are much, much smaller. The day is probably not too far off when such unions can be prevented through DNA analysis of the child and his or her potential mate without revealing anything about the identity of the donor.

The strong recommendation of the American Association of Tissue Banks Reproductive Council and the preference of most donors and sperm recipients are that the parties involved remain unknown to each other. However, in the future a health condition may arise in the child whose proper treatment requires more information from the donor than he provided on the initial questionnaire, or, conversely, a genetic condition might appear in the child that could have health implications for the donor's children or family. Therefore, responsible sperm banks keep donor and patient files and continue to track the whereabouts of donors and patients.

Moreover, while children born through donor insemination currently do not have at age eighteen the same legal rights as adopted children do to trace their biological parents, D.I. children may well gain such rights in the future, especially since the medical and psychological needs that propelled the change in legislation for adopted children are similar in D.I. children. That is another reason for couples using D.I. to make sure that the sperm bank that they are using keeps careful and current records of their donors and recipients.[11]

Disclosure of the identities of donors and recipients is still preferable for the physical reasons described above and the psychological reasons delineated below, but the common practice of confidential donor insemination is permissible if the sperm bank keeps thorough records on all its donors and recipients and conscientiously updates them as necessary. Furthermore, as much as possible of the donor's medical history must be revealed to the child in order to prevent possible genetic diseases in that child's own offspring.

3. *The identity of the father.* While adoption was applauded in Jewish law, it did not gain the legal power to replace the child's natural parentage. For example, if an orphan is the child of a *kohein* but his adoptive father is a *yisra'el,* the child retains his natural father's status at birth. The same would presumably be true for the child born through D.I. But what if the biological father's status is not known? And what if the donor is a non-Jew—or, at least, is not known to be a Jew? In addition to these questions of personal status, there are related questions of inheritance. Would the child of D.I. inherit from the sperm donor, the husband (the "social father"), neither, or both? And there is the question of the commandment to "be fruitful and multiply." Does a man fulfill that obligation if he consents to have his wife impregnated with the semen of another man? Does he fulfill it if his own semen is artificially implanted in his wife's uterus? What if he himself is a semen donor?

By and large, rabbis have ruled that the provider of the semen is the father. Nevertheless, some rule that a semen donor does not fulfill the obligation to procreate because there is no sexual act involved, and some do not see either the donor or the social father as the father for purposes of Jewish law.[12] These varying positions would directly affect the answers to the questions raised above regarding personal status (*kohein, levi,* or *yisra'el*) and inheritance within Jewish law in addition to the question of the commandment to procreate.

Let us take them one by one. With regard to personal status, if the donor's status as a *kohein, levi,* or *yisra'el* is known, the child inherits that. If the donor's status is not known, the child is usually treated as a *yisra'el* as a default status. If it is not certain that the donor of the semen is a Jew, that does not matter with regard to the Jewish identity of the child, for Jewish law determines a person's Jewish identity according to the bearing mother. Her religion can usually be determined, and then, if necessary, the child can be converted to Judaism as an infant. The more complicated questions of personal status regarding the possibility of incest in the next generation have been treated above.

As for inheritance, thirty-one American states [as of 1994] have passed laws making the child of a married couple who uses D.I. the legal child of the couple. No court order or other official action is required for this to be the case (unlike requirements for adoption), but some states restrict this parentage to cases in which a physician performed the procedure, and most states (twenty-six) require that the husband's consent to the donor insemination be in writing. Eighteen of these thirty-one states have adopted some form of the Uniform Parentage Act, which defines the donor as not being the father with regard to either rights or responsibilities, as long as a physician was involved in the insemination.[13] Donors who want to protect their property may want to remain anonymous in states that have not passed the act, where a physician was not involved, or where the husband did not provide written consent to the procedure (or the donor has no way of knowing whether the husband did). In any case, since Jewish law does not govern inheritance in the United States or Canada, the implications of D.I. for inheritance within Jewish law need not concern us; it is, after all is said and done, a moot issue for Jewish law, determined by the law of the state.

What Jewish law does determine, though, is whether a Jewish man fulfills the commandment to be fruitful and multiply through agreeing to have his wife impregnated by a donor, and the answer to that has generally been no.[14] Rabbi Joseph Soloveitchik, however, has said that raising adopted children does fulfill the commandment,[15] and the same reasoning would seem to apply to a child conceived through D.I.

The first point that must be mentioned is that donor insemination stretches our understanding of fatherhood. We normally assume that the same man who sired a child will be the one who raises him or her. When that does not happen, the legal category of fatherhood and the concept underlying it must be applied to new circumstances, and then we should not be surprised if the attribution of fatherhood does not fit exactly right, no matter which way we rule.

In our case, some factors would lead us to call the semen donor the father for purposes of the commandment of propagation. Unless there has been a formal, legal act of adoption, in U.S. law we call the man who brings up a child but who did not sire it the "foster father" or the "stepfather," depending upon the circumstances. That usage, which exists in rabbinic law as well (*apotropos*), would argue for seeing only the biological father as the one official "father." As we shall describe in more detail in the section on adoption [see chapter 3], while the Jewish tradition applauded adoption as a way of providing parental support and education for orphaned children, it never ascribed legal parentage to the adoptive parents but rather saw them as the agents of the child's natural parents. That precedent would seem to apply to the biological and social fathers of a child born through D.I. as well, making the social father the agent of the biological father and not his legal substitute. Underlying both the linguistic usage and the law on adoption is the genetic fact that it is the natural father's DNA that the child inherits, not the social father's. Modern research has made us increasingly aware of the impact of our genes on who we are as people, not only biologically, but in a number of character traits as well. That genetic contribution of the semen donor, while shaped by the child's upbringing, is ultimately indelible. It influences the medical history of the child, and it determines the identity of the people whom it is genetically dangerous to marry, lest the children born of that marriage suffer from the diseases rooted in their consanguineous union.

On the other hand, there are other factors that would lead us to classify the social father as the one who fulfills the command to propagate. According to the biblical law of levirate marriage, when a man dies childless, it is the duty of his brother to have conjugal relations with the deceased man's widow so that a child might be born bearing the parentage of the deceased brother. That precedent would argue that the semen donor is not the father.[16] In addition, one classical rabbinic source ascribes fatherhood to the man who raises a child, not to the one whose semen gave him birth. It is a homiletical (midrashic) source, and therefore not one that intends to announce law, but it does invoke a parable that places its ruling in a legal context, the writing of a marriage contract, and, contrary to other sources, it specifically proclaims the guardian the father and does not regard him *as if* he were the father. Based on Isa. 64:7, "But now, O Lord, You are our Father," the midrash says:

> The Holy One, blessed be He, said: "You have abandoned your ancestors, Abraham, Isaac, and Jacob, and you are calling Me father." They said to Him: "We are recognizing You as [our] father." Parable: An orphaned girl grew up with a guardian [*apotropos*], and he was a good and faithful man who raised her and watched over her as is fitting. He wanted to marry her off, and the scribe came to write her marriage contract. He said to her: "What is your name?" She said: "So-and-so." He said to her: "And what is the name of your father?" She began to be silent. Her guardian said to her: "Why are you silent?" She said to him: "Because I know no father except you," for the one who raises [a child] is called father and not the one who begets. Similarly, these orphans, Israel, for it says, "We were orphans without a father" (Lam. 5:3); their good and faithful guardian is the Holy One, blessed be He, [and] Israel began to call Him "our Father," as it says, "But now, O Lord, You are our Father" (Isa. 64:7). The Holy One, blessed be He, asked: "You have abandoned your ancestors and you call Me 'Our Father'?" as it says, "Look back to Abraham, your father, [and to Sarah who brought you forth]" (Isa. 51:2). They said to Him: "Master of the world, the one who raises [a child] is the father and not the one who begets [him or her]," for it says, "For You are our father, for we have not known Abraham" (Isa. 63:16).[17]

Furthermore, the fact that the semen donor never intended to raise the child makes him somewhat like the Gentile who renounces the idolatrous status of a given idol and thereby converts it into a mere statue;[18] similarly—although obviously with no implications whatsoever that a child is an idol!—the donor's explicit intention to have someone else raise the child might, it could be argued, amount to a renunciation of his status of fatherhood and a transfer of it to the social father. Yet another precedent that argues in this direction is that of Jacob, who adopts Ephraim and Menasheh, even though he did not beget them, and their descendants thus become two of the twelve tribes of Israel, along with the descendants of the rest of Jacob's sons.[19]

Aside from these arguments based on facets of Jewish law, a number of contemporary realities would argue in this direction. U.S. law, as we have seen, construes the man who raises the child to be his or her father for all legal purposes. With the exception of the physician who asks for a medical history of the child's family, all the people who come into the child's life see the social father as the father, too. That is right and proper, for the social father, after all, invests a lifetime of energy, love, and substance in the child, while in most cases the donor never even meets the child. Jewish law generally awards privileges only to those who bear concomitant responsibilities, and that would certainly suggest in this case that the man who raises the child, rather than the man who merely ejaculates, should merit the status of fulfilling the commandment of propagation. Such a ruling would accord with the intentions and the actions of both men involved.

Whichever way we rule, then, some aspects of the ruling will seem counterintuitive, for in some ways the semen donor really is the father, and in some ways the social father is. Seeing exclusively one or the other as the father hides important aspects of the child's being. We need to craft a ruling that recognizes the fatherhood of both men involved in the distinctive ways in which they are the child's father.

For purposes of the commandment of propagation, we must see the semen donor as the father of the child. In part, this is because of the precedents in section B of the previous chapter—although, as I indicated there, those stories are not really on point as analogies for the modern practice of D.I. More substantively, it is the ultimate fact that the child's genetic heritage is that of the semen donor that motivates this ruling. That fact is important legally for two reasons. First, Jewish law abhors incest, counting it among only three prohibitions that one may never violate, even at the cost of one's life.[20] Second, aside from this legal and moral factor, we also have a medical concern, for we now know the genetic basis of family diseases imparted through consanguineous unions. For both these reasons, we must consider the semen donor to be the father for purposes of the commandment of propagation. As we shall note below, this imposes upon him some duties from which U.S. law makes him exempt, and that must be part of his understanding and undertaking when agreeing to be a semen donor.

This is not to deny the critical input of the social father in the raising of the child. Another important point to make here is that the command to procreate, like all other commandments, does not apply to those who cannot fulfill it. "In cases of compulsion [*ones*], the All-Merciful One exempts him," the Rabbis say.[21] Thus, men who cannot impregnate their wives should not see themselves as thereby failing to obey Jewish law; their inability to procreate frees them of the responsibility to do so. In that way, they are legally in a better status than those men who have had many children, but all of the same gender, for such men presumably could still fulfill the commandment of begetting a boy and a girl but technically have not done so.[22] Even then, we would probably be inclined to say that the man is exempt from having any more children after having two, regardless of their gender, because no man can consciously control the gender of his children; how much the more is that man exempt who cannot have any children at all. Moreover, the social father should be aware that there are more than enough other commandments he can and must fulfill, including many dealing with the children the man has with his wife through D.I. The fact that the social father is not legally the father in Jewish law gives the man who assumes all the obligations of raising the children conceived through D.I. a special status. As the Talmud says,

> "Happy are they who act justly, who do right at all times" (Ps. 106:3). Is it possible to do right at all times? . . . Rabbi Samuel bar Naḥmani said: This refers to a person who brings up an orphan boy or girl in his house and enables him or her to marry.[23]

Thus, while the social father—that is, the one who rears the child—is not the father in the technical sense of being the biological parent and therefore does not fulfill through D.I. the specific commandment to procreate, he is the "real" father in most significant ways for the child and "does right at all times."

I would suggest that we go yet further in recognizing this paternal connection. According to traditional sources, one who raises another person's biological child does not assume the biblical prohibitions associated with one's own child. Thus, intercourse between an adoptive parent and the adopted child is not a violation of the biblical laws of incest,[24] and adopted children raised in the same home may, according to the Talmud, marry each other.[25]

Even though there is no biological relationship between the social father and the child adopted or born through D.I., and despite the permissive rulings on adoption cited above, I think that the emotional and educational relationships are sufficiently strong for us to apply the category of secondary relations (*sheniyot*) to D.I. children—and also to adopted children. That is, in most cases of D.I., the wife's eggs are used for all the couple's children, and then sexual relations between two of the children, who are biologically half-brothers and half-sisters, are prohibited according to the Torah itself. But even if a couple has a girl and a boy who were both born using another woman's eggs and another man's sperm, we would see it as incest of the second degree for them to have sexual relations, and consequently we would not marry them. The same would be true for two adopted children, even if their biological parents are four separate people, all different from the social parents. Moreover, we would see intercourse between adoptive parents and their adopted children, or between the social father and the donor-inseminated child he is raising, as prohibited incest of the second degree. That is a stringency over the traditional sources, but one that the close relationship created in raising a child warrants.

In sum, in either D.I. or adoption, because the child's genetic heritage is not the social father's and because traditional sources define an adoptive parent as the agent of the natural parent, we cannot consider the social father as fulfilling the commandment of propagation. Our marital law, though, must recognize the strong bonds that social parents create between themselves and all the children they raise and among all the children themselves, whether they became the social parents' children through artificial insemination, egg donation, or adoption. Consequently, sexual relations between the parents and children or between the children themselves are prohibited at least in the second degree.[26] Furthermore, the social father's name may be invoked when the child is being identified by his or her Hebrew name, as, for example, when being called to the Torah.[27] Similarly, children of donor insemination should consider themselves obligated to fulfill the Torah's commands to honor one's parents (Exod. 20:12; Deut. 5:16) and to respect them (Lev. 19:3) as applied to the social parents, and, conversely, the social parents should consider themselves responsible to fulfill the duties that the Torah and the Jewish tradition impose upon parents vis-à-vis their children.[28]

These rulings openly recognize the ways in which the semen donor (i.e., the biological father) has a relationship to the child as well as the ways in which the social father does. Donor insemination has real import for both men involved and for the child, and both men must be seen as the "real" father of the child in the critical, but different, ways in which they both are.

B. Artificial Insemination with a Donor's Sperm: Moral Concerns

1. Licentiousness. Since these strictly legal concerns can be met, most rabbis who have objected to donor insemination have done so on moral grounds. In my own view, positive law and morality are one undifferentiated web, where each can and should influence the other. That is especially true in a religious legal system like the Jewish one, where a fundamental assumption is that the law must express the will of a moral—indeed, a benevolent—God. Thus, the moral concerns that donor insemination raises are not for me "merely" moral, but fully legal.[29]

It is especially interesting to see rabbis who usually shun moral arguments in their legal decisions resort to them when they cannot find legal grounds to deny the legitimacy of donor insemination. Rabbi J. David Bleich, for example, claims that since, according to Jewish law, the provider of the semen is the father, the adoptive father does not fulfill the mitzvah of procreation by consenting to have his wife impregnated by another man's seed, even if he subsequently assumes all the responsibilities of parenthood. In Rabbi Bleich's view, this reduces artificial insemination by a donor to a matter of personal desire that must be weighed against the potential legal problems of adultery, wasting of seed, and incest in the next generation. Despite this, he hesitantly permits it under certain circumstances.[30]

Others have similarly voiced concerns about the morality of using someone else's body or semen in this way, and others worry that artificial insemination will increase the prospects of widespread licentiousness. Rabbi Jakobovits voices these moral concerns in strong language:

> If Jewish law nevertheless opposes A.I.D. [artificial insemination by a donor] without reservation as utterly evil, it is mainly for moral reasons, not because of the intrinsic illegality of the act itself. The principal motives for the revulsion against the practice is the fear of the abuses to which its legalization would lead, however great the benefits may be in individual cases. By reducing human generation to stud-farming methods, A.I.D. severs

> the link between the procreation of children and marriage, indispensable to the maintenance of the family as the most basic and sacred unit of human society. It would enable women to satisfy their craving for children without the necessity to have homes or husbands. It would pave the way to a disastrous increase of promiscuity, as a wife, guilty of adultery, could always claim that a pregnancy which her husband did not, or was unable to, cause was brought about by A.I.D., when in fact she had adulterous relations with another man. Altogether, the generation of children would become arbitrary and mechanical, robbed of those mystic and intimately human qualities which make man a partner with God in the creative propagation of the race.[31]

We, however, should take a much more positive attitude toward artificial insemination, even when the wife of an infertile man is being inseminated with a donor's semen. After all, people who want to be licentious will find many ways to do so without artificial insemination. Indeed, donor insemination is so onerous a mode of illicit sex—if it be that at all—that it is downright implausible that people would go to the trouble and expense of using it for such purposes. Furthermore, the couple is, by hypothesis, using D.I. when they have no other way to achieve a precious goal in Jewish law and thought, the bearing of children. As will be discussed below in greater detail, we should applaud their efforts, because the Jewish tradition has always valued children and also because having and raising Jewish children is a demographic imperative for the Jewish community in our time.

2. The impact on the marriage and on the parent-child relationship. Rabbi Jakobovits's point about severing the tie between generation and parenting is more complicated. We clearly do not want to transform generation into stud farming, we certainly want to acknowledge the importance of fathers in the rearing of children, and we do want to preserve the tie between children and loving families.

These concerns should not, however, lead us to prohibit artificial donor insemination. At the very most, they would lead us to restrict our approval of it to married couples who cannot have children in any other way, and it may not even do that. This responsum specifically will not treat the issue of artificial insemination of single women because that would require a much more extensive analysis of our developing understanding of "family" and of the evidence available regarding the well-being of children raised by single, but loving, parents. We shall not undertake that analysis here. The question that led to this responsum asks about artificial insemination in the context of infertile, married couples. To weigh the morality of donor insemination in that situation, we must analyze what it does to the relationship between husband and wife and between parents and child.

In a philosophically penetrating article probing the nature of parenthood, Paul Lauritzen, whose own wife was artificially inseminated, notes that one need not deny the significance of genetic relationships to affirm that the more important parental relationship to a child is that of caring for it:

> Caring for, nurturing, and nourishing a child in the context of an ongoing social, emotional, and loving relationship is more important than physically begetting a child, however ineradicable and significant the physical/biological connection that is created thereby. . . . While genetic connection may foster relational bonds, it is the bonds that are crucial, not the genetic ties.[32]

Lisa Sowle Cahill has argued against artificial insemination (and adoption) on the grounds that biological relation offers children greater moral protection from abandonment than the parental bonds to which individuals freely consent, but, as Lauritzen says, that is not necessarily so:

> While it may be true that biological relation will often, in Cahill's words, "undergird and enhance" the interpersonal relation between parent and child, this biological relation is not necessary to the development of an intense, ongoing social relationship; nor does the existence of biological relation ensure a social commitment to care. . . . Parental responsibilities are, in a sense, inalienable, but it is not genetic connection that makes them so; rather it is the intense, person-specific nature of the interpersonal bonds constituting the parental relation that makes parental responsibility largely nontransferable.[33]

The real moral problems in donor insemination for Lauritzen, then, are those that threaten the purpose of parenthood and the relationship between husband and wife. Chief among those are secrecy and the genetic asymmetry that donor insemination creates in the relationship between each of the parents and the child. In addition, as Jews we must ask how our moral evaluation of donor insemination should be affected, if at all, by the demographic realities of the low Jewish birthrate and high rates of Jewish intermarriage and assimilation in which this question is being asked.

a. Secrecy. The secrecy that often surrounds artificial insemination is sometimes justified as a protection for the child, sometimes as protection for the husband, and sometimes as protection for the donor. We shall consider each in turn.

Children, the argument goes, may feel perplexed and odd if they know they were conceived in an unusual way, especially as they approach puberty. Moreover, when they have their inevitable quarrels with their parents, children born through artificial insemination, like adopted children, may feel and say that they would not be having such problems if their *real* fathers were there. Secrecy presumably shields children from such feelings and helps them accept their social parents, even in time of tension.

Secrecy about how a child was conceived, though, undermines the trust that must be at the core of a child's relationship with his or her parents—especially on a subject as critical to a child's identity and self-image as his or her origins. Since secrecy almost definitely will require one or both social parents to lie to the child on a number of occasions, the potential damage is even worse. As Sissela Bok notes in her book, *Lying,* lies are particularly corrosive and contagious within families. "The need to shore up lies, [to] keep them in good repair, the anxieties relating to possible discovery, the entanglements and threats to integrity—are greatest in a close relationship where it is rare that one lie will suffice."[34] Indeed, as Lauritzen points out, this is possibly the most egregious case of "living a lie," for when the truth about a child's origins through artificial insemination is kept from the child, everything about the parent-child relationship is based on a presumed or explicit lie. That surely is "incompatible with the commitments that responsible parenthood entails,"[35] not only theoretically, but practically, for it engenders shame and guilt, fear and suspicion.

Secrecy does not protect the husband's ego, either. It is perfectly normal for men who cannot impregnate their wives to feel angry, inadequate, ashamed, and even guilty. The only hope of coping with such feelings over the long run is not through denial, but rather through expressing them (literally, pushing them out of himself) through open communication with those who are likely to sympathize and support him.

If he can talk about this with his wife, she can reassure him that she still considers him a manly mate, whatever his sperm count or motility may be. Furthermore, he will soon discover, if he does not already know, that marriage is not exclusively based on the ability to procreate, that it includes, more importantly, sharing life together. Given the possibilities of artificial insemination and adoption, that can even include the raising of children, which, after all, takes much more of one's time, energy, and commitment and offers a much more sustained basis for sharing than procreation alone does. If the man is sufficiently self-assured to talk with his male friends about this, too, he may well find that he is not alone, that some of his friends may be experiencing the same problems or know of others who are, and that, in any case, they will not abandon him as a friend and will not think less of him as a man.

On the other hand, if the man cannot muster enough self-confidence to have such discussions with his wife and friends, he ironically cuts himself off from the very strengthening he so desperately needs. Secrecy about his wife's donor insemination thus will not help him, but instead will compound the problems in making the necessary adjustments in his thoughts, feelings, and plans. As Lauritzen says:

> Unfortunately, to mask a problem is not to resolve it, and the secrecy only serves to delay an acknowledgement of the emotional and psychological effects of sterility. Infertile individuals need to mourn and grieve the children they will not produce; they need to resolve any feelings of inadequacies that sterility may engender, and secrecy is an obstacle to meeting both needs.[36]

Moreover, the secret of a woman's artificial insemination can be revealed at any time in an angry moment, and that cannot help but add stress to a marriage. Furthermore, relatives and friends who do not know about the artificial insemination will quite innocently add to the man's pain when they talk about whom the child resembles. All these factors mean that the husband's manliness is much better protected if he does not keep the artificial insemination of his wife a secret.

Jewish law would encourage the husband to avoid secrecy. "Be fruitful and multiply" is a commandment, one that North American Jews, who statistically have a 1.6 or 1.7 reproductive rate, nowadays all too often ignore. As we have noted above, however, if one cannot fulfill this commandment, one ceases to be obligated by it. Therefore, an infertile man should not feel any shame or guilt for failing to fulfill this commandment, since it does not apply to him. Procreation is not the only duty we have regarding children. Those who cannot procreate may not be able to fulfill that commandment, but they surely can raise children through artificial insemination or adoption. In so doing, they fulfill many commandments and act with real, ongoing *ḥesed* (loving-kindness, fidelity) to the children who are, in most significant ways, their sons or daughters. For these reasons, an infertile Jewish man whose wife is artificially inseminated or whose children are adopted has nothing to hide—and nothing to gain by secrecy.

That leaves the donor. Secrecy surrounding artificial insemination is most often justified to protect the potential pool of donors, for if the donor's identity were known, it is feared, he might be held financially, morally, and perhaps legally responsible for the care of the child or the mother. This might include not only child support and a claim on the biological father's estate when he dies, but also monetary compensation for any disease or disability that passed through the semen from the donor to the child, especially given the general lack of regulations governing sperm banks.[37] Moreover, according to Yeh and Yeh, "many potential donors would be reluctant to give specimens if they knew that their names would be given out publicly."[38] Conversely, the social parents may want to keep the identity of the donor secret to prevent unwanted intrusions by that man into their lives and into the life of their child on the grounds of his biological connection to the child.

Some of these are real concerns, and some are not. As noted above, since the 1970s, most American states have enacted the Uniform Parentage Act or other legislation that makes the husband, not the donor, the legal father of the child, with most of these states requiring that the husband agree to the procedure in writing and that there be a physician involved in the insemination. The only legal concerns of donors with regard to inheritance or child support involve donations in those states that did not pass the Uniform Parentage Act or its equivalent and donations where the requirements were not met in the laws of those states that did pass such legislation. The latter situation occurred in a recent case in which lesbians used a friend as a sperm donor, and he subsequently won the right in court to be involved in the child's upbringing.[39]

Potential liability for diseases contracted through the insemination is a more serious possibility that might lead potential donors to remain anonymous. Indeed, three recent law review articles argued that legal notions of warranty should be invoked or legislation should be passed to prosecute such claims, at least if the donor knowingly hid important genetic information or lied about it.[40] This is especially important in light of the fact that donors are usually paid, and even though the sums are modest (typically, $25 for each donation), the money may encourage donors to be careless or evasive in their answers to questions about their physical histories or even to lie. Only three states—California, Florida, and Indiana—have enacted legislation going beyond the required testing of sperm donors for HIV, and no state has statutorily imposed regulations sufficient to meet the recommended guidelines of the American Fertility Society.[41] This is undoubtedly because in-depth testing of donors and their sperm could cost recipients an additional $800 to $900.[42] That would make donor insemination much more expensive than the $200 to $500 that it commonly costs now, but it is nothing in comparison with the costs of caring for a genetically defective or diseased child. No legal action has yet been brought against a donor on these grounds, but one could understand why a donor might want to avoid any chance of that through anonymity.

The social parents may also want to preserve the donor's anonymity in order to keep him out of their lives and the life of the child. Those states that have passed the Uniform Parentage Act or its equivalent have thereby established protection against that, since the sperm donor, according to such statutes, is legally not the father in any way; but that applies only when all details of the law are carried out, such as written permission of the husband and supervision by a physician, where these are mandated by law. Courts have given donors paternal rights where these aspects of the law have not been fulfilled and where the donor has evidenced through his actions that he wanted to serve as the child's father.[43] Thus, even in those states that have laws governing this, and all the more so in those that do not, the social parents may want to guarantee their freedom from the donor through keeping his identity secret.

Australia, which pioneered open adoptions, has enacted laws that mandate that donors, donors' spouses (if married), and infertile couples be counseled not to preserve anonymity before participating in donor programs. A registry in which donors are identified is open to children at age eighteen, equivalent to the law on adoption.[44]

American states, however, have uniformly protected the identity of the donor, and even those who keep records of the donation only allow them to be opened for "cause" or "good cause," some requiring a court order to do so, and this was the position incorporated into the Uniform Parentage Act as well.[45] Thus American states apparently do not want to go as far as Australia has gone in revealing donors, social parents, and children to one another.

Even so, one can protect the confidentiality of the donor without keeping the fact of the donation a secret. One can even divulge to the child many facts about the donor without compromising his privacy—an important point, given that children often want to know and, one might even say, have the right to know many genetic characteristics of their biological fathers.

At present, only three states—California, Illinois, and Ohio—require the physician to keep records of the attributes of the donor, and fifteen others require that some state agency have such records.[46] We should encourage registration at least of the donor's medical history and, if possible, of other personal characteristics that the donor would like his progeny to know about him. As Mahlstedt and Greenfeld say, "Considering donors real people with specific interests, skills, and family histories enables the donor children to identify positively with their genetic heritage."[47] Moreover, as we noted above, it enables the children to avoid having incestuous sex, either within or without marriage. That is not only important legally and morally, but also physically, for one wants to avoid the genetic problems that can arise in the progeny of a consanguineous relationship. For psychological and physical reasons, then, if the donor insists on confidentiality, his sperm may be used for insemination within the bounds of Jewish law as we interpret it only if information about his medical history, and preferably tidbits about his character and interests, be made available to both the social parents and to the child.

The above approach to matters of secrecy is based on the best advice available in the psychological literature that, in turn, is based on the experience of the many people—couples, donors, and children—involved in donor insemination. Still, even with all this input, some couples may choose to keep the donor insemination a secret from their children, family, and friends—just as they do not reveal other matters, such as the times they have intercourse, to anyone else—in order to make themselves and their child feel as close to them and as "normal" as possible. We should understand and permit that decision, but only after sharing with parents the advice that has emerged from those who have dealt with donor insemination extensively and the reasons for that advice, as described above.

b. Asymmetry. The fact that a child born through donor insemination is the biological descendant of the mother but not that of her husband makes for an asymmetry in their relationship to their child. That can cause problems in their spousal relationship if the husband never works out his feelings of anger, impotence, shame, and even guilt at not being able to father a child. Every time he sees the child, he may be reminded of his own infertility and, in contrast, his wife's ability to procreate. He may once again resent his predicament and, through psychological transference, his wife. The asymmetry involved in donor insemination also may cause problems in the father-child relationship. In Lauritzen's words:

> When the child is young, there will be the inevitable speculation about whom the child resembles. For the father this is likely to be painful and to frustrate rather than further the parent-child bond. If the child develops in ways or with interests different from the father's, or if the child is particularly close to his mother, the father may well feel left out, an outsider in the family. If the child is told about the conception, he is likely at some point to wield this information to inflict pain. He may shout in anger that he hates his mother, but only to his father will he say that he, the father, is not his real parent. So the absence of genetic relation is likely to be painful and isolating, and in this pain the mother cannot fully share.[48]

Adoption engenders some of the same feelings, and adjusting to them is in some ways easier and in some ways harder than adjusting to donor insemination. On the one hand, neither of the parents can see an adopted child as their biological progeny, and so the problems for the husband-wife relationship caused by the asymmetry of donor insemination would not affect adoption. On the other hand, the parent-child relationship may be more difficult, for in donor insemination the child knows that at least one of the social parents (the mother) is also his or her biological parent, while in adoption both biological parents are unknown. Thus, the child's genetic uncertainty and the lure to blame the parents' lack of biological connectedness in moments of tension are doubled. Many adopted children feel that they have been fundamentally rejected by their genetic parents, leading some, as adults, to seek the identity of, and a meeting with, their genetic parents. That often produces less than desirable results for all parties concerned: the child may be deeply disappointed in the reality, as against the dream, of the kind of human beings the genetic parents are; the genetic parents may find being discovered by the child after all these years to be most unwelcome, making the child feel rejected yet again; and the social parents feel that they were somehow inadequate as parents, that they never succeeded in overcoming the lack of biological relationship between them and the child despite years of love and effort, if the child now seeks to know and be connected with his or her biological parents.[49]

While these dangers in both donor insemination and adoption should not be minimized, they should not be exaggerated, either. We do, after all, have many "blended" families today, in which children are raised by a biological parent and by a nonbiological parent. That may not be ideal for the same reasons of asymmetry that artificial insemination is not ideal, and yet we know that committed spousal and parent-child relationships based on honesty, trust, and respect most often overcome the difficulties. One must remember, too, that in marriages in which fertility is not a problem, the families that result from them are not always ideal; each marriage and family has its difficulties that the people involved must overcome, and the asymmetry of artificial insemination is just a pitfall of a specific sort. The couple and child will need to talk out the issues fully, perhaps with professional help, but it certainly is not impossible for a marriage and family to survive the asymmetry of donor insemination and even to emerge stronger as those involved join in dealing with its challenges.

The same point applies to grandparents. As Mahlstedt and Greenfeld point out, if grandparents remain distant from grandchildren conceived through artificial insemination, it is generally not in reaction to the means of conception, but is rather a continuation of the poor relationships that the social parents had with them from the start on other grounds entirely. It is *those* personal problems that must be addressed before the special issues deriving from donor insemination can be successfully confronted. This is very important for the social parents to recognize, for family support is critical to meeting the challenges that the asymmetry inherent in donor insemination poses. According to Mahlstedt and Greenfeld,

> [T]he social attitudes which concern infertile couples most are *not* those of the church or the law, but those of their families. . . . It is their support that most effectively enables confidence, conviction, and courage to emerge in the couple's experience with donor conception. Couples who receive family love and support reflect less ambivalence about their choice, more com-

fort in sharing their means of conception with others, and more confidence in their abilities to cope with negative social attitudes.[50]

Thus with grandparents, with other family members, and with friends, as with the social parents themselves, good relations apart from this issue will help everyone deal with it, and bad relations will make that task harder. Within a reasonably strong network of relationships, however, including especially their own, the asymmetry inherent in donor insemination need not become an insurmountable obstacle to a strong marriage and to good parenting, and it therefore should not be prohibited on that moral ground.

3. Demographic concerns. In addition to these moral issues that presumably affect couples of all faiths involved in donor insemination, there are specific Jewish issues in judging its morality. Rabbi Jakobovits mentioned adultery and the diminution of the role of the father as reasons to oppose donor insemination, despite his inability to find legal grounds to do so. For reasons discussed above, we have rejected those contentions of his. There is one important moral factor that, on the contrary, argues for permitting donor insemination: the demographic context in which this question is being asked.

Jewish families in the past had numerous children. This was in part, no doubt, because so many children died in childbirth or of childhood diseases; as a result, one could only have a few children survive to adulthood if one had significantly more than that in the first place. Thus, while birth control was known and used when medically necessary for either the mother or the infants she was nursing, it was not even contemplated, as far as we can tell from the sources, for purposes of family planning.[51]

Contemporary Jews generally do not share this ethic. Survival rates to adulthood are much better now, so that Jewish couples need no longer conceive many more children than they ultimately want to have. Moreover, they commonly want to provide substantial educational and material benefits to the children they do have, and that argues for smaller families so that they can afford to do so. Economic necessity and the women's movement have made the dual-career marriage commonplace, and so couples are reluctant to have many children when they know that they will have limited time to care for them. These factors, combined with the loss of a third of world Jewry in the Holocaust, and assimilation and intermarriage, have together produced the serious demographic problems that our contemporary Jewish community has.

This must enter into our moral evaluation of donor insemination because a Jewish examination of any moral issue cannot be adequate to Jewish concerns if it only narrowly considers the specific legal issues involved. Any tradition based on law must grapple with its sources if it is to be true to itself and if it is to reap the many benefits inherent in a legal system,[52] and I have done that in some detail above. The law, though, must be interpreted with full cognizance of the specific context to which it is to be applied, for otherwise it risks two opposite dangers: it could either be ignored and thus dishonored; or—perhaps the greater danger—it could be obeyed despite the personal, social, and moral havoc it wreaks on the situation it was meant to guide with sensitivity and wisdom. Certainly, Jewish law, which tries to delineate the will of God as we understand it, must now, as it has in the past, pay attention to the welfare of the Jewish community and of the specific people involved as any good God would. Moreover, the Conservative movement, with its commitment to historical analysis, must surely not only recognize the influences of historical circumstances on the legal judgments of the past, but must also take the responsibility to meet the needs of Judaism and the Jewish community in its responsa of the present.

In our case, when the demographic statistics are as threatening as they are for the continuity of the Jewish tradition and the Jewish community, any room in the law to enable Jews who are otherwise infertile to have children must be used. The moral scales, in other words, are decisively balanced by these communal concerns in favor of donor insemination when the couple cannot have children in any other way.

4. Compassion. These communal considerations stand quite apart from, and in addition to, the compassion that one must surely have for couples who have tried to have children and cannot. In such situations, both members of the couple suffer immensely. In addition to the frustration of being unable to have children when they deeply want to do so, they often have feelings of inadequacy as men or as women. Infertility certainly requires couples to alter their understandings of what it means to be a man, a woman, and a couple, for one important part of all those concepts is no longer true. Thankfully, the greater publicity about infertility in our time, including its frequency and the availability of support groups and helpful publications, has enabled many couples to overcome the emotional hurdles involved; but more than a few couples have broken apart because of their inability to have children. In addition to our communal concerns mentioned above, our attention to the needs of Jews who are trying to fulfill Jewish law and actualize Jewish ideals and our interest in preventing divorce to the extent that we can should also prompt us to prefer the permissive lines of reasoning in the sources described above.

Compassion in these cases goes in two directions. Just as we want to be responsive and affirming to the couples who want to use these new techniques to have children, we also want to recognize that some couples will choose not to engage in these procedures. In some cases, the cost will be a factor. In others, the psychological problems engendered by the asymmetry of donor insemination and egg donation pose too much of a threat to the marriage. For these and other reasons, couples may legitimately refuse to use either donor insemination or egg donation, and we should not make them feel as though they have let down the Jewish people, their partners, or potential grandparents. The commandment to procreate does not apply to a couple who cannot have children through their own sexual intercourse, and that recognition will surely be liberating for some couples. There are many commandments and many opportunities in life to do good deeds, and so as much as we may individually or collectively support those couples who decide to use D.I. or egg donation, we must also be sensitive to the good reasons that will motivate other couples not to use these techniques.

C. The Scope and Tenor of This Responsum

All the above conclusions concerning artificial insemination and egg donation assume the case of the question asked—i.e., a married couple who cannot have children. [Similar assumptions would apply to egg donation as well, as discussed in chapter 3.] This responsum does not treat, and therefore expresses no opinion about, the more complicated case of single women who wish to be inseminated (and, in some cases, also implanted with the egg of another woman), single men who artificially impregnate surrogate mothers, or single men or women who adopt children for purposes of becoming parents.

Jewish law clearly assumes that it is best for children to have both a mother and a father, as it describes differing roles for both parents.[53] Furthermore, recent studies reaffirm the importance of fathers in the raising of a child, and a recent movie was based on the search for her father by a child born through D.I. to a single mother.[54]

An adequate treatment of the use of artificial insemination, egg donation, or adoption by a single person thus requires a full-fledged analysis of Jewish law and of contemporary psychological and sociological studies to determine how Jewish law should treat these new family configurations.

Such an analysis would also have to take into account the complications raised by U.S. law, for protections against the paternity of the semen donor built into the Uniform Parentage Act and similar legislation have not been applied by recent court decisions to single parents.[55] Moreover, some states do not recognize the right of lesbians or gay men to be parents, even if they are the biological parents.[56]

Adoption by single people on the face of it poses fewer problems, since the child is already born and is, by hypothesis, an orphan; but in contrast to cases of divorce or the death of a spouse, this involves consciously creating a single-parent home. Single parents often do a remarkable job of raising their children, and it is certainly better for a child to have one caring parent than foster parents or no parents at all. Still, if the child could be adopted by two parents, that might well be better for the welfare of the child.

This responsum, in any case, has not carried out the necessary analysis of these situations.[57] Its task, instead, is to respond to the far more numerous cases of artificial insemination, and [in the next chapter] egg donation and adoption, being used by *infertile couples* to have children.[58]

As medicine becomes ever more adept at helping infertile couples conceive on their own, donor insemination, while necessary and permissible now, may no longer be necessary. Just recently, Belgian scientists invented a new treatment for male infertility that they say may allow "virtually any man, no matter how few or misshapen or immobile his sperm cells, to father a child" through the direct injection of a single human sperm cell into a human egg in a petri dish.[59] One hopes that someday, egg donation will not be necessary for infertile women, either.[60] Then the emotional, moral, and legal problems that these procedures raise may resolve themselves.

D. Summary

When other interventions do not work, artificial insemination using donor sperm is permissible. In this case, as much about the donor as possible should be revealed to the social parents and, through them, to the child so that the child can have as strong a sense of his medical history and personal identity as possible. Secrecy about the artificial insemination should be avoided on all sides and for everyone's benefit—although, for legal reasons and out of respect for a donor's wish for privacy, confidentiality, but not total anonymity, is permissible.

Donor insemination does not constitute licentiousness or adultery, and the child so conceived is fully legitimate. For purposes of priestly status, the child follows the status of the semen donor, if that is known, or else adopts the default status of a *yisra'el.* While the social father does not fulfill the commandment to procreate through D.I., he does fulfill many other commandments connected to the raising of children, making him the child's father in many important senses even if not in the biological one. All of the woman's children conceived through D.I. are prohibited to each other by the Torah as sexual partners and as candidates for marriage, since they share a mother and are thus half-brother and half-sister.[61] Furthermore, children raised in the same household, whatever their genetic origins, are prohibited to each other as mates because we consider them minimally as relatives of the second degree (*sheniyot*).

While donor insemination is permissible, infertile couples are not required to use it to have children, for, in any case, the husband does not fulfill the obligation to procreate through donor insemination. If the husband cannot procreate, he is exempted from the commandment, and he should feel no guilt on that account. Thus, if the psychological problems engendered by the asymmetry of donor insemination pose a significant threat to the marriage or if other concerns make them feel reluctant, a couple may, in full compliance with Jewish law, elect not to use donor insemination to have children. If they wish to raise children, they should think of adoption as an alternative, but even that is not required by Jewish law.

Notes

1. Deut. 23:3.
2. *Tzitz Eliezer* 9:51, chap. 5, sec. 1, p. 251.
3. For the prohibition of adultery, see Lev. 18:16 and 20:10. For the rationale that observing this will make us holy and pure, see Lev. 18:24 and 20:8, 26. For sep-

aration from the practices of the Egyptians and Canaanites as an explicit component of the meaning of those terms, see Lev. 18:3, 27, 30; 20:23, 24, 26. For avoiding pollution of the Land of Israel as another component of the meaning of these terms, see Lev. 18:25–29; 20:22.

4. Rabbi Paul Plotkin has suggested that, biblically at least, the ban of adultery is based not on the breach of trust involved, but on the violation of the husband's acquisition of his wife (*kinyan*). In D.I., though, the husband agrees to the procedure, so presumably his rights of possession are not violated.
5. B. *Shevuot* 18a; cf. M. *Yevamot* 6:1 (53b), B. *Yevamot* 54a, and B. *Horayot* 4a. *M.T., Laws of Forbidden Intercourse* 1:10–11. This is also the opinion of Rabbi David Halevi (the "Taz") of the seventeenth century, who bases it on the responsa of Rabbi Peretz, an eleventh-century scholar; see *Turei Zahav* in *S.A., E.H.* 1:8. Rabbi Peretz is quoted there as asserting that "in the absence of sexual intercourse, the child resulting from the mixing of sperm and egg is always legitimate." Rabbi Bleich, who vigorously opposes A.I.D., nevertheless notes the following modern authorities (*aḥaronim*) who require sexual contact for a sexual act to be termed adulterous: Rabbi Shalom Mordecai Schwadron, *Teshuvot Maharsham* (Brezany, 1910), III, no. 268; Rabbi Aaron Walkin, *Teshuvot Zekan Aharon* (New York, 1951), II, no. 97; Rabbi Yehoshua Zion Uziel, *Mishpetei Uziel* (Tel Aviv, 1935), *E.H.* I, no. 19; Rabbi Moshe Feinstein, *Iggerot Moshe* (New York, 1961), *E.H.* I, no. 10; and Rabbi Eliyahu Meir Bloch, *Hapardes,* Sivan 5713. On the other hand, he cites the following authorities who do not require sexual contact for the prohibition of adultery to take effect: Rabbi Yehudah Leib Zierlson, *Teshuvot Ma'arekhei Lev,* no. 73 and Rabbi Ovadiah Hadaya, *No'am* 1 (5718): 130–37, with reference also to Rabbi Eliezer Waldenberg, *Tzitz Eliezer* 9:51, sec. 4. These latter authorities stress that Lev. 18:20 reads literally, "and to the wife of your fellow you shall not give your intercourse for seed to defile her," which, in their view, would include providing semen even without sexual intercourse. See J. David Bleich, *Judaism and Healing: Halakhic Perspectives* (New York: Ktav, 1981), 84 nn. 1–2.

   In the discussion of this responsum by the CJLS, Rabbi Paul Plotkin noted that for those who insist on contact of the genital organs to establish adultery, there is a parallel in the Talmud's insistence that the Torah's prohibition against eating blood is violated only when the blood is ingested in the normal way, through the throat. Therefore, contrary to the Jehovah's Witnesses, who interpret the biblical command more broadly, we Jews permit blood transfusions, even when they are precautionary and not clearly essential for the saving of a life. See B. *Sanhedrin* 63a, and another responsum of mine (Elliot N. Dorff, "A Jewish Approach to End-Stage Medical Care," *Conservative Judaism* 43, no. 3 [spring 1991]: 35) [chap. 20, p. 349 of this vol.], in which I use this precedent along similar lines to permit the withdrawal of artificial nutrition and hydration. While I would agree that this case is parallel to the one at hand—and I thank him for calling my attention to that—and while that strengthens the point being made here, we do not need to depend on it to establish that adultery occurs only where there is genital contact because the Talmud and later authorities already make that point.

6. See *M.T., Laws of Forbidden Intercourse* 1:1, 9, 12 (and see the commentary of the *Maggid Mishneh* there).
7. B. *Yevamot* 98a; cf. Tosafot, B. *Yevamot* 22a, s.v. *ervah lakol mesurah. M.T., Laws of Forbidden Intercourse* 14:13; *S.A., Y.D.* 269:3.
8. Feinstein, *Iggerot Moshe, E.H.* (New York, 1961), I, nos. 10, 71, pp. 12–14, 169–71; II (New York, 1963), *Ḥ.M.* no. 11, pp. 322–24. On the pressure that ultimately caused him to withdraw these responsa, see Zvi Hirsch Friedman, *Sefer Sedeih Ḥemed* (Brooklyn, 1965/66), 34.
9. Daniel J. Lasker, "Kabbalah, Halakhah, and Modern Medicine," *Modern Judaism* 8, no. 1 (Febr. 1988): 1–14, esp. 7–11.
10. Curie-Cohen et al., "Current Practice of Artificial Insemination by Donor in the United States," *New England Journal of Medicine* 300 (1979): 585–90. Thirty-one percent of the inseminating doctors surveyed in that study indicated that they use the sperm of several donors within one menstrual cycle, while 51.1 percent reported that they use a single donor, but change donors with each new cycle, and one donor had been used to produce fifty pregnancies (p. 587). If the subject is a donor for a minority ethnic group in the area, the chances of intermarriage by the children become even greater (p. 589 n. 9). Medical students are the most tapped resource; cf. George Annas, "Fathers Anonymous: Beyond the Best Interests of the Sperm Donor," *Family Law Quarterly* 14 (1980): 7. Apparently one such case actually took place in Tel Aviv, and in another case in the United States, incest was avoided only by the intervention of a doctor who knew of the couple's common paternal roots; see Hoffer, "The Legal Limbo of Artificial Insemination by Donor," *Modern Medicine* (1 Nov. 1979): 27.

    I was not able to find any definitive study of the practice of sperm banks on this issue after the Cohen study of 1979. Although that may have changed, none of the sources I consulted—including a 1993 summary of law regarding artificial insemination published by the American Bar Association—reported any new legislation prohibiting such multiple uses of one donor's sperm. See Julia J. Tate, *Artificial Insemination and Legal Reality* (n.p.: American Bar Association, Section of Family Law, 1992).

    On the contrary, in a booklet published by California Cryobank (Fader, *Sperm Banking: A Reproductive Resource* [Los Angeles: California Cryobank, Inc., 1994]), the practice is that sperm donors must agree to donate sperm twice a week for a minimum of a year, and preferably two years. They have that policy because they freeze the man's sperm for six months while they continue to test him for AIDS and venereal diseases to make sure that his sperm is not infected, and "without the year minimum commitment from donors, this safety measure could not be carried out" (21). They report that "the number of live births from one donor usually ranges between two and ten" (21), and they retire a donor after his sperm has produced ten live births. Nevertheless, they maintain that the chance of offspring from a single donor inadvertently marrying and having children, "although not impossible, . . . is extremely remote," especially because they distribute frozen sperm internationally (21–22).

11. See Fader, *Sperm Banking,* 26–27.
12. See chap. 1, n. 31 of this vol.
13. John Yeh and Molly Uline Yeh, *Legal Aspects of Infertility* (Boston: Blackwell Scientific Publications, 1991), 41–48. See especially the charts appearing on pp. 43–46 of that book. The Uniform Parentage Act, 9A U.L.A. 592 (1979), drafted in 1973 by the National Conference of Commissioners on Uniform State Laws and approved by the House Delegates of the American Bar Association in 1974, has since been passed in whole or in part by the following states: Ala., Calif., Colo., Del., Hawaii, Ill., Kan., Minn., Mo., Mont., Nev., N.J., N.M., N.Dak., Ohio, R.I., Wash., and Wyo. Section 5(A) deals with donor insemination.

    This acceptance of donor insemination in American law took some time. In 1964, Georgia became the first state to pass a statute legitimizing children conceived by donor insemination, on condition that both the husband and the wife consented in writing, and the first American appellate court ruling affirming that stance was in 1968 in the California Supreme Court case *People v. Sorenson.* The court there upheld Mr. Sorenson's criminal conviction for not supporting a D.I. child conceived with his consent during his marriage. The court held that the sperm donor had no more responsibility for the use of his sperm than a blood donor had for the use of his or her blood. This was in sharp contrast to the 1954 ruling of the Supreme Court of Cook County, which held that regardless of the husband's consent, D.I. was "contrary to public policy and good morals, and constituted adultery on the mother's part," so that the child so conceived was the mother's exclusively and "the father has no rights or interest in said child." See Fader, *Sperm Banking,* 4–5. Thus, the 1973 recommendation of the Commissioners on Uniform State Laws that children born through D.I. be considered legitimate was, for most jurisdictions, breaking new ground. It has, however, been widely followed: see *S. v. S.,* 440 A.2d 64 (N.J. 1981); *In re* Adoption of Anonymous, 345 N.Y.S.2d 430 (1973); *Noggle v. Arnold,* 338 S.E.2d 763 (Ga. 1985); *R.S. v. R.S.,* 670 P.2d 923 (Kan. 1983); *Mace v. Webb,* 614 P.2d 647 (Utah 1980); *In re* Custody of D.M.M., 404 N.W.2d 530 (Wis. 1987); *L.M.S. v. S.L.S.,* 312 N.W.2d 853 (Wis. 1981); *In re* Baby Doe, 353 S.E.2d 877 (S.C. 1987). Thus, the man who consents to the artificial insemination of his wife is now legally obligated to support the resulting children, either on the theory of equitable estoppel (since he, after all, consented to the insemination), or on the theory of adoption, according to which the husband, by his consent, has formally or informally adopted the children.
14. E.g., Bleich, *Judaism and Healing,* 80.

15. Melech Schachter, "Various Aspects of Adoption," *Journal of Halacha and Contemporary Society* 4 (fall 1982): 107.
16. Deut. 25:5–10. This law may only refer to inheritance rights, but the language of Deuteronomy seems to indicate a stronger relationship, for the levir is to have a child with his sister-in-law, whom he takes "as his wife," but "the first son that she bears shall be accounted to the dead brother, that his name may not be blotted out in Israel" (Deut. 25:6).
17. *Exodus Rabbah* 46:5. In contrast, another, deservedly famous source (B. *Sanhedrin* 19b) proclaims, "Whoever brings up an orphan in his home, Scripture ascribes it to him *as if* he had begotten him." This source in *Exodus Rabbah,* however, removes the "as if."
18. M. *Avodah Zarah* 4:4–7; T. *Avodah Zarah* 6:2; B. *Avodah Zarah* 43a, 52a–55a; *M.T., Laws of Idolatry* 8:9–12; *S.A., Y.D.* 146:1–12.
19. Gen. 48:5–6. As Rabbi Reuven Kimelman has pointed out to me, Jacob, while not the biological father of Ephraim and Menasheh, was their biological grandfather, unlike the social father of a D.I. child. Furthermore, biblical terminology often does not discriminate between children and grandchildren, and since Joseph was Jacob's firstborn son by Rachel, Ephraim and Menasheh may represent Joseph's double portion through primogeniture—although we do not hear of a similar provision for Reuven, Leah's firstborn son. In any case, these factors would argue against using this last example to support the social father's claim to fulfilling the command to procreate, while the specific language of the verses in Genesis, by which Ephraim and Menasheh are legally taken as Jacob's sons even though they are not biologically his sons, would seem to support his claim.
20. B. *Sanhedrin* 74a; *M.T., Laws of the Foundations of the Torah* 5:1–3; *S.A., Y.D.* 157:1.
21. The principle is announced in B. *Nedarim* 27a, B. *Bava Kamma* 28b, and B. *Avodah Zarah* 54a. There is some discussion among medieval commentators as to whether in cases of compulsion the obligation continues but the person is not culpable for failing to fulfill it (that is, the exemption applies only to culpability for failure to perform the commanded act), or whether the obligation ceases to apply altogether (that is, the exemption is from the obligation itself). The answer depends on whether the person, although unable to fulfill the obligation now, could fulfill it later, in which case the obligation continues and the principle excludes only culpability at this time; or whether the compulsion will continue indefinitely, in which case the obligation itself ceases. In any case, Tosafot (B. *Gittin* 41a, s.v. *lisa shifḥah eino yakhol*) apply the principle directly to the obligation to be fruitful and multiply, claiming that in such an instance the obligation itself ceases. In general on this topic, see *Encyclopedia Talmudit* (Hebrew) 1:346–60, esp. 347, 360, s.v. "*Ones.*"
22. See chap. 1, n. 2 of this vol.
23. B. *Ketubbot* 50a. See chap. 3, n. 18 of this vol. for further, similar sources.
24. *S.A., E.H.* 15:11.

25. B. *Sotah* 43b. One medieval authority, Rabbi Judah ben Samuel, decreed that such marriages may not be performed; cf. Judah ben Samuel of Regensburg (Heḥasid), *Sefer Ḥasidim,* sec. 829. This decree, however, has not been generally accepted; see Rabbi M. Sofer, *Responsa,* 2 *Y.D.* 125. As Michael Broyde notes, however, although legally permitted, few such marriages are performed; see Michael Broyde, "Marital Fraud," *Loyola of Los Angeles International and Comparative Law Journal* 16, no. 1 (Nov. 1993): 98 n. 15. The rabbinic prohibition I am proposing below takes that reluctance one step further by giving it legal form.
26. I would like to thank Rabbi Gordon Tucker for suggesting this approach in the meeting of the CJLS on 8 Dec. 1993. The Torah's definition of sex between half-siblings as incest: Lev. 18:9; 20:17. The rabbinic category of incest in the second degree: B. *Yevamot* 21a; *M.T., Laws of Marriage* 1:6; *S.A., E.H.* 15:1ff. In line with this treatment of adoptive and D.I. relationships on a rabbinic, rather than a biblical, level we would maintain the rabbinic rulings that award the possessions, earnings, and findings of a minor child to the custodial, rather than the natural, parents (B. *Bava Metzia* 12b; *S.A., Ḥ.M.* 370:2), and, despite the laws prohibiting unmarried and unrelated people from living together (*yiḥud*), we would permit, for example, an adopted son whose adoptive father has died to continue living alone with his adoptive mother. See Broyde, "Marital Fraud," 98–99.
27. This has been the ruling of the CJLS, which validated a responsum in 1988 by Rabbi Avram Reisner to the effect that an adopted child may use the patronymic and matronymic of his or her adoptive parents, and if a convert, need not use *ben/bat Avraham avinu.* The same would apply to children born through D.I. That responsum will soon be published in the collection of the CJLS's responsa from 1985 to 1990.
28. For a brief description of the obligations of children to parents as defined by Jewish tradition, see my "Honoring Aged Mothers and Fathers," *Reconstructionist* 53, no. 2 (Oct.–Nov. 1987): 14–20. For a more extended description, see Gerald Blidstein, *Honor Thy Father and Mother* (New York: Ktav, 1975). For a description of the duties of parents toward their children, see Ben-Zion Schereschewsky, "Parent and Child," *Encyclopaedia Judaica* 13:95–100. Vol. 10 of *The Jewish Law Annual* (Boston: Boston University Institute of Jewish Law, and Philadelphia: Harwood Academic Publishers, 1992) was devoted in its entirety to legal aspects of the relationships between parents and children. While the Talmud and later Jewish law codes do not speak of D.I. children specifically, they do require that children honor and respect their stepparents (B. *Ketubbot* 103a; *S.A., Y.D.* 240:21), and the same would clearly apply to the social parents of D.I. children.
29. I have written about this in several contexts: "The Interaction of Jewish Law with Morality," *Judaism* 26, no. 4 (fall 1977): 455–66; "Judaism as a Religious Legal System," *Hastings Law Journal* 29, no. 6 (July 1978): 1331–60, esp.

1347–60; and (with Arthur Rosett) *A Living Tree: The Roots and Growth of Jewish Law* (Albany: State University of New York Press, 1988), 249–57.

30. Bleich, *Judaism and Healing*, 80.
31. Immanuel Jakobovits, *Jewish Medical Ethics* (New York: Bloch, 1959, 1972), 248–49. Cf. 244–50 and 272–73 generally. Cf. also Bleich, ibid., 81–84; Alex J. Goldman, *Judaism Confronts Contemporary Issues* (New York: Shengold, 1978), 74–86. This was also the opinion of Rabbi Jacob Breish, who engaged in a vigorous debate with Rabbi Moshe Feinstein, agreeing with him that donor insemination was technically legal, but asserting that it would result in a general decline of moral values, that "from the point of view of our religion these ugly and disgusting things should not be done, for they are similar to the deeds of the land of Canaan and its abominations." 3 *Ḥelkat Ya'akov*, 45–51. For the debate with Rabbi Feinstein: *Dibbrot Moshe, Ketubbot*, 232–48.
32. Paul Lauritzen, "Pursuing Parenthood: Reflections on Donor Insemination," *Second Opinion* (July 1991): 63. I thank Rabbi Aaron Mackler for calling my attention to this article and those listed on this topic in n. 36 below.
33. Ibid., 65, 66.
34. Sissela Bok, *Lying: Moral Choice in Public and Private Life* (New York: Vantage Books, 1978), 224; cited in Lauritzen, "Pursuing Parenthood," 69.
35. Ibid.
36. Ibid., 69. Cf. Rona Achilles, "Anonymity and Secrecy in Donor Insemination: In Whose Best Interests?" in *Sortir la maternité du laboratoire* (Montreal: Government of Quebec, 1988), 156–63 (nn. on 407–8); and Patricia P. Mahlstedt and Dorothy A. Greenfeld, "Assisted Reproductive Technology with Donor Gametes: The Need for Patient Preparation," *Fertility and Sterility* 52, no. 6 (Dec. 1989): 908–14.
37. Richard Doren has stressed this point in arguing for greater control of sperm donations while preserving donor confidentiality; see Richard Doren, "The Need for Regulation of Artificial Insemination by Donor," *San Diego Law Review* 22 (1985): 1193–1218.
38. Yeh and Yeh, *Legal Aspects of Infertility*, 48.
39. *Jhordan C. v. Mary K. and Victoria T.*, 179 Cal. App. 3d 386, 224 Cal. Rptr. 530 (1986).
40. Doren, "The Need for Regulation of Artificial Insemination by Donor"; L. Thomas Styron, "Artificial Insemination: A New Frontier for Medical Malpractice and Medical Products Liability," *Loyola Law Review* 32 (1986): 411–46; Anita M. Hodgson, "The Warranty of Sperm: A Modest Proposal to Increase the Accountability of Sperm Banks and Physicians in the Performance of Artificial Insemination Procedures," *Indiana Law Review* 26 (1993): 357–86. Styron, 443 n. 190, records the donor agreement recommended by the American Fertility Society to preserve the donor's anonymity while making him responsible to notify a designated party "should I contract any contagious or venereal disease."

41. Hodgson, ibid., 359 and n. 10 there. See 1991 Cal. Adv. Legis. Serv. 801 (Deering); FLA. STAT. ch. 381.6105 (1990); IND. CODE, par. 16-8-7.5–6 (1988).
42. Hodgson, ibid., 360 and n. 12 there.
43. *C.M. v. C.C.*, 377 A.2d 82, 152 N.J. Super 160 (Juvenile and Domestic Relations court, Cumberland County, N.J.), 1977; *Jhordan C. v. Mary K. and Victoria T.* (see n. 39 above); *In the Interest of R.C.*, 775 P.2d 27, 34 (Colo. 1989). The condition that the donor show interest in serving as the father through his consistent actions is critical, for the U.S. Supreme Court, in ruling that a biological father who had no relationship with the child was not entitled to notice of the child's adoption proceedings, held in *Lehr v. Robertson* 463 U.S. 248, 103 S.Ct 2985, 77 L.Ed.2d 614 (1983) that "the mere existence of a biological link does not merit equivalent constitutional protection" to one who did maintain a relationship with the child.
44. S. Elias and G. J. Annas, "Social Policy Considerations in Noncoital Reproduction," *Journal of the American Medical Association* 255 (1986): 62, cited in Mahlstedt and Greenfeld, 911. These laws also prohibit payment for specimens and mixing of donor and husband sperm.
45. Yeh and Yeh, 45–46.
46. The Health Department is mandated to keep such records in Alabama, Colorado, Minnesota, Montana, Nevada, New Jersey, and Wisconsin; a local court or the Registrar of Vital Statistics keeps such records in Connecticut, Idaho, Kansas, New Mexico, Oklahoma, Oregon, Washington, and Wyoming. See Yeh and Yeh, *Legal Aspects of Infertility,* 45–46.
47. Mahlstedt and Greenfeld, 911.
48. Lauritzen, "Pursuing Parenthood," 71.
49. For a recent, poignant article about this, see Susan Chira, "Years After Adoption, Adults Find Past, and New Hurdles," *New York Times,* 30 Aug. 1993, A1, C11. I thank Prof. Vicki Michel and Rabbi Elie Spitz for calling my attention to this article.
50. Mahlstedt and Greenfeld, 913.
51. On this topic and on many others relevant to this responsum, see David M. Feldman, *Birth Control in Jewish Law* (New York: New York University Press, 1968), esp. chaps. 9–13.
52. I spell out some of the advantages of encasing values in law in my article "The Interaction of Morality and Jewish Law," *Judaism* 26, no. 4 (fall 1977): 455–66, and in my book *Knowing God: Jewish Journeys to the Unknowable* (Northvale, N.J.: Jason Aronson, 1992), 71–75.
53. Thus, in the case of divorce, children under the age of six must be put into the custody of their mother, for they are mainly in need of the physical care and attention that mothers typically give children at that age; and above the age of six, boys must be with their father, so that he can carry out his obligation to teach his male children Torah, while girls must be with their mother so that she can instruct them in the ways of modesty; see B. *Ketubbot* 102b, 103a; *M.T., Laws of*

Marriage (*Ishut*) 21:17; *S.A., E.H.* 82:7. One talmudic passage even describes differing contributions of each parent in the physical makeup of the child, the mother contributing red matter (probably because menstrual blood is red) and the father contributing white matter (probably because semen is white), while God, each person's third parent according to the Rabbis, breathes life into the child; see B. *Niddah* 31a. These differing roles lead to differing reactions of the child to each parent, which, according to the Rabbis, explains why the Torah commands us to honor the father before the mother (Exod. 20:12), but to revere the mother before the father (Lev. 19:3); see *Mekhilta,* "Masekhta de-Baḥodesh" (ed. Horowitz-Rabin), 8, p. 232 and its parallel in B. *Kiddushin* 30b–31a (although that version lacks the significant phrase "Where a deficiency exists, He filled it"), and see *Sifra,* "Kedoshim" 1:9 (87a) and M. *Keritot,* end (trans. H. Danby), 572, according to which even the mother must honor the father.

In modern times, we would certainly have a different understanding of what and how each parent contributes to the biological makeup of the child, and we would probably dispute the rigid roles for mothers and fathers delineated in the sources, too; but the underlying point that parents of both genders have distinctive roles to play is, I think, still right. This is one instance of my general approach to matters of gender, for I have long affirmed that men and women are equal, but, at least in some significant ways beyond their anatomies, different; see my article "Equality with Distinction," in Judith Glass and Elliot N. Dorff, *Male and Female God Created Them* (Los Angeles: University of Judaism [the *University Papers* series], 1984), 13–23. More current research, e.g., Deborah Tannen, *You Just Don't Understand: Women and Men in Conversation* (New York: Ballantine Books, 1990), confirms that thesis all the more. This makes it all the more important for children to have caring adults of both genders in their lives.

54. For a popular summary of this, see Lee Smith, "The New Wave of Illegitimacy," *Fortune,* 18 Apr. 1994, 81–94. According to Smith:

Data on thousands of children collected for the Department of Health and Human Services show that:

> —Kids from single-parent families, whether through divorce or illegitimacy, are two to three times as likely to have emotional or behavioral problems, and half again as likely to have learning disabilities, as those who live with both parents.
>
> —Teenage girls who grow up without their fathers tend to have sex earlier. A 15-year-old who has lived with her mother only, for example, is three times as likely to lose her virginity before her 16th birthday as one who has lived with both parents. (82)

Smith also cites David Popenoe, a Rutgers University sociologist, who says that while the social sciences can seldom prove anything in the strict sense of proof, there remains "a strong likelihood that the increase in the number of fatherless children over the past 30 years has been a prominent factor in the growth of violence and juvenile delinquency." More than half of the 14,000 inmates surveyed by the Justice Department in 1991 did not live with both parents while they were growing up (82). The consensus of the experts Smith consulted indicates that "a father shows a child, especially a boy, how to fit into the community. Dr. Frank Pittman, an Atlanta psychiatrist, says in his recent book, *Man Enough,* that a father's role is not to make his sons more aggressive or to show them how to take what is theirs. On the contrary, his function is to define the limits of manhood. A boy doesn't have to be John Wayne. Jimmy Stewart is man enough" (94).

The movie cited is *Made in America* (1993), with Whoopi Goldberg and Ted Danson, in which the daughter presumably born using the sperm Danson's character donated to a sperm bank in his teens seeks him out when she is a senior in high school. The movie bespeaks two worries about D.I.—that the children will have a deep-seated need to know their biological fathers, and that sperm banks will not keep accurate records.

55. That was the ruling of the Juvenile and Domestic Relations Court in *C.M. v. C.C.* (1977), the California Court of Appeals in *Jhordan C. v. Mary K. and Victoria T.,* and the Colorado Supreme Court in *In the Interest of R.C.* (1989), all at n. 43 above, and also the Oregon Court of Appeals in *McIntyre v. Crouch,* 780 P.2d 239, 98 Or. App. 462 (1989).
56. This was the basis of the recent Virginia ruling that Sharon Bottoms could not retain custody of her daughter, born by artificial insemination. Va. is one of just four states where legal precedent deems gay parents unfit (Ark., Mo., and N.Dak. are the others), and N.H. and Fla. categorically bar gays as adoptive parents. On the other hand, in the nation's capital, local officials held a seminar in the summer of 1993 to instruct gays on how to adopt, and N.J., Mass., and six other states explicitly permit a lesbian to adopt her lover's child and become a second parent. See "Gay Parents: Under Fire and on the Rise," *Time,* 20 Sept. 1993, 66–71. American law, in all its diversity, is another factor that must be considered in artificial insemination of single women, and the matter is clearly complicated further if the women involved are lesbians.
57. Our colleague Rabbi David Golinkin has written a responsum on one aspect of these questions; see his paper "Artificial Insemination for a Single Woman," *Responsa of the Va'ad Halakhah of the Rabbinical Assembly of Israel* (Jerusalem: The Rabbinical Assembly of Israel and the Masorti Movement, 5748/49), 3:83–92. I am sure that his is only the first of many responsa that will deal with what is, for all of us, a very new kind of family. The question is no longer whether such families exist, for a considerable number of women have already been artificially impregnated; the question is rather what Jewish law should say about such procedures, and why.

Newsweek (2 Aug. 1993, Michele Ingrassia et al., "Daughters of Murphy Brown," 59) reported:

> The greatest burden of single parenthood falls on the children. As research increasingly shows, children reared in one-parent families tend to have more educational, emotional, and financial difficulties than those who grow up with two parents. Since the problems are often economic, some of the effects may be eased for children of well-educated, middle-class women. Psychologist Anna Beth Benningfield argues that children can accept any situation as normal, as long as there's a strong sense of family. Though [single parent Jane] Saks would have preferred a more conventional setup, she believes it makes little difference in an era of sky-high divorce rates. . . . What is critical is how mother responds when her child asks: where's Dad?

In checking with some child psychologists, current research indicates that children, on average, indeed do worse with one parent rather than with two, but only when that single parent is isolated as the only caregiver for the child. If the parent has sufficient funds to hire help, or if, in poor or rich families, there is a strong network of support from family and friends, children do no worse, on average, than they do with two parents. In making these comparisons, one must remember that the criteria for measuring adjustment and well-being are themselves sometimes at issue and that many contemporary families with two parents are themselves dysfunctional. Still, this remains a concern.

The one clear thing is that children born to a Jewish woman through artificial insemination are fully Jewish.

58. According to the 1987 national survey commissioned by the United States Office of Technology Assessment [see chap. 1, n. 8 of this vol.], 11,000 physicians around the country provided artificial insemination services to approximately 172,000 women. Eighty percent of the requests for artificial insemination were prompted by male infertility in the husband of a couple; only 4 percent (approximately 5,000 women) were cases of single women seeking to become pregnant. On the other hand, the California Cryobank, based on its own records, estimates that approximately 25 percent of the women requesting artificial insemination today (1994) are without male partners. That is quite some discrepancy! Still, even with the 25 percent figure, the vast majority (75 percent) of artificial inseminations are done for infertile couples, the subject of this responsum. See Fader, *Sperm Banking*, 6, 11.
59. Gina Kolata, "New Pregnancy Hope: A Single Sperm," *New York Times*, 11 Aug. 1993, C11. I thank Rabbi Avram Reisner for drawing my attention to this. Fader maintains that Alan Trounson reported success with microinjection of an individual human sperm into a human egg at the Sixth World Congress on Human Reproduction in Tokyo in 1987; see Fader, *Sperm Banking*, 10.
60. In any case, many health insurance plans do not include payment for IVF, and since egg donation requires that, it may become the privilege of only the rich and therefore, quite rare.

donation. In cases in which a woman cannot produce eggs but can carry a fetus, she may have eggs of a donor woman fertilized in a test tube with either the sperm of her (that is, the infertile woman's) husband or of a donor, and then the zygote is implanted in her uterus for gestation. Even if a woman over the age of forty can produce eggs, the success rate of IVF (in vitro fertilization) in such women is so dismal that doctors generally recommend the use of a younger woman's eggs instead.

This procedure is much newer than artificial insemination because semen can be obtained through simple ejaculation, while the techniques for harvesting and preserving eggs for donation have been developed only in recent years. Egg donation is also more dangerous to the donor than artificial insemination is. A man who produces sperm for purposes of donation does not thereby entail any physical danger (although there may be psychological or legal risks for him in such donations, as discussed above [in the previous chapter]). The same immunity from physical danger does not apply to the woman who produces eggs for donation. To increase the chances of producing a baby, and to reduce the number of times the donor must undergo the procedure to harvest the eggs, the woman's ovaries must be stimulated by drugs to produce multiple eggs. As discussed below, there is some evidence that this increases her risk of having ovarian cancer and some other maladies, especially if she does this often. The number of women who are willing to donate eggs is therefore considerably and understandably smaller than the pool of semen donors.

One can understand why the recipients want to use donated eggs. Unlike adoption, egg donation allows the woman to go through pregnancy, and many women want to have that experience. Moreover, a woman who can bear a child but who cannot produce eggs may seek a woman with characteristics similar to her own to donate eggs so that the offspring will look like her and, assuming that her husband's sperm is used, like her husband as well. The same desires often lead couples who need D.I. (donor insemination) to seek a donor similar in characteristics to the husband.

Couples sometimes want children who look like them to maximize their own feelings and those of the child of belonging to each other while simultaneously minimizing the awareness of family, friends, and others that the child became the couple's through any process other than the usual way. This is understandable; for all of us, part of the lure of having children is that they represent one of the ways in which we gain eternity, a piece of us that remains after we die. There is, however, inherent racism involved in refusing to adopt a child of a race different from one's own, and that is theologically and legally problematic. God, according to our tradition, created all people, with no race inherently more worthy than any other, and membership in a particular race is not a necessary condition for being Jewish—as the plethora of races among Israel's Jews amply attests. Race is not a sufficient condition for being Jewish, either, as the many non-Jews of all races demonstrate. Consequently, while such discrimination may be acceptable in the name of enabling the couple and the child to overcome some of the problems inherent in egg donation, D.I., or adoption so that the parents and child can bond all the more effectively, rabbis must help couples see that these procedures are possible and fully valid within Jewish law with donors and children of any race as long as conversion takes place when necessary.

One critical factor that makes egg donation less acceptable than artificial insemination, though, is the extra danger for the donor. Jewish law does not permit one to endanger oneself unduly: "[The strictures against] endangering oneself are more stringent than [those against violating] a prohibition," says the Talmud.[1] One must not "stand idly by the blood of one's neighbor," according to the Torah, and so some risk is required or at least permitted to save the life of another; but in the case of egg donation, we are not talking about saving a life but rather enabling a couple to conceive a new life. Since no physical danger will ensue to the couple if they fail in that project, we cannot justify the danger to the egg donor on that basis. While the risks to the donor are not so great as to force us to ban the procedure entirely out of concern for the life or health of the donor, they are significant enough for us to say that egg donation should only be used when the couple has seriously considered all other options for having children, including adoption.

2. Moral and psychological issues in egg donation. For the infertile couple, most of the moral and psychological issues in egg donation are the same as those we already have encountered in artificial insemination [see chapter 2 of this volume]. If the sperm used is the husband's, the couple will face the asymmetry mentioned above—although in the opposite direction, for the husband will be biologically related to the offspring while the wife will not be a provider of the child's gametes. Unlike a husband in the case of donor insemination, though, a woman in the case of egg donation has a biological link to the child. A woman who carries a child, even if the egg came from another woman, has the satisfaction of being the gestational mother, a source of meaning and connection to the child that a man can never experience. If the husband cannot produce sperm with sufficient number or motility so that the couple must use both donated sperm and eggs, both social parents will not be the biological parents of the child, in which case they must face the problems that adoptive parents encounter. The openness in communication required of all parties involved in artificial insemination must therefore characterize cases of egg donation as well. Finally, the same demographic crisis and the same compassion for the infertile couple that should affect our understanding of artificial insemination should likewise incline us to permit egg donation when the couple cannot have a child in any other way.

Legally, in egg donation, as in artificial insemination, contact of the genital organs and intent to have an adulterous relationship are both missing, so that the prohibition against adultery is not relevant. In light of the added expense and the significantly decreased chances of success over artificial insemination, egg donation is even less plausibly construed as a form of licentiousness.

The paucity of egg donors makes it permissible for a fertile sister to donate eggs to an infertile one. Since donor sperm is readily available and inexpensive, it is generally inadvisable for a fertile brother to donate sperm for the impregnation of his infertile brother's wife, for while that is not technically incest, it feels very close to it and raises all kinds of boundary problems for the brothers and the child later on ("Is Uncle Barry really only my uncle, or is he my substitute father when I want him to be?").[2] Since donated eggs are less available and more expensive, and since the lack of genital contact means that legally there is no taint of incest, we would allow a fertile sister to donate eggs to her infertile sibling, but only after appropriate counseling and careful consideration of how the sisters are going to handle these boundary questions as the child grows.

3. *The Jewish identity of the child.* There is only one source in the Jewish tradition, to my knowledge, that even contemplates anything close to egg donation. Noting that the Torah specifically calls Dinah "the daughter of Leah" (Gen. 30:21) rather than following its more usual practice of identifying the child by her father's name, the Talmud tells a story to explain why the Torah did this. When Jacob already had ten sons, the story goes, Leah became pregnant. She knew that Jacob was to father a total of twelve sons, and she did not want her sister, Rachel, to bear him fewer than the two sons whom each of the maidservants, Bil-

hah and Zilpah, had already produced. Consequently, Leah prayed that the child she was carrying not be a boy, and ultimately Dinah was born to her. The most common understanding of that story is that in response to Leah's prayers, God changed the gender of the child in utero. (For some reason, the commentators never imagined that Leah could have been carrying a girl in the first place!) The *Targum Jonathan,* however, understands the story to mean that in response to Leah's prayers, God exchanged the female child (Dinah) in Rachel's womb with the male child (Joseph) in Leah's, thus effecting an embryo transfer so that Leah would give birth to a girl and Rachel to her first son. Rabbi Samuel Edels (the "Maharsha," 1555–1631) also claims that this is the correct interpretation of the talmudic story.

The question is whether this interpretation of the story, which is ultimately built on the Torah's identification of Dinah as Leah's daughter, should serve as a precedent for determining the identity of the mother of a child conceived through egg donation. Even if we assume that the story is indeed one of embryo transfer, and even if we ignore the fact that in the story God is the one who effects the embryo transfer rather than human beings, there are real questions as to whether any story should be used for legal rulings, and all the more so one such as this, which is really only one possible interpretation of what is, in turn, a talmudic tale. Rabbi J. David Bleich, who called attention to the story, himself casts doubt on the use of it for this purpose.[3]

Other grounds, however, support the holding that the bearing mother, rather than the egg donor, should be identified as the mother of the child. Specifically, Jewish law, in general, defines a child's native religion according to the religion of the birth mother at the time of birth.[4] Therefore, if a woman converts to Judaism during pregnancy, the child is born a Jew.[5] For purposes of redemption of the firstborn son, Jewish law defines that child as the one who "opens the womb."[6] All these precedents assume that the birth mother provides genetic materials as well, but the law clearly focuses not on conception or gestation, but on birth. The only factor that would argue against defining the status of the child according to the birth mother is the parallel to fatherhood, for, as we have noted, it is the sperm donor, rather than the social father, who counts as the genetic father in Jewish law. There, however, the social father is never physically involved with the child until after birth, while in the case of egg donation, the birth mother's body nurtures the child throughout gestation. As a result, in accordance with the line of precedents noted above that make the status of the mother at birth the defining factor for determining the religious identity of the child, we hold that a child born to a Jewish woman is Jewish, regardless of the religious status of the ovum donor.[7]

4. The problem of selective abortions. Because the rate of success with IVF, GIFT, and ZIFT is currently so low, the standard practice in North America among infertility specialists is to implant four or five sets of gametes (GIFT) or zygotes (IVF or ZIFT) each cycle in the hope of raising the odds of success to 25 percent or so. The use of multiple eggs in any attempt at impregnation, however, produces the need in some cases to abort one or more fetuses. Women can generally safely carry up to three children, but being able to bear more than three healthy babies without undue threat to the mother's health is rare, and so the common practice is to abort all but three fetuses if more than that number successfully implant into the uterus. In most cases, the couple is lucky if even one of the implants "takes"—indeed, they are then beating three-to-one odds—but in some instances, all four or five attach themselves to the uterus and begin to develop.

The Jewish tradition requires abortion when the mother's life or health is at stake, and it sanctions it when there is a risk to her life or health beyond that of normal pregnancy. Abortion, though, is generally prohibited, and the burden of proof is always on the one who wants to abort. We therefore do not want to create situations where we know ahead of time that we may well have to abort one or more fetuses.

Moreover, abortion often engenders psychological issues, even if it is necessary. Those are likely to be all the more severe for a couple with fertility problems.[8] Therefore, to avoid the need for selective abortions as much as possible, Jews may implant preferably two, or at most three, zygotes for IVF or ZIFT and may use preferably two, or at most three, eggs for GIFT.

5. The obligation to procreate. Couples who choose not to use egg donation as a means of overcoming their infertility need not feel guilty. As noted above,[9] even though men clearly cannot have children without women, the Rabbis restricted the commandment to procreate to men. Since women do not fall under that legal obligation, infertile women are not failing to fulfill any commandments relevant to them by refusing to be impregnated by donated eggs. Given the potential psychological problems engendered by the asymmetry involved in producing a child with the husband's sperm but another woman's egg, one can understand why some women would refuse to undergo the procedure, and that refusal must be respected.

This will mean that the woman's husband will not be able to procreate with his wife (assuming that his sperm is fit to produce children), and the Mishnah rules that a man who cannot procreate with his wife after trying for ten years must divorce her and marry another in an attempt to fulfill the commandment to procreate.[10] By the late Middle Ages, though, that rule had largely fallen into disuse, as Rabbi Moses Isserles ultimately codifies:

> Today it is not the custom to force somebody on this issue. Similarly, anybody who has not fulfilled the commandment "be fruitful and multiply" and goes to marry a woman who is not capable of having children because of sterility, age, or youth, because he loves her or [even] for her wealth, even though by law we should prevent such a marriage, it has not been the practice for many generations for the court to interfere in the affairs of couples. Similarly, if a man marries a woman and waits ten years [without children], we do not force him to divorce her, although he has not fulfilled the commandment "be fruitful and multiply." And the same applies to other matters regarding couples.[11]

Infertile couples who choose not to pursue egg donation need not feel that they are thereby violating Jewish law. Again, they may use egg donation as a means to have children, but they are not required to do so. Those who opt not to use this method should consider adoption, which will satisfy many of the same needs and will open the couple to the possibility of fulfilling many other commandments associated with children.

B. Donating One's Sperm or Eggs

Until now, we have considered artificial insemination and egg donation from the point of view of the couple seeking children. What about the donors? As we have said above [in chapter 1], virtually all halakhic authorities to date have permitted a husband to produce sperm for A.I.H. when he cannot impregnate his wife otherwise. But is it permissible for a Jewish man to donate his sperm for purposes of donor insemination? Conversely, may a Jewish woman donate her eggs for purposes of enabling another woman to become pregnant? If the answers to either or both of these questions is affirmative, are there any restrictions on that permission?

Donor insemination, it will be remembered, constitutes procreation in Jewish law on the part of the donor. This introduces an appropriate note of seriousness to semen donation. It is not, and should not be construed as, simply another job for a college or medical student to earn some spare change. The (typically) young man involved should recognize that he is making it possible for a couple to have a child, with all the positive implications of that for the couple and, if Jews are the recipients, for the Jewish people. He should approach this whole process, in other words, with a sense of mitzvah, duly appreciative of the awesomeness of the human ability to procreate and of his role in helping that happen for an infertile couple.

He should also understand that, like it or not, he will have an important, biological relationship to the offspring. He may want to keep his identity confidential so as not to incur any risk of personal or legal problems with the couple or with the child later on. Since the laws on this are not universal and not totally clear, he may indeed have to retain confidentiality to avoid such consequences, at least as many state laws in the United States are written now.

The donor should recognize, however, that since the child will inherit his genes, he should supply him or her with as much information about his physical and personal characteristics as possible without compromising the confidentiality of his identity. Only then can the child know enough about his or her medical history to take appropriate preventive and curative steps against genetically inherent diseases or susceptibilities to disease, and only then can the child avoid having sex with a genetic relative. Furthermore, as we have said above [in chapter 2], the more the donor reveals about his personal characteristics and interests, the more the child can achieve a sense of self-identity; thus, the donor should provide at least some of that information to the social parents and, through them, to the child.

The donor should also be concerned about his own future children not unwittingly marrying a genetic relative. This, too, argues for sharing as much information as possible with the child born of artificial insemination so that at least someone is guarding against such an occurrence. All these problems disappear if both he and the social parents decide to reveal their identities to each other and to the child, but that raises other problems, and he must consider those, too.

None of these difficulties should make semen donation forbidden; the great good of enabling an infertile couple to have a child outweighs them all. This includes any objections to the masturbation through which the semen will be procured, for the intent to produce a child removes any stigma of "wasting the seed." The donor, though, must at least understand the complications involved, as described above, and plan for how he will respond to them.

The same concerns apply to egg donation, but that procedure incurs the additional risks involved in procuring the eggs. Because doctors can now be guided by ultrasound to the ovaries so that they can remove eggs vaginally, surgery is no longer necessary to harvest eggs. To minimize the number of times that a woman must undergo the procedure and to maximize the possibility of pregnancy in the recipient, the woman must be treated with drugs to produce more than one egg. (Eggs cannot yet be frozen.) Recent studies have found, however, that there is some increased risk in egg donors of a number of maladies, including even stroke and heart attack, and that "women who had used fertility drugs had three times the risk of invasive epithelial ovarian cancer compared to women without a history of infertility . . . [and] four times the risk of ovarian tumors of low malignant potential (borderline tumors) seen among women lacking a history of infertility." On the other hand, as of 1988, 1.9 million women aged fifteen to forty-four years were estimated to have taken fertility drugs, and only a very small percentage of those have contracted ovarian cancer. As a result:

> At present, there is no need to change medical practice regarding use of fertility-enhancing drugs. There is enough cause of concern, however, to slightly alter the physician's approach to counseling patients. We suggest advising patients receiving fertility drugs as to the possible increased risk of ovarian cancer. Especially careful consideration should be given to counseling women who wish to donate eggs, particularly repeat donors, because they derive no reproductive benefit from their fertility drug exposure.[12]

With this state of medical knowledge, a Jewish woman may take on the risks of egg donation, but not repeatedly, and only if she is assured by physicians after due examination that she personally can do so without much danger to her own life or health, for that clearly takes precedence in Jewish law to the good of enabling an infertile couple to have children, as great a good as that is.

Egg donors face some of the same issues of confidentiality as do semen donors, but several of the factors are different. Sperm is not in short supply, but eggs are. Furthermore, no state currently has laws unequivocally declaring the social mother, and not the egg donor, to be the legal mother (perhaps because of the newness of the procedure); thus, the legal risks of future obligations are substantially greater for egg donors than they are for semen donors. These elements would argue for a greater measure of acceptance of confidentiality in egg donation than we would be prepared to accept in semen donation. On the other hand, the egg donor, no less than the semen donor, contributes substantially to the child's genetic structure, and so she, too, should reveal as much as possible of her medical history and personal characteristics for the good of the child.

C. Adoption

When a couple cannot have children, adoption is an available option. Several passages in the Bible suggest that adoption existed during biblical times,[13] although the evidence is equivocal and is not specified in any legal source of the Bible. In later Jewish law, adoption is not a defined institution as such, but rabbinic law provided for the approximate equivalent. The rabbinic court, "the father of all orphans,"[14] appoints guardians for orphans and children in need, and the guardians have the same responsibilities as natural parents have. They must care for the child's upbringing, education, and physical accommodations, and they must administer the child's property. If the guardian dies, his or her estate is responsible to continue providing for the child's care. The sense of guardianship in Jewish law is so strong that it was once invoked in a New York case to extend the obligations of the adoptive father beyond the demands of civil law.[15]

Contrary to modern, American adoption, however, in Jewish law the adoptive parents do not become the legal parents, but rather function as the agents of the natural parents.[16] Therefore, natural parents continue to have the usual parental obligations to the child, and the guardian fulfills those obligations on behalf of, but not in legal substitution for, the natural parents. Along the same lines, the personal status of the child in matters of Jewish identity, ritual, and marriage depends upon the status of the natural parents.[17] Therefore, when it is not known that the gestational mother was Jewish, the child must be formally converted.

At the same time, rabbinic sources express immense appreciation for the adoptive parents; taking a child who is, in essence, an orphan into one's home and raising that child is a *ḥesed* (an act of faithfulness, loving-kindness) of the first order. The Talmud says that one who does so "is as if he has given birth to him," and, in a source quoted earlier [in chapter 2] but that bears repeating, the Talmud notes that the adoptive parents manage to act rightly at all times:

> "Happy are they who act justly, who do right at all times" (Ps. 106:3). Is it possible to do right at all times? . . . Rabbi Samuel bar Naḥmani said: This refers to a person who brings up an orphan boy or girl in his house and enables him or her to marry.[18]

This appreciation has legal consequences. As we have noted above, the possessions, earnings, and findings of minor, adopted children go to their custodial, rather than their natural, parents; this is probably a matter of equity, for this provision is in partial compensation for the expenses of raising children.[19] Similarly, according to Rabbi Moses Sofer, adopted children do not incur the obligations of mourning upon the death of their natural parents, but they do have such obligations when their adoptive parents die.[20] In appreciation of the immensely significant role that adoptive parents have in their children's upbringing, and in recognition of the close bonds that adopted siblings create with one another, we consider adopted children, like children born through donor insemination, to have the status of relatives of the second degree (*sheniyot*), and therefore sex or marriage between them is prohibited. Furthermore, as with children born through D.I., the social father's (or parents') name(s) may be invoked when the child is being identified by his or her Hebrew name, as, for example, when being called to the Torah.

Many infertile Jewish couples cannot find Jewish children to adopt because of the high rate of abortion among Jews. That argues for two things: first, Jews should understand that while Jewish law requires abortion when the life or health of the mother is at stake and permits it when there is a risk to the mother's life or health above that of normal pregnancy, by and large the Jewish tradition prohibits abortion. Jews often wrongly assume that because Jewish law requires or permits abortion in some cases, it does so in all cases, and so all too many of our people are using abortion as a *post facto* form of birth control. They need to be disabused of this error in Jewish law—and made aware of the physical and psychological dangers involved in abortion. They also should come to understand that even if they cannot or will not care for the child, there is an abundance of infertile couples who would do so willingly and lovingly, and that makes nontherapeutic abortions even less justifiable.

Second, Jewish couples contemplating adoption need to widen their search to include non-Jewish children, including ones who are not of their own race. Conversion will be necessary, but for children that is a relatively easy process. As noted above, race is not a factor in Jewish identity—or in the joy (and troubles!) of raising children.[21] Similarly, it is not only infants and able-bodied children that a couple should consider for adoption; older children and those with some disability are also God's children—and are more available for couples seeking to adopt. Indeed, Jews should consider the possibility of adoption of such children even when they already have two or more children through their own sexual intercourse and have thereby fulfilled the demands of Jewish law to procreate.

At the same time, couples need to be aware of special legal and psychological issues that may arise in adoption. The highly publicized Baby Jessica case, in which a two-and-a-half-year-old child was taken in August 1993 from the adoptive parents who had raised her from birth and returned to her biological parents, indicates the importance of attending to the legal details of adoption—and of changing the laws in many states that made such a case possible. That is undoubtedly among the adoptive parents' worst nightmares, and it probably is not in the child's best interests, either. Biological parents do have a right and an obligation to care for their children, but if they give up the rights and obligations of parenthood in a formal, legal way, adoptive parents and children have the right to be secure in their status as a family.

More commonly, adoptive parents must face psychological issues. Family members may say insensitive things—or bend over backward in avoiding mention of the adoption. Adopted children will be reminded of their special status each time school forms ask for their medical history. During adolescence, when all children need to differentiate themselves from their parents and often feel misunderstood in the process, adopted children may think that their biological parents would understand them if they were present. That may be the occasion for some angry and hurtful remarks as the child attacks the adoptive parents where they are most vulnerable. Adopted children sometimes seek out their biological parents when they reach adulthood, and the adoptive parents need to understand that that does not usually mean that the child is rejecting them as parents. To cope with such issues, adoptive parents are well advised to get appropriate counseling even before the child comes into their home and should avail themselves of subsequent counseling as needed.

Along the same lines, Jewish men and women who are not able or willing to adopt should seriously consider becoming Jewish Big Brothers or Jewish Big Sisters to enable children who have lost their fathers or mothers through death or divorce to have a close, adult male or female model to balance the gender of their single parents as they grow up. Both adoption and service as a Jewish Big Brother or Big Sister are significant acts of *ḥesed* whose beneficial effects often last throughout the child's life, and thus those who perform these acts should feel religiously as well as personally confirmed and appreciated.

In sum, adoption is an honored course of action in our tradition. In light of the physical risks of egg donation, and in view of the tradition's overwhelmingly positive attitude toward adoption, we must urge couples to consider adoption before engaging in egg donation.

D. Summary

1. Egg donation. Similar conclusions to those seen in the preceding chapters on artificial insemination apply to egg donation. The act is not licentious, since there is no contact of the genital organs of the egg donor and the husband; thus, the child so conceived is fully legitimate. The bearing mother determines the Jewish identity of the child, regardless of the source of the egg. The same need for openness about the child's origins within the family—and the same desirability for the child to know as much as possible about the egg donor—apply to egg donation just as they apply to donor insemination. Because of the shortage of donated eggs, a fertile sister may donate eggs to her infertile sibling, despite the potential psychological problems involved, but only after appropriate counseling and only after all concerned determine that, on balance, the advantages of this arrangement outweigh its disadvantages.

way the commandment to procreate has been interpreted in Jewish sources, because of the physical dangers sometimes incurred, and because of the psychological problems involved in the asymmetry that these methods of having children sometimes create, infertile couples are not required to engage in these procedures to have children. For those who do use them, our endorsement of their choice to have children by these methods is not grudging, but enthusiastic. May God grant them the children they seek, and may they raise their children to Torah, the wedding canopy, and to good deeds.[22]

Notes

1. B. *Ḥullin* 10a. See B. *Berakhot* 32b; B. *Shabbat* 32a; B. *Bava Kamma* 15b, 80a, 91b; *M.T., Laws of Murder and the Guarding of Life* 11:4–5; *S.A., O.Ḥ.* 173:2; *Y.D.* 116:5, gloss.
2. A brother's sperm was used in levirate marriages (Deut. 25:5–10), but there the husband had died, and so there is no threat of the complications inherent in the blurring of roles between the brothers. Indeed, in that case, it would actually be in the child's best interest if the uncle acted as a substitute father.
3. The talmudic story: B. *Berakhot* 60a. The comment of *Targum Jonathan* is on Gen. 30:21. Maharsha's support of that interpretation: B. *Niddah* 31a. Rabbi J. David Bleich's refusal to use this source to determine the identity of the child's mother on the basis of parturition (along with Rabbi Joshua Feigenbaum) because halakhic principles are not derivable from aggadic sources (quite remarkable, given Rabbi Bleich's usual methodology): J. David Bleich, "Maternal Identity," *Tradition* 19, no. 4 (winter 1981): 359–60. See also Fred Rosner, *Modern Medicine and Jewish Ethics,* 2d ed. (Hoboken, N.J.: Ktav, and New York: Yeshiva University, 1991), 115–16. I would like to thank Rabbi Aaron Mackler for calling my attention to these materials.

   I think that we not only can use aggadic material as the source of general principles, but commonly do so in halakhic practice. Moreover, I think we should do so, for only then can our beliefs have impact on our actions. We must just be intelligent enough to understand that stories, unlike laws and judicial precedents, are not generally told in a form intended to be examined in legal detail but rather are to be read as articulating general principles, and we must also remember that stories, perhaps even more than legal precedents, may conflict with each other. In the use of stories for legal purposes, we must examine them, as we analyze potential precedents, for the analogies and false analogies between them and the case at hand. In the case here, I would agree with Rabbi Bleich that this story is a very thin reed on which to determine the mother's identity, not so much because it is aggadic, but because it represents only one reading of what is already a fantastic tale designed more to indicate the kindness of Leah and the miracles of God than the way rabbis should rule in cases of egg donation. For the general point about the use of stories within the context of legal reasoning, see my articles "Methodology in Jewish Medical Ethics," in *Jewish Law Association Studies VI: The Jerusalem 1990 Conference Volume,* ed. B. S. Jackson and S. M. Passamaneck (Atlanta: Scholars Press, 1992), 35–57 (reprinted as chap. 11 of *Contemporary Jewish Ethics and Morality: A Reader,* ed. Elliot N. Dorff and Louis E. Newman [New York: Oxford University Press, 1995]), and "A Jewish Approach to End-Stage Medical Care," *Conservative Judaism* 43, no. 3 (spring 1991): 4–7 [chap. 18, pp. 294-97 of this vol.]. See also Elliot N. Dorff, *Matters of Life and Death: A Jewish Approach to Modern Medical Ethics* (Philadephia: Jewish Publication Society, 1998), 404–17.

4. M. *Kiddushin* 3:12; B. *Kiddushin* 70a, 75b; B. *Yevamot* 16b, 23a, 44a, 45b; *M.T., Laws of Forbidden Intercourse* 15:3.
5. *S.A., Y.D.* 268:6.
6. Exod. 13:2, 12, 15; 34:19; Num. 3:12; 18:15.
7. When this responsum was approved by the CJLS, this matter had not yet been determined, and so I maintained then that unless both the ovum donor and the birth donor were Jewish, the child should undergo the rites of conversion. Subsequently, the CJLS approved the responsum of Rabbi Aaron Mackler ("In Vitro Fertilization, Draft No. 3," Nov. 1995, p. 12 [chap. 4, p. 109 of this vol.]), according to which "the woman who gestates [a donated ovum] and gives birth to the child is to be treated as the child's mother for purposes of Jewish law, including the determination of Jewish identity." I have therefore adjusted this printed version of my responsum to reflect that subsequent CJLS decision [see also chap. 8 of this vol.].

   This would mean that in the reverse situation, when a Jewish woman's egg is implanted into a non-Jewish surrogate for gestation and birth, the child would not be Jewish by birth and would need to undergo conversion.
8. I want to thank Rabbi Judah Kogen for calling my attention to the psychological aspects of this situation.
9. See chap. 1, n. 2 of this vol.
10. M. *Yevamot* 6:6. In mishnaic times, the man legally could have taken a second wife to fulfill the commandment to procreate, but the Mishnah does not mention that possibility, probably because by mishnaic times polygamy, while legal, was already frowned upon. Thus, not one of the more than 2,000 sages mentioned in the Talmud has a second wife, and a second wife was called a *tzarah,* trouble. See also the story of Rabbi Judah Hanasi's son, who could not have children with his wife. His father told him to divorce her, but he said, "People will say, 'This poor one waited all these years in vain.' " His father said, "Take a second wife," but he said, "People will say, 'This is his wife, and this is his concubine.' " He therefore prayed for her, and she was able to conceive (B. *Ketubbot* 62b). In any case, by the Middle Ages, polygamy was outlawed altogether in

Ashkenazic communities through the revision of the law (*takanah*) accredited to Rabbi Gershom of Mayence (d. 1028).

11. *S.A., E.H.* 1:3, gloss.
12. Robert Spirtas, Steven C. Kaufman, and Nancy J. Alexander, *Fertility and Sterility* [= the journal of the American Fertility Society] 59, no. 2 (Febr. 1993): 291–92. I thank my friend, Dr. Michael Grodin, for sharing this article with me. The 1988 congressional report also reported a number of other possible complications caused by commonly used drugs to stimulate the ovaries, including early pregnancy loss, multiple gestations (fetuses), ectopic pregnancies, headache, hair loss, pleuropulmonary fibrosis, increased blood viscosity and hypotension, stroke, and myocardial infarction; see U.S. Congress, Office of Technology Assessment, *Infertility: Medical and Social Choices,* OTA-BA-358 (Washington, D.C.: U.S. Government Printing Office, 1988), 128–29. Once again, the demonstrated risks are not so great as to make stimulation of the ovaries for egg donation prohibited as a violation of the Jewish command to guard our health, but they are sufficient to demand that caution be taken and that the number of times a woman donates eggs be limited.
13. For example, Gen. 15:2–3 and 48:5–6 are probably the most plausible cases, but some suggest that all or some of the following passages refer to adoption as well: Gen. 16:2, 30:3, 38:8–9, 50:23; Exod. 2:10; Lev. 18:9; Deut. 25:6; Ps. 77:16; Ruth 4:16–17; Esther 2:7, 15; Ezra 2:61, 10:44; and 1 Chron. 2:35–41, 4:18. The evidence is murky, especially when one tries to differentiate adoption from fosterage and from inheritance rights alone. See Jeffrey Tigay, *Encyclopaedia Judaica* 2:298–301, s.v. "Adoption"; and Michael Broyde, "Marital Fraud," *Loyola of Los Angeles International and Comparative Law Journal* 16, no. 1 (Nov. 1993): 97 n. 11.
14. *Bava Kamma* 37a; *Gittin* 37a.
15. *Wener v. Wener* 59 Misc. 2d 959, 301 N.Y. Supp. 2d 237 (Sup. Ct. 1969); and cf. appeal, 35 App. Div. 2d 50, 312 N.Y. Supp. 2d 815 (2d Dept. 1970), where the judgment was affirmed but not its religious grounds.
16. Michael Broyde claims ("Marital Fraud," 97 n. 11) that there are four instances in the Bible in which adoptive parents are called natural parents, but, as noted in n. 13 above, all the biblical instances of possible adoption are unclear. In any case, the Talmud assumes those ascriptions of parentage not to be legal pronouncements, but rather descriptions of the close relationships between the children and adoptive parents: see 1 Chron. 4:18; Ruth 4:17; Ps. 77:16; 2 Sam. 21:8; and B. *Sanhedrin* 9b.

    Broyde (ibid., n. 10) calls attention to the disparate approaches taken by Roman and U.S. law, which severed all previous relationships between the biological parents and the adopted children (to the point that, until recent amendments, the parties to the adoption were to remain anonymous to each other), as against British common law, which rejected the institute of adoption altogether, as against the intermediate position taken by Jewish law, which saw the adopted parents as agents of the biological parents. He cites, among other articles, C. M. A. McLauliff, "The First English Adoption Law and Its American Precursors," *Seton Hall Law Review* 16 (1986): 659–60, and Sanford N. Katz, "Rewriting the Adoption Story," *Family Advocate* 5 (1982): 9–13. Because of the theory underlying U.S. law, most states still ascribe to adoption law the ability to re-create maternal and paternal relationships even if the child, under the new legislation passed in many states, knows the biological parents.

17. Cf. *Encyclopaedia Judaica* 2:298–303, s.v. "Adoption"; 3:218–22, s.v. "Apotropos"; and 12:1478–80, s.v. "Orphan," for a summary of all the laws in this and the last paragraph. See especially B. *Sanhedrin* 19b; *S.A., E.H.* 15:11. Cf. also Broyde, "Marital Fraud," 96–100, who points out that in this way Jewish law is in marked contrast to Roman law as well as American law, but in agreement with British common law.
18. B. *Megillah* 13a; B. *Ketubbot* 50a. See also *Exodus Rabbah,* chap. 4; *S.A., O.Ḥ.* 139:3; Abraham Gombiner, *Magen Avraham, S.A., O.Ḥ.* 156; Moshe Feinstein, *Iggerot Moshe, Y.D.* 161.
19. B. *Sanhedrin* 12b awards such possessions to the child's father; *S.A., Ḥ.M.* 370:2 specifies that this means the child's custodial father; and Rabbi J. Falk, *Me'irat Einayim,* on *S.A., Ḥ.M.* 370:2, suggests that this is a matter of equity. Thus, a financially independent minor does not transfer his income to his parents because he is supporting himself; cf. *S.A., Ḥ.M.* 370:2.
20. M. Sofer, *Responsa,* 1 *O.Ḥ.* 164. Sofer assumes that mourning is a rabbinic institution, which itself is a matter of dispute: compare *S.A., Y.D.* 398:1 with Moses Isserles, *Y.D.* 399:13, gloss. For other examples of rabbinic institutions not strictly applied in the context of custodial parentage, see, generally, *S.A., O.Ḥ.* 139:3; *Magen Avraham, S.A., O.Ḥ.* 156; *Iggerot Moshe, Y.D.* 161.
21. Despite the thousands of black children waiting to be adopted, it may not be easy for white people to adopt them, for state and private adoption agencies, often backed by state laws, prohibit such adoption for fear that white parents will undermine the ethnic identity of the child. See Lynn Smith, "Salvation or Last Resort?" *Los Angeles Times,* 3 Nov. 1993, E-1, 3.
22. I would like to thank the following physicians for helping me with the medical and general ethical aspects of this responsum [this chapter and the two preceding chapters in this volume]: Dr. Brenda Fabe, M.D., a gynecologist/obstetrician at Kaiser Permanente Medical Center in West Los Angeles and director of physicians for Camp Ramah in California; Dr. Michael Grodin, M.D., professor of medical ethics at Boston University School of Medicine; and Dr. Cappy Miles Rothman, a male-infertility specialist and urologist in Los Angeles. I would also like to thank Professor Vicki Michel, J.D., past cochair of the Los Angeles County Joint Commission on Bioethics of the American Bar Association and the American Medical Association, and Professor Arthur Rosett of UCLA School of Law, both of whom helped me with the sections of this responsum referring to U.S. law and some general ethical concerns as well. In addition, Rabbis Kassel

Abelson, David Feldman, Aaron Mackler, Avram Reisner, and Joel Roth, my fellow members of the Subcommittee on Bioethics of the Committee on Jewish Law and Standards, had significant input on many aspects of this responsum, and I am indebted to them. As usual, none of the people mentioned here is responsible for any of the errors or judgments of this responsum, but they all have contributed immensely to my own thinking on these complicated issues, and they have my sincere appreciation as colleagues and as friends.

B. IN VITRO FERTILIZATION

Introduction

This paper by Rabbi Aaron L. Mackler addresses halakhic questions entailed by in vitro fertilization (IVF). In this procedure, a human egg cell is fertilized outside the human body, and transferred to a woman's uterus for gestation. After a brief statement of relevant Jewish values, the paper presents relevant background material on the medical procedure of IVF and the biology of the early stages of embryonic development. Attention is then given to the "simple case" of IVF, in which a wife's egg and a husband's sperm are joined. It is argued that this procedure is halakhically acceptable in appropriate cases, though never obligatory.

A number of more particular questions are examined. IVF and preimplantation genetic testing may be used by a couple to avoid having a child with a severe genetic disease, but should not generally be used for gender selection. To avoid risks associated with multifetal pregnancy, no more than three embryos (and preferably two) should be transferred for implantation. Embryos that are not transferred may be frozen for later use. Couples could maintain embryos in their frozen state indefinitely, but it would be permissible to thaw (and thereby discard) embryos that the couple does not want to implant.

The use of donated sperm, eggs, or embryos raises significant halakhic and personal concerns. Couples considering these procedures should consider these issues; following reflection and counseling, they could appropriately decide to use donated material, or not to pursue this option. Conversely, after careful consideration of the implications of their actions, a couple may choose to donate an embryo formed from their sperm and egg to enable another couple to have a child.

CHAPTER 4

In Vitro Fertilization*

Aaron L. Mackler

She'eilah (Question):

In vitro fertilization (IVF) involves the fertilizing of a human ovum (egg cell) by sperm outside the human body. The resulting embryo can be transferred to a woman's uterus for gestation and (when successful) the birth of a child. This technique gives rise to a number of important questions:

1. May an infertile couple utilize IVF, using the husband's sperm and the wife's egg, to have a child? What is the status of the offspring?
2. Does halakhah provide any guidance regarding the transfer of embryos to the woman's uterus for gestation?
3. May more embryos be created by IVF than are needed for immediate use? What may be done with extra embryos, including those that are cryopreserved (frozen)?
4. Is IVF using donated sperm or ova permitted? What is the status of the offspring?

Teshuvah (Response):

Judaism values children as a blessing for their parents and for the broader community. For those able to do so, having children represents the fulfillment of a mitzvah, one that can be traced back to God's

*Approved by the Rabbinical Assembly Committee on Jewish Law and Standards, Dec. 1995.

charge to "be fruitful and multiply" (*peru urevu*) in the biblical account of creation.[1] In vitro fertilization, like other reproductive technologies, offers the potential to bring a new child into the world. In appropriate cases, this can provide life to a child who otherwise would not have been born, add joy and harmony to the family, and contribute to the strengthening of the Jewish (and human) community.[2] At the same time, reproductive technologies can impose significant personal, financial, and physical costs on the individual or couple using them and, in some cases, on children born of the procedure.

More broadly, the use of reproductive technologies can affect communal values and practices concerning children, reproduction, and the family. The United States and other societies have explored these concerns through a variety of means, including examination by professional associations and interdisciplinary commissions and developments in civil law. In the Jewish tradition, the central means of responding to these concerns is through halakhah, or Jewish law.[3]

A. In Vitro Fertilization and Embryonic Development

In vitro fertilization involves the fertilization of an ovum outside the body; "in vitro," literally meaning "in glass," refers to the petri dish in which sperm and ova are combined. In the first successful use of IVF as a reproductive technology, British researchers Robert Edwards and Patrick Steptoe fertilized an ovum produced by Leslie Brown with sperm produced by her husband, and transferred the fertilized ovum to her uterus, leading to the birth of Louise Brown in July 1978.

As typically practiced today, a woman preparing for IVF receives hormones to stimulate the development of several ova. Shortly before ovulation would occur, a physician uses ultrasound to guide a needle through the cervix to the ovaries to gather or "retrieve" developed ova. After inspection and appropriate preparation, the ova are combined with prepared sperm. The resulting embryo is allowed to develop for up to a few days, reaching the stage of two to eight cells, and is then transferred to a woman's uterus, using a catheter inserted through the cervix. When the procedure is successful, the embryo continues to develop and implants in the uterus, leading to pregnancy and the birth of a child. At the two- to eight-cell stage, the embryo could be cryopreserved or "frozen" for transfer at a later time.[4]

In vitro fertilization was originally developed to assist women with damaged or absent fallopian tubes. The fallopian tube, connecting the ovary and the uterus, is typically the site of fertilization as well as the path by which the fertilized ovum reaches the uterus. IVF has also been used in response to other female infertility factors (such as endometriosis or ovulatory problems), for male factors, and for "unexplained infertility."[5] The Society for Assisted Reproductive Technology and the American Society for Reproductive Medicine report that in 1993, IVF and related procedures were performed for 50,844 cycles, leading to 8,741 deliveries. The most common procedure, IVF using the recipient's ova and without embryo freezing, led to the delivery of a child following 18.6 percent of egg retrievals. An individual's prospects might be significantly higher or lower, depending on personal and medical factors. For example, success rates have been found to be higher when no male factor is involved, and for women under the age of forty.[6]

The process of fertilization begins with the sperm penetrating the ovum. After about twenty-four hours, the chromosomes of the sperm and egg combine, a process referred to as syngamy. The embryo soon begins a series of cell divisions, but does not yet change in overall size. Within a few days, when the embryo has reached the eight-cell stage, the fusion of genetic material is complete and gene expression (functioning) begins. Transfer of an IVF embryo to a woman's uterus generally occurs between the two-cell and the eight-cell stage.[7]

A series of changes takes place between this stage—about day 3 after fertilization—and day 14. Through day 3, each cell has the ability to develop into any type of cell or to divide off and develop into a separate embryo. With increasing differentiation within the embryo, cells begin to lose this ability after day 3, but some such abilities may persist until about day 14. In the uterus, implantation begins at about seven days after fertilization, and is completed by about fourteen days. During this second week of development, the embryo begins to gain internal organization of a basic sort, such as the differentiation of the embryo itself from the placenta. At about day 14, the embryo first exhibits a "primitive streak," a clustering of cells at one end of the embryo. Formation of the neural groove, the rudimentary beginning of the nervous system, occurs in the third week. Current scientific capabilities generally cannot maintain an embryo in vitro beyond about the first week of development. As noted above, transfer of an embryo for reproduction occurs well before this time, at about day 3 of development.[8]

B. In Vitro Fertilization Using a Couple's Own Ova and Sperm

Most halakhic authorities who have addressed the issue of in vitro fertilization have treated this issue as similar to artificial insemination. Many permit in vitro fertilization using a wife's egg and a husband's sperm. Central issues typically include whether the husband violates the prohibition against "wasteful emission of seed," whether the couple can be sure that the embryo transferred to the woman in fact derives from their gametes (sperm and ova), and whether the husband fulfills the mitzvah of procreation. Thus, for example, Rabbi Ovadiah Yosef rules that IVF is permitted when it represents the only way for a couple to have children, and that the child is to be considered the parents' offspring in all regards.[9]

Rabbi Eliezer Yehudah Waldenberg represents an exception to this rule, arguing that IVF is more problematic than artificial insemination on technical grounds, and should be absolutely forbidden.[10] Rabbi Avigdor Nebenzal, writing in response to Waldenberg, raises a number of objections to his position. Prohibiting IVF, even as a last resort, could prevent the husband from fulfilling the mitzvah of procreation, increase the couple's anguish and bitterness of spirit, or lead to divorce. Producing sperm in order to fertilize an egg would not represent "emission of seed in vain," for the husband's intention is procreative. While IVF raises some legitimate concerns, these must be weighed against the "happiness of the couple among the people Israel."[11]

Rabbi J. David Bleich raises two additional concerns with the procedure. First, IVF is objectionable if it entails a risk for the embryo and increases the likelihood of a seriously impaired child. Bleich argues that the uncertainties inherent in the first uses of IVF would represent an unacceptable risk: "it will require the birth and maturation through adolescence into adulthood of a significant number of healthy and normal test-tube babies before the technique may be viewed as morally acceptable." Second, Bleich objects to the possible destruction of embryos that might result if more are created than are to be transferred for implantation. He expresses hope that, in time and given proper safeguards, IVF "can be a welcome means of bestowing the happiness and fulfillment of parenthood upon otherwise childless couples."[12]

Finally, Rabbi David Feldman observes that "with so pronatalist a . . . tradition, the Jewish response has been understandably affirmative to new reproductive techniques, such as in-vitro fertilization." He notes the concerns of some that technological interventions such as IVF interfere with the natural process of reproduction.[13] He nonetheless argues that, given safeguards against abuse, IVF can provide an appropriate way for humans to act as partners with God in improving upon nature, and represents a positive response to the deeply human desire for offspring.[14]

I would agree with Feldman and others that the technological interventions required for IVF do not in themselves rule out the procedure. The Jewish ideal, when it is possible, is for children to be conceived through marital intercourse.[15] In the case of an infertile couple, however, this is not possible. Medical interventions to assist the natural process of reproduction can enable the couple to have a child. The use of IVF in such situations accords with our responsibility to be both reverent and active in our partnership with God. Similarly, I would agree with Nebenzal and others that producing sperm for the purpose of reproduction does not violate any prohibition.[16]

Bleich's concern about the destruction of embryos will be addressed in section D below. The issue of risk to children born of IVF must be taken seriously by halakhah. Current information, however, suggests that the procedures do not involve prohibitive risks. Studies indicate that children born of IVF do not suffer from congenital anomalies to a greater extent than the general population. IVF as currently practiced is associated with an increased likelihood of multiple pregnancies and births (such as triplets and quadruplets), and multiple births entail an increased risk of low birth weight, which in turn is associated with increased risk of disability. In addition, the risk of perinatal death may be somewhat higher for births following IVF than for other births.[17]

The biomedical community should monitor long-term effects of IVF and continue to work to lessen all risk involved with this procedure. Couples using IVF should do their best to ensure that any potential harm to children is minimized. While risks must be considered carefully by the couple in deciding about IVF, as they must be considered in any medical decision, currently available information suggests that they should not preclude the practice.

Risks to the couple, specifically the woman, must be taken seriously as well; Jewish law and values prohibit us from endangering our lives or exposing ourselves to excessive risk.[18] Currently available information suggests that medical risks of the procedures are not, in general, prohibitive. Commonly used techniques to retrieve ova and transfer an embryo to the uterus do not require use of a general anesthetic and are fairly noninvasive. Potential harms associated with drugs that promote ovulation should be carefully evaluated by individuals and their physicians, but would not, in general, rule out the practice.

Couples—in particular, women—should be aware of these risks. They should also be aware of the personal and psychological toll that the use of reproductive technologies such as IVF often entails. Financial costs of IVF should be considered as well. Finally, all should be aware that many couples who undergo these procedures do not have a child, and they should have a realistic sense of the likelihood of a child in their specific circumstances. Some studies suggest that "the stress of repeated failures of treatment is particularly difficult for couples to cope with."[19] Thorough counseling and social support are important for all who consider using IVF or other reproductive technologies.

In light of these factors, it is clear that couples are not required by Jewish law to utilize procedures such as IVF. Given the risks, burdens, and uncertainty involved, the use of reproductive technologies such as IVF is clearly not obligatory, and probably would be ill-advised in some cases. Such interventions should not occur without the fully informed and voluntary consent of those involved, and the decision of a couple or an individual not to use these procedures would be fully justifiable and must be respected. As expressed by Rabbi Elliot Dorff, "The Jewish tradition would have all people, fertile or infertile, understand that our ability to procreate is not the source of our ultimate, divine worth; that comes from being created in God's image."[20] Individuals who cannot have children can make other vital contributions to strengthening the Jewish (and human) community.[21] In particular, they should strongly consider adoption, which provides an opportunity to raise a child, strengthen the community, and provide a life-changing benefit for a child who cannot be cared for by biological parents.[22]

Having said this, it is clear that IVF is permissible for those who choose to utilize these procedures. For these couples, technical and other halakhic concerns are outweighed by the great good of a new human life, the addition to the harmony and joy of the family, and the contribution to the strengthening of the Jewish community and humanity.[23] A child born as a result of IVF using a couple's sperm and egg is fully the parents' child in all respects, and causes the mitzvah of "be fruitful and multiply" to be fulfilled.

C. Transferring In Vitro Embryos for Gestation

1. *Preimplantation genetic testing.* Genetic information about embryos can be obtained through a number of techniques. In one approach, a cell is removed from an embryo at an early stage of development, when the embryo consists of eight cells. While the embryo can continue to develop normally, the DNA (genetic material) of the single cell is amplified to provide a sufficient quantity of material to allow for genetic testing. In research reported in 1992, genetic diagnosis was performed on embryos created from the sperm and ova of couples, both members of which were carriers for the (recessive) disease of cystic fibrosis. For two couples, some embryos were identified that would be affected by the disease and were not transferred, and other embryos (representing carriers or noncarriers) were transferred. One of the women became pregnant and gave birth to a girl unaffected by the disease.[24]

Asked about genetic testing, Rabbi Y. Zilberstein responded that "one cannot close the door in the face of despondent people who suffer mental anguish in fear of giving birth to sick children, pressure that can drive the mother mad. Therefore, in the case of a serious genetic disease that affects the couple, it is difficult to forbid the suggestion [for genetic testing through IVF]."[25]

Genetic diagnosis and selective transfer of embryos is clearly no more problematic than prenatal diagnosis and abortion of a fetus affected with a severe genetic disease, which has been accepted in the Conservative movement and by some in Orthodoxy.[26] If anything, selective nontransfer of an early in vitro embryo would be preferable to abortion of a more fully developed fetus in utero. The use of IVF for genetic testing faces great practical obstacles, and the risks and uncertainties of IVF will preclude requiring such use for the foreseeable future. For those couples who desire to use IVF and preimplantation genetic testing to avoid having a child with a severe genetic disease, the procedure is certainly fully acceptable.

2. *Gender selection.* Similar (and often somewhat simpler) techniques can be used to determine the gender of an embryo. In some cases, a severe genetic disease may be linked to a sex chromosome, and so affect primarily children of only one gender, generally males. For example, if a woman is a carrier for Duchenne's muscular dystrophy, half her sons but none of her daughters would be likely to be affected by the disease.

In such situations, preimplantation sex selection of embryos would represent a form of testing for a severe genetic defect, and would be acceptable.

Sex selection in other situations would be more problematic. The desire for a child of a particular gender would not be enough to justify the risks and other problems associated with IVF. Moreover, sex selection by any means raises important concerns. It is offensive to regard one gender as better than or preferable to the other, and it would be wrong to choose the gender of a child or take any other action on the basis of sexist views. Moreover, some studies suggest that couples with a strong preference regarding their child's gender disproportionately would choose boys. If sex selection were to be widely practiced, this might lead to an overabundance of males in society, entailing significant social problems.[27]

Bleich observes that classical rabbinic sources do not object to sex selection, and the Talmud provides advice on increasing the likelihood of a male birth. These sources would be more concerned with legitimacy of the method used for sex selection than with the attempt to influence the gender of one's offspring. Bleich nonetheless argues that, based on demographic concerns, "society would find ample justification in the teachings of Judaism for discouraging widespread sex preselection."[28] Rabbis Y. B. Shafran and Y. Zilberstein have specifically ruled against the use of IVF for sex selection.[29] I would agree that (with the exception of sex-linked disease) IVF should not be used solely for the purpose of sex selection.[30]

3. *Number of embryos transferred.* A question can also be raised with regard to the number of embryos to be transferred to the woman's uterus. A number of embryos are generally transferred together in order to increase the likelihood of at least one implanting. At the same time, transferring a large number of embryos increases the risk of multifetal pregnancies. Multifetal pregnancy, especially when involving more than two fetuses, increases risks for the woman and for the fetuses.[31]

A procedure of multifetal pregnancy reduction has been developed to selectively abort some of the fetuses in order to lessen the risk for the woman or the other fetuses. If a woman is pregnant with more than two fetuses, multifetal pregnancy reduction would be halakhically acceptable in appropriate cases—certainly in order to protect the woman from a serious threat to her health, and arguably with the independent justification of protecting the remaining fetuses.[32] At the same time, this procedure may itself entail risks for the woman and especially for the remaining fetuses. From the standpoint of Judaism, it would be important to take reasonable steps to lessen the likelihood of the need for multifetal pregnancy reduction, as it would be appropriate to lessen the likelihood of recourse to abortion in other circumstances.

Many who have examined the practice of IVF have recommended limiting the number of embryos transferred to no more than three. This limit is found in guidelines of Britain's Human Fertilisation and Embryology Authority, Canada's Royal Commission on New Reproductive Technologies, and the European Society of Human Reproduction. The Canadian Commission, for example, argues that transferring more than three embryos increases the risk of multifetal pregnancy but does not increase the likelihood of success, and in fact may lessen the likelihood of the live birth of a child.[33] The specific concern of Jewish law and ethics to minimize risk to the woman and the fetuses provides additional support for this limit. No more than three embryos should be transferred in a procedure. To the extent possible, transferring only two embryos would be preferable.[34]

D. Embryos That Are Not Transferred for Gestation

While it would be possible to only use one or two ova in an IVF procedure, current IVF practices involve attempts to fertilize all ova retrieved from the woman's ovaries, often five to ten or more. One reason is that fertilization does not always occur, and exposing all available ova to sperm maximizes the chance that the needed number of embryos will be created. In addition, current capabilities allow for the successful cryopreservation or freezing of early-stage embryos, but not of unfertilized ova. "Extra" embryos, beyond the number appropriate for immediate transfer, could be frozen for later use, in case the current transfer does not result in the birth of a child or the couple wishes to have additional children using IVF. Embryos are generally frozen between the one-cell and eight-cell stage. Embryo freezing avoids the need for additional egg retrieval procedures, and may be desirable for other medical or personal reasons.[35]

Creating extra embryos and freezing embryos, as currently practiced, would be halakhically acceptable.[36] These procedures enhance the likelihood of success and minimize the medical risks and burdens faced by the woman. This permissibility is based on the assumption that cryopreservation of embryos is safe, as appears to be the case. While the freezing of embryos is permissible, it poses problems as well, as will be seen below. If it becomes technically possible to freeze and thaw unfertilized ova, this would be preferable.[37]

Freezing embryos with the possibility of future transfer and maintaining them in the frozen state also appear to be consistent with any obligations concerning appropriate treatment of the embryos.[38] Other options for frozen or newly created embryos are more problematic (although not necessarily prohibited). These include: 1) thawing a frozen embryo without transferring it (or not transferring a newly created embryo), so that the embryo dies; 2) using the embryo for scientific research; and 3) donating the embryo for use by another.

Some halakhic authorities have ruled that in vitro embryos, at least those that are not intended to be transferred, have no significant halakhic status and may be discarded. Rabbi Hayyim David Halevi, for example, holds that "all ova that are fertilized in vitro do not have the legal status of an embryo; one does not violate the Sabbath on their behalf, and it is permissible to discard them if they were not chosen for transfer, since the law of abortion only applies to [an embryo] in the womb. . . . In vitro, there is no prohibition whatsoever."[39] Rabbi Mordechai Eliyahu, while somewhat less categorical, agrees: "Fertilized ova that have been designated for transfer to a woman's uterus should not be destroyed, since a live fetus will develop from them, but fertilized ova that have not been designated for transfer may be discarded."[40]

In contrast, Bleich objects that "there are no obvious grounds for assuming that nascent human life may be destroyed simply because it is not sheltered in its natural habitat, i.e., its development takes place outside the mother's womb." He suggests that in vitro embryos that are viable should not be destroyed.[41]

My own view is that the early embryo should be accorded a significant degree of respect and sanctity as a wondrous divine creation and potential human life. It would seem implausible to claim that Jewish restrictions with regard to in-utero embryos and fetuses are simply irrelevant because of the embryo's location. At the same time, the fact that the embryo is in vitro does make its potential development more complicated and less likely. Moreover, embryos at the early stage at which freezing occurs are still a mass of undifferentiated cells that can give rise to two or more embryos.[42]

A non-Jewish ethicist has suggested that frozen embryos should not be destroyed; he argues that freezing the embryo indefinitely would be preferable, and could be defended either on grounds of respect for the embryo's status, or as a symbolic expression of respect for human life generally.[43] Such an approach would accord well with Jewish law and values. Nonetheless, it does not seem to be required halakhically. Thawing a frozen embryo in order to discard it would be halakhically permissible.

The use of embryos for nontherapeutic research, in order to gain scientific knowledge but without the expectation that the embryo would be transferred for gestation, is a topic of current controversy in the United States and other countries. Many have suggested that in vitro embryos that a couple does not wish to implant could be used for research under certain conditions—for example, that the information is important and could not be gained in any other way, that the experiment has been appropriately reviewed, and that embryos are not maintained beyond the fourteenth day of development.[44]

A full analysis of the issue of embryo research is beyond the scope of this paper. Allowing an embryo to be observed for scientific research does not seem intrinsically more objectionable than simply discarding the embryo. On the other hand, using an embryo for research becomes more troubling as the embryo reaches further points of development. *A Compendium on Medical Ethics*, edited by Rabbi David Feldman and Dr. Fred Rosner, allows the use of "a fertilized egg not in the womb . . . for the advancement of scientific knowledge."[45] The rationale for this position and guidance for its application require further examination beyond the scope of this paper.

The donation of embryos is discussed in section E below.

E. Donor Sperm, Eggs, and Embryos

1. Using donor gametes and embryos. Some couples are unable to have children using their own sperm and eggs, even with the assistance of procedures such as IVF. These cases raise the difficult question of whether sperm, eggs, or embryos donated by another person may be used by a couple to have a child.[46] This question has been addressed at length by Dorff. Dorff acknowledges that the use of donated gametes raises significant concerns in Jewish law, including the possibility of incest in future generations, and ambiguity with regard to the identity of the child's parents. Even more significant, the use of donor gametes entails personal and psychological difficulties for all involved; it has the potential to add strain to the marriage and complicate the relationship of the child to his or her (social) parents.[47]

Nonetheless, motivated largely (but not exclusively) by compassion for couples who desire the procedure, Dorff deems the use of donor gametes permissible, providing that certain guidelines are met. The couple should seriously investigate alternatives, including adoption. They should be aware of all that the use of donor gametes involves, including the likely strain entailed. As well, they should receive thorough counseling and plan for the best ways to meet these challenges. Couples who use donor gametes should not keep this use secret, especially within the family. Based on the experience of many families who have used reproductive technologies, an open approach promotes the ability of family members to receive needed support, and contributes to the family's harmony and the psychological health of all involved.[48]

I would concur with Dorff's position with regard to the use of sperm in IVF, including the guidelines and restrictions that accompany his permission for the use of donor gametes, and extend this position to the use of donated eggs and embryos.[49] I would emphasize that no couple or individual should use donated gametes without careful reflection and a fully informed and voluntary decision. A decision by either member of the couple not to make use of these procedures must be fully respected, and would be strongly supported by ethical and halakhic considerations.

2. Maternal identity. In the case of sperm donation, as Dorff argues, the sperm donor is the genetic father, and should be viewed as the father both with regard to technical issues of Jewish identity and in order to prohibit marriage (or sexual relations) with genetic relatives. At the same time, the social father of a child conceived using donor insemination, like the social father of an adopted child, is "the 'real' father in most significant ways," and is accorded by Jewish tradition the special status of one who "does right at all times."[50]

Paternal identity is complicated by the use of donor sperm in that two men might be seen as fathers: the genetic father and the social father. The use of donated eggs complicates maternal identity to an even greater extent, for not two but three factors are relevant. The donor of the eggs could be seen as the genetic mother; the woman who is pregnant with and gives birth to the child could be seen as the gestational or birth mother; and the woman who raises the child could be seen as the social mother.

A number of halakhic authorities have addressed the issue of maternal identity in such cases. Many of these statements have been summarized in a review article by Bleich.[51] These sources suggest that maternal identity is to be determined primarily by gestation and birth.[52]

A central precedent in the discussion is the case of a pregnant woman who converts: conception is by a non-Jew, from an ovum from a non-Jew; the fetus is gestated by a non-Jew and then by a Jew; and a woman who is Jewish gives birth. Orthodox sources debate whether the child requires immersion, and the rationale for the requirement or lack of requirement. The Conservative position, however, is clear. Following the *Shulḥan Arukh,* Rabbi Isaac Klein rules: "If a woman converts while pregnant, the child does not require conversion, even if it was conceived before conversion, because at the time of its birth its mother was already Jewish."[53] The woman's status at the time of birth determines the child's identity. By extension, the status of the birth mother determines the child's identity for IVF. While this argument provides the central basis for a Conservative position on maternal identity, this position may be supported by additional considerations as well.[54]

Accordingly, the woman who gestates and gives birth to the child is to be treated as the child's mother for purposes of Jewish law, including the determination of Jewish identity. If a Jewish woman gives birth to a child, that child should be considered Jewish, whether the egg came from a Jewish or a non-Jewish woman. If a non-Jewish woman gives birth to a child, that child would not be Jewish (and so would require conversion in order to be recognized as a Jew), whether the egg came from a Jewish or a non-Jewish woman. [Further development of this position and its supporting rationale may be found in chapter 8 of this volume.]

A less satisfactory alternative position to identifying the birth mother as mother, which might also be compatible with halakhic precedent, would be to recognize *both* the genetic and birth mothers as having maternal status: even if birth is the primary determinant of maternal identity, the genetic mother would be treated as mother because of doubt, or to follow a more stringent position. This alternative is in some ways attractive at the theoretical level, for it would formally recognize the contributions of both women to the child's birth. At the practical level, however, it would impose unnecessary complications for the use of donated ova.[55] If an anonymously donated ovum were used, the presumption (outside of Israel) would be that the donor is not Jewish; accordingly, the child (born to a Jewish mother) would require conversion in order to be fully Jewish. Moreover, the child would have obligations of honoring her or his (genetic) mother (*kibud av va'em*) that likely would be unfulfilled.

Furthermore, ova from a known or designated donor are used in about a quarter of ovum-donation procedures in the United States and Canada,[56] in part because donating ova is more invasive and entails greater risks than donating sperm, and ova are thus less readily available (and more expensive). Accordingly, I agree with Dorff that a fertile sister (or other relative) may donate ova to an infertile woman, provided that all involved receive appropriate counseling and consider ways in which they would deal with "boundary questions" (Is my aunt also my mother? Is my niece also my child?).[57] In such a case, officially recognizing the genetic mother as mother would complicate this enterprise by answering these boundary questions in the affirmative: my aunt is indeed my mother (in addition to my birth/social mother). Such a halakhic stance would be likely to undermine family harmony and the psychological well-being of all involved.

While the genetic mother should not be viewed as mother halakhically, genetic siblings should not marry (or engage in sexual relations with) each other. The most basic reason for this prohibition is that offspring of a consanguineous union face a high risk of genetically based disease; this concern alone would suffice to support a rabbinic prohibition. Combining this ruling with those found in Dorff's paper, one comes to the unsurprising conclusion that one should not marry (or engage in sexual relations with) children of one's genetic, gestational, or social parents. Technically, the prohibition would be Toraitic with regard to children of one's genetic father and birth mother and would reflect the category of secondary relations (*sheniyot*) for children of other parents.[58]

Based on the reasoning allowing a couple to use donor sperm or eggs in order to have a child, couples could use both donor sperm and eggs in IVF when necessary to have a child. Similarly, a couple could use a donated embryo. This might be required in an unusual case in which the husband had a medical indication for donor sperm and the wife had an indication for donor eggs, but was able to gestate and give birth to a child. It might also be suggested if the couple had indications for a donated egg, and donor embryos but no donor eggs were available.[59]

3. Donating embryos. A final and difficult issue concerns whether a couple may donate extra embryos formed from their gametes. Here my inclination is to follow, and expand upon, Dorff's permission for Jews to donate sperm and eggs to enable another couple to have a child. I would emphasize that such donation is not required, and may be done "only after due consideration of the implications of what they are doing and only with due respect and, indeed, awe for the whole procedure."[60]

Dorff notes that donating sperm or eggs entails a biological connection with resulting children that may have great personal significance, and that has importance in halakhah. Thus, for example, a sperm donor should take steps to ensure that no marriages or sexual relations occur among genetic offspring arising from donated sperm and genetic offspring within the man's own family. An egg donor would face similar responsibilities (even though they would be rabbinic rather than Toraitic in their basis). Other responsibilities for one's genetic children, as well as any medical risks, must be faced as well.[61]

An additional concern raised by the donation of eggs or embryos must be addressed, but can be dealt with readily on the basis of the position developed above. If (disagreeing with my position) the genetic mother were to be considered the child's mother, then a child born of an embryo that develops from a Jewish woman's egg, or a child born from an egg donated by a Jewish woman, would be Jewish. I can see no way that halakhah would permit a Jewish woman or couple to make donations that would lead to a Jewish child who would be raised as a non-Jew. If this alternative position were followed, either Jews would not be able to donate eggs or embryos, or they would be able to do so only if the clinic could guarantee that these would be used to help infertile Jews but not non-Jews. Such a position would be highly problematic, to say the least.[62]

As argued above, however, the birth mother is the sole halakhically recognized mother, so a child born to a non-Jew from an egg or embryo donated by Jews would not be Jewish. Accordingly, Jews can donate eggs and embryos, within the guidelines developed above and in Dorff's paper. This position accords with the traditional mandates of *tikun ha'olam,* improving the world and maintaining social order, and *darkhei shalom,* the ways of peace. If Jews are willing to accept donated embryos, then allowing Jews to donate embryos as well helps to maintain the system, fulfilling one sense of *tikun ha'olam,* as well as contributing to the improvement of the world, fulfilling another sense. This permission promotes harmonious relations between Jews and non-Jews, fulfilling one sense of *darkhei shalom,* as well as promoting the value of harmony and peace.

"Great is peace [*shalom*], for all blessings are contained within it."[63] We hope that in vitro fertilization and other reproductive technologies, used responsibly in accordance with the guidance of halakhah, will contribute to wholeness and healing (*sheleimut*) for infertile couples who choose to use these procedures, harmony (*shelom bayit*) in their families, and healthy new life that will add to the peace of Israel and the world.[64]

F. Conclusions

1. An infertile couple may utilize IVF, using the husband's sperm and the wife's egg, to have a child. They are under no obligation to do so. Before undergoing IVF procedures, the couple should consider medical risks as well as the personal and psychological toll that IVF often entails. A child born as a result of such an IVF procedure is fully the parents' child in all respects, and causes the mitzvah of "be fruitful and multiply" to be fulfilled.

2. Couples who wish to use IVF and preimplantation genetic testing to avoid having a child with a severe genetic disease may do so.

3. IVF should not be used solely for the purpose of gender selection. If used to avoid having a child with a severe disease that is gender-linked, however, preimplantation testing would represent a form of genetic testing and would be acceptable.

4. To avoid risks to the mother and child and to decrease the likelihood of abortion, no more than three embryos should be transferred in an IVF procedure. To the extent possible, transferring only two embryos would be preferable.

5. Creating extra embryos and freezing embryos are halakhically acceptable. Embryos may be maintained as frozen indefinitely, but thawing a frozen embryo that the couple does not wish to implant, in order to discard it, would be halakhically permissible.

6. Couples considering the use of donated sperm, ova, or embryos should consider the halakhic and personal concerns involved, should receive thorough counseling, and should seriously investigate alternatives,

including adoption. Those wishing to use donated sperm, ova, or embryos may do so.

7. The woman who gestates and gives birth to a child is to be treated as the child's mother for purposes of Jewish law, including the determination of Jewish identity. One should not marry or engage in sexual relationships with the offspring of one's birth, genetic, or social parents.

8. After careful consideration of the implications of their actions, a couple may donate an embryo formed from their sperm and egg to enable another couple to have a child.

Notes

1. M. *Yevamot* 6:6 states:

> לא יבטל אדם מפריה ורביה אלא אם כן יש לו בנים בית שמאי אומרים שני זכרים ובית הלל אומרים זכר ונקבה שנאמר זכר ונקבה בראם

> One must not abstain from "fruitfulness and increase" unless one has children. The School of Shammai say: two males. The School of Hillel say: a male and a female, as it is written, "male and female He created them" [Gen. 1:27].

Jewish law follows Hillel's view but encourages continuing to engage in procreation even if one already has a son and a daughter. While having children (specifically, a boy and a girl) represents the fulfillment of a mitzvah, those unable to have children are exempt from the obligation. Indeed, J. David Bleich argues that the mitzvah of procreation is best understood not as having children, which is beyond one's control, but as continuing one's practice of potentially procreative intercourse with one's spouse at least until a boy and a girl are born (*Judaism and Healing* [New York: Ktav, 1981], 113). Jewish law describes the obligation to procreate as incumbent upon the male. This formulation (exegetically based on the wording of Gen. 1:28) may reflect a sociological background in which men have greater control than women over whether they would marry and procreate, or a view that women should be encouraged but not technically obligated to entail the risks of pregnancy and childbirth. M. *Yevamot* 6:6; *S.A., E.H.* 1; David M. Feldman, *Health and Medicine in the Jewish Tradition* (New York: Crossroad, 1986), 69–71; David M. Feldman, *Marital Relations, Birth Control, and Abortion in Jewish Law* (New York: Schocken, 1978), 46–59; Elliot N. Dorff, "Artificial Insemination, Egg Donation, and Adoption" (Committee on Jewish Law and Standards, 1994) [chap. 1, pp. 18-21 of this vol.]. Unspecified citations of Dorff below refer to this paper [which appears as chaps. 1–3 of this vol.].

2. Dorff; Michael Gold, *And Hannah Wept* (Philadelphia: Jewish Publication Society, 1988); Richard V. Grazi, ed., *Be Fruitful and Multiply* (Jerusalem: Genesis, 1994); Mordechai Halperin, "Applying the Principles of Halakhah to Modern Medicine: In-Vitro Fertilization, Embryo Transfer, and Frozen Embryo[s]," in *Proceedings of the Association of Orthodox Jewish Scientists* (New York: Sepher-Hermon, 1987), 8–9: 198–200. Here and elsewhere, I draw on Dorff's responsum. Like Dorff, I only address the case of a married couple that seeks to have offspring. While some unmarried women wish to use donated sperm to reproduce, relatively few seek (or require) IVF procedures. In any case, the use of IVF by unmarried women raises concerns beyond the scope of this paper.
3. See, e.g., Elliot N. Dorff, "A Methodology for Jewish Medical Ethics," in *Contemporary Jewish Ethics and Morality,* ed. Elliot N. Dorff and Louis E. Newman (New York: Oxford University Press, 1995), 161–76.
4. Canada, Report of the Royal Commission on New Reproductive Technologies, *Proceed with Care* (Ottawa, 1993) [cited below as Canada]; Ethics Committee, American Fertility Society, "Ethical Considerations of Assisted Reproductive Technologies," *Fertility and Sterility* 62 (1994): 35S [cited below as AFS]. The term "embryo" is used broadly in this paper to refer to the product of fertilization throughout its early development. Because of the rudimentary nature of its development at this stage, many prefer the term "preembryo" (AFS) or "zygote" (Canada). Similar techniques are employed in two related alternative procedures. In GIFT (gamete intrafallopian transfer), ova and sperm are mixed and placed directly in the fallopian tube. With ZIFT (zygote intrafallopian transfer), the embryo produced in vitro is transferred to the fallopian tube rather than to the uterus. Both these procedures require laparoscopy, a somewhat more invasive procedure than the transcervical procedures used in IVF (Canada; Grazi; AFS, 38S–40S). While this responsum focuses on IVF, its conclusions would in general apply to these procedures as well.
5. Canada; AFS, 35S–36S.
6. Society for Assisted Reproductive Technology, American Society for Reproductive Medicine, "Assisted Reproductive Technology in the United States and Canada: 1993 Results Generated from the Society for Reproductive Medicine/Society for Assisted Reproductive Technology Registry," *Fertility and Sterility* 64 (1995): 13–21 [cited below as SART]. For the sake of comparison, the average monthly likelihood of fertilization leading to live birth among sexually active fertile couples not using contraception in the general population is about 20–25 percent.
7. Canada, 149–60; AFS, 29S–31S; U.S. National Institutes of Health, "Final Report of the Human Embryo Research Panel," 27 Sept. 1994, 20–36, 57–63; Thomas A. Shannon and Allan B. Wolter, "Reflections on the Moral Status of the Pre-embryo," *Theological Studies* 51 (1990): 606–10.
8. Ibid.
9. Cited in Moshe Drori, "Genetic Engineering: Preliminary Discussion of Its Legal

and Halakhic Aspects," *Teḥumin* 1 (1980): 287–88. On "wasteful emission of seed" (*hotza'at zera levatalah;* or "destruction of seed," *hashḥatat zera*), see Feldman, *Marital Relations,* 109–31.

10. Waldenberg asserts that IVF violates the prohibition against "wasteful emission of seed," for while artificial insemination transfers a husband's sperm to his wife's reproductive system, in IVF sperm remains outside her body. IVF diverges more dramatically from natural reproduction, "upsetting the order of creation" (*meshanim bazeh sidrei bereishit*), making it impossible to view the husband or wife as parents of the offspring. Finally, Waldenberg argues that it is much more difficult to be certain that a transferred embryo represents the product of the couple's gametes than it is to ensure that the husband's sperm is used in artificial insemination (*Tzitz Eliezer* 15, siman 45, 115–20). This responsum appears as well in *Assia,* no. 33 (1982): 5–13.
11. Avigdor Nebenzal, "In Vitro Fertilization: Comments," *Assia,* no. 35 (1983): 5.
12. "Test-Tube Babies," in *Jewish Bioethics,* ed. Fred Rosner and J. David Bleich (New York: Sanhedrin Press, 1979), 80–85.
13. As noted above (n. 10), such concerns have been raised by R. Eliezer Waldenberg. They also have been expressed within the context of Christian and secular ethics. See Leon R. Kass, *Toward a More Natural Science* (New York: Free Press, 1985), 72; Congregation for the Doctrine of the Faith, *Instruction on Respect for Human Life in Its Origin and on the Dignity of Procreation: Replies to Certain Questions of the Day* (Washington, D.C.: United States Catholic Conference, 1987). A somewhat differing Roman Catholic view may be found in Lisa Sowle Cahill, "Moral Traditions, Ethical Language, and Reproductive Technologies," *Journal of Medicine and Philosophy* 14 (1989): 515–16.
14. Feldman, *Health and Medicine,* 71–72.
15. As expressed by the medieval *Iggeret Hakodesh:* "The union of man with his wife, when it is proper, is the mystery of the foundation of the world and its civilization. Through the act they become partners with God in the act of creation. This is the mystery of what the sages said, 'When a man unites with his wife in holiness, the *Shekhinah* is between them in the mystery of man and woman.' " *The Holy Letter,* trans. Seymour J. Cohen (Northvale, N.J.: Jason Aronson, 1993; reprint of New York: Ktav, 1976), 92. This point is nicely expressed in a paper by Rabbi Daniel Schiff of the Reform movement, "Developing Halakhic Attitudes to Sex Preselection," 1995, pp. 21–22 of typescript (since published in *The Fetus and Fertility in Jewish Law,* ed. Walter Jacob and Moshe Zemer [Pittsburgh: Rodef Shalom Press, 1995], 91–117).
16. Nebenzal, 5; Dorff, 23 [chap. 1, p. 29 of this vol.].
17. Canada, 527–34; Norma C. Morin et al., "Congenital Malformations and Psychosocial Development in Children Conceived by In Vitro Fertilization," *Journal of Pediatrics* 115 (1989): 222–27.
18. As expressed by the Talmud (*Ḥullin* 10a), *ḥamira sakanta mei'isura,* that which is dangerous is to avoided even more stringently than that which is ritually for-

bidden. The rabbinic tradition finds this value expressed positively in Deut. 4:15: *venishmartem me'od lenafshoteikhem,* "you should take care of yourselves diligently." See Feldman, *Health and Medicine,* 24–26; Dorff, 64 [chap. 3, p. 77 of this vol.].

19. Canada, 527–34, esp. 532. For a popular discussion of the potential frustrations and personal costs of these procedures, see Sharon Begley, "The Baby Myth," *Newsweek,* 4 Sept. 1995, 38–47.
20. Dorff, 25 [chap. 2, p. 38 of this vol.]. Dorff accordingly states that "infertile couples are under no Jewish obligation to use modern technology to have children. If they nevertheless choose to do so, they must recognize and take into account all of the factors involved in order to make a reasonable and Jewishly responsible decision" (Dorff, 17 [chap. 1, p. 25 of this vol.]).
21. See Dorff, 25 [chap. 2, p. 38 of this vol.]; Gold. While this paper is addressed in particular to Jews, all humans have intrinsic value as beings created in the image of God and participants in God's covenant with the children of Noah; see Louis Finkelstein, "Human Equality in the Jewish Tradition," in *Aspects of Equality,* ed. Lyman Bryson et al. (New York: Harper and Brothers, 1956), 179–205. The message of Isa. 56:3–5 is relevant as well. God assures those "who have chosen what I desire and hold fast to My covenant—I will give them, in My House and within My walls, a monument and a name better than sons or daughters. I will give them an everlasting name that shall not perish."
22. See Dorff, 75–80 [chap. 3, pp. 84–87 of this vol.].
23. Cf. Nebenzal.
24. Alan H. Handyside et al., "Birth of a Normal Girl after In Vitro Fertilization and Preimplantation Diagnostic Testing for Cystic Fibrosis," *New England Journal of Medicine* 327 (1992): 905–9; Joe Leigh Simpson and Sandra Ann Carson, "Preimplantation Genetic Diagnosis," *New England Journal of Medicine* 327 (1992): 951–53. See also AFS, 64S–66S; William Edward Gibbons et al., "Preimplantation Genetic Diagnosis for Tay-Sachs Disease: Successful Pregnancy after Pre-Embryo Biopsy and Gene Amplification by Polymerase Chain Reaction," *Fertility and Sterility* 63 (1995): 723–28.
25. Responsum to Richard Grazi, Shevat 5751 (1991), cited in Richard V. Grazi and Joel B. Wolowelsky, "Preimplantation Sex Selection and Genetic Screening in Contemporary Jewish Law and Ethics," *Journal of Assisted Reproduction and Genetics* 9 (1992): 321 (brackets original); this material appears also in Grazi, 189.
26. E.g., Kassel Abelson, "Prenatal Testing and Abortion," in *Proceedings of the Committee on Jewish Law and Standards, 1980–85* (New York: Rabbinical Assembly, 1988): 3–10 (the vol. is cited below as *PCJLS*). [This paper appears as chap. 13 of this vol.]
27. See Schiff, 18–19, and Owen D. Jones, "Sex Selection: Regulating Technology Enabling the Predetermination of a Child's Gender," *Harvard Journal of Law and Technology* 6 (fall 1992): 12–17, cited therein. Schiff argues that, assuming that it is not sexist in application, sex preselection is not inherently objection-

able; nonetheless, the use of a fully efficient method of sex selection would represent hubris and an inappropriate overreliance on technology. See also AFS, 64S–66S.

28. "Sex Preselection," in *Judaism and Healing,* 110–15.
29. In Grazi and Wolowelsky, 320–21.
30. One possible exception would be the case of a couple undergoing IVF for independent reasons who gain knowledge about the sex of embryos. If the couple has only children of one sex, one could argue that they could use available information to choose embryos of the other sex for implantation. This would help them to achieve the classical goal articulated by Hillel of having at least one child of each gender (M. *Yevamot* 6:6; see n. 1 above). A practice of sex selection limited to this situation would avoid the concerns with sexism and demography noted above.
31. Canada, 527–30; Fred Rosner, "Pregnancy Reduction in Jewish Law," *Journal of Clinical Ethics* 1 (1990): 181.
32. Richard V. Grazi and Joel B. Wolowelsky, "Multifetal Pregnancy Reduction and Disposal of Untransplanted Embryos in Contemporary Jewish Law and Ethics," *American Journal of Obstetrics and Gynecology* 165 (1991): 1268–71; J. David Bleich, "Pregnancy Reduction," *Tradition* 29, no. 3 (1995): 55–63; Yitzchak Mehlman, "Multi-Fetal Pregnancy Reduction," *Journal of Halacha and Contemporary Society* 27 (1994): 35–68; Rosner, 181–86; and numerous sources cited in these articles.
33. Canada, 527–30; Great Britain, Human Fertilisation and Embryology Authority, *Manual for Centres* (1990), Code of Practice, 7.i.
34. This agrees with the position of Dorff, 68–69 [chap. 3, p. 80 of this vol.]. A group of Belgian researchers found that "limiting the number of embryos transferred to only two did not influence the take-home baby rate but eliminated triplet and quadruplet gestations. Moreover, the number of patients with good-quality supernumerary [extra] embryos available for cryopreservation increased." Martine Nijs et al., "Prevention of Multiple Pregnancies in an In Vitro Fertilization Program," *Fertility and Sterility* 59 (1993): 1245–50.

    The Ethics Committee of the American Fertility Society (37S), while expressing similar concerns, has offered a somewhat more complex recommendation. "The goal of this procedure is to maximize pregnancy rates while minimizing multiple gestation rates." Variations among particular cases, however, argue against establishing a standard numerical limit. Rather, "the number of preembryos transferred should be limited . . . to anticipate that no quadruplet pregnancies will occur and that triplet pregnancies will be minimized to 1% to 2%." I would suggest that this criterion could be used to determine when the number of embryos transferred should be limited to two, and when transferring three would be indicated. Unusual cases in which transferring more than three embryos would be necessary for a reasonable chance of pregnancy—and would be consistent with the AFS guidelines—should be dealt with on a case-by-case basis.

35. Canada, 507–512, 595–96; AFS, 56S–59S. For 1993, 6,869 transfers of frozen embryos for gestation were reported, and 9,100 IVF procedures gave rise to frozen embryos (SART, 18).
36. See similarly Halperin, 207–8.
37. See AFS, 54S–55S.
38. Transfer of the embryo for gestation in most cases would not raise any special concerns. In some cases, one member of the couple may oppose transfer of an embryo deriving in part from his or her gametes; this might occur following divorce, or be due to other considerations. Given the personal and halakhic concerns involved, and the understanding of the status of the embryo developed in the body of this paper, such opposition should be respected. Those using IVF should be encouraged to indicate at the time of cryopreservation their preferences regarding disposition of embryos under various circumstances that might arise, but should have the right to alter their decisions. As a moral matter, an individual should reflect carefully before opposing transfer that accords with a prior decision, or that (e.g., following divorce) would provide important benefits for one spouse without entailing significant difficulties for the other (*zeh neheneh vezeh lo ḥaser*). Still, an individual could have valid personal and halakhic reasons to oppose transfer. Transfer for gestation should not occur over the opposition of either individual.
39. "Fetal Reduction," *Assia,* no. 47–48 (1990): 15.
40. "Destroying Fertilized Eggs and Fetal Reduction," *Teḥumin* 11 (1990–91): 272–73. *A Compendium on Medical Ethics,* ed. David M. Feldman and Fred Rosner, similarly states (51): "A fertilized egg not in the womb, but in the environment—the Petri dish—in which it can never attain viability, does not yet have humanhood. It may be discarded or used for the advancement of scientific knowledge" (6th ed., New York: Federation of Jewish Philanthropies of New York, 1984).
41. Bleich, "In Vitro Fertilization," *Tradition* 25, no. 4 (1991): 97. Unspecified citations of Bleich below refer to this article.
42. This fits relatively well with the legal category of "mere fluid" (*maya be'alma*) found in the Talmud in connection with the early fetus (*Yevamot* 69b; see Feldman, *Marital Relations,* 266). Given the current state of scientific knowledge, it may be less plausible to see as "mere fluid" later stages of embryonic and fetal development, especially beyond the fourteenth day. None of the CJLS papers on abortion relies on this view of the embryo or fetus, and none distinguishes between abortion before or after the fortieth day of development.

    On this issue, my position would be similar to those of the AFS Ethics Committee; Shannon and Wolter, "Reflections on the Moral Status of the Pre-embryo"; and Richard McCormick, "Who or What Is the Preembryo?" *Kennedy Institute of Ethics Journal* 1 (1991): 1–15. These contrast with the Vatican's position that "the human being must be respected—as a person—from the very first instant of his existence," i.e., the moment of conception (Congregation for the Doctrine of the Faith, *Instruction on Respect for Human Life in Its Origin and on the Dignity of Procreation,* 12).

43. David T. Ozar, "The Case Against Thawing Unused Frozen Embryos," *Hastings Center Report* 15, no. 4 (1985): 7–12.
44. AFS, 78S–80S; NIH. Yet additional concerns would be raised by the creation of an embryo specifically for purposes of research, a prospect beyond the scope of this paper. Nontherapeutic research discussed in the body of the paper is distinct from therapeutic research, in which IVF procedures take place within the context of a research protocol, intended to increase the likelihood of success and benefit the couple and/or the fetus. Like other therapeutic research, this would not be inherently problematic, provided that the couple is aware of the research protocol and consents to participation, and risks and benefits are appropriately weighed.
45. Feldman and Rosner, 51.
46. Reporting on procedures conducted in 1993, the Society for Assisted Reproductive Technology notes 2,766 IVF procedures using donated eggs, leading to 716 deliveries, and an additional 625 procedures using donated embryos, leading to 108 deliveries. (The paper also reports 246 procedures involving gestational surrogacy, resulting in 78 deliveries [SART, 17–18]. A halakhic analysis of surrogate motherhood is beyond the scope of this paper. [See chaps. 5–9 of this vol.])
47. Dorff, 24–62 [chap. 2 of this vol.]. On the psychological challenges posed by the use of donor gametes, see also Patricia P. Mahlstedt and Dorothy A. Greenfeld, "Assisted Reproductive Technology with Donor Gametes: The Need for Patient Preparation," *Fertility and Sterility* 52 (1989): 908–14. Most Orthodox sources either do not address the issue of donated sperm, eggs, or embryos, or argue against these practices; see, e.g., Halperin, 203–7. For a somewhat differing view, see Richard V. Grazi and Joel B. Wolowelsky, "Donor Gametes for Assisted Reproduction in Contemporary Jewish Law and Ethics," *Assisted Reproduction Reviews* 2 (1992): 154–60.
48. Ibid. Couples should also be aware that in many states, legal issues concerning the use of donor eggs and embryos have been less clearly addressed in legislation than have corresponding issues in the use of donor sperm, although this difference seems unlikely to have any practical effect (AFS, 47S–49S).
49. Dorff (26–29 [chap. 2, pp. 38–40 of this vol.]) notes, and rejects, the argument of some authorities that donor insemination constitutes (or is akin to) adultery in introducing another man's sperm into a woman's reproductive system. This concern is even less significant with IVF, in which an embryo, and not sperm, is placed in a woman's uterus.
50. Dorff, 40, citing B. *Ketubbot* 50a [chap. 2, p. 47 of this vol.].
51. Bleich, 82–102.
52. The argument presented below is more fully developed in chap. 8 of this vol.
53. Klein, *A Guide to Jewish Religious Practice* (New York: Jewish Theological Sem-

nary of America, 1979), 446. *S.A., Y.D.* 268:6 states this conclusion, but does not offer a rationale:

עובדת כוכבים שנתגיירה והיא מעוברת בנה אין צריך טבילה

If a non-Jewish woman converts when she is pregnant, her child does not require immersion.

The talmudic source of this ruling, *Yevamot* 78a, is not in itself decisive on the issue of maternal identity. Bleich argues that *Yevamot* 97b, discussing the status of twins born to a woman who converts while pregnant, supports the identification of the birth mother as halakhic mother.

54. Among the supporting arguments:

1. Halakhah views the status of a fetus as subservient to that of the woman. As the talmudic phrase *ubar yerekh imo* (*Ḥullin* 58a) is explicated by Feldman: "The fetus is deemed a 'part of the mother' rather than an independent entity" (David M. Feldman, "Abortion: The Jewish View," *PCJLS,* 11 [chap. 11 of this vol.]). This phrase is also cited in the *teshuvot* of Rabbi Robert Gordis ("Abortion: Major Wrong or Basic Right?" *PCJLS,* 22 [chap. 14 of this vol.] and Rabbi Isaac Klein ("A *Teshuvah* on Abortion," *PCJLS,* 33 [chap. 12 of this vol.]. Accordingly, the status of the gestating woman determines the status of the fetus, and the status of the birth mother determines the status of the child.

2. The above argument is strengthened by the fact that embryo transfer takes place well within the first days of development of the embryo, when the talmudic designation of the embryo/fetus as "mere fluid" (*maya be'alma, Yevamot* 69b) most clearly applies. See n. 42 above, and Bleich, 93–94, who rejects this view in part because of his belief that "the developing fetus is a 'person' in its own right."

3. Halakhic identification of a firstborn son as one who "opens the womb" supports defining the birth mother as the child's mother. See Exodus 13 and Dorff, 68 [chap. 3, p. 79 of this vol.].

4. Some have suggested that one reason for basing Jewish identity on matrilineal descent is that the child's mother can always be identified; see, e.g., Walter Jacob, ed., *Contemporary American Reform Responsa* (New York: Central Conference of American Rabbis, 1987), 63; Shaye J. D. Cohen, "The Origins of the Matrilineal Principle in Rabbinic Law," *AJS Review* 10 (1985): 40–41, who reports but argues against this view. This consideration would support determining the child's status on the basis of the birth mother.

5. *Targum Jonathan* (Gen. 30:21) and Rabbi Samuel Edels (Maharsha, commenting on *Niddah* 31a) relate that, prior to the birth of Joseph and Dinah, Leah was pregnant with a male, and Rachel with a female. Leah prayed that Rachel would give birth to the male, and God switched the embryos. Dinah, conceived by Rachel but born to Leah, is considered Leah's child; Joseph, conceived by Leah but born to Rachel, is considered Rachel's child. Thus, the status of the birth mother determines the child's identity. See Bleich, 84; Dorff, 66–68, 104–5 [chap. 3, pp. 78–79, 90–91 of this vol.].

6. As discussed below, identifying the birth mother but not the genetic mother as the halakhic mother facilitates the use of donated eggs and embryos, and enables Jews to donate eggs and embryos. This policy/ethical concern, while not necessarily decisive, represents an important halakhic consideration that minimally serves to reinforce the above arguments.

55. Some analogous complications are accepted in the use of donor sperm (Dorff). However, because Jewish identity (for those who do not convert to Judaism) is based on the mother's status, egg donation would entail additional problems. More important, the complications do not seem to be avoidable with sperm donation, and may be avoided here simply by following the position most clearly suggested by halakhic precedent.
56. In 599 out of 2,766 cycles (SART, 17).
57. Dorff, 65–66 [chap. 3, p. 78 of this vol.].
58. See Dorff, 41 [chap. 2, pp. 47–48 of this vol.]; *S.A., E.H.* 15. A child born from IVF who unknowingly engaged in sexual relations with a genetic sibling would not be culpable. Children born of these procedures should in no way be stigmatized.
59. AFS, 50S. Donated embryos generally are not created for the purpose of donation, but represent "extra" embryos that another couple does not wish to use. Accordingly, genetic screening may be less complete than is usually the case for donated sperm or ova.
60. Dorff, 84 [chap. 3, p. 88 of this vol.].
61. Dorff, 71–75 [chap. 3, pp. 82–84 of this vol.]; AFS, 47S–49S. While the ovum donor is not halakhically considered the child's parent, her responsibilities for the welfare of the child as another human being are similar to those faced by the sperm donor.
62. A similar concern is raised by Bleich, 94–95, although my response to this issue differs markedly from his. In discussing the permissibility of autopsies, Rabbi Yehudah Leib Graubart argues that to discriminate against non-Jews, so as to appear to care little for the life and health of non-Jews, would represent a desecration of God's name. He argues that concern to avoid such desecration not only would support ruling in accord with a lenient position (as in

this paper), but could suffice to allow what otherwise would be prohibited. *Responsa Ḥavalim Bane'imim,* vol. 3, sec. 64 (Jerusalem: Feldheim, 1975, reprint); cited in part in Isaac Klein, *Responsa and Halakhic Studies* (New York: Ktav, 1975), 41. I am grateful to Rabbi Elliot Dorff for alerting me to this reference.

63. *Leviticus Rabbah* 9:9.
64. For their suggestions and thoughtful insights, which have contributed greatly to this paper, I would like to thank Dr. David Kelly, Lorraine Newman Mackler, and members of the Committee on Jewish Law and Standards, including my fellow members of the Subcommittee on Bioethics: Rabbis Kassel Abelson, Elliot Dorff, David Feldman, Shoshana Gelfand, Avram Reisner, Joel Roth, and Elie Spitz.

C. SURROGATE MOTHERHOOD

Introduction

A surrogate mother gestates and gives birth to a child with the intention that the child will be raised by others. Most commonly, the surrogate is artificially inseminated by the sperm of a man to whom she is not married, and the child is raised by the man and his wife. This procedure may be called simply "surrogate motherhood" or "surrogacy," "full surrogacy," or "ovum surrogacy." Alternatively, in "gestational surrogacy," the surrogate mother gestates and gives birth to a child from an embryo fertilized in vitro, resulting (most commonly) from the sperm of a husband and an ovum of a wife. Many aspects of this practice are controversial, including the very term "surrogate mother." Some would refer to her as a "birth surrogate," others simply as "mother," and some prefer to call the practice "surrogate parenting."

The controversial status of this practice is reflected in the diverse views found in this volume. This section begins with a summary statement of the views of Rabbi Elie Spitz and Rabbi Aaron L. Mackler, "On the Use of Birth Surrogates." Rabbi Spitz's paper, "On the Use of Birth Surrogates," follows. The paper begins with a presentation of the medical, legal, and social background of surrogacy. Values implicit in

Jewish law are then considered, including views of procreation, third-party intervention, and science. All these values support an infertile couple's use of surrogacy to have a child. Spitz then considers and responds to ethical and legal objections that have been raised against surrogacy. He concludes that surrogacy is acceptable and advocates legislation to safeguard against potential abuses.

In "Surrogate Parenting," Rabbi Mackler argues that surrogacy cannot be recommended, and in at least most cases would be forbidden by Jewish law and ethics. He begins by considering the significance of birth and gestation, and discusses the potential harms that surrogacy may impose on children as well as on the surrogate. He concludes with specific provisions that would be required if surrogacy were practiced in any case. A companion paper by Mackler follows, entitled "Maternal Identity and the Religious Status of Children Born to a Surrogate Mother." The paper opens with consideration of intuitions on maternity, which are important, though not necessarily decisive. Mackler turns to halakhic discussion of maternal identity and religious status, including the precedent of children born to a woman who converts to Judaism while she is pregnant. He concludes that the woman who gestates and gives birth to a child should be recognized as the child's mother.

This section concludes with a paper by Rabbi David H. Lincoln, "Surrogate Motherhood." Here Lincoln focuses on issues concerning the artificial insemination of the surrogate. Although this paper was written more than a decade before the other papers in this section, many of the issues raised continue to be important in current discussions.

CHAPTER 5

On the Use of Birth Surrogates*

Aaron L. Mackler and Elie Kaplan Spitz

The practice of surrogacy involves powerful and sometimes conflicting Jewish concerns, including the value of procreation, respect for persons (*kevod haberiyot*), and concern for the well-being of all the vulnerable people who are involved. The Rabbinical Assembly Committee on Jewish Law and Standards has approved two papers on this sensitive subject, by Rabbi Aaron Mackler and Rabbi Elie Spitz, respectively. Both agree that, on the one hand, traditional Jewish law does not mandate an absolute prohibition of surrogacy in all cases. On the other hand, surrogacy entails serious potential problems that would make it inappropriate in at least some cases. The two papers differ, however, in their general evaluation of surrogacy and on some more particular points.

General Evaluation

For Rabbi Spitz, the great benefit of providing a child to an infertile couple is decisive. Concerns with avoiding exploitation of the surrogate and harm to children born of the procedure are real but manageable. These must be addressed by couples considering surrogacy, and ideally would be dealt with at the policy level by civil legislation. At the same time, the data of the last fifteen years indicate that problems as a result

*Approved by the Rabbinical Assembly Committee on Jewish Law and Standards, Sept. 1997.

of these risks occur only in a small number of cases, and that the vast majority of surrogacies have resulted in offering the couple the joy of parenthood without harming or exploiting the surrogate or others. "From a Jewish perspective, it would be wrong to outlaw a procedure that has the potential to help so many couples overcome infertility and that works smoothly in the overwhelming majority of cases."

Rabbi Mackler expresses greater concern with potential harms and exploitation. There is a danger of treating people as commodities, and in some extreme cases, contracting/intended parents have sought to refuse custody of a child born with birth defects or of the undesired gender. When the surrogate has other children, those children face the potential psychological harm of seeing their mother go through pregnancy and give birth to a child who is given to others. The risk of exploitation (*oshek*) of surrogates is real, as well. While such harms have been documented in some cases, their extent is debated and difficult to ascertain precisely. Still, these have been enough to lead secular groups such as the Ethics Committee of the American Fertility Society, which generally supports reproductive technologies, to express "serious ethical reservations," and "not to recommend widespread clinical application of clinical surrogate motherhood at this time." From a Jewish perspective, "surrogacy cannot be halakhically recommended, and in at least most cases would be forbidden by Jewish law and ethics."

Particular Guidelines

Whether surrogacy agreements might be appropriate in most cases or only in exceptional cases, both rabbis agree on some important guidelines:

1. Couples contemplating the use of a surrogate should consider the halakhic and personal concerns involved, receive thorough counseling, and seriously investigate alternatives, including adoption. Either member of the couple would be fully justified in a decision not to proceed with surrogacy, and such refusal must be fully respected.

2. The surrogate should be protected from pressure to continue pregnancy when she judges abortion to be required to avoid serious threat to her health, and conversely, she should be protected from pressure to abort.

3. In the formulation of surrogacy agreements, and all actions

taken with regard to surrogacy, greatest concern must be given to the well-being and rights of the child to be born of the procedure, as well as any other children who might be affected. Concern must be given to avoid exploitation of other vulnerable parties, including the surrogate, as well.

4. Rabbi Spitz and Rabbi Mackler agree that a surrogate may receive reimbursement for her expenses, and that any money that the surrogate receives cannot be contingent on her giving up custody of the child. For Rabbi Spitz, it is appropriate that a surrogate be paid a reasonable sum for her services, which is separate and distinct from payment for a child. This payment is compensation for time engaged in the medical, psychological, and legal procedures; physical restrictions due to pregnancy; medical risk; and the use of her womb. The permissibility of payment is rooted in the reality that not everyone has a volunteer family member or a friend to assist in the much wanted blessing of a child. For Rabbi Mackler, any payment to a surrogate mother beyond reimbursement of expenses would be discouraged as dangerously close to baby-selling, or minimally the selling and purchase of parental relationships, which are inconsistent with halakhah.

5. Rabbi Spitz and Rabbi Mackler address the possibility of a dispute arising over the custody of the child, and each discusses the response he views as most consonant with Jewish law and ethics. For Rabbi Spitz, during the pregnancy a surrogate has the right to withdraw from the agreement, an extension of her freedom of choice. Upon birth to a gestational surrogate, the surrogate should have no right to challenge custody. In contrast, an ovum surrogate may assert her maternal rights, but the burden of proof is upon her to show cause as to why the original intent should not be honored. For Rabbi Mackler, the surrogate mother, as gestational and birth mother, is halakhically recognized as mother and should have the right to contest the assumption of custody by the intended parents (one of whom would be halakhically recognized as the child's father). This right would be held by both ovum surrogates and gestational surrogates. Custody of the child—in these, as in other cases—should be determined on the basis of the child's best interest, as required by Jewish ethical values as well as halakhic precedent. The views of Rabbi Spitz and Rabbi Mackler on this matter are not necessarily offered as decisive halakhic rulings, however, and both rabbis recognize that, in practice, custody likely would be determined by general civil law.

6. The sole position approved by the Committee on Jewish Law

and Standards is that the religious status of a child follows that of the gestational/birth mother in cases involving surrogacy, as in all other cases. Children born to a non-Jewish surrogate (whether a gestational or an ovum surrogate) would require conversion to be halakhically recognized as Jewish. Rabbis should display personal and pastoral sensitivity in such cases.

Any individuals considering surrogacy, as well as other interested readers, are strongly advised to read the full papers [which follow as chapters 6–8 of this volume].

CHAPTER 6

On the Use of Birth Surrogates*

Elie Kaplan Spitz

She'eilah (Question):

Is an infertile couple's use of a surrogate mother acceptable? Specifically:

1. Is it permissible to use an ovum surrogate?
2. Is it permissible to pay her for her services?
3. Is it permissible to employ a gestational surrogate?
4. Is the mitzvah of procreation met through a surrogate birth?

Teshuvah (Response):

A. Surrogates: Some Background

The Rabbinical Assembly Committee on Jewish Law and Standards dealt with the permissibility of ovum surrogacy in 1988. In that opinion, authored by Rabbi David Lincoln, the committee concluded: "The mitzvah of having children is so great that we should not deny couples this opportunity." [See chapter 9 of this volume.] That opinion was written while there was still relatively little experience with ovum surrogacy. Gestational surrogacy had not yet taken place. In order to evaluate the increased data of the last decade and to analyze in greater detail the ramifications of surrogacy, this paper is presented.

*Approved by the Rabbinical Assembly Committee on Jewish Law and Standards, June 1997.

Jewish law lacks direct precedent for surrogate birth. Much of the rabbinic debate that has taken place has focused on theoretical risks.[1] Halakhic authorities are in agreement that a couple has no duty to resort to surrogacy to fulfill the mitzvah of procreation. The difference of opinion is in whether an infertile couple may choose to do so.

Before an analysis of the ethics of surrogacy, let us clarify terms and examine the data that encompass the experience of the last fifteen years.

1. *What is a surrogate?* There are two categories of surrogate motherhood, based on the surrogate's genetic relationship to the child. Currently, in the majority of cases the surrogate is an ovum surrogate: both her ovum and womb are used. She is impregnated by artificial insemination with the sperm of the intended father and agrees to give the newborn over to him and his wife.[2] The first acknowledged paid surrogacy arrangement occurred in 1980.[3] As many as 4,000 children have been born to surrogates[4] since then, and the present pace is estimated at 1,000 new agreements a year.[5]

A gestational surrogate, the second category, essentially serves as an incubator. Referred to as a "tummy mummy," the gestational surrogate is impregnated through in vitro fertilization with a fertilized ovum of the intended parents.[6] In vitro ("in glass") fertilization produced a child for the first time in 1978.[7] The first birth of an infant carried by a gestational surrogate was in 1986.[8] Yet gestational surrogacy is increasing quickly and may soon outnumber "traditional surrogacy" activity.[9]

2. *Dollars and sense: What are some of the conditions and costs of a surrogate agreement?* Surrogacy arrangements usually involve payment and a written agreement. This is not always the case, however. There are moving stories of family members using the technology to facilitate birth.[10] A well-publicized example is the case of Arlette Schweitzer, who was the gestational surrogate for her daughter, who lacked a uterus. Schweitzer gave birth to her granddaughter![11]

Yet most couples lack the family member or friend who will incur the inconvenience and run the risks of pregnancy as a gift. In the 1970s, surrogacy couples often found their own surrogates for pay and entered into private contracts. Today, people overwhelmingly use an established center that includes the guidance of an attorney, well-drafted agreements, and a psychologist. To date, 60 percent of surrogacy births have been arranged through such a surrogacy center.[12]

A couple who contracts with a paid ovum surrogate will spend approximately $42,000; of that amount, the surrogate will typically receive $12,000.[13] For the couple, the most uncertain variable in cost is the expense of medical procedures, particularly for gestational surrogacy. Each in vitro attempt, which commonly uses three fertilized eggs, has a less than one-in-six success rate. The average medical cost for a successful in vitro fertilization is $22,000.[14]

Surrogacy contracts serve to protect the surrogate's interests and to ensure clear expectations for all parties involved.[15] Among the items often contained in an agreement:

- Complete freedom of choice for the surrogate prior to conception, including the right to withdraw from the agreement.
- Payment for the surrogate of all medical costs, psychological counseling, attorney fees, and living expenses or pay (not to exceed a reasonable amount); to be paid on a monthly installment basis.
- A commitment of the intended parents to accept the newborn, regardless of the child's physical condition, and the surrogate's agreement to turn the newborn over to the intended parents upon birth.
- A guarantee of the surrogate's right over her body during pregnancy, which includes the right to operations to protect her health and abortion (which would affect payment). In addition, the surrogate agrees not to abuse her body, including the use of illicit drugs, which if violated to the detriment of the fetus allows for compensatory damages.

3. *Who agrees to be a surrogate?* At least eight Ph.D. dissertations and other professional-level studies have been conducted to ascertain the emotional, psychological, and financial profiles of surrogates.[16] The American Bar Foundation, consistent with other research, found that the typical surrogate mother was twenty-eight years old, married with two children, employed full time, and had thirteen years of education. Her husband was supportive of her decision to serve as a surrogate. Most were Caucasian, middle-range in income bracket, in good health, and had had positive experiences in past pregnancies.[17] While money

was a factor in choosing to become a surrogate, it rated consistently lower than the desire to help another couple.[18]

4. *Why hire a surrogate?* Surrogacy is a last-resort solution for female infertility. Infertility is defined as the inability to achieve a pregnancy after one year of regular, unprotected sexual relations or the inability of the woman to carry a pregnancy to live birth. Approximately one out of seven couples will experience some degree of infertility.[19] In 40 percent of those cases, the infertility is directly linked to the woman.[20]

Not so long ago, biology was destiny. Only recently have doctors learned to manipulate the mechanics of pregnancy and birth. There are many interventions short of surrogacy. Today medical intervention may open closed passageways, concentrate the sperm of a man with a low sperm count, or circumvent absent or dysfunctional tubes through in vitro fertilization. In addition to using refined medical technology, couples often utilize new social arrangements. The American Fertility Society estimates that as many as 50,000 couples each year use a third party to have a child.[21] A third party participates either as a sperm donor, an ovum donor, or as a surrogate.

Donor insemination, which overcomes the inability of a man to produce healthy sperm, is the most widely practiced third-party intervention. Since the 1950s, donor insemination has been responsible for as many as 300,000 births.[22] Donor insemination is conception in a doctor's office: the donor produces the sperm by masturbating, and that semen is then injected with a syringe into the woman's vagina. Surrogacy, which addresses a woman's infertility, is the female equivalent of donor insemination.

In the case of the ovum surrogate, the wife either lacks healthy ovaries or the ability to produce ova for retrieval and is unable to carry a baby to term. Gestational surrogacy is a solution for women with one of a variety of fertility problems: a malformed or absent uterus; a medical condition that would make pregnancy dangerous for her, such as severe hypertension, diabetes, or lupus; or a condition that would endanger the fetus, such as phenylketonuria.[23]

An infertile couple approaching an adoption agency is likely to encounter a long wait and a complex selection process before succeeding in adopting a child.[24] The advantage in using a third party, either through artificial insemination by a donor or surrogacy, is that the offspring is genetically linked to one—or, in the case of gestational surrogacy, to both—of the prospective parents. The genetic link meets the psychological need for continuity of a genetic chain, provides the gratification of a child who looks and may act like one of the parents, and may allow for more than one child who is genetically linked to his or her siblings.

There are serious potential problems entailed by surrogacy. It involves a third party who may change her mind and assert her maternity of the child. For the future child, there is the potential stigma of having been born to a woman who is not part of the child's life. There is also an ethical concern in barring access of a genetic mother to her child. Additionally, in contrast to adoption, in surrogacy arrangements parents accept responsibility for a future child who may turn out to be impaired. To better assess the nature of these risks, it is important to examine the legal data from the past two decades.

5. *Surrogate lawsuits.* In recent years, failed surrogacy arrangements have led to highly publicized, painful lawsuits. The most infamous of the surrogacy cases and among the first was the matter of Baby M,[25] in which Mary Beth Whitehead, a twenty-nine-year-old surrogate, reneged on a contract to surrender the baby she bore for a childless couple. William Stern had supplied the sperm for the artificial insemination of Whitehead, and had paid her $10,000 to carry the fetus to term. In 1988, the New Jersey Supreme Court held that the agreement between Whitehead, the surrogate, and the Sterns, the intended parents, was not binding because it violated the rule against payment for an adoption. The judge treated the matter as a custody case and awarded the child to her biological father, Stern.

Most of the lawsuits filed to date are products of the surrogate changing her mind and wishing to keep the newborn. A recent example is the marriage of Moschetta case,[26] in which the ovum surrogate asserted her maternal rights when she learned that the intended couple had separated. The surrogate said that she had implicitly agreed to give the child only to a stable, married couple. The judge ruled that the contract was not binding and dealt with the case as one of custody. The biological father and surrogate were given joint custody, and the intended mother—who lacked a biological link—was denied any privileges.

Although the emotional costs of failed surrogacy arrangements are high, surrogacy overwhelmingly succeeds. According to the Health Department of the State of New York, from an estimated 4,000 children born to surrogates from the late 1970s to the early 1990s, only twelve surrogacy-related cases had been filed in the U.S. courts, and in every case except one, custody was awarded to the intended parents.[27]

Only one gestational surrogate case has wound up in court. In *Anna Johnson v. Mark and Crispina Calvert*,[28] the paid surrogate, Anna Johnson, asserted a maternal right to the child. The California Supreme Court upheld the lower courts and ruled that the contract between the parties for turning over the child was binding. Moreover, the court held that the intended mother, who was also the biological mother, was "the natural mother under California law." Currently in California, it is only the genetic-intended mother's name that appears on the birth certificate of a child born by a gestational surrogate.

Legal cases reveal only some of the complications entailed by surrogacy. There is little psychological data on the emotional costs of surrogacy to the surrogate's family, who see their wife or mother turn over a child she has borne. The long-term feelings of surrogates concerning the process are still unclear because of the limited number of years that surrogacy has taken place, and this issue warrants ongoing evaluation.

To date, the rabbis who have written on surrogacy have done so from a theoretical vantage point and have largely concluded that surrogacy is unacceptable. Jewish law is worth reexamining in light of the positive track record of surrogacy to date, the growing use of surrogacy, and the fact that surrogacy has successfully allowed for the blessing of children.

B. Values Implicit in Jewish Law

Jewish law has no direct precedent for modern surrogacy. Until recently, the possibility of gestational surrogacy was restricted to the realm of science fiction.[29] Similarly, ovum surrogacy in a monogamous context did not take place. Early rabbis, however, possessed a prescient imagination and were able to envision embryo transfer. *Targum Jonathan* says that Dinah was conceived by Rachel and transferred to the womb of Leah, and Joseph was conceived by Leah and transferred to the womb of Rachel.[30] Such speculation, however, has no legal significance, since the commentator derived no legal lesson from this legend and, in the Rabbis' account, neither mother intended or even knew that the embryo transfer had occurred.

Surrogacy is a matter of legal first impression in Jewish law, as in American law. The analysis of jurists to date, both in the U.S. courts and in the writing of rabbis, has largely tried to analyze it within previously existing categories. Yet ovum surrogacy is something new, a constellation of five factors: artificial insemination; payment of fees to a biological mother; agreement by a biological mother to relinquish rights; legitimation by a biological father; and adoption by his wife.[31] Gestational surrogacy, in which the birth mother has no genetic link to the newborn, is totally new. To define surrogacy with partial analogies to existing laws is a distortion and a disservice to halakhah.

Whether surrogacy is worthy of halakhic support comes down to a balancing test of moral, financial, communal, and personal costs coupled with the gains to the intended parents. Since there is no direct legal precedent for surrogacy in Jewish law, a place to begin such an analysis is with the underlying values found in Judaism that touch on surrogacy.

1. Procreation. Children are among God's chief blessings. Indeed, procreation is the first command in the Torah: *peru urevu umile'u et ha'aretz,* "Be fruitful and multiply and fill up the earth."[32] So important are offspring that the Mishnah contains a debate between Hillel and Shammai as to the number—each says two—and genders of children—males for Shammai, one of each for Hillel—needed to fulfill the biblical mandate.[33] Nonetheless, the Tosafot criticizes those who fulfill only the minimum requirement.[34]

Abundance of offspring is a recurring promise to the patriarchs—your descendants shall be "like the stars in the heavens and sands of the sea."[35] The promise, however, required parental effort—hence the statement in the midrash that there are three partners to creation: the father, mother, and God.[36] Rabbi Eleazar ben Azariah is quoted in a midrash as saying, "He who does not engage in procreation is as if he diminished the divine image," for without human descendants, there is no one to embody God's image.[37] In light of the importance of procreation, permission was given even to sell a Torah scroll to enable a marriage in which procreation had yet to be fulfilled.[38] In the words of Isaiah, "The world was created to be inhabited."[39]

Despite God's promise of progeny, each of the patriarchs had wives who confronted infertility.[40] Reflective of the pain of these couples are Rachel's words to Jacob: "Give me children lest I die!" In response, "Jacob was incensed at Rachel, and said, 'Can I take the place of God, who has denied you fruit of the womb?' "[41] Jacob's anger reveals both his frustration and limitation. There was no medical knowledge in his day that could have solved Rachel's or Jacob's infertility. An infertile couple only had prayer and the possibility of the aid of a third party—which, we will see, was Rachel's solution.

2. *Third-party intervention.* In response to infertility, the Torah provides for third-party intervention. Interestingly, there is such a possibility for both female and male infertility, the categories of *shifḥah* and *yibum*. These two responses of last resort are not the direct equivalent of modern-day surrogacy or artificial insemination by a donor, but are worth examining closely to uncover underlying values.

a. The shifḥah.[42] Unable to conceive, Rachel says to Jacob:

הנה אמתי בלהה בא אליה ותלד על ברכי ואבנה גם אנכי ממנה

> Here is my handmaid Bilhah, come unto her, and she shall give birth on my knees and I will be built up through her.[43]

Rachel's use of Bilhah, her *shifḥah* (Hebrew for "handmaid"), as her surrogate had precedent both among the patriarchs and the society in which she lives. Sarah, too, resorts to a *shifḥah*. "Look, the Lord has kept me from bearing," Sarah says to Abraham. "Consort with my handmaid, Hagar; perhaps I shall have a child through her."[44] Abraham consents, and Hagar gives birth to Yishmael. Later on when Leah (Rachel's sister) is unable to continue to bear children, she asks Jacob to consort with her handmaid, Zilpah.[45]

The handmaids are subservient to the matriarchs. Their rights are limited. Hence, when Sarah is displeased with Hagar, who at this point is pregnant by Abraham, Abraham says to Sarah:

הנה שפחתך בידך עשי לה הטוב בעיניך ותענה שרי ותברח מפניה

> Behold, your *shifḥah* is in your hands, do with her that which is good in your hands.[46]

Subsequently, Sarah is so harsh with Hagar that she runs away.[47] Consistent with the matriarchs' primacy in the marriage, when children are born to Bilhah and Zilpah, it is Rachel and Leah who give the children their names.[48] When Rachel says, "She shall give birth on my knees," she uses language similarly found as a formal act of adoption in contemporaneous Hittite documents.[49] The children born to the handmaids are considered Jacob's sons and are included among the twelve tribes along with the natural sons of Leah and Rachel.

Parallel to the biblical *shifḥah* are legal accounts found in ancient Near Eastern documents. The Code of Hammurabi warns expressly that a slave girl elevated by her mistress could not claim equality.[50] A Nuzi marriage document stipulates: "If Gillimninu bears children, Shennima shall not take another wife. But if Gillimninu fails to bear children, she shall get for him a slave girl as concubine. In that case, Gillimninu herself shall have authority over the offspring."[51] Despite the second-class status of the *shifḥah* in the Torah, she also has certain privileges that are absent in modern surrogacy arrangements. The *shifḥah* is part of the patriarch's family and apparently helps to raise her own children.

Some critics of surrogacy have pointed to the case of Hagar as a warning. To quote Arlene Agus: "Despite many circumstances—the status and rights offered Hagar, the absence of payment, the shared custody arrangement—the arrangement failed. Perhaps there is a lesson to be learned here."[52] But holding out Hagar and Sarah's relationship as typical overlooks the apparent success of Rachel and Leah with their handmaids.[53]

Moreover, modern surrogacy offers the advantage of simplifying the family arrangement so that two women do not need to compete for the affection of the same man. Indeed, the most obvious difference between the *shifḥah* and the modern-day surrogate is that the *shifḥah* existed in a polygamous context. Then it was socially acceptable for a man to impregnate a woman in addition to his primary wife. With Rabbenu Gershon's mandate in the tenth century, monogamy was required, a restriction that some critics construe as a prohibition of surrogacy today.[54]

Yet there is a fundamental difference between procreation in the past and today. In the ancient world, the only way a man had children with a woman was through sexual intercourse. Today, children may be born without violating the sacred sexual intimacy of marriage. In that light, artificial insemination by a donor is not considered an act of adultery, across a broad spectrum of halakhic authorities.[55] Because of the division between sex and procreation and even between gestation and providing the ovum, modern surrogacy is not easily dismissed by reference to the category of monogamy alone.

Despite some differences between the *shifḥah* and the contemporary surrogate, there are significant shared values to glean from the Bible's acceptance of a third party to procreation. First, the use of a third party is a permitted last resort to assure genetic continuity for the husband. Although the patriarchs and matriarchs could have adopted a child—a legal category in the ancient world, too—they chose the option of using a *shifḥah*. Second, although children were born to the *shifḥah*, the Torah recognized the maternal role of the "intended mother" and gave her rights. The offspring were adopted by the matriarchs and named by them. Third, although the *shifḥah* was not recognized as a wife, her offspring were treated as descendants of the patriarch, which entailed full inheritance rights.

b. Yibum. A second biblical category of third-party intervention, *yibum*, offered a form of artificial insemination. An analysis of *yibum* demonstrates the Bible's willingness to redraft familial lines to overcome infertility. Moreover, the history of the category of *yibum* reveals that the halakhah evolves and responds to changing social mores.

When a man died childless, his next of kin was commanded to procreate with the widow in order to perpetuate the deceased's name and memory. This duty, called *yibum*, is present in Genesis. When Tamar's husband, Er, died without issue, her father-in-law, Judah, said to his second son, Onan: "Join with your brother's wife and do your duty by her as a brother-in-law [*veyabeim otah*] and provide offspring for your brother"[56] Onan was an intended surrogate for his deceased brother. This form of artificial insemination required sexual intercourse, the only conceivable way to fertilize a woman in the ancient world. The law of *yibum*, levirate marriage, is codified in Deuteronomy[57] as follows:

> When brothers dwell together and one of them dies and leaves no son, the wife of the deceased shall not be married to a stranger, outside the family. Her husband's brother shall unite with her: take her as his wife and perform the levir's duty. And the firstborn she bears shall succeed in the name of his brother who is dead, that his name not be blotted out of Israel.

Normally, marriage between a man and his brother's former wife was forbidden.[58] *Yibum* was the exception to the rule. Apparently, familial continuity and having a child was so great a value that it overrode the societal norm of familial boundaries. Deuteronomy did, however, provide a brother-in-law with a way out of the levirate duty, too. The man could publicly refuse to perform *yibum*. The widow had to agree, which was marked by a public ritual, called *ḥalitzah* ("removal"), whereby she removed her brother-in-law's shoe, spit toward his face, and declared, "This is what shall be done to the man who will not build up a family for his brother."[59]

Recent scholarship documents that *yibum* was not unique to the Bible. It was part of a legislative pattern of the ancient Near East. A fragmentary text from the Middle Assyrian Empire's compendium of laws (fifteenth–fourteenth century B.C.E.) requires a widow who has no son to be married off by the father-in-law to the son of his choice.[60] In the Hittite laws, approximately from Abraham's lifetime, is the statement that if a married man dies, "his brother shall take his wife, then [if he dies] his father shall take her."[61] These laws offered financial and physical protection for a widow, and they also treated the woman as the property of the clan.

Yibum in Jewish law evolved in response to changing societal mores. As Judaism moved away from polygamy, the Rabbis of the Talmud interpreted the Torah to make *ḥalitzah* easier. *Yibum* was restricted to the case of a brother who died without any issue,[62] instead of the previous gloss of a male child, and the brother-in-law could fulfill the command only if his motives were pure.[63] Therefore, if he were drawn to the widow by her attractiveness, he was barred from having sex with her. The Rabbis also made it easier for the widow to release her brother-in-law. Rather than spitting in his face, she was permitted to symbolically spit on the ground in front of her brother-in-law.[64]

Although the biblical law's interpretation evolved, the Rabbis of the talmudic period and even later halakhic authorities remained divided over the preference of *ḥalitzah* to *yibum*.[65] The difference in opinion correlates with whether the Rabbis lived in a polygamous or a monogamous society.[66] Only in 1950 did the two chief rabbis of Israel, a state that prohibited polygamy, issue an edict (a *takanah*) that prohibited *yibum*. They explained that in modern society, most levirs do not undergo levirate marriage for the sake of fulfilling a mitzvah, and that there is a need to maintain a norm of monogamy to protect society's stability.[67]

Yibum and *shifḥah* are two biblical examples of third-party intervention in the context of polygamy. Each was a last resort. Although they are significantly different from contemporary surrogacy, we may learn the following values and lessons from these precedents:

- Social norms are dynamic, and halakhah responds to evolving societal mores.

- Extraordinary effort and even crossing familial lines is accepted as a last resort in assuring genetic continuity.
- Recognition is warranted for the investment made by an initiating mother and her role in shaping the identity of her adopted child.

In contrast to the days of the patriarchs, sex is no longer needed for procreation. Hence, polygamy and monogamy may no longer define reproductive boundaries. Two distinct questions emerge in assessing the novelty of contemporary surrogacy: Does Judaism accept scientific intervention to overcome infertility? And is it moral for a couple in our day to use a third party to enable procreation?

3. *Science as blessing and mandate.* When the Torah commands "be fruitful and multiply," it continues, "and conquer it (the earth) [*vekhivshuha*]."[68] The phrase "and conquer it" is interpreted as a mandate to serve as God's partner in maintaining and assisting nature.[69] In that light, Rabbi Seymour Siegel writes:

> We are called upon to care for nature and to preserve it—but not to worship it. We are also called upon to use our ingenuity, our imagination, and intelligence to improve nature when human happiness and well-being [are] thwarted. This is the basis for the whole medical enterprise.[70]

Physicians, in the Jewish tradition, help fashion creation. Their role is beautifully illustrated in the following midrash[71] of a pair of leading Rabbis in second-century Palestine:

> Once Rabbi Yishmael and Rabbi Akiva were strolling in the streets of Jerusalem along with another man. They met a sick person, who said to them, "Masters, tell me how I can be healed." They quickly advised him to take a certain medicine until he felt better.
> The man with them turned to them and said, "Who made this man sick?"
> "The Holy One, Source of Blessing," they replied.
> "And do you presume to interfere in an area that is not yours? He is afflicted and you heal?!"
> "What is your occupation?" they asked the man.

> "I'm a tiller of the soil," he answered, "as you can see from the sickle I carry."
> "Who created the field and the vineyard?"
> "The Holy One, Source of Blessing."
> "And you dare to move in an area that is not yours? God created these and you eat their fruit?"
> "Don't you see the sickle in my hand?" the man said. "If I did not go out and plow the field, cover it, fertilize it, weed it, nothing would grow!"
> "Fool," the Rabbis said, "just as a tree does not grow if it is not fertilized, plowed, and weeded—and even if it already grew, but then is not watered—it dies. So the body is like a tree: the medicine is the fertilizer and the doctor is the farmer."

Medicine, in this account, is seen as a way to actualize God's blessing. Rabbi Akiva and Rabbi Yishmael's words are a compelling response to those, such as the Catholic Church,[72] that speak of natural law and restrict greatly the use of technology to overcome infertility. The imagery of the two Rabbis speaking of seed, field, and fruit is well suited to the area of medical intervention and procreation.

Rabbis universally accept the use of medical technology, but may question the ethical implications of the process. Hence, Rabbi Jakobovits, the former chief rabbi of England and among the first to write on the ethics of reproductive technology, said in 1975:

> Artificial insemination utilizing an outside donor (A.I.D.) is, however, considered to pose grave moral problems. Such operations, even if they may not technically constitute adultery, would completely disrupt the family relationship. Moreover, a child so conceived would be denied its birth-right to have a father and other relations who can be identified. Altogether, to reduce human generation to "stud-farming" methods would be a debasement of human life, utterly repugnant to Jewish ideals and traditions. . . .
>
> Hardly less offensive to moral susceptibilities is the proposal to abort a mother's naturally fertilized egg and to reimplant it into a "host-mother" as a convenience for women who seek the gift of a child without the encumbrance and disfigurement of preg-

> nancy. To use another person as an "incubator" and then take from her the child she carried and delivered for a fee is a revolting degradation of maternity and an affront to human dignity.[73]

Rabbi Jakobovits's words are a sample of the alarm generated by the new tools of medical reproductive intervention. It is not the use of the tools that is objectionable, but the social and ethical implications. Regrettably, the concerns have rarely encompassed the data of the last two decades and instead have focused on theoretical scenarios, often of the most extreme kind. Surrogacy is something fundamentally new that warrants a balancing test of the gains and risks and must be seen as a new composite of legal concerns.

C. Ethical and Legal Objections to the New Social Arrangements

A private arrangement such as that of the Sterns and Mary Beth Whitehead would not bind a court, according to Jewish law, because traditionally parents do not have the right to independently determine the status of their children. In all such matters of parental responsibility and rights, including custody, it is the court that makes an authoritative determination, based on the best interests of the child.[74]

Whether surrogacy is in the best interests of children and a societal good is a widely debated question. If these novel social arrangements are ethical, enhance family, and serve to protect the child, then the courts might choose to oversee and validate such agreements. The following analysis of the ethical and legal concerns that stem from surrogacy affirms the needs of the child as the priority.

1. *Baby-selling.* Baby-selling is repugnant to the Jewish tradition and illegal in all fifty states. Hence, a mother in the United States may not receive payment for her child when she turns her offspring over to another couple for adoption. Nonetheless, most surrogate birth arrangements involve payment. Is the payment to a surrogate mother the equivalent of baby-selling? When a subcommittee of the California Legislature gave its findings on surrogates in 1991, the majority equated surrogacy with adoption and wrote that paid surrogacy arrangements would "treat the child as a commodity and would set up a distinction between ordinary

adoptions and surrogacy adoptions that would be neither defensible nor practically enforceable."[75] The recommendation of the California Legislation Committee was to permit surrogacy for free, but to make it a criminal offense to participate on any level in enabling surrogacy for pay. While the California Legislature is still debating the question, four states have made it outright illegal to receive payment as a surrogate.[76]

There are, however, some critical differences between adoption and surrogacy. First, the intended father—in either ovum or gestational surrogacy—is the genetic and intended father of the child.[77] Second, the intended parents accept responsibility from the moment of conception. The interests of the child to enter a secure home where he or she is wanted is therefore protected. Third, there is limited duress on the woman agreeing to give up the child, because she makes her decision even before conception.

Distinctions between the typical surrogate and adoption-giving mother further demonstrate that surrogacy and adoption are dissimilar. The profile of a typical adoption mother is an unmarried teenager who lacks financial security and is giving birth for the first time. The adoption-oriented mother has usually gotten pregnant unintentionally, which both she and the biological father regret. She is vulnerable to the manipulation of baby-brokers who may offer her a small monetary fee and care during pregnancy in exchange for the child.[78] Adoption law seeks to protect a vulnerable pregnant mother and to facilitate giving up an unwanted child, rather than to orchestrate a child's conception.[79]

The chances of an adoptive mother changing her mind about giving up a child are also significant, commonly put at between 5 and 15 percent.[80] In one study, adoption specialist Carol Wolfe, MFCC, interviewed 250 birth mothers who had agreed to place their children with prospective adoptive parents. In ninety-five of these cases (38 percent), one or the other party withdrew from the agreement prior to or following the birth.[81]

In contrast, surrogate mothers make a decision prior to conception—usually with the aid of an attorney and a therapist—to give the child to parents who very much want to establish a family. Because of the time frame, there is no need for hurried decisions, no rival bidding, and no unwanted pregnancy. The studies on surrogates consistently show that surrogates are usually married, have already borne at least one child, and are financially and psychologically stable.[82] An ovum surrogate mother, let alone a gestational surrogate, does not experience the stress of an unplanned pregnancy. Nor is she likely to feel guilty about giving away her child if she views herself as performing a good deed for the natural father and his wife.[83] The fact that less than 1 percent of surrogate arrangements have ended up in the courts is strong evidence that surrogacy is different from adoption after birth.

Critics of paid surrogacy say that the payment to the surrogate is for the child because that is what the intended parents really want and that such payments demean human life. Sharon Huddle, who founded the National Coalition Against Surrogacy, argues: "The ultimate victims are children. Their very existence was pre-negotiated, pre-designed, and contracted for just like any other commercial transaction."[84] While it is tempting (and rhetorically effective) to characterize the money that changes hands as a payment for a commodity (the child), it is unclear that this is true. Pregnancy entails lost time, medical risk, and pain, all of which warrant remuneration.[85] In addition, payments to an ovum surrogate may be viewed as the biological father's attempt to protect the welfare of his child by ensuring that the mother is provided with proper care.[86]

If payment is banned, there is the need to pressure a friend or a relative to serve as an unpaid surrogate, an act of persuasion that may be even more coercive and problematic than remuneration. It is unrealistic to expect that couples who wish to have a child through a surrogate will be able to find one without participating in the cost, including the living costs, entailed by pregnancy. To ban paid surrogacy is to encourage a "surrogacy underground," because the law will not eliminate a strong desire to utilize medical technology to have one's own children through a third party.

Money linked to pregnancy does not mean that the resulting child is any less loved or is reduced to a mere commodity. Currently, $1 billion a year is spent in medical clinics to assist procreation. The money does not detract from the uniqueness of the child; it only underscores that a child is a much wanted blessing.

The best interests of a child are served if the child is loved, cared for, and nurtured, which has little to do with the manner of conception and gestation. Payment compensates the surrogate for the hardship of pregnancy and helps ensure that the intended child is properly taken care of, beginning with conception. Surrogacy is not baby-selling, unless there is exploitation.

2. *Oshek—exploitation. Oshek,* which translates as "exploitation," is condemned in Jewish law. The prohibition stems from the biblical in-

junction *lo ta'ashok et rei'akha,* "You shall not oppress your neighbor."[87] Technically, this mandate is identified by its biblical context and in later Jewish law as the wrongful withholding of funds, usually that of wages.[88] Nonetheless, *oshek* may also be understood more broadly as a moral condemnation of taking advantage of the distress, weakness, or inexperience of another person.[89] If there were exploitation, a Jewish court might disregard an agreement, as it does with gambling contracts.[90] Marc Gellman, among others, argues that *oshek* is inherently present in surrogacy arrangements.[91] He goes on to cite the statement in the Talmud that it is better to do a little good with what is yours than to do much good by exploiting that which belongs to others.[92]

The charge that surrogacy is exploitative is rooted in a variety of concerns: abuse of poor women by the rich; insensitivity to the birth mother's sacrifice in surrendering a child; frivolous avoidance of natural childbirth by fertile women; and undue risk with devaluing and commodifying the body. Put succinctly by George Annas: "The core reality of surrogate motherhood is that it is both classist and sexist: a method to obtain children genetically related to white males by exploiting poor women."[93]

On the other side is the argument articulated by Carmel Shalev that "the exclusion of domestic reproduction labor from the public economy is the ultimate manifestation of a patriarchal double standard."[94] Shalev says that it is the historical failure to value the domestic work of mothers and housewives that has contributed to the sense that gestation has no value as a form of productive labor. She argues that women may exercise reason with respect to reproduction and may responsibly share birth power with those less fortunate.[95] As men get paid for their muscles, Shalev says, women should get reimbursed for their wombs.

Much of the debate to date has taken place in the theoretical realm. For instance, there is no evidence that women have used surrogates to avoid the hardship of pregnancy, as Rabbi Jakobovits had feared. Indeed, looking at the actual data on exploitation and surrogacy, Judge Parnelli in *Anna Johnson v. Calvert*[96] wrote for the California Supreme Court:

> Although common sense suggests that women of lesser means serve as surrogate mothers more often than do wealthy women, there has been no proof that surrogacy contracts exploit poor women to any greater degree than economic necessity in general

exploits them to accept lower-paid or otherwise undesirable employment.

The service as a surrogate is not to be equated with slavery, which some have done. The woman makes the choice in a freewill manner and is given the right to withdraw at any point. She is not giving up her womb permanently, but using it for a specific purpose that is inherently time bound.

In reference to the ovum surrogate, who is giving up a child who is genetically her own, a larger perspective is helpful. We as a committee have approved the donation of sperm and ovum. An ovum surrogate is essentially donating her ovum. Rather than it being placed in another woman, she is donating the ovum and serving as the gestational surrogate for that donated egg.

Another challenge to surrogacy, as articulated by Andrea Dworkin, among others,[97] is that surrogacy is a form of prostitution. There are, however, fundamental differences between surrogacy and prostitution. The goal of prostitution is a fleeting moment of carnal pleasure. In contrast, surrogacy enables a profound societal gain—the creation of a child. Second, prostitutes are easily and often exploited. Those who use their services usually have little regard for the prostitutes' well-being. In contrast, intended parents are committed to a surrogate during the extended time frame of conception and gestation. They are concerned for the surrogate's lifestyle, home life, emotional and psychological stability, physical health, and a myriad of other factors that could affect the baby's health. It is hard to imagine an employer who cares more for his or her workers than do intended parents for a surrogate. Last, the use of a surrogate, as in the case of artificial insemination, does not violate the marital bond, as would adultery. A third party who assists procreation does not harm a marriage, but strengthens it.

Oshek is of critical concern and warrants oversight by the courts and legislators, but is not inherent to surrogacy. If payment for the use of a womb is accepted as legitimate, then surrogacy for payment is defensible. If we recognize women as responsible and accountable for their decisions, we should acknowledge that surrogacy provides women the opportunity to give the blessing of a child to a couple in need and allows the surrogate to get paid legitimately for her efforts.

3. Unjustified risk. God commands *venishmartem me'od lenafshoteikhem,* "Guard your lives carefully."[98] This charge led the codifiers of Jewish law to say that a person should not unreasonably risk his or her life.[99] There is no doubt that giving birth entails risk. As Dr. Jay Masserman, an obstetrician, told me, the day a woman gives birth is generally the most dangerous of her life. Rabbi Marc Gellman has challenged surrogacy on this basis, saying that a surrogate cannot justify self-endangerment, because she has no *ḥiyuv,* legal obligation, to give birth for another couple.[100] However, in the technical sense of *ḥiyuv,* a woman is never obligated to procreate. The command is only binding upon men.[101]

Yet the rabbis have seen pregnancy as worthy of risk-taking by women. As a wife undertakes a risk to allow her husband to fulfill a mitzvah, so does the surrogate. As a woman derives joy from giving birth to her own child, so may a woman gain fulfillment in enabling another couple to be blessed with a child. The exception to self-endangerment can be read more broadly than Gellman's definition of *ḥiyuv* and may be understood as a risk that provides a substantial good.

In that light, Rabbi Elliot Dorff permits ovum donation despite medical risks and notes that the risks are smaller than those for kidney donation from a live donor, who only has two kidneys to start with, and which is permitted.[102] Moreover, the sages permitted the performance of paid tasks, such as sailing, which in their day entailed substantial risks to safety. And today, we would allow a Jew to serve as an astronaut despite the risks and with only theoretical gains. In the case of surrogacy, it is technically a mitzvah for the man in the couple to have a child, and it benefits family life. To enable a couple to have a child justifies risk.

A woman who is at greater risk than most during pregnancy should not serve as a surrogate because of the prohibition of self-endangerment. Fortunately, the risks of pregnancy and childbirth have declined in recent decades because of improved monitoring of the pregnant woman and the fetus and safer C-section techniques. Nonetheless, when a woman and her husband consider her serving as a surrogate, they must take risk into account and be sure that her health is sound.

4. Asmakhta—finality of conditions. Another contractual concept that is discussed as a challenge to surrogacy agreements is that of *asmakhta,*[103] which literally means "lean on," and means that a contract is binding only if we can reasonably presume that the intentions of both parties are serious, deliberate, and final.[104] Maimonides goes so far as to void all contracts that are bound by an "if" clause, because the condition precedent implies that the contract only takes effect in the future.[105]

Yet Maimonides and later *posekim* did accept commercial futures contracts when written with the language of "from now" (*mei'akhshav*), clarifying that the parties were bound from the moment of entering the agreement.[106] The symbolic act of acquisition (*kinyan*), often marked by the exchange of a handkerchief, served to show that the parties had made up their minds to enter into an immediately binding transaction. Consequently, social agreements of future marriage (*shidukhim*), when properly composed, were enforced with penalties for breach of promise.[107] Nonetheless, the moral question remains as to whether a woman can, in fact, make a final decision to relinquish a yet unborn child.[108]

In response to such concerns, Carmel Shalev is vehement in her objection to the "insinuation that it is unreasonable to expect a woman to keep her promise because her faculty of reason is suspended by the emotional facets of her biological constituency."[109] Shalev says that as an artist may grow attached to a work of art, he or she is still bound by the agreement to part with the work. Likewise, Rabbi Seymour Siegel argued that a woman has the capacity to make a decision and should be bound by her word.[110] On a contract level, the response to *asmakhta* is that surrogacy is an agreement for services that binds the parties from the moment they enter into the agreement.

During the pregnancy, a surrogate should have the right to withdraw from the agreement—an extension of her freedom of choice. But once the child is born, it should be assumed that it goes to the intended parents. After all, it is their responsibility to accept the child from the moment of birth regardless of birth defects. After birth, an ovum surrogate may assert her maternal rights, but the burden of proof is on her to show cause as to why the original intent should not be honored. *Asmakhta* is a legal concern in Jewish law to ensure predictability of outcomes, which the court should protect in a surrogacy case as well, unless there is a violation of the best interests of the child.

5. Davar shelo ba la'olam—futures. Another contractual concern related to *asmakhta* is the prohibition against contracts for "something that is not yet in existence"—*davar shelo ba la'olam.*[111] Parties could not technically give title to what did not yet exist. Yet here, too, the problem was overcome with language that shifted the focus to the parties themselves, who did exist, and their obligation to act in a certain way.[112] Hence, the concern is moot when a surrogate agreement is understood as a contract for services of pregnancy that binds the conduct of the respective parties, rather than the determination of the status of the future child.

6. *Family integrity.* Surrogacy is challenged in broad terms as contrary to a public policy of preserving family life. Some of the objections are as follows: "Frivolous motivations [for surrogacy] soon become socially acceptable";[113] "To use another person as an 'incubator' and then take from her the child she carried and delivered for a fee is a revolting degradation of maternity."[114]

Jewish tradition values family integrity, which includes the ability to define who is in the family; forging secure family bonds; fashioning personal identity; and preserving the sanctity of marriage.[115] It is precisely the value of family that motivates an advocacy of surrogacy, for such arrangements allow for much wanted children who enhance and create families. Infertility imposes a great strain on a marriage, which, for the couple with an infertile woman, may find a solution in the benign assistance of another woman.

There is currently no evidence of harm to a family unit that has had a child through surrogacy, such as the jealousy of the nongenetic parent or half-siblings of either family. If anything, the stories to date are overwhelmingly of the joy of gaining a child. No doubt, there are risks worthy of monitoring through careful consideration and counseling before entering such an agreement. But most persuasive is the fact that with thousands of children born to surrogates—thousands of children who otherwise would not have been born—only a minuscule percentage have resulted in litigation or reported problems. Surrogacy, evidenced anecdotally by the successes, strengthens family.

D. A Path for Surrogacy

The novelty of a woman carrying a child for another couple will take time to gain social acceptance. Comfort with surrogacy will properly increase and theoretical fears will dissipate as the data build an unimpeachable case of happy families that successfully overcame the infertility of the female spouse.

Jewish law contains many examples of the power of the courts to redefine family relationships and rights. Such change comes slowly and is a response to shifting societal norms and new variables. Moreover, the legislation of the state, as in the case of adoption, may give Jewish courts authority to foster entirely new social arrangements. Yet the reality is that Jewish courts, particularly in our movement, refrain from monitoring social arrangements and adjudicating disputes. Largely, our *batei din* deal with matters of marriage and divorce.

Jewish law espouses the principle of *dina demalkhuta dina*, the law of the land is the law. This principle, originally enunciated by Samuel in the Talmud in reference to civil matters,[116] would apply on a broader basis to any practice in violation of local law. Consequently, if legislatures prohibit surrogacy, Jewish courts and lawyers would need to abide by that holding.[117] If we believe in the benefits of surrogacy, we need to encourage our legislators to pass supportive legislation. We need to caution our members that if the law of their state prohibits surrogacy, they must not violate the law, including the participation in writing "illegal" contracts.

Although surrogacy is a potentially positive use of new technology, controls are needed to protect against abuses and to oversee the best interests of the child. Without effective legislation, there is the threat of reproductive anarchy. Recent alleged unauthorized use of ova by fertility physicians at the University of California at Irvine demonstrates the potential havoc created by an abuse of consent. Legislation must ensure that the expectations of all parties involved are clearly defined in an agreement and that there is oversight of the professionals.[118]

Wise legislation would require that even prior to conception, parties would appear before a state court and request permission to enter into a surrogacy agreement. The judge would confirm the surrogate's physical health, emotional stability, informed consent, prior experience with pregnancy, and, if she were married, confirm her husband's approval. The court would also determine that the initiating couple would make good parents and that their motive was infertility. The court would oversee fair compensation to any involved parties, including agencies or professionals, and require that insemination be done by a licensed physician. The court would also ascertain that there would be professional counseling and psychological preparedness for all parties prior to entering the agreement.

Guidelines for surrogacy agreements coupled with court oversight would offer the following necessary ingredients for the child's security: certainty, efficiency, and finality. Such legislation is a means for making workable that which might otherwise create social disorder. There is a need for such control to avoid underground, unscrupulous practices. Indeed, legislatures could make it a crime to enter a surrogacy agreement absent court approval and thereby put teeth into a law that would limit abuse of a potential blessing.

Couples should consider surrogacy as a last option to overcome infertility because of its great financial and emotional costs. Among the substantial emotional costs are the uncertainty of success—which may entail great psychological stress—and the possibility of a change of mind by the surrogate, which might entail a lawsuit or simply great disappointment. In addition, ongoing ethical concerns remain that warrant ongoing evaluation, such as the impact of surrogacy on the family of the surrogate. Nonetheless, when a couple is aware of these risks, the Rabbinical Assembly Committee of Law and Standards should affirm in light of the current evidence that surrogacy is permitted by halakhah.

E. Additional Concerns

Does surrogacy allow for fulfilling the mitzvah of "be fruitful and multiply"?

Yes. A man, according to Jewish law, is considered the natural father of the offspring of his sperm. Hence, with the aid of a surrogate, a man would fulfill the mitzvah of procreation, which is incumbent only upon the man. In the same vein, whether the child was a *kohein, levi,* or *yisra'el* would be determined by the biological father.[119]

Must an infertile couple hire a surrogate to fulfill the mitzvah?

No. Surrogacy is an extraordinary method to conceive and gestate a child. A couple is only obligated to use natural means to fulfill the procreative mandate.[120]

F. Summary

Surrogacy—both ovum and gestational—is a new legal construct. Jewish law has no precedent for child-making without sex, let alone the splitting of biology and gestation. This is a time to acknowledge that new variables provide a need to craft law. To determine whether Jewish law should support surrogacy is to balance the gains of surrogacy over its potential damage.

Adoption is to be encouraged, but some couples will prefer a genetic link to the father (artificial insemination, ovum donation, or ovum surrogacy) or to the mother (gestational surrogacy). At first impression, there may be a visceral discomfort with these relatively new modes of reproduction—specifically, the transfer of genetic material or the use of a womb for another couple. Yet when we examine this new technology in the context of its outcome, we find the blessing of children to couples who want them very much. The bigger picture, which includes the intended result, makes surrogacy more acceptable upon reexamination.

A contemporary surrogate is not the equivalent of the *shifḥah,* because the surrogate may have a husband and children of her own and she is not involved in raising the intended child. Yet the new medical technology allows the surrogate to help an infertile couple without violating her own sexual, marital commitment to her husband. And the intended child is given a home by parents who are genetically linked to the intended child and accept responsibility for the newborn from the point of conception.

The precedents of *shifḥah* and *yibum* evidence that such constructs evolve in response to changing variables, including shifting social mores. Surrogacy has grown dramatically over the past two decades because it meets the needs of many couples. As a new social construct, related to but different from *shifḥah,* it warrants an open-minded examination. It is not ostensibly forbidden by Jewish law, and, if anything, the past constructs suggest the possibility of new social forms as a last-resort solution to female infertility. There are potential abuses in surrogacy, and some cases have already led to lawsuits. Before a couple opts to use a surrogate, they should explore all their reproductive options and be aware of the serious costs and risks entailed by depending on a third party to their child's birth.

Legislation would help overcome potential abuses, such as exploitation of surrogates. The test of a new social construct is not whether it can thrive in the absence of legislation, but whether legislation can control abuse.[121] In the context of surrogacy, the success of the surrogacy centers in screening potential surrogates and writing contracts with clearly stated expectations reveals the potential of the courts to make surrogacy workable for all parties. To ban a technique based on potential psychological harm may cause even greater psychological harm by its absence. Jewish ethical concerns, including baby-selling, exploitation, family integrity, and contractual needs for a meeting of the minds, are each balanced in favor of surrogacy upon close examination.

From a Jewish perspective, it would be wrong to outlaw a procedure that has the potential to help so many couples overcome infertility and that works smoothly in the overwhelming majority of cases. On balance, surrogacy offers the joy of parenthood, a profound benefit to society. Judaism, we see in this analysis, affirms couples who say, as did the matriarch Sarah: "Through her I too shall bear a child."[122]

G. Halakhic Conclusions

It is permissible to employ a surrogate, whether gestational or ovum, to overcome infertility and to serve as a surrogate. A man fulfills the mandate of procreation in having a child with a surrogate.

Notes

1. Noam Zohar of Jerusalem writes: "Regarding surrogacy the rejection is almost universal" ("Artificial Insemination and Surrogate Motherhood: A Halakhic Perspective," *Svara* 2, no. 1 [1991]: 13–19). Little, in fact, has even been written. To quote Pinhas Shifman of Hebrew University in Jerusalem: "Rabbinic opinion has [not] yet addressed itself to religious problems created by surrogate motherhood" ("The Right to Parenthood and the Best Interests of the Child: A Perspective on Surrogate Motherhood in Jewish and Israeli Law," *Human Rights Annual* 4 [1987]: 560).

   Among the Orthodox rabbis, I have not found a rabbi in favor of ovum surrogacy; among the non-Orthodox rabbinate, opinions are divided. A selection of rabbinic views to date:

   Immanuel Jakobovits: "To use another woman as an 'incubator' . . . for a fee . . . [is a] revolting degradation of maternity and an affront to human dignity" (*Jewish Medical Ethics* [New York: Bloch, 1959, 1975], 264–65).

   Moshe Tendler is opposed to both ovum and gestational surrogacy, as undermining a woman's dignity: "If the surrogate is a married woman . . . this is not a curative modality. It substitutes illness for illness, pathology involving many for the pathology of one woman" ("Infertility Management: Cure or Ill," *Sh'ma* 17, no. 334 [15 May 1987]: 109–10).

   Daniel H. Gordis: "Jewish women should not serve as surrogates for pay, nor should Jewish couples seek to hire such women. Our commitment to human dignity and social good and our desire to forge a link between halakhah and morality requires a stance no less inflexible than this" ("Give Me Progeny

. . . : Jewish Ethics and the Economics of Surrogate Motherhood," in *University of Judaism Papers* 8, no. 1 [Los Angeles: University of Judaism, 1988]: 21).

Marc Gellman: "The sanctity of family life requires a single husband and wife" ("The Ethics of Surrogate Motherhood," *Sh'ma* 17, no. 334 [15 May 1987]: 105–7).

David Feldman says that the ovum-surrogacy contract is unenforceable as a matter of public policy and that courts should determine custody based on the best interests of the child (*Sh'ma* 17, no. 334 [15 May 1987]: 108–9). Feldman supports gestational surrogacy as a last resort, *Health and Medicine in the Jewish Tradition* (New York: Crossroad, 1986), 71–75.

The Rabbinical Assembly Committee of Law and Standards voted in favor of surrogacy (5 June 1985); a responsum by Rabbi David Lincoln says that anything that helps overcome the low Jewish birthrate is welcome [see chap. 9 of this vol.].

Walter Jacob, on behalf of the Central Conference of American Rabbis (*American Reform Responsa* [New York: Central Conference of American Rabbis, 1983]), cautiously permits surrogacy because of the importance of procreation.

Seymour Siegel: "Our society rests on the expectation that contracts made in good faith will be honored." He says that the surrogacy contract is moral and hence should be enforced ("The Ethics of Baby M's Custody," *Sh'ma* 17, no. 334 [15 May 1987]: 108–9).

Michael Gold accepts surrogacy as a last-resort response to infertility, although he prefers adoption and sees the need for surrogacy legislation (*And Hannah Wept* [Philadelphia: Jewish Publication Society, 1988], 120–27).

Fred Rosner permits gestational surrogacy as a last resort (*Modern Medicine and Jewish Ethics,* 2d ed. [Hoboken, N.J.: Ktav, 1991], 114).

2. Overwhelmingly today, the initiating couple is a husband and wife. Beyond the scope of this paper are the possibilities of single and gay parents and the anonymous donation of the sperm and/or the ovum.
3. Lori B. Andrews and Lisa Douglass, "Alternative Reproduction," *Southern California Law Review* 65 (1991): 637.
4. No official statistics are maintained by any agency, and the 4,000 figure is only an estimate, but it is widely cited. *Minority Report of the Advisory Panel to the Joint Legislation Committee on Surrogate Parenting,* California Legislature (Sacramento, 1991), M8 (hereafter, *Minority Report*); Andrews and Douglass, 670; Susan Edmiston, "Whose Child Is This?" *Glamour* 89 (Nov. 1991): 234, 276; estimate of New York Health Department cited in *Center for Surrogate Parenting Newsletter* 1 (spring 1993): 1.
5. Edmiston, 236.
6. In this procedure, an egg is removed from a ripe follicle and is fertilized by a sperm cell outside the human body. The fertilized egg is allowed to divide in a protected environment for about two days and is then inserted into the uterus of the gestational surrogate.

7. Louise Brown was born in England in 1978. Andrews and Douglass, 625.
8. Andrews and Douglass, 670, citing Wulf H. Utian et al., "Preliminary Experience with In Vitro Fertilization-Surrogate Gestational Pregnancy," *Fertility and Sterility* 52 (1989): 633–38.
9. *Minority Report,* M9: "[T]he Center [for Surrogate Parenting] reports that approximately 50 percent of current surrogate activities involving their professional program involve gestational arrangements."
10. See Deborah Diamond, "Labor of Love," *Ladies Home Journal,* Sept. 1994, 173, the story of a sister carrying a child for her sister, who, until then, had been unsuccessful at getting pregnant but simultaneously got pregnant with twins by in vitro fertilization. Consequently, the once infertile couple began parenthood with three children.
11. "Miraculous Babies: The Woman Who Bore Her Own Grandchild," *Life,* Dec. 1993, 78–79; *Time,* 19 Aug. 1991, 58.
12. Andrews and Douglass, 671 n. 236.
13. Sums supplied by the Center for Surrogate Parenting, Beverly Hills, Calif. (1994). Other costs include approximately $5,000 for medical costs; $13,600 for administrative costs; $4,000 for psychological costs; $3,000 to retain legal counsel; and $4,000 for miscellaneous costs.
14. Andrews and Douglass, 635, citing the U.S. Congress, Office of Technology Assessment, *Infertility: Medicine and Social Choices* (Washington, D.C.: U.S. Government Printing Office, 1988), 50.
15. William Handel of the Center for Surrogate Parenting (8383 Wilshire Blvd., Ste. 750, Beverly Hills, CA 90211; [213] 655–1974) is the most accomplished attorney in the area of surrogacy-agreement drafting.
16. *Minority Report,* 16 n. 9, contains a list of the studies, which include: H. Daniel and K. Linkins (Harvard Medical School), "Surrogate Mother Demographies," which concludes that the primary motivation of surrogates is altruism; "Psychiatric Evaluation of Women in the Surrogate Mother Process," *American Journal of Psychiatry* (Oct. 1981), a favorable evaluation of surrogate mother candidates; Hilary Hanafin, "Surrogate Parenting: Reassessing Human Bonding," which claims no evidence of regret by surrogates, and [that] open contact between parties was an important variable.
17. Lisa Douglass, "Empirical Studies of Surrogate Mothers and Their Children," in *Minority Report,* 16.
18. Not one surrogate in Hanafin's study said that money was the deciding factor for participation (cited in Andrews and Douglass, 673–74).
19. Andrews and Douglass, 626, citing the U.S. Congress, *Infertility.*
20. In 40 percent of the couples, the trouble is traced to the man, in another 40 percent it is traced to the woman, and in the rest of the couples, the source of the problem cannot be identified. "Miraculous Babies"; Andrews and Douglass, 634.
21. Edmiston, 236.

22. *Minority Report,* 7 n. 2: Donovan, "New Reproductive Technologies: Some Legal Dilemmas," *Family Planning Perspectives* 18, no. 2 (Mar./Apr. 1986).
23. Andrews and Douglass, 670; phenylketonuria is a genetic defect that may lead to mental retardation unless identified very early in the child's life.
24. Avi Katz, "Surrogate Motherhood and the Baby-Selling Laws," *Columbia Journal of Law and Social Problems* 20 (1986): 4 n. 12: "While there is an abundance of older, handicapped, or minority children waiting for adoption, healthy white infants are in scarce supply."
25. 537 A2d 1227 (N.J. 1988).
26. 25 Cal. App. 4th 1218, 30 Cal. Rptr. 893 (1994); the appellate court has redirected the trial court to examine the criteria of custody, but has also held that the surrogacy agreement was in no way binding. See the trial court opinion at LA Super CT., no. D324348; featured on NBC's *48 Hours,* 23 Nov. 1991.
27. *Center for Surrogate Parenting Newsletter* (spring 1993): 1; Edmiston puts the number at 15; *Minority Report* cites only 10 lawsuits to date; an editorial in *USA Today* (26 Sept. 1990, 126) says: "Of the 1,000 babies born [to surrogates] in the past decade, only a handful have wound up in court."
28. 5 Cal. 4th 84, 19 Cal. Rptr. 494 (1993).
29. Surrogacy has been mentioned in futuristic literature, including George Orwell's *1984* (New York: Harcourt, Brace, 1949), 66, reference to a totalitarian "Junior Anti-Sex League," which advocated all reproduction by artificial insemination or "artsem"; Aldous Huxley's *Brave New World* (New York: Harper and Row, 1932), 1–14, description of hatcheries used for human reproduction in a totalitarian world; Margaret Atwood, *The Handmaid's Tale* (New York: Houghton Mifflin, 1986).
30. *Berakhot* 60a, discussed in Rosner, *Modern Medicine,* 122. The background on the legend is the story that knowing that Jacob would become the father of a total of twelve sons and not wishing her sister Rachel to bear fewer sons than the maidservants Bilhah and Zilpah, Leah prayed that her already conceived fetus be born a female. In *Berakhot,* her prayer is answered by a sex change. However, *Targum Jonathan,* on Gen. 30:2, suggests that an embryo transfer occurred to solve the problem. Bleich cites the talmudic commentary of Rabbi Samuel Edels as supporting the embryo-transfer idea as a way to understand *Berakhot* 60a.
31. Andrea E. Stumpf, "Redefining Mother: A Legal Matrix for New Reproductive Technologies," *Yale Law Journal* 96 (1986): 191–92.
32. Gen. 1:28.
33. *Yevamot* 6:6. Shammai sees Adam's two sons as the model; Hillel looks to Adam and Eve.
34. Tosafot to *Bava Batra* 60b, s.v. *din hu.*
35. Gen. 15:5, 22:17, 26:4; Exod. 32:13; Deut. 1:10, 10:22, 28:62.
36. *Niddah* 31a.
37. *Genesis Rabbah* 34:14; it is incorporated by Joseph Karo, *S.A., E.H.* 1:1; even

stronger were the words of Eliezer ben Hyrcanus, "Who brings no children into the world is like a murderer" (*Yevamot* 63b).

38. *Megillah* 27a.
39. Isa. 45:18.
40. A description of Sarai offering Avram her handmaid Hagar in order to have children through her is Genesis, chap. 16. In regard to Rebecca, the Torah records: "And Isaac entreated the Lord for his wife, because she was barren, and the Lord was entreated of him, and Rebecca his wife conceived" (Gen. 25:21).
41. Gen. 30:1–2.
42. *Shifḥah* and *amah* are used interchangeably in the Torah to describe a slave of the patriarch's wife, who, as property of the patriarch, was also a member of the extended family (see Gen. 16:1 and 30:3, 9). Pilegesh, a concubine, was one of a harem of freeborn or freedwomen belonging directly to the patriarch as a secondary wife. See L. Epstein, *Marriage Laws in the Bible and Talmud* (Cambridge, Mass.: Harvard University Press, 1942), 34–62.
43. Gen. 30:3.
44. Gen. 16:2.
45. Gen. 30:9.
46. Gen. 16:6.
47. Gen. 15:6.
48. Rachel—Gen. 30:6 (Dan), 8 (Naftali); Leah—Gen. 30:10 (Gad), 13 (Asher).
49. Sarna says that the origin of placing a child on its knees as an act of adoption is in the idea of the knee as the seat of generative power. Indeed, in Akkadian, "knee" is *birku,* which is used as a euphemism for sexual parts. This act of adoption is also found in ancient Greece and Rome. Sarna, *Genesis: The JPS Torah Commentary* (Philadelphia: Jewish Publication Society, 1989) (hereafter, JPS), 207.
50. Code of Hammurabi 146, in *Ancient Near Eastern Texts,* ed. James B. Pritchard, rev. ed. (Princeton: Princeton University Press, 1955), 172, cited in *The Torah: A Modern Commentary,* ed. W. Gunther Plaut (New York: Union of American Hebrew Congregations, 1981) (hereafter, UAHC), 111.
51. Quoted by Ephraim A. Speiser, *Genesis* (Garden City, N.J.: Doubleday, 1964), 120; cited in UAHC, 111.
52. Arlene Agus, "Surrogacy," *Lillith* 19 (spring 1988): 31.
53. Yishmael, Hagar's son, is only one of five children born to a biblical surrogate. The other four are treated as the full sons of Jacob, and no problems for their mothers are reported. In addition, when Hagar leaves the surrogate arrangement, she does so with her son.
54. Gellman.
55. Only a small number of the authorities permit artificial insemination by a donor, because of concern with potential incest. Elliot Dorff, in his responsum for the R.A. Law Committee, 24–27 [chap. 2, pp. 37–42 of this vol.], has per-

mitted the use of donor insemination and in response to the concern of incest encourages as much information as possible to be shared with the prospective parents and for them to share it with their child. In addition, Rabbi Dorff notes Rabbi Feinstein's position that incest is a limited concern when the donor is not Jewish.

56. Gen. 32:8.
57. Deut. 25:5–6.
58. Lev. 18:16, 20:21.
59. Deut. 25:8–9.
60. A, par. 33, cited in Sarna, *Genesis,* JPS, 266 note to v. 8.
61. Par. 193, cited in Sarna, ibid.
62. *Yevamot* 2:5 and 22b; *Nedarim* 5:3.
63. *Berakhot* 1:7 and Rashi there; also Tosefta *Yevamot* 6:9—Abba Saul said, "I am inclined to think that the child of such a union is a *mamzeir.*"
64. *Yevamot* 12:6; *M.T., Yibum* 4:1–23; *S.A., E.H.* 169.
65. In the third generation of tannaim, levirate marriage was customarily upheld (*Yevamot* 8:4). Although the majority of Babylonian amoraim left the choice between marriage and *ḥalitzah* to the levir (*Yevamot* 39a–b), the Palestinian amoraim held that *ḥalitzah* took priority. This summary is from *Encyclopaedia Judaica* 11:125–26, s.v. "Levirate Marriage and Halizah."
66. In the medieval rabbinic period, Sephardic rabbis gave priority to levirate marriage; see Alfasi to *Yevamot* 39b; Maimonides, *M.T., Yibum* 1:2; and *S.A., E.H.* 165:1; the rabbis of northern France and Germany held that *ḥalitzah* took priority over *yibum*—see Rashi and Rabbenu Tam; Asher b. Yeḥiel, *Tur, E.H.* 165; and Moses Isserles, *Rema, E.H.* 165:1.
67. Cited in *Encyclopaedia Judaica* 11:129.
68. Gen. 1:28.
69. An important essay on this theme is Joseph Soloveitchik's "The Lonely Man of Faith," *Tradition* 7 (1965): 1–67.
70. Seymour Siegel, an unpublished paper, prepared for the CJLS (1978), quoted in Gold, 83.
71. Midrash Samuel 4:1; Midrash Temurah, as cited in *Otzar Midrashim,* ed. J. D. Eisenstein (New York: n.p., 1915), 2:580–81.
72. "Instruction on Respect for Human Life in Its Origin and on the Dignity of Procreation," *Origins* 16, no. 40 (19 Mar. 1987): 700. Cited by Gold, chap. 5, n. 3: prohibition of procreation by non-natural means.
73. Jakobovits, 264–65.
74. See *Encyclopaedia Judaica* 13:99, s.v. "Parent and Child," citing *Piskei Din shel Batei Hadin Harabaniyim Beyisra'el* 2:3, 171–77; 5:171, 173.
75. *Advisory Panel Report, Joint Committee on Surrogate Parenting,* Sunny Mojonnier, chair, California Legislature (1991), 15.
76. Ariz., Ky., Mich., and Utah. Five more states ban payment but have the caveat of allowing "expenses": Fla., N.H., N.Y., Va., and Wash.

77. A father has a duty to maintain his minor children—*M.T., Ishut* 13:6; *S.A., E.H.* 73:6, 7—and is responsible whether or not he is married to the woman, e.g., the child is born out of wedlock—Resp. *Ribash* no. 41; Resp. *Rosh* 17:7—cited in *Encyclopaedia Judaica* 13:96, s.v. "Parent and Child."
78. Avi Katz, 8.
79. Margaret D. Townsend, "Surrogate Mother Agreements: Contemporary Aspects of a Biblical Notion," *University of Richmond Law Review* 16 (1982): 486.
80. *Center for Surrogacy Parenting Newsletter* 1, no. 4 (spring 1993): 1.
81. *Center for Surrogacy Parenting Newsletter.*
82. Andrews and Douglass, 673–74.
83. Avi Katz, 18.
84. Cited in Lori B. Andrews, "Surrogacy Wars," *California Law Journal* 12 (Oct. 1992): 47.
85. In the Talmud are parallel categories of compensation for willful injury: *nezek*—loss or damage; *tza'ar*—pain and suffering; *ripui*—medical expenses; *shevet*—loss of earnings; *boshet*—humiliation. See *Bava Kamma,* chap. 8; *Ḥ.M.* 420.
86. Carmel Shalev, *Birth Power: The Case for Surrogacy* (New Haven: Yale University Press, 1989), 159. Shalev points out that giving life a monetary value took place in the nineteenth century with respect to life insurance, which was thought to represent a form of trafficking in human lives. Shalev wrote the book as her doctoral dissertation at Yale Law School and currently practices law in Jerusalem.
87. Lev. 19:13.
88. See Rashi to Lev. 19:3; *M.T., Gezeilah Va'aveidah* 1:4; and *Encyclopaedia Judaica* 12:1435–36, s.v. "Oppression."
89. *Bava Metzia* 59b; also note Rashi there.
90. *Sanhedrin* 25b; *M.T., Gezelah* 6:6–16.
91. Gellman, 106.
92. *Sukkot* 29b, cited by Gellman as an argument against ovum surrogacy.
93. George Annas, "Fairy Tales Surrogate Mothers Tell," *Law, Medicine and Health Care* 16 (1988): 27.
94. Shalev, 164.
95. Shalev, 142.
96. 5 Cal. 4th, 97; 19 Cal. Rptr. 2d, 503.
97. Andrea Dworkin, *Right-Wing Women: The Politics of Domesticated Females* (New York: Coward, McCann, 1983), 181–83, cited in Andrews and Douglass, and cited in Shalev, 148.
98. Deut. 4:15.
99. *Ḥullin* 10a; see *Berakhot* 32b; *Shabbat* 32a; *Bava Kamma* 15b, 80a, 91b; *M.T., Hilkhot Rotzeaḥ* 11:4–5; *O.Ḥ.* 173:2; *Rema* to *Y.D.* 116:5.
100. Gellman, 106.
101. *Yevamot* 6:6. The majority holds that only men are required. A dissenting opin-

ion is voiced by Rabbi Yoḥanan ben Beroka, who would obligate both men and women. Feldman, *Health and Medicine,* 71, presents this law and explains it as based on the possibility of man engaging in polygamy and with the gloss of Rabbi Meir Simchah of Dvinsk (d. 1927) that since the pain and risk of child-bearing is upon the woman, the Torah could not in fairness command a woman to undergo that pain and risk.

102. Elliot Dorff, "Donor Insemination, Egg Donation, and Adoption," unpublished 2d draft, Sept. 1993, written for the CJLS, 53 [chap. 3, pp. 83–84 of this vol.].
103. Gold, 122.
104. *Bava Metzia* 48b, 66a–b; *Bava Batra* 168a.
105. *M.T., Mekhira* 11:2, 6.
106. *M.T., Mekhira* 11; see discussion by A. Zvi Ehrman, "Asmakhta," in *Principles of Jewish Law,* ed. Menahem Elon (Jerusalem: Keter, 1974), 171–74.
107. Ehrman, "Asmakhta," Tosefot to *Bava Metzia* 66a; *Sanhedrin* 24b–25a and *S.A., Ḥ.M.* 207:16, although Ashkenazic authorities widely argue that the penalty was not a matter of contract law, but compensation for damage and insult.
108. This question is raised by Michael Gold, 122, who does not answer it, but goes on to emphasize that a woman who makes such an agreement still has a moral duty to fulfill it; he quotes the sages: "He who exacted punishment from the generations of the Flood and from the generations of the Tower of Babel will also exact punishment from one who does not abide by his word" (*Bava Metzia* 4:2).
109. Shalev, 121.
110. Siegel, 107–8.
111. Tosefta, *Nedarim* 6:7; see also *Bava Metzia, Hamafkid* (chap. 3).
112. *Bava Batra* 157a; *Tur* and *S.A., Ḥ.M.* 60:6.
113. Tendler.
114. Jakobovits.
115. Concerns cited by Agus, "Surrogacy."
116. *Nedarim* 28a; *Gittin* 10b; *Bava Kamma* 113a; *Bava Batra* 54b, 55a.
117. There is no state in the union that has legislated surrogacy contracts as legal and enforceable. Only nineteen states have any laws on the subject as of the end of 1993, and most placed limits—some even made it a crime to engage in surrogacy for profit (editorial in *USA Today,* 19 Nov. 1993, 12A). State legislatures are actively considering legislation; in 1992, there were fifteen states with legislation, the most common—applicable in eleven states—is voiding paid surrogacy contracts (Andrews, "Surrogacy Wars," 50).
118. Examples of model legislation include the Uniform Status of Children of Assisted Conception Act, National Conference of Commissioners of Uniform State Law, 1988; analyzed and supported in Paul J. Greco, "Parental Guidance Suggested: A Proposal for Regulating Surrogacy," *Columbia Journal of Law and Social Problems* 22 (1989): 115ff.; favorable legislation was drafted by Calif.

state senator Watson, Senate bill 2635 (1988), passed by the California Legislature, but vetoed by Gov. Pete Wilson.

119. Dorff similarly holds according to the link to the biological father that the tribal identity follow the source of the sperm, 64 [chap. 2, p. 63 of this vol.].

120. Dorff similarly writes in reference to the use of donor insemination, 66 [chap. 2, p. 63 of this vol.].

121. Greco, 180.

122. Gen. 16:2.

CHAPTER 7

Surrogate Parenting*

Aaron L. Mackler

She'eilah (Question):

May an infertile couple use a surrogate mother to gestate and give birth to a child? Does halakhah provide guidance regarding such cases?

Teshuvah (Response):

The practice of surrogate parenting touches on powerful and sometimes conflicting ethical values and has the potential to dramatically affect the lives of all involved in cases in which it occurs. In the United States over the past decades, the practice has been the topic of vigorous ethical, legislative, and popular debate.[1] Sharply differing and powerfully expressed views may be found among Jewish thinkers as well.[2] In the Jewish context, central values include those of procreation and raising children, respect for persons (*kevod haberiyot*), and appreciation for the human role as active but reverent partners with God in improving the world.[3]

In an extensive, thoughtful, and eloquent paper, "On the Use of Birth Surrogates," Rabbi Elie Spitz argues in favor of surrogacy.[4] For Rabbi Spitz, the great benefit of providing a child to an infertile couple is decisive. Concerns with avoiding exploitation of the surrogate and harm to children born of the procedure are real but manageable. In my judgment, a different halakhic conclusion is required. I appreciate

*Approved by the Rabbinical Assembly Committee on Jewish Law and Standards, June 1997.

Rabbi Spitz's careful work and sincere intentions and hope that my disagreements with him will be part of a *maḥloket lesheim Shamayim,* helping to clarify the best direction for development of halakhah.

I would agree with Rabbi Spitz that the real life experience of an infertile couple, for whom surrogacy could provide a child, bears great weight. I have argued elsewhere that such concerns, together with the Jewish tradition's valuing of procreation, would suffice to justify the use of in vitro fertilization in a variety of cases. Objections by some that reproductive technologies are artificial, as well as additional concerns, would be outweighed by the great good of enabling the birth of the child. In that paper, I emphasized as well that the members of the couple are in no way required to use reproductive technologies, and that their value as persons does not depend on their ability to have a child, but rather is intrinsic, stemming from the creation of all humans in God's image (*betzelem Elohim*).[5] In the case of surrogate parenting, however, precisely this value of respect for persons and human dignity is at risk. The real life experiences of all the vulnerable persons involved, including the surrogate and especially her children, are weighty and must be considered. In light of these concerns, I argue, surrogacy cannot be recommended by halakhah, and would be ill-advised in most cases.

My paper will focus on three particular concerns: a Jewish understanding of gestation and birth; the risk of harms and exploitation (*oshek*) and the appropriate halakhic response; and more specific questions raised by surrogacy agreements. A companion paper, "Maternal Identity and the Religious Status of Children Born to a Surrogate Mother," addresses that issue [and appears as chapter 8 of this volume].

A. The Significance of Gestation and Birth

Gestation and birth are profoundly significant for halakhah, on the basis of traditional halakhic texts, and because of broader ethical and theological concerns that I believe are important factors in the halakhic process. Appreciation of this significance is not necessarily decisive in determining the acceptability of surrogacy and related issues, but it is likely to influence both the articulation of halakhic guidelines and the application of these guidelines in particular cases.

As I argue elsewhere, halakhic sources indicate that maternal identity is determined primarily by gestation and birth. A woman who gives birth to a child is identified as that child's mother. Indeed, this represents the sole position authorized by the Committee on Jewish Law and Standards with regard to maternal identity.[6]

More generally, gestation and birth represent powerful experiences of intimacy and nurturing that have great significance. Parents' feelings of attachment at the birth of their children reflect not only awareness of genetic linkage, but also the lived experience of months of physical changes, observations, and caregiving, as well as the intense and miraculous event of birth. The mother's experience has included unique connections of biology, combined with the conscious acceptance of risks and burdens, and emotional and intellectual responses of often surprising power. Perhaps for this reason, the Hebrew word for intense and other-regarding love, *raḥamim,* is linked to the word for womb, *reḥem.*

Accordingly, Jewish law and ethics would not agree that a "gestational surrogate" who gestates and gives birth to a child "essentially serves as an incubator," as Rabbi Spitz at one point suggests, nor would it agree to refer to her as a "tummy mummy."[7] It is not her tummy, but her womb, and with it her experience of biological connection and intense other-regarding care, that need to be acknowledged. According to halakhah, she simply is the mother of the child.

Such acknowledgment of the importance of gestation and birth has been reflected by non-Jewish as well as Jewish writers. Lawyer George Annas, for example, argues that in cases of dispute, the relationship of gestational mother to the child should be recognized as primary, in part because of the extent of her biological and psychological investment in the child.[8] Rosemarie Tong notes a feminist objection to surrogacy, that "such arrangements privilege a possible relationship over an actual one, an abstract intention over concrete experience." Concerns are also expressed with treating persons and relationships as commodities.[9] As Rabbi Spitz notes, not all feminists agree in rejecting surrogacy, but Tong's feminist claims focusing on relationships and responsibilities resonate importantly with general Jewish values. While some thinkers have speculated that a woman's role of gestation and birth might be replaced by an artificial womb, others have speculated that with developments in genetic engineering, the role of sperm and eggs in conveying genetic information might be replaced, strengthening the claims of gestation as primary. Both sets of claims are speculative; the important point is to avoid an unwarranted assumption that genetics are somehow essential and gestation and birth somehow accidental to parental identity.[10]

B. Potential Harms and Exploitation

While appreciation of the significance of birth and gestation will affect judgments on surrogacy, the central issues are the assessment of risks of harm and exploitation, and the proper halakhic response. Here my greatest concern is for children affected by the procedures, although concern to avoid harm for any of the vulnerable people who might be involved is warranted. There is a danger of treating children as commodities; in some extreme cases, contracting/intended parents have sought to refuse custody of a child born with birth defects or of the undesired gender. The risk of this occurring, and less extreme dangers, are present in a broader range of cases.[11]

Another type of concern arises when the surrogate has other children, as in the case of the "typical" surrogate, who is married and has two other children.[12] The potential for psychological harm for these children, as they see their mother go through pregnancy and give birth to a child who is given to others, is very real.[13] Another ethical concern to which halakhah would be sensitive is the interference of surrogacy with the sexual relations of a (married) surrogate and her husband, and the potentially negative effect on their relationship more broadly.[14]

Additional concerns involve the potential of harm to and exploitation of the surrogate. One type of exploitation is that of coercion or unfair treatment by intended parents or surrogacy agencies. While relatively few surrogates have brought lawsuits, this says little either way about the existence of *oshek*. Victims of *oshek* are precisely those who are least likely to sue. Think, for example, of recent immigrants working in sweatshops, or oppressed agricultural workers. Victims of *oshek* not only lack financial resources, but tend to feel intimidated and unsure of their self-worth, and are unlikely to assert themselves against those whom they correctly perceive as more powerful. On the basis of available information, it is difficult to determine how many surrogates are satisfied, and how many suffer in silence.[15]

Other concerns are of the type that would be more prominent in

Jewish law and ethics than in U.S. law, for example. An important precedent for Rabbi Spitz is the case of Sarah, who said of Hagar, "Through her I, too, shall bear a child." Appeals are also made to more general halakhic precedents of *shifḥah* (handmaid/concubine) and *yibum* (levirate marriage).[16] All these precedents are problematic for contemporary Jewish law and ethics. Over the centuries, Judaism has become increasingly sensitive to the demand not to use people. This stems from a number of factors, including the unfolding in the Oral Torah of the significance of humans being created *betzelem Elohim,* and (more recently) the influence of Kantian ethics. Largely in response to these ethical concerns, halakhah has abolished (at least de facto) the institutions of *shifḥah* and *yibum,* replacing the latter with *ḥalitzah.* In light of such developments, Sarah's intention to have her child through another woman is troubling. Similarly, as Robert Gordis observes, the elimination of *yibum* represents "the dual process of extending the rights of women, on the one hand, and limiting the powers of men, on the other."[17] Whatever the acceptability or excusability of these practices in the past, the development of halakhah reflects an understanding that it would be wrong for a person to use someone else in these ways in order to have a child. While Rabbi Spitz notes distinctions between *shifḥah/yibum* and surrogacy, he appeals to these precedents precisely because of important common features, and these commonalities raise ethical problems.

As Rabbi Spitz rightly notes, the extent of harm and exploitation is unproven and uncertain. The difficult question, then, is how halakhah should respond to plausible but uncertain harms and exploitation, what might be termed *safeik oshek. Safeik oshek* does not carry the same decisive power as *safeik pikuaḥ nefesh* (possible saving of or danger to life), but cannot be ignored. One instructive model is offered by the Ethics Committee of the American Fertility Society. This committee is composed of scientists and health care professionals involved in developing and providing assisted reproductive technologies, as well as others sympathetic with such practices. For this committee, however, the potential harms of surrogacy mandate great caution, if not rejection.

> The Committee continues not to recommend widespread clinical application of clinical surrogate motherhood at this time. Because of the legal risks, ethical concerns, and potential physical and psychological effects of surrogate motherhood, it would

> seem to be more problematic than most of the other reproductive technologies. . . . The Committee recommends that if surrogate motherhood is pursued, a number of unresolved issues need to be addressed in the research, [including] the psychological effects of the procedure on the surrogates, the couples, and the resulting children; the effects, if any, of bonding between the surrogate and the fetus in utero; . . . the effects on the surrogate's own family due to her participation in the process. . . . The Committee has serious ethical reservations about surrogacy that cannot be fully resolved until appropriate data are available for assessment of the risks and possible benefits of this alternative. In light of these reservations, some members of the Committee judged that surrogacy could not be ethically recommended. Others concluded that it could be cautiously recommended while research on the key issues continued.[18]

C. Deciding about Surrogacy and Surrogacy Agreements

Minimally, halakhah would share the "serious reservations" expressed by the American Fertility Society Ethics Committee and others. It also would be concerned with broader, if less tangible, dangers of the commodification of human persons and relationships. Surrogacy cannot be recommended by halakhah, and would be ill-advised in most cases.

In light of Rabbi Spitz's paper, however, I must admit that the question of whether the reservations are strong enough to support an absolute prohibition on surrogacy in all cases is less clear. If grounds to permit surrogacy are found in a particular case, at a minimum, certain requirements would be clearly mandated by halakhah to protect the well-being, rights, and dignity of any children affected, and all other vulnerable persons, including the surrogate:

1. Couples contemplating the use of a surrogate mother should consider the halakhic and personal concerns involved, receive thorough counseling, and seriously investigate alternatives, including adoption. Either member of the couple would be fully justified in a decision not to proceed with surrogacy, and such refusal must be respected.

2. The surrogate mother, as gestational and birth mother, is halakhically recognized as the child's mother. She should have the right to contest the assumption of custody by the intended parents (one of whom would be halakhically recognized as the child's father). This right would be held whether the ovum originally came from the surrogate, the intended/social mother, or another woman. The exact parameters of this right are beyond the scope of this paper, and in practice would be determined by general civil law. Custody of the child—in these, as in other cases—should be determined on the basis of the child's best interest, as required by Jewish ethical values as well as halakhic precedent.[19]

3. The gestational/birth mother should be protected from pressure to continue pregnancy when she judges abortion to be required to avoid serious threat to her health, and from pressure to abort when she judges continuation of the pregnancy to be consistent with her physical and psychological health.

4. Halakhah would discourage, if not prohibit, payments to a surrogate mother beyond reimbursement of expenses. Any money the surrogate receives cannot be contingent on her giving up custody of the child. For the surrogate to receive money if she gives over custody of the child would represent baby-selling, or minimally the selling and purchase of parental relationships, which are inconsistent with halakhah.

5. In the formulation of surrogacy agreements, and all actions taken with regard to surrogacy, greatest concern must be given to the well-being and rights of the child to be born of the procedure, as well as any other children who might be affected. Concern must be given to avoid exploitation of other vulnerable parties, including the surrogate, as well.

While these provisions represent the minimal requirements of Jewish law and ethics, they would be difficult to implement in commercial surrogacy. If these provisions are followed, surrogacy would likely be limited to cases in which all parties are well-intentioned and trust one another. Such a limitation would itself be appropriate.

A final note concerns the acceptability of a woman serving as surrogate mother, gestating and giving birth to a child to be raised by another couple. Minimally, all the above requirements would apply. In addition, if a Jewish woman gives birth to a child, the child would be Jewish. As argued in this paper and my accompanying paper, and authorized by the Committee on Jewish Law and Standards, the birth mother's status would define the child's in all cases. Accordingly, allowing Jewish women to serve as surrogates entails either the birth of Jewish children who will be raised as non-Jews, or the surrogate's willingness to serve only for Jewish couples. Either option would be highly problematic. Unless this problem is explicitly and satisfactorily addressed, I do not see how halakhah can authorize Jewish women to serve as surrogates.[20] If this is the case, this provides an additional consideration against halakhically supporting surrogacy. To authorize Jews to use others as surrogates but not serve as surrogates would itself be problematic, as reflected in the Jewish tradition's commitment to *darkhei shalom,* the paths of peace.

D. Conclusion

Surrogacy cannot be halakhically recommended, and in at least most cases would be forbidden by Jewish law and ethics. Any exceptional cases in which surrogacy is accepted would need to meet specific requirements safeguarding the well-being, rights, and dignity of any children affected, and all other vulnerable persons, including the surrogate.[21]

Notes

1. See, e.g., Rosemarie Tong, "Reproductive Technologies: Surrogacy," in *The Encyclopedia of Bioethics,* ed. Warren T. Reich, rev. ed. (New York: Simon and Schuster Macmillan, 1995), 4:2225–29; American Fertility Society Ethics Committee, "Ethical Considerations of Assisted Reproductive Technologies," *Fertility and Sterility* 62 (1994): 67S–77S; New York State Task Force on Life and the Law, *Surrogate Parenting* (New York: New York State Task Force on Life and the Law, 1988); Larry Gostin, ed., *Surrogate Motherhood: Politics and Privacy* (Bloomington: Indiana University Press, 1990).
2. See, for example, David M. Feldman, "The Case of Baby M," in *Jewish Values in Health and Medicine,* ed. Levi Meier (Lanham, Md.: University Press of America, 1991), 163–69; Fred Rosner, *Modern Medicine and Jewish Ethics,* 2d ed. (Hoboken, N.J.: Ktav, 1991), 113–16. Most authors do not develop an extensive halakhic argument about the practice of surrogacy; while many express

misgivings, some suggest that the practice is halakhically permitted, and others suggest that it should not occur. Immanuel Jakobovits, for example, argues: "To use another person as an 'incubator' and then take from her the child she carried and delivered for a fee is a revolting degradation of maternity and an affront to human dignity" (*Jewish Medical Ethics,* rev. ed. [New York: Bloch, 1975], 265). In a brief paper written for the Committee on Jewish Law and Standards [CJLS] in 1984 [appearing as chap. 9 of this vol.], Rabbi David H. Lincoln states that "we should not deny couples this opportunity" of using a surrogate, though he does not explicitly address halakhic issues other than those of artificial insemination. At the same time, he expresses significant concerns: "Are we not degrading [the surrogate], however noble her intentions? Can we really allow a single woman to become pregnant? If [the surrogate is] married, there is something very distasteful in [her] carrying another man's baby, even if the woman has not committed adultery." In light of psychological and legal concerns, "great caution must therefore be exercised." The ensuing decade and a half have provided more extensive experience with surrogacy and discussion of the issues involved, most prominently in connection with the Baby M trial. These developments now allow for a more extensive evaluation of surrogacy.

3. See Aaron L. Mackler, "An Expanded Partnership with God? In Vitro Fertilization in Jewish Ethics," *Journal of Religious Ethics* 25 (1997): 279–81.
4. Elie Spitz, "On the Use of Birth Surrogates," paper approved by the CJLS, June 1997 [chap. 6 of this vol.].
5. Mackler, "In Vitro Fertilization," approved by the CJLS, Dec. 1995 [chap. 4 of this vol.].
6. Mackler, "Maternal Identity and the Religious Status of Children Born to a Surrogate Mother," approved by the CJLS, Sept. 1997 [chap. 8 of this vol.], and "In Vitro Fertilization." There is no reason to speculate that the identification of the birth mother as mother in earlier sources is based on an assumption of a genetic link, unless one simply assumes or has established on other grounds that genetics should be primary. In fact, the few cases that reflect a divergence of gestation/birth and genetics support gestation and birth as primary. A central precedent is the case of a pregnant woman who converts: the child is Jewish because, while the ovum was originally from the woman when she was not Jewish, the woman's status at the time of birth determines maternity.
7. Spitz, 3 [chap. 6, p. 130 of this vol.].
8. George J. Annas, "Death Without Dignity for Commercial Surrogacy: The Case of Baby M," *Hastings Center Report* 18, no. 2 (1988): 23–24.
9. Rosemarie Tong, "The Overdue Death of a Feminist Chameleon: Taking a Stand on Surrogacy Arrangements," in *The Ethics of Reproductive Technology,* ed. Kenneth D. Alpern (New York: Oxford University Press, 1992), 291, 285, 289.
10. Intuitively, it might seem to some that gestation is a relatively straightforward process that science likely will develop ways to replace artificially, while the ge-

netic material of the human genome is hopelessly complex and will elude scientists. On the other hand, the understanding of human genetics and the ability to synthesize genetic material have been progressing rapidly and at accelerating rates, while the capacity to nurture the developing human are only very slowly, if at all, moving later than the first week of embryonic development in vitro, and earlier than about week 23–24 of development for extremely premature infants (New York State Task Force on Life and the Law, *Fetal Extrauterine Survivability* [New York: New York State Task Force on Life and the Law, 1988]). More generally, speculation on future scientific progress is uncertain at best. Writing in 1957, Isaac Asimov was able to envision a world of interstellar space travel and human-like robots, in which most of the process of gestation and human development could be managed artificially, but in vitro fertilization remained elusive, and fertilization itself could only take place in the body (*The Naked Sun* [New York: Doubleday, 1957]).Within a few decades, this apparently elusive element had, in fact, been achieved, while other developments remained distant.

11. See, for example, the discussion of the Malahoff case, "Parenting through Contract When No One Wants the Child," in Alpern, ed., *The Ethics of Reproductive Technology,* 335–37; Angela R. Holder, "Surrogate Motherhood and the Best Interests of the Child," in Gostin, ed., *Surrogate Motherhood,* 79. In a Michigan surrogacy case, Patty Nowakowski unexpectedly became pregnant with twins. The contracting couple told her that they would not accept responsibility for a boy, and when a girl and a boy were born, they only took the girl home (New York State Department of Health, *The Business of Surrogate Parenting* [Albany: New York State Department of Health, 1992], 8). As Holder (79) observes:

> In the usual situation of babies born with unexpected handicaps, parents may be shocked but they do not attempt to solve their problems by displacing custody onto anyone else. In the surrogate situation, however, the mother has doubtless attempted not to think of herself as the baby's "mother" or to become too attached, since she plans to surrender it for adoption. Thus it is certainly not surprising that, if a problem occurs, her response is, "Here, take it. I did what I was supposed to do, so give me my money." The father-by-contract, as well, having thought of the arrangement as placing an order for a baby, not surprisingly takes the position that there has been some sort of breach of warranty of quality and doesn't want the baby either. Regardless of obligation to support, the situation does not bode well for love and acceptance of the handicapped child.

12. Spitz, 5 [chap. 6, p. 131 of this vol.].
13. Evidence regarding this harm remains largely anecdotal, as does evidence about the benefits and harms of surrogacy in general. One example is provided by a surrogate mother named Sally, responding to Phyllis Chesler's question as to

whether Sally's (other) children ask about Jason, the child in the surrogacy arrangement (Phyllis Chesler, *Sacred Bond: The Legacy of Baby M* [New York: Vintage, Random House, 1988], 66–67):

> Yes. Quite often. My daughter Rebekah says that if she has a baby she'll never give it away. She's been asking me, "Did you really have to give Jason away?" It's on her mind a lot. It's on my son Matthew's mind, too, but he tries not to talk about it. I've begun to encourage them to talk about it.

Similarly, Kathleen King agreed to serve as a surrogate, but came to feel attached to the child during pregnancy. She reports that after she surrendered the child, one of her other children asked, "I heard you're giving my brother away. Are you going to give me away?" (New York State Department of Health, 7). While careful counseling likely would lessen the harm to the surrogate's other children, these children still would be exposed to the risk of significant harm, without their consent.

14. I am grateful to Rabbi Susan Grossman for this observation.
15. See Chesler for interviews with surrogates and accompanying discussion.
16. Spitz, 30, 10–15 [chap. 6, pp. 153, 136–38 of this vol.].
17. Robert Gordis, *The Dynamics of Jewish Law* (Bloomington: Indiana University Press, 1990), 150–53. Other developments in halakhah have increasingly supported the practice of adoption, and have in at least many aspects recognized adopting parents as the child's parents for halakhic purposes. See Elliot N. Dorff, "Artificial Insemination, Egg Donation, and Adoption," *Conservative Judaism* 44, no. 1 (1996): 51–54 (a responsum approved by the CJLS, Mar. 1994 [chap. 3 of this vol.]); Rabbi Avram Reisner, "On the Conversion of Adopted and Patrilineal Children," approved by the CJLS, Tevet 5748 (1988).
18. American Fertility Society Ethics Committee, 76S–77S.
19. See *S.A., E.H.* 82:7, where Karo states that in case of divorce, a child should stay with the mother until age six, and Isserles adds that this should only be the case when it serves the best interests of the child, which should be decisive. George Annas (23) supports the ruling of the New Jersey Supreme Court in the Baby M case that custody of children in surrogacy disputes should be decided according to the best interests of the child, and that the child should remain with the mother until permanent custody can be determined. In at least some situations, the surrogate mother's seeking of custody would be a morally appropriate course of action. David Feldman (163) comments that in the Baby M case, the judge should have thanked Mary Beth Whitehead "for reminding us of the special bond of attachment that a mother forms with her child; and he should have gratefully acknowledged her message that surrogacy as an option ought to be discouraged."
20. While Rabbi Spitz in earlier drafts of his paper approved Jews serving as surrogates, his final draft as approved by the CJLS does not offer this permission.

21. For their suggestions and thoughtful insights, which have contributed greatly to this paper, I would like to thank Lorraine Newman Mackler, and members of the Committee on Jewish Law and Standards, including my fellow members of the Subcommittee on Bioethics: Rabbis Kassel Abelson, Elliot Dorff, Shoshana Gelfand, Avram Reisner, Joel Roth, and Elie Spitz.

CHAPTER 8

Maternal Identity and the Religious Status of Children Born to a Surrogate Mother*

Aaron L. Mackler

She'eilah (Question):

How do we determine maternal identity and religious status for a child born to a surrogate mother?

Teshuvah (Response):

I argue elsewhere that surrogacy cannot be halakhically recommended, and in at least most cases would be forbidden by Jewish law and ethics. Nonetheless, the issue of the status of a child born to a surrogate mother must be addressed for cases in which surrogacy does occur. These cases might represent exceptional circumstances that I do not preclude, or people following a more lenient ruling such as that of Rabbi Elie Spitz, or simply people proceeding with surrogacy without necessarily having sought halakhic guidance.[1]

When the surrogate mother is artificially inseminated by the contracting/intended father, it is clear that she is the child's mother in the eyes of halakhah. Her ovum is fertilized in her body, she gestates the child, and she gives birth. I am aware of no halakhic source that claims otherwise. Accordingly, the child's religious status follows that of the (surrogate) mother.

*Approved by the Rabbinical Assembly Committee on Jewish Law and Standards, Sept. 1997.

Things become more complicated in the case of a gestational surrogate. Here, one woman provides an ovum that is fertilized in vitro, and she could be seen as the genetic mother. Another woman gestates and gives birth to the child, and she could be seen as the gestational/birth mother. While I will conclude that in such cases (as in all others), halakhah recognizes the birth mother as mother, more of an argument is required.

A. Intuitions on Maternity

People's gut feelings or intuitions on maternal identity are not halakhically decisive.[2] Still, these can affect the extent to which people are receptive to and convinced by more formal halakhic considerations. More generally, gestation and birth represent powerful experiences of intimacy and nurturing that have great significance. Parents' feelings of attachment at the birth of their children reflect not only awareness of genetic linkage, but also the lived experience of months of physical changes, observations, and caregiving, as well as the intense and miraculous event of birth. The mother's experience has included unique connections of biology, combined with the conscious acceptance of risks and burdens, and emotional and intellectual responses of often surprising power. Perhaps for this reason, the Hebrew word for intense and other-regarding love, *raḥamim,* is linked to the word for womb, *reḥem.*

Such acknowledgment of the importance of gestation and birth has been reflected by non-Jewish as well as Jewish writers. Lawyer George Annas, for example, argues that in cases of dispute, the relationship of gestational mother to the child should be recognized as primary, in part because of the extent of her biological and psychological investment in the child.[3] Rosemarie Tong notes a feminist objection to surrogacy, that "such arrangements privilege a possible relationship over an actual one, an abstract intention over concrete experience." Concerns are also expressed with treating persons and relationships as commodities.[4] As Rabbi Spitz notes, not all feminists agree in rejecting surrogacy, but Tong's feminist claims focusing on relationships and responsibilities resonate importantly with general Jewish values. While some thinkers have speculated that a woman's role of gestation and birth might be replaced by an artificial womb, others have speculated that with developments in genetic engineering, the role of sperm and eggs in conveying genetic information might be replaced, strengthening the claims of gestation as primary. Both sets of claims are speculative; the important point is to avoid an unwarranted assumption that genetics are somehow essential, and gestation and birth somehow accidental, to parental identity.[5]

B. The Precedent of a Woman Who Converts while Pregnant

A number of halakhic authorities have addressed the issue of maternal identity in cases in which one woman gestates and gives birth to a child deriving in part from the ovum of another. Many of these statements have been summarized in a review article by Rabbi J. David Bleich. These sources suggest that maternal identity is to be determined primarily by gestation and birth.[6]

A central precedent in the discussion is the case of a pregnant woman who converts: conception is by a non-Jew, from an ovum from a non-Jew; the fetus is gestated by a non-Jew and then by a Jew; and a woman who is Jewish gives birth. Halakhah is clear that the child is Jewish. As stated by the *Shulḥan Arukh* (*Y.D.* 268:6):

עובדת כוכבים שנתגיירה והיא מעוברת בנה אין צריך טבילה

> If a non-Jewish woman converts when she is pregnant, her child does not require immersion.

The rationale for this ruling is less clear. For some later authorities, such as Rabbi Isaac Klein, this is simply because the woman's status at the time of birth determines the child's identity. "If a woman converts while pregnant, the child does not require conversion, even if it was conceived before conversion, because at the time of its birth, its mother was already Jewish."[7] For Rabbi Ezekiel Landau (*Dagul Merevavah*), however, the reason is that the woman's own immersion in a mikvah at her conversion serves as the immersion required for the child's conversion.[8]

Some support for Landau's interpretation is found in the talmudic source of the *Shulḥan Arukh*'s ruling, *Yevamot* 78a, where at least one opinion holds that the reason the child's immersion is not required is that the woman's body does not constitute a barrier to the immersion of the fetus. This interpretation becomes less plausible, however, in light of another passage, *Yevamot* 97b, which discusses the status of twins born to a woman who converts while pregnant. (This position was later codified in the *Shulḥan Arukh, Y.D.* 269:4.)

ת"ש שני אחים תאומים גרים וכן משוחררים לא חולצין ולא מייבמין ואין חייבין משום אשת אח היתה הורתן שלא בקדושה ולידתן בקדושה לא חולצין ולא מייבמין אבל חייבין משום אשת אח היתה הורתן ולידתן בקדושה הרי הן כישראל לכל דבריהן

> Come and hear: twin brothers who are converts, and similarly if they are emancipated slaves, they do not participate in *ḥalitzah* or *yibum* [levirate marriage], and they are not liable for the prohibition of marrying a brother's wife.
>
> If they were conceived when the woman was not Jewish [lit., "not in holiness"] but were born when she was Jewish, they do not participate in *ḥalitzah* or *yibum,* but they are liable for the prohibition of not marrying a brother's wife.
>
> If they were conceived and born when the woman was Jewish, they have the status as Jews in all regards.

The first clause reflects the Talmud's understanding that when an individual converts to Judaism, his or her familial relations are understood to start from a blank slate for purposes of Jewish law; the convert is considered to be newly born (*ketinok shenolad*). But according to the second clause, the twin brothers born to a woman who converted while pregnant are in a different category. They must be brothers, and Jews, from the moment of birth.[9] Hence, they must be recognized as having the status of Jews simply because of their mother's status at the time of birth. Indeed, Rashi gives this rationale explicitly in his commentary. He explains that the twins do not participate in *ḥalitzah* or *yibum* because these practices apply to brothers with the same father, and their biological father is not technically recognized as their father for these purposes.

אבל חייבין - כרת משום אשת אח מן האם שהרי היא כישראלית שילדה בנים

> "But they are liable": for the penalty of excision [*kareit*] for the prohibition of not marrying a brother's wife, because they are brothers who share the same mother, because she was Jewish when she gave birth.

Klein's rationale for the Jewish status of a child born to a woman who converted while pregnant is supported by, and is virtually a paraphrase of, this explanation.

As surveyed by Bleich, a number of Orthodox authorities have suggested varied understandings of these sources, and of the status of children gestated and given birth to by one woman but deriving in part from the genetic material of another. Among the most significant views:

Rabbi Avraham Yitzḥak Halevi Kilav argues that in general, the birth mother is decisive for the child's identity. However, there is a difference between "national" relations and "familial" relations. A child's status as Jewish depends on the woman in whose body conception and early development takes place, but if the child is Jewish, the birth mother is decisive for all other purposes. While this provides an ingenious reconciliation of the talmudic sources, it seems excessively speculative and far-fetched. Kilav does not explicitly address the issue of a genetic mother who provided an ovum that was fertilized in vitro. He might be interpreted to offer some support for the genetic mother's religious status determining that of the child, though the genetic mother would not be considered to be the child's mother for any other purposes. (On the other hand, his discussion of the importance of gestation in accounting for differences between maternal and paternal identity suggests that he might not extend his argument to the case of in vitro fertilization.) Kilav specifies that his discussion is only for purposes of theoretical discussion and *pilpul* and is not intended to offer halakhic guidance.[10]

For Rabbi Moshe Sternbuch, the birth mother simply is the mother, for all halakhic purposes. In fact, the child could marry children of the woman who provided the ovum, for they would in no way be considered siblings. Rabbi Sternbuch understands the discussion of immersion not to involve conversion to become Jewish, but rather a purification process to remove what he perceives as "impurity of Gentileness" (*tum'at akum*). According to this view, a child born to a non-Jewish gestational mother would not be Jewish. Since Conservative Jewish authorities (and many others) reject his understanding of "impurity of Gentileness," the child's status would simply follow that of the birth mother in all cases.[11]

Rabbi Moshe Soloveitchik discusses a number of views, including positions that the mother is the woman who gestated the fetus on its fortieth day of development, or the first woman to gestate the fetus on or after the fortieth day without another maternal relationship having been already established. For cases such as gestational surrogacy where fertilization occurs in vitro, the birth mother's status would be decisive, the genetic mother's irrelevant. Similarly, in the case of ovum donation, the birth mother would be recognized as mother.[12]

For Rabbi Zalman Nehemiah Goldberg, the maternal relationship is determined by the mother who gives birth. Another woman in whose body fertilization and early gestation took place would not have halakhic status as mother. All the more so, a woman who provides an ovum that is fertilized in vitro would not have halakhic status as mother. If conception takes place in the body of a non-Jew from her ovum, and a Jewish woman then gestates the fetus and gives birth, the child would be Jewish according to the view that the fetus's status is subservient to the mother's (*ubar yerekh imo*). For those who hold the view that the fetus's status is not subservient, conversion should take place, but the child would then be regarded as the child of the birth mother in all regards. According to this view, a child born to a non-Jewish gestational surrogate would not be Jewish. In the case of ovum donation from a non-Jew to a Jew, the birth mother would be recognized as mother. Conversion would not be required for those agreeing that *ubar yerekh imo*, but should occur for those disagreeing with this view.[13]

The talmudic sources and ensuing halakhic discussion are thus rather complicated. Virtually all authorities would agree, however, that birth (or gestation) represents the prime determinant of maternal status, and that a child born to a non-Jewish gestational surrogate would require conversion to Judaism. In my judgment, Klein's position, while not addressing all the questions raised by the talmudic sources, makes the most sense for deriving a conclusion for practical halakhah. The talmudic sources may well simply reflect differing views among talmudic authorities, which contributed to differing views among halakhic authorities. Klein's view certainly represents the most authoritative statement on this issue by a Conservative authority to this point.

C. Additional Considerations

Halakhah recognizes the gestational/birth mother as mother in all regards. The above discussion of cases involving a woman who converts while pregnant provides the key halakhic evidence. At the same time, a number of additional considerations provide further support of this position. While I do not claim that each of these by itself would be decisive, together I believe that they are compelling.

1. Halakhah views the status of a fetus as subservient to that of the woman. As the talmudic phrase *ubar yerekh imo* (*Ḥullin* 58a) is explicated by Rabbi David Feldman: "The fetus is deemed a 'part of the mother' rather than an independent entity." While this is not the unanimous view of all halakhic authorities, it seems to be the most common. This has been the position of all Conservative authorities who have addressed the issue, and has helped to shape Conservative positions on abortion.[14] Accordingly, the status of the gestating woman determines the status of the fetus, and the status of the birth mother determines the status of the child.

2. The above argument is strengthened by the fact that embryo transfer takes place well within the first forty days of development and, in fact, within the first few days of embryonic development, when the talmudic designation of the embryo/fetus as "mere fluid" (*maya be'alma, Yevamot* 69b) most clearly applies. The embryo at this stage consists of only a few cells, without any specialization of cells or embryonic structure.[15]

3. The halakhic identification of a firstborn son as one who "opens the womb" offers some additional support for defining the birth mother as the child's mother.[16]

4. Some have suggested that one reason for basing Jewish identity on matrilineal descent is that the child's mother can always be identified. This consideration would support determining the child's status on the basis of the birth mother.[17]

5. Some (non-Jewish) thinkers have advocated identifying the birth mother as mother on policy grounds, to best assure the welfare of newborns. As George Annas argues, the birth mother "will of necessity be present at birth and immediately thereafter to care for the child."[18] These considerations would be important to halakhah under the rubric of *hatov vehayashar* (Deut. 6:18), the injunction to do "the right and the good."

6. *Targum Jonathan* (Gen. 30:21) and Rabbi Samuel Edels (Maharsha, commenting on *Niddah* 31a) relate that, prior to the birth of Joseph and Dinah, Leah was pregnant with a male, and Rachel with a female. Leah prayed that Rachel would give birth to the male, and God switched the embryos. Dinah, conceived by Rachel but born to Leah, is considered Leah's child; Joseph, conceived by Leah but born to Rachel, is considered Rachel's child. Abstracting from the issue of the historical accuracy of this account, it does reflect rabbinic understandings and assumptions regarding maternity. This offers some support for the view that the status of the birth mother determines the child's identity.[19]

Accordingly, the woman who gestates and gives birth to the child is to be treated as the child's mother for purposes of Jewish law, including the determination of Jewish identity. If a Jewish woman gives birth to a child, that child should be considered Jewish, whether the ovum came from a Jewish or a non-Jewish woman. If a non-Jewish woman gives birth to a child, that child would not be Jewish (and so would require conversion in order to be recognized as a Jew), whether the ovum came from a Jewish or a non-Jewish woman.

A less satisfactory alternative position to identifying the birth mother as mother, which might also be compatible with halakhic precedent, would be to recognize *both* the genetic and birth mothers as having maternal status: even if birth is the primary determinant of maternal identity, the genetic mother would be treated as mother because of doubt, or to follow a more stringent position. For the case of surrogacy, this would lead to little practical difference. As I argue elsewhere, in a paper approved by the Committee on Jewish Law and Standards (CJLS), this would prove far less satisfactory for the much more common practice of ovum donation and in vitro fertilization (IVF). The alternative is in some ways attractive at the theoretical level, for it would formally recognize the contributions of both women to the child's birth. At the practical level, however, it would impose unnecessary complications for the use of donated ova. If an anonymously donated ovum were used, the presumption (outside of Israel) would be that the donor is not Jewish; accordingly, the child (born to a Jewish mother) would require conversion in order to be fully Jewish. Moreover, the child would have obligations of honoring its (genetic) mother (*kibud av va'em*) that likely would be unfulfilled. Furthermore, recognizing only the birth mother and not additionally the genetic mother as mother for purposes of halakhah enables Jews to donate eggs and embryos, an important consideration in light of Jewish ethics and the halakhic mandate of *darkhei shalom*.[20]

While the genetic mother should not be viewed as mother halakhically, genetic siblings should not marry (or engage in sexual relations with) each other. The most basic reason for this prohibition is that offspring of a consanguineous union face a high risk of genetically based disease; this concern alone would suffice to support a rabbinic prohibition. Combining this ruling with those found in Rabbi Elliot Dorff's paper on artificial insemination, one comes to the unsurprising conclusion that one should not marry (or engage in sexual relations with) children of one's genetic, gestational, or social parents. Technically, the prohibition would be Toraitic with regard to children of one's genetic father and birth mother and would reflect the category of secondary relations (*sheniyot*) for children of other parents.[21]

D. Intentions as Determinative?

Rabbi Elie Spitz has argued that intentions can be determinative for maternal identity. He has done so in an academic paper and in a thoughtful paper prepared for the CJLS but subsequently withdrawn from consideration.[22] In these papers, Rabbi Spitz agrees that a child born to an "ovum surrogate," who provides genetic material as well as gestation and birth, follows the status of that mother. He argues, however, that in the case of a gestational mother, the child's status should follow that of the genetic/intended social mother instead of that of the gestational/birth mother. In advancing this position, he relies on an argument of David Kraemer that parents' feelings about their fetus/child-to-be can affect its status in thinking about abortion.[23]

In my best judgment, halakhah cannot support such an exception. First, the precedents supporting the status of the gestational/birth mother in determining identity are powerful. As well, Kraemer's arguments for the importance of feelings in thinking about abortion do not translate easily to determining halakhic status. Kraemer presents his paper on abortion as exemplifying an approach to Jewish ethics that is sharply distinguished from halakhah; he seeks "to do ethics with traditional sources without accepting the ways of Halacha." On the specific issue of the status of the fetus, Kraemer argues that this should depend on the parents' feelings; the status "may change as a function of our emotional connections to it."[24] His claim that decisions about abortion hinge in large part on subjective feelings, known fully only to the individual and to God, is plausible and thought-provoking. To base the religious status of a child on such factors is more troubling. The problems are clearest in cases of ambivalence or dispute. For example, what if a gestational surrogate becomes subjectively convinced at some point in pregnancy that the child is really hers and should be raised by her, and gives birth with this subjective intentionality in mind? We would have a situation in which factors indicating the child's status would be evenly divided. Things would be further complicated if the genetic/social mother's feelings were ambivalent. In real life, subjective feelings and emotional connections are likely to vary widely. That is one reason that such factors generally are not, and should not be, decisive in determining parental identity and status.

An alternative position, which I do not believe that Rabbi Spitz advocates, would determine religious status on the basis of contract. In U.S. contract law, "intent" can be understood in a technical sense, as expressed in the wording of contracts rather than the thoughts and feelings of the persons involved. Kraemer's example of giving a gift to one's fetus, however, argues against such contractual intent being decisive. One generally cannot give a gift to a fetus, whatever language is used, unless these emotional and subjective feelings are present. More general halakhic grounds argue against defining parenthood and status on the basis of contract. One cannot buy or sell, or achieve by intent and formal agreement, the status of parent, child, *kohein,* Jew, and so on. Such attribution of status would diverge more strongly from traditional precedent than does the Reform movement's acceptance of patrilineal descent. It also unacceptably treats relations as commodities.

Other practical difficulties can be anticipated as well. Imagine the case of two women (perhaps a lesbian couple) who decide to have children together by having the ova from one fertilized in vitro and gestated by the other. They plan for one of them to assume primary custody for the first child born, and the other to assume custody for the next. One woman is Jewish, and the other is not. According to the proposal (once) advocated by Rabbi Spitz, this could result in the birth of twins, one of which was Jewish from birth, the other of which was not Jewish. I do not believe that such a result would be an acceptable development for halakhah.[25]

In addition, the reasons given in Rabbi Spitz's paper for this dramatic change in halakhah do not seem compelling. He argues that requiring conversion for a child born to a non-Jewish gestational mother would offend the genetic/social parents. The conversion of infants, and ritual circumcision performed in this context, are common—for example, in cases involving adoption, or children born to a Jewish husband and a non-Jewish wife who are raised as Jews. These ceremonies are joyful, welcoming, and affirming, especially when guided by rabbis with thought and sensitivity. These children are really the couple's children, as Rabbi Dorff argues in his discussion of adoption.[26]

Finally, Rabbi Spitz argues that to follow the birth mother in determining status would make Judaism seem "behind the times" to parents who live in states where the genetic/social parents are recognized as sole parents. Such states remain in the minority.[27] It could be argued that to disregard the status of the gestational/birth mother in states where this is legally important would make Judaism seem less respectful of women's experience of gestation and birth (or of Jewish tradition) than secular authorities. Determining Jewish status using different criteria in different states of the U.S., not to mention other countries, is clearly unacceptable. Most basically, however, halakhah cannot follow *dina demalkhuta dina* (deference to civil law) in determining the religious status of children.

E. Conclusion

Halakhah recognizes the woman who gestates and gives birth to a child as the child's mother. Accordingly, the religious status of a child follows that of the gestational/birth mother in cases involving surrogacy, as in all other cases. Children born to a non-Jewish surrogate would require conversion to be halakhically recognized as Jewish. Rabbis should display personal and pastoral sensitivity in such cases.[28]

Notes

1. See Aaron L. Mackler, "Surrogate Parenting," paper approved by the Committee on Jewish Law and Standards [CJLS], June 1997 [chap. 7 of this vol.]; Elie Spitz, "On the Use of Birth Surrogates," paper approved by the CJLS, June 1997 [chap. 6 of this vol.].

2. Some material in this section may be found as well in my companion paper, "Surrogate Parenting" [chap. 7 of this vol.].
3. George J. Annas, "Death Without Dignity for Commercial Surrogacy: The Case of Baby M," *Hastings Center Report* 18, no. 2 (1988): 23–24.
4. Rosemarie Tong, "The Overdue Death of a Feminist Chameleon: Taking a Stand on Surrogacy Arrangements," in *The Ethics of Reproductive Technology*, ed. Kenneth D. Alpern (New York: Oxford University Press, 1992), 291, 285, 289.
5. Intuitively, it might seem to some that gestation is a relatively straightforward process that science likely will develop ways to replace artificially, while the genetic material of the human genome is hopelessly complex and will elude scientists. On the other hand, the understanding of human genetics and the ability to synthesize genetic material have been progressing rapidly and at accelerating rates, while the capacity to nurture the developing human are only very slowly, if at all, moving later than the first week of embryonic development in vitro, and earlier than about week 23–24 of development for extremely premature infants (New York State Task Force on Life and the Law, *Fetal Extrauterine Survivability* [New York: New York State Task Force on Life and the Law, 1988]). More generally, speculation on future scientific progress is uncertain at best. Writing in 1957, Isaac Asimov was able to envision a world of interstellar space travel and human-like robots, in which most of the process of gestation and human development could be managed artificially, but in vitro fertilization remained elusive, and fertilization itself could only take place in the body (*The Naked Sun* [New York: Doubleday, 1957]). Within a few decades, this apparently elusive element had, in fact, been achieved, while other developments remained distant.
6. J. David Bleich, "In Vitro Fertilization: Maternal Identity and Conversion," in *Contemporary Halakhic Problems IV* (New York: Ktav, 1995), 237–72; an earlier version of this chapter appeared in *Tradition* 25, no. 4 (1991): 82–102. As Bleich notes, a few writers have articulated minority positions according to which the child in such cases has no mother, or the genetic mother is primary. As I indicate in the body of the paper, I believe that stronger justification supports the view that has been advocated by most authorities who have addressed these issues, that maternal identity is to be determined primarily by gestation and birth.
7. Isaac Klein, *A Guide to Jewish Religious Practice* (New York: Jewish Theological Seminary of America, 1979), 446. This would seem to be the view of Rabbi Boaz Cohen as well. In a letter dated 5 Dec. 1955, he wrote: "If the woman is converted while she is still pregnant, her children will be born Jewish; otherwise they will need conversion."
8. *Dagul Merevavah*, on *S.A., Y.D.* 268:6. Accordingly, Landau suggests that if the *beit din* at her conversion did not know that she was pregnant, another immersion might be required.
9. Further casting doubt upon Landau's view, if the brothers are seen as undergo-

ing conversion, either they are not officially Jewish until their circumcision eight days after birth, or one would have to postulate that it is possible for a male to convert to Judaism without circumcision. See Zalman Nehemiah Goldberg, "Yiḥus imahut behashtalat ubar bereḥem shel aḥeret," *Teḥumin* 5 (5744): 255.

10. Kilav, "Mihi imo shel yilud, hahorah o hayoledet," *Teḥumin* 5 (5744): 260–74.
11. Sternbuch, "Tinok mavḥanah," *Bishvilei Harefu'ah* 8 (5747/1986): 29–37. See Elliot N. Dorff, "Artificial Insemination, Egg Donation, and Adoption," *Conservative Judaism* 44, no. 1 (1996): 21 (a responsum approved by the CJLS, Mar. 1994 [chap. 2, pp. 40–41 of this vol.]).
12. Soloveitchik, "Bedin tinok hamavḥanah," *Or Hamizraḥ* (1980/5741): 122–28.
13. Goldberg, 245–59.
14. David M. Feldman, "Abortion: The Jewish View," in *Proceedings of the Committee on Jewish Law and Standards, 1980–85,* ed. Kassel Abelson (New York: Rabbinical Assembly, 1988), 11 [chap. 11, p. 196 of this vol.]. The phrase is also cited in the *teshuvot* of Rabbi Robert Gordis, "Abortion: Major Wrong or Basic Right?" ibid., 22 [chap. 14, p. 224 of this vol.]; and Rabbi Isaac Klein, "A *Teshuvah* on Abortion," ibid., 33 [chap. 12, p. 208 of this vol.].
15. See David M. Feldman, *Birth Control in Jewish Law,* 3d ed. (Jerusalem: n.p., 1995), 266.
16. See Exodus 13, and Dorff, 46 [chap. 3, p. 79 of this vol.]. It should be noted that this argument serves only in a secondary, supportive role in this paper. If a child were born by cesarean section, for which halakhah would not apply the category of opening the womb (*peter reḥem*), this would in no way affect the recognition of the birth mother as the child's mother.
17. See, e.g., Walter Jacob, ed., *Contemporary American Reform Responsa* (New York: Central Conference of American Rabbis, 1987), 63; Shaye J. D. Cohen, "The Origins of the Matrilineal Principle in Rabbinic Law," *AJS Review* 10 (1985): 40–41, who reports but argues against this view.
18. Annas, 23–24.
19. See Bleich, 247–48; Dorff, 45–46 [chap. 3, pp. 78–79 of this vol.].
20. See Mackler, "In Vitro Fertilization" [chap. 4 of this vol.]. Reporting on procedures conducted in 1993, the Society for Assisted Reproductive Technology notes 2,766 IVF procedures using donated eggs, leading to 716 deliveries, and an additional 625 procedures using donated embryos, leading to 108 deliveries. The paper also reports 246 procedures involving gestational surrogacy, resulting in 78 deliveries (Society for Assisted Reproductive Technology, American Society for Reproductive Medicine, "Assisted Reproductive Technology in the United States and Canada: 1993 Results Generated from the Society for Reproductive Medicine/Society for Assisted Reproductive Technology Registry," *Fertility and Sterility* 64 [1995]: 13–21).
21. See Dorff, 29–30 [chap. 2, pp. 47–48 of this vol.]; *S.A., E.H.* 15.
22. "The Religious Identity of Offspring Born to a Surrogate," submitted to the

CJLS but withdrawn, 1997; " 'Through Her I Too Shall Bear a Child': Birth Surrogates in Jewish Law," *Journal of Religious Ethics* 24 (1996): 89–91.

23. David Kraemer, "Jewish Ethics and Abortion," *Tikkun* 8, no. 1 (1993): 55–58, 77.
24. Ibid., 55, 58.
25. I am grateful to Rabbi Avram Reisner for raising this issue.
26. Dorff, 51–54 [chap. 3, pp. 84–87 of this vol.]; Rabbi Avram Reisner, "On the Conversion of Adopted and Patrilineal Children," approved by the CJLS, Jan. 1988.
27. Furthermore, states currently recognizing the genetic mother as mother in cases of gestational surrogacy could well change. In California, the minority report of a legislative committee, supported by six of its members, recommended identifying the genetic mother as mother in such cases; but the majority report, supported by twelve members, argued that the birth mother should be recognized as mother irrebuttably ("Commercial and Noncommercial Surrogate Parenting," a report to the California Legislature from the Joint Legislative Committee on Surrogate Parenting, 1990).
28. For their suggestions and thoughtful insights, which have contributed greatly to this paper, I would like to thank Lorraine Newman Mackler, and members of the Committee on Jewish Law and Standards, including my fellow members of the Subcommittee on Biomedical Ethics: Rabbis Kassel Abelson, Elliot Dorff, Shoshana Gelfand, Avram Reisner, Joel Roth, and Elie Spitz.

CHAPTER 9

Surrogate Motherhood*

David H. Lincoln

She'eilah (Question):

A question has been raised regarding a case involving a Jewish married couple. The wife has had a hysterectomy; the husband's sperm is fertile; and a Gentile, divorced woman has agreed to be artificially inseminated with this husband's sperm. Should the procedure prove successful, the surrogate mother would hand over the child at birth. Is this arrangement permissible? Does it matter whether the surrogate mother is Gentile or Jewish, married or single?

Teshuvah (Response):

Although we should mainly confine ourselves to answering the questions as posed, there are certain ancillary matters that need to be mentioned, such as: Is the father the father? Has he fulfilled the mitzvah of *periyah ureviyah* ("Be fruitful and multiply")? What is the status of the child? If a boy, would he need *pidyon habein?* These have been addressed in other papers, including one by Rabbi Moses Shapiro, "Artificial Insemination in Jewish Law."[1] We need to note as well the uncertainties in civil law regarding surrogate mothers and their offspring. A paper by Carolea Goldfarb of New York Law School outlines some of our problems.[2]

In 1970, the office of the chief rabbi in London raised objections to

*Approved by the Rabbinical Assembly Committee on Jewish Law and Standards, June 1985.

A.I.D. (artificial insemination by donor) [in general], and [in particular] to reimplanting a fertilized egg into a host mother.[3] This idea of a host mother is also discussed by Rabbi J. David Bleich.[4] Attention should also be given to Rabbi Seymour Siegel's personal statement on the Brown baby, which ends with, "We hail the brilliant achievement of science, which has made possible the fulfillment of the profound desire for a child. . . . We should continue to use our God-given intelligence to wrest from nature her secrets. We can improve man's lot. We must be vigilant so that our achievements do not become our tribulations. We have reason to believe that an informed public, an intelligent government, and a dedicated scientific community will achieve even more wonders in the future."[5]

Much has been written in rabbinic responsa on both A.I.D. and A.I.H. (artificial insemination by husband). Rabbi Isaac Klein in *A Guide to Jewish Religious Practice* has a short note.[6] *American Reform Responsa* has two responsa by Rabbi Solomon Freehof and one by the [Reform] Law Committee.[7] Rabbi Morris Shapiro's aforementioned paper quotes many authorities. Rabbi Moshe Feinstein's responsa have achieved worldwide acclaim, and even notoriety in some quarters.[8]

All these writings yield the same conclusion: the child born of a non-Jewish mother is not Jewish. Of course, it is possible to convert the child, but do we really want to encourage a Jewish father to have a non-Jewish child so that we can convert it? What impact would this have on Jews who are married to Gentiles for whom we do not make it so easy? Should the couple not, rather, look for a baby to adopt? In the case presented, it does not matter halakhically whether the host mother is married or single, or, as we shall see below, whether she is Gentile or Jewish.

A more complicated case [for determining the child's religious status] would be if the fertilized ovum of a Jewish woman would be transferred to a non-Jew. The status of the child would depend on whether Jewish law defines maternal identity as established by conception, by parturition, or by genotype. Rabbi Moshe Hershler quotes *Yevamot* 97b, which discusses a pregnant woman who became a convert to Judaism and then gave birth to twins. Since conception happened before her conversion, there is no halakhic paternity, and hence no levirate obligations devolve upon the twins since they are not deemed to be paternal siblings, and so on. (There are, however, restrictions, as they are "related" [as maternal siblings].)[9] This all would need a separate paper, and we are not asked that here. [More extensive discussion may be found in chapter 8 of this volume, written after the completion of this paper.]

If the recipient [of artificial insemination, the surrogate mother] is an unmarried Jewish woman, and we know her identity, I would feel that it would be "permitted" based on Rabbi Moshe Feinstein's various [responsa] that this [donor insemination—i.e., insemination of the surrogate mother by a man who is not her husband] is not considered *bi'ah* [intercourse] and is permissible.[10] However, there are authorities, including the Satmar rebbe, who state that it is forbidden for the recipient to be a Jewish married woman, for offspring from such a pregnancy would be *mamzeirim* (illegitimate). For Rabbi Feinstein, however, adultery and illegitimacy apply only in cases in which there is lust, broken faith, and physical intercourse.

A problem of which Rabbi Feinstein is constantly aware, and that should be noted in cases of artificial insemination, is the possibility of incest [among children with the same genetic father in future generations]. Rabbi Aaron Soloveitchik of the Brisk Yeshiva in Chicago relates a case in which he was invited to officiate at a wedding on the West Coast. One of the bridal couple had been conceived through artificial insemination. A doctor had found that they were brother and sister. The Talmud warns of this in *Yevamot* 37b:

> **לא ישא אדם אשה במדינה זו וילך וישא אשה במדינה אחרת שמא יזדווגו זה לזה ונמצא אח נושא את אחותו**
>
> One should not marry a woman in this country and go marry a woman in another country, lest [the child of] one have relations with [the child of] the other, and only then discover that he is marrying his sister.

That is why it is better to know to whom the sperm is given, and be certain that some record is kept.

There is a problem that I did not see mentioned in other authorities but that was raised by Rabbi Soloveitchik, based on the talmudic discussion in *Yevamot* 76a, of *nashim hamesolelot zo bazo,* women who "commit lewdness" with one another. [Exactly what "lewdness" is being referred to is discussed by various authorities, who generally understand some sort of lesbian sexual behavior to be involved.[11] Some interpretations describe the women as transferring among themselves semen that had come from their husbands.] All this is described as *ma'aseh mitzrayim* (immorality of Egypt [proscribed in Lev. 18:3]). I would, with respect, tend to believe that the *ma'aseh mitzrayim* is not the transfer of semen, but rather, the lesbian behavior, although the *Maggid Mishneh* could be interpreted as Rabbi Soloveitchik suggests.

Nevertheless, might there not be an element of *ma'aseh mitzrayim,* something unsavory, about the whole process? If the surrogate mother is not Jewish, is it desirable for Jews to father Gentiles, even if the children's birth may be quickly followed by conversion? If the surrogate mother is unmarried, are we not degrading her, however noble her intentions? Can we really allow a single woman to become pregnant? If [the surrogate is] married, there is something very distasteful in [her] carrying another man's baby, even if the woman has not committed adultery.

Conclusion

In spite of these reservations, artificial insemination is permitted in Jewish law, and we recognize that. The mitzvah of having children is so great that we should not deny couples this opportunity. If, however, the surrogate mother is not Jewish, the child requires conversion.

Colleagues who recommend such procedures and who counsel couples in such a predicament must be aware of psychological and legal difficulties that may arise. In the latter, especially, each state and country has different laws. The legal ramifications have not as yet been fully discussed or formulated by the courts and legislatures. Great caution must therefore be exercised.

Notes

1. A paper presented to the Committee on Jewish Law and Standards but not voted upon, Aug. 1978. [More extensive discussion may be found in chaps. 1–3 of this vol., written after the completion of this paper.]
2. Carolea Goldfarb, "Two Mothers, One Baby, No Law," *Human Rights* 11 (summer 1983): 27–29, 54–56.
3. Immanuel Jakobovits, *Jewish Medical Ethics* (New York: Bloch, 1975), 264–66.
4. J. David Bleich, *Contemporary Halakhic Problems I* (New York: Ktav, 1977), 106–9; *Contemporary Halakhic Problems II* (New York: Ktav, 1983), 91–93.
5. Seymour Siegel, "The Brown Baby and the Jewish Tradition," a paper presented to the CJLS but not voted upon, Aug. 1978.
6. Isaac Klein, *A Guide to Jewish Religious Practice* (New York: Jewish Theological Seminary of America, 1979), 417–18.

7. *American Reform Responsa* (New York: Central Conference of American Rabbis, 1983), no. 159, "Surrogate Mother," 505–7.
8. *Iggerot Moshe, E.H.*, pt. 1:10, 71; pt. 2:11.
9. *Halakhah Urefu'ah* 1 (Jerusalem: Regensberg Institute, 5740), 316.
10. *Iggerot Moshe, E.H.*, pt. 1:10, 71; pt. 2:11.
11. Rashi, ad loc.; Maimonides (*M.T., Hilkhot Isurei Bi'ah* 21:8); and the *Maggid Mishneh*'s commentary to Maimonides.

II. RESPONSIBILITIES FOR FETAL LIFE

D. ABORTION

Introduction

Abortion is a controversial issue within Jewish ethics, as it is in Western societies generally. Most Jewish writers would agree that a fetus does not have the status of a full human person, so that abortion is not homicide. At the same time, the fetus is a developing life and potential person. Abortion is morally wrong prima facie—that is, unless serious ethical considerations mandate an exception. Such an exception could be justified, however, in particular when required to protect the pregnant woman from severe harm. The severity of the harm required to justify abortion and the authority of the woman herself to make this judgment vary among diverse Jewish writers.

This section begins with a consensus statement of Conservative Jewish views on this issue: "An abortion is justifiable if a continuation of pregnancy might cause the mother severe physical or psychological harm, or when the fetus is judged by competent medical opinion as severely defective." At the same time, "the fetus is a life in the process of development, and the decision to abort it should never be taken lightly." Four papers follow. The first two papers focus on presenting classical sources, ranging from the Bible and the Mishnah to developing responsa over the centuries. In "Abortion: The Jewish View," Rabbi

David M. Feldman presents varied strands within the tradition. Initially stringent positions "build down" to allow exceptions to a general prohibition of abortion, while initially lenient positions "build up" to avoid indiscriminate abortion. A common thread is the criterion of maternal welfare. In "A *Teshuvah* on Abortion," Rabbi Isaac Klein presents the decisive issue as "whether the fetus is considered a living being." He concludes that "abortion is morally wrong [in general]. It should be permitted only for therapeutic reasons."

Rabbi Kassel Abelson draws on analyses of Klein and Feldman, as well as his own presentation of sources, in "Prenatal Testing and Abortion." He concludes that prenatal testing should be encouraged in appropriate cases. "If the tests indicate that the child will be born with major defects that would preclude a normal life and that would make the mother and family anxious about the future, it is permitted to abort the fetus." Rabbi Robert Gordis devotes significant attention to social factors and public policy in "Abortion: Major Wrong or Basic Right?" He ideally would desire liberal societal laws on abortion, to allow for abortion in appropriate cases, together with a more demanding ethical understanding expressed by society and individuals. Pragmatically, laws should be crafted to reflect "a basically liberal attitude toward abortion with conservative safeguards."

CHAPTER 10

A Statement on the Permissibility of Abortion*

Ben Zion Bokser and Kassel Abelson

Jewish tradition is sensitive to the sanctity of life and does not permit abortion on demand. However, it sanctions abortion under some circumstances because it does not regard the fetus as an autonomous person. This is based partly on the Bible (Exod. 21:22–23), which prescribes monetary damages when a person injures a pregnant woman, causing a miscarriage. The Mishnah (*Oholot* 7:6) explicitly indicates that one is to abort a fetus if the continuation of pregnancy might imperil the life of the mother. Later authorities have differed as to how far we might go in defining the peril to the mother in order to justify an abortion. The Rabbinical Assembly Committee on Jewish Law and Standards takes the view that an abortion is justifiable if a continuation of pregnancy might cause the mother severe physical or psychological harm, or when the fetus is judged by competent medical opinion as severely defective. The fetus is a life in the process of development, and the decision to abort it should never be taken lightly. Before reaching her final decision, the mother should consult with the father, other members of her family, her physician, her spiritual leader, and any other person who can help her in assessing the many grave legal and moral issues involved.

*Approved by the Rabbinical Assembly Committee on Jewish Law and Standards, Nov. 1983.

CHAPTER 11

Abortion: The Jewish View*

David M. Feldman

She'eilah (Question):

Is abortion permitted according to Jewish law?

Teshuvah (Response):

The abortion question in talmudic law begins with an examination of the fetus's legal status. For this the Talmud has a phrase, *ubar yerekh imo*, a counterpart of the Latin *pars viscera matris*. The fetus is deemed a "part of its mother" rather than an independent entity. Of course, this designation says nothing about the right of abortion; this is found only in more theoretical contexts. In the case of an embryo found in a purchased animal, the embryo is intrinsic to its mother's body; its ownership is defined—it belongs to the buyer. Moreover, in the religious conversion of a pregnant woman, her unborn child is automatically included and requires no added ceremony. Nor does the fetus have power of acquisition. Gifts or transactions made on its behalf, except by its father, are not binding; it inherits from its father only, in a natural rather than a transactional manner.

Germane as such information might seem to the question of abortion, it tells us little more than, in the words of a modern writer on Roman and Jewish law, that in both systems the fetus has no "juridical

*Approved by the Rabbinical Assembly Committee on Jewish Law and Standards, Aug. 1983. The explicit statement of the *she'eilah* (question) has been added by the editor.

personality" of its own. The morality of abortion is a function, rather, of the legal attitude to feticide as distinguished from homicide or infanticide. The law of homicide in the Torah, in one of its several formulations, reads: *Makeih ish . . .* (He who smites a man . . .) (Exod. 21:12). Does this include any "man," say, a day-old child? Yes, says the Talmud, citing another text: *ki yakeh kol nefesh adam* (If one smite any *nefesh adam* [Lev. 24:17]—literally, any human person). The "any" is understood to include the day-old child, but the *nefesh adam* is taken to exclude the fetus in the womb, for the fetus in the womb is *lav nefesh hu* (not a person) until he is born. In the words of Rashi, only when the fetus "comes into the world" is it a "person."

The basis, then, for denying capital-crime status to feticide in Jewish law, even for those rabbis who may have wanted to rule otherwise, is scriptural. Alongside the *nefesh adam* text is another basic one in Exod. 21:22, which provides:

> If men strive, and wound a pregnant woman so that her fruit be expelled, but no harm befell [her], then shall he be fined as her husband shall assess, and the matter placed before the judges. But if harm befell [her], then shall you give life for life.

The Talmud makes this verse's teaching explicit: only monetary compensation is exacted of him who causes a woman to miscarry. Though the abortion spoken of here is accidental, the verse is still a source for the teaching that feticide is not a capital crime (since even accidental homicide cannot be expiated by monetary fine).

This important passage in Exodus has an alternate version in the Septuagint. One word change there yields an entirely different statute on miscarriage. Prof. Viktor Aptowitzer's essays analyze the disputed passage; he calls the school of thought that it represents the Alexandrian school, as opposed to the Palestinian, that is, the talmudic view set forth above. The word in question is *ason,* rendered above as "harm"; hence, "If [there be] no harm [i.e., death, to the mother], then shall he be fined. . . ." The Greek renders the word *ason* as "form," yielding something like: "If [there be] form, then shall you give life for life." The "life for life" clause is thus applied to the fetus instead of to the mother, and a distinction was made, as Augustine would formulate it, between *embryo informatus* and *embryo formatus,* a fetus not yet "formed" and one already "formed"; for the latter, the text so rendered prescribes the death penalty.

Among the church fathers, the consequent doctrine of feticide as murder was preached by Tertullian (second century), who accepted the Septuagint, and by Jerome (fourth century), who did not (whose classic Bible translation renders the passage according to the Hebrew text accepted in the Church). The *Didache,* a handbook of basic Christianity for the instruction of converts from paganism, follows the Alexandrian teaching and specifies abortion as a capital crime. Closer to the main body of the Jewish community, we find the doctrine accepted by the Samaritans and the Karaites and, more important, by Philo, the popular first-century philosopher of Alexandria. On the other hand, Philo's younger contemporary Josephus bears witness to the Palestinian (halakhic) tradition. Aside from its textual warrant, the latter is the more authentic in the view of Aptowitzer, while the other is a later tendency, "which, in addition, is not genuinely Jewish but must have originated in Alexandria under Egyptian-Greek influence."[1]

In the rabbinic tradition, then, abortion remains a noncapital crime at worst. But a curious factor further complicates the question of the criminality of the act. This is the circumstance that one more biblical text (this one in Genesis and hence "before Sinai" and part of the laws of the "Sons of Noah") served as the source for the teaching that feticide is indeed a capital crime—for non-Jews. Gen. 9:6 reads, "He who sheds the blood of man, through man [i.e., through the human court of law] shall his blood be shed." Since the Hebrew (*shofeikh dam ha'adam ba'adam*) allows for a translation of "man, in man," as well as "man, through man," the Talmud records the exposition of Rabbi Ishmael: "What is this 'man in man'? It refers to the fetus in its mother's womb." The locus of this text in Genesis, standing as it does without the qualifying balance of the Exodus (Sinaitic) passage, made feticide a capital crime for non-Jews (i.e., those not heir to the Sinaitic covenant) in Jewish law. Some modern scholars hold this exposition to be more sociological than textually inherent, representing a reaction against abuses among the heathen. In view of rampant abortion and infanticide, they claim, Rabbi Ishmael "forced" the above exegesis out of the Genesis text to render judgment against the Romans.

Regardless of its rationale, the doctrine remains part of theoretical Jewish law, as Maimonides systematically defines it:

> A "Son of Noah" who killed a person, even a fetus in its mother's womb, is capitally liable. . . . (The Jewish court is obliged to provide judges for the resident alien to adjudicate for

> them in accordance with these laws [of the Sons of Noah] so that society not corrupt itself. The judges may come either from their midst or from the Israelites.) (*Hilkhot Melakhim* 9:4; 10:11)

Therapeutic abortion is not, of course, included in this Noahide restriction. Nor is an abortion during the first forty days of pregnancy included, according to some. The implications of this anomaly of a different law for the "Sons of Noah" were dealt with in a responsum of the eighteenth century:

> It is not to be supposed that the Torah would consider the embryo as a person [*nefesh*] for them [Sons of Noah] but not a person for us. The fetus is not a person for them either: the Torah merely was more severe in its practical ruling in their regard. Hence, therapeutic abortion would be permissible to them, too.[2]

In the rabbinic system, then, abortion is not murder. Nor is it more than murder, as would be the case if "ensoulment" were at issue. Talmudic discussions speak of the moment—conception, birth, post-birth, and so on—at which the soul joins the body. This is seen to be irrelevant to the abortion question, because the soul is immortal no matter when it enters or leaves the body. And, more important than being immortal, it is a pure soul, free of the taint of "original sin." In the sixth century, Saint Fulgentius ruled that "original sin" is inherited by the soul of the fetus at conception, which made baptism in utero necessary in cases of miscarriage, and which made abortion worse than murder, in the sense that the fetus was being "killed in this world and the next." Judaism has no concept of "original sin" of this kind and, in the words of the Talmud and the daily prayer book, "My God, the soul with which Thou has endowed me is pure."

Murder (of the innocent) is forbidden even to save life. But with abortion removed from the category of murder, therapeutic abortion becomes permissible and, in fact, mandated. The Mishnah sets forth the basic talmudic law in this regard:

> If a woman has [life-threatening] difficulty in childbirth, the embryo within her should be dismembered limb by limb, because her life takes precedence over its life. Once its head (or its

> greater part) has emerged, it may not be touched, for we do not set aside one life for another. (*Oholot* 7:6)

In analyzing such provisions, the Talmud suggested that the reason could well be that the fetus is in the category of an "aggressor"; its life is forfeit under the law that permits killing a "pursuer" in order to save the intended victim. The Talmud, however, dismisses this reasoning, since the fetus is an innocent being, and since one cannot know "who is pursuing whom"; the pursuit must therefore be deemed an "act of God," and this factor does not apply. In the *Mishneh Torah,* Maimonides also used the term "aggressor," but only figuratively; in truth, he and his commentators concluded that the argument does not apply. It is either inapplicable or, at best, superfluous, because the fetus is not yet a person and murder is not involved. Maimonides formulates the talmudic law as follows:

> This, too, is a [negative] commandment: not to take pity on the life of a pursuer. Therefore, the Sages ruled that when a woman has difficulty in giving birth, one may dismember the child in her womb, either with drugs or by surgery, *because it is like a pursuer seeking to kill her.* Once its head has emerged, it may not be touched, for we do not set aside one life for another; this is the natural course of the world. (*Hilkhot Rotzeaḥ Ushmirat Nefesh* 1:9)

Some commentators of thc *Mishneh Torah* suggest that although abortion is not technically murder, it is still so grave an offense that Maimonides resorted to the aggressor argument in order to buttress the permission for abortion; its justification is that the fetus is at least *like* an aggressor.

The subsequent rabbinic tradition seems to align itself either to the right, in the direction of Maimonides, or to the left, in the direction of Rashi. The first approach can be identified especially with the late chief rabbi of Israel, Issar Unterman, who sees any abortion as "akin to homicide" and therefore allowable only in cases of corresponding gravity, such as saving the life of the mother. This approach then builds down from that strict position to embrace a broader interpretation of lifesaving situations, which include a threat to her health, for example, as well as a threat to her life. The second approach, associated with another former chief rabbi of Israel, Ben Zion Uziel, and others, assumes that no real prohibition against abortion exists and builds *up* from that lenient position to safeguard against indiscriminate abortion. This includes the example of Rabbi Yair Bachrach in the seventeenth century, whose classic responsum saw no legal bar to abortion, but would not permit it in the case before him. The case was one of a pregnancy conceived in adultery; the woman, in "deep remorse," wanted to destroy the fruit of her sin. The author concludes by refusing to sanction the abortion, not on legal grounds but on sociological ones, as a safeguard against further immorality. Other authorities disagreed on this point, affirming the legal sanction of abortion for the woman's welfare, whether life or health, or even avoidance of "great pain."

The criterion in both approaches becomes maternal rather than fetal. The principle in Jewish law is *tza'ar gufah kadim,* that her welfare is primary. Rabbinic rulings on abortion are thus amenable to the following generalization: if a possibility or probability exists that a child may be born defective, and the mother seeks abortion on the grounds of pity for a child whose life would be less than normal, the rabbi would decline permission. Since we do not know for sure that it will be born defective, and since we do not know how bad such a defective life would be for the child, and since no permission exists in Jewish law to kill born defectives, permission on those grounds would be denied. If, however, an abortion for the same potentially deformed child were sought on the grounds that the possibility was causing severe anguish to the mother, permission would be granted. The fetus is unknown, future, potential, part of the "secret of God"; the mother is known, present, alive, and asking for compassion.

One rabbinic authority, writing in Rumania in 1940, responded to the case of an epileptic mother who wanted to interrupt her pregnancy for fear that her child, too, would be epileptic. He first discusses the question of epilepsy itself, then writes:

> For fear of possible, remote danger to a future child that, maybe, God forbid, he will know sickness—how can it occur to anyone to actively kill him because of such a possible doubt? This seems to me very much like the laws of Lycurgus, king of Sparta, according to which every blemished child would be killed. . . . Permission for abortion is to be granted only because of fear of mental anguish for the mother. But for fear of what might be the child's lot—"the secrets of God are none of your business."[3]

In the current Tay-Sachs screening controversy, rabbinic authorities recommend screening before, rather than during, the pregnancy. This is because the alternative would be to resort to amniocentesis after the first trimester of pregnancy, with possible abortion on the basis of its results. This abortion for fetal, rather than maternal, indications would not ordinarily be sanctioned by Jewish law. True, rabbinic opinion permitting abortion for fetal reasons alone is not altogether lacking, but the normative rabbinic view is to permit it for maternal indications only. Yet the one can blend into the other, as fetal risk can mean mental anguish on the part of the mother, so that the fetal indication becomes a maternal one. The woman's welfare is thus the key to warrant abortion.

Implicit in the mishnah above is the teaching that the rights of the fetus are secondary to the rights of the mother all the way up until the moment of birth. This principle is obscured by the current phrase "right to life." In the context of abortion questions, the issue is not the right to life, which is very clear in Jewish law, but the right to be born, which is not as clear. The right to be born is relative; the right to life for existing persons is absolute. "Life" may begin before birth, but it is not the life of a human person; animal life, plant life, or even prehuman life are not the same as human life. Rabbinic law has determined that human life begins with birth. This is neither a medical nor a court judgment, but a metaphysical one. In the Jewish system, human life in this sense begins with birth. Of course, potential life already partakes of the potential sacredness of actual life, since the latter can have its inception only through the former.

Another slogan-like phrase is dealt with in the same mishnah, wherein it is ruled that "once the fetus has emerged from the womb, it cannot be touched," even to save the life of the mother, "for we cannot set aside one life for another." The "quality of life" slogan or concept is thus inadmissible. The life of the mother has more "quality"; she is adult, has a husband, children, and associations, while the newborn has none of these yet. Still, the sanctity-of-life principle means that life is sacred regardless of differences in quality; mother and newborn babe are equal from the moment of birth.

Talmudic statements do use the term "murder" in a figurative sense, of course, to describe even the neglect to conceive. Procreation is a positive mitzvah, and he who fails to fulfill this mitzvah is called "guilty of bloodshed." And much of the pro-natalist attitude of Judaism helps account for its abhorrence of casual abortion. There may be legal sanction for abortion when necessary, but the attitude remains one of hesitation before the sanctity of life and a pro-natalist respect for potential life.

Accordingly, abortion for "population control" is repugnant to the Jewish system. Abortion for economic reasons is also not admissible. Taking precaution by abortion or birth control against physical threat remains a mitzvah, but never to forestall financial difficulty. Maternal considerations are improper in this connection. In the Jewish community today, with a conscious or unconscious drive to replenish ranks decimated by the Holocaust, contemporary rabbis invoke not the more lenient, but rather the more stringent, responsa of the earlier authorities. The more permissive decisions, they point out, were, in any case, rendered against the background of far greater instinctive hesitation to resort to abortion. Against today's background of more casual abortion, rabbis are moving closer to the position associated with Maimonides and Unterman, allowing abortion only for the gravest of reasons.

Notes

1. Viktor Aptowitzer, "Observations on the Criminal Law of the Jews," *Jewish Quarterly Review* 15 (1924): 85ff.
2. R. Isaac Schorr, *Responsa Koaḥ Shor,* vol. 1, no. 20 (Kolomea, 1888).
3. R. David Sperber, *Responsa Afarkasta D'Anya,* no. 169 (Satmar, 1940).

CHAPTER 12

A Teshuvah on Abortion*

Isaac Klein

She'eilah (Question):

Is abortion permitted according to Jewish law?

Teshuvah (Response):

We first have to define the word "abortion." Medically, abortion is the term indicating the spontaneous or artificial termination of a pregnancy before the twenty-eighth week, at which time the infant, theoretically, first becomes able to carry on an independent existence.[1] In our case, the question applies only to the artificial (not spontaneous or natural) termination of the pregnancy at any time before the complete birth of the child and involves the death of the embryo or the fetus.

The main talmudic source for this question is found in the mishnah that states:

> האשה שהיא מקשה לילד מחתכין את הולד במעיה ומוציאין אותו אברים אברים מפני שחייה קודמין לחייו יצא רובו אין נוגעין בו שאין דוחין נפש מפני נפש

> If a woman is having difficulty in giving birth, it is permitted to cut up the child inside her womb and take it out limb by limb because her life takes precedence. If the greater part of the child

*Approved by the Rabbinical Assembly Committee on Jewish Law and Standards, Aug. 1983.

> has come out, it must not be touched because one life must not be taken to save another. (*Oholot* 7:6)

This is repeated in the Tosefta with slight variations:

> **האשה שמקשה לילד מחתכין העובר במעיה ואפי׳ בשבת ומוציאין אותו איברים איברים מפני שחייה קודמין לו יצא ראשו אפי׳ ביום השיני אין נוגעין בו שאין דוחין נפש מפני נפש**

> If a woman is having difficulty in giving birth, it is permitted to cut up the child in her womb even on the Sabbath, and take it out limb by limb because her life takes precedence. If its head came out, it may not be touched even the second day, because one life may not be taken to save another. (T. *Yevamot* 9:9)

On the above mishnah, we have the following comment of the Talmud:

> **יצא ראשו אין נוגעין בו לפי שאין דוחין נפש מפני נפש ואמאי רודף הוא שאני התם דמשמיא קא רדפי לה**

> Once his head has come forth, he may not be harmed because one life may not be taken to save another. But why so? Is he not a pursuer? There it is different, for she is pursued by heaven. (*Sanhedrin* 72b)

What is the reason that we permit taking the life of the unborn child when it endangers the life of the mother? Rashi, in his comment on the above passage, gives the following reason:

> **דכל זמן שלא יצא לאויר העולם לאו נפש הוא וניתן להורגו ולהציל את אמו אבל יצא ראשו אין נוגעים בו להורגו דהוה ליה כילוד ואין דוחין נפש מפני נפש**

> For as long as it did not come out into the world, it is not called a living thing and it is permissible to take its life in order to save its mother. Once the head has come forth it may not he harmed because it is considered born, and one life may not be taken to save another.

Thus, according to Rashi, the reason for the permission to take the life of the unborn child is that the embryo is not considered a living thing, and hence, taking its life cannot be called murder. This view is supported by the biblical law concerning harm done to a pregnant woman, in which case the Bible prescribes:

> וכי ינצו אנשים ונגפו אשה הרה ויצאו ילדיה ולא יהיה אסון ענוש יענש כאשר ישית עליו בעל האשה ונתן בפללים: ואם אסון יהיה ונתתה נפש תחת נפש

> If men strive and hurt a woman with child, so that her fruit depart from her, and yet no mischief follow: he shall surely be punished, according as the woman's husband will lay upon him; and he shall pay as the judge determines. And if any mischief follow, then thou shalt give life for life. (Exod. 21:22–23)

The mischief in the verse refers, of course, to the death of the woman. It is only in the case that death results to the mother from the hurt that capital punishment follows. The death of the unborn child is punishable by fine only.

From Maimonides, it would appear that the reason the life of the unborn child may be taken when it endangers the life of the mother is based on the law of the "pursuer" (*rodeif*). In his code, Maimonides says:

> הרי זו מצות לא תעשה שלא לחוס על נפש הרודף. לפיכך הורו חכמים שהעוברה שהיא מקשה לילד מותר לחתוך העובר במיעיה בין בסם בין ביד מפני שהוא כרודף אחריה להורגה, ואם משהוציא ראשו אין נוגעין בו שאין דוחין נפש מפני נפש וזהו טבעו של עולם

> This is, moreover, a negative commandment, that we have no pity on the life of a pursuer. Consequently, the Sages have ruled that if a woman with child is having difficulty in giving birth, the child inside her may be taken out, either by drugs or by surgery, because it is regarded as one pursuing her and trying to kill her. But once its head has appeared, it must not be touched, for we may not set aside one human life to save another human life, and what is happening is the course of nature. (Rambam, *Hilkhot Rotzeaḥ Ushmirat Nefesh* 1:9)

This opinion of Maimonides is followed by Joseph Karo in *Ḥoshen Mishpat* 425:2.

There is a clear distinction between the reasoning of Rashi and that of Maimonides. According to Rashi, the embryo is not considered a living thing and therefore the life of the mother takes precedence. According to Maimonides, the life of the mother takes precedence because the embryo is in the position of a *rodeif*, a "pursuer." From this difference in interpretation may also result differences in legal decisions. According to Maimonides, we would permit abortion only when there is clear danger to the life of the mother. According to Rashi, there might be other adequate reasons besides the threat to the life of the mother.

The interpretation of Maimonides offers many difficulties. There is no indication in the Mishnah that in the case of an embryo, the law of the pursuer applies. On the contrary: the Mishnah clearly states that the life of the mother takes precedence as long as the child is unborn. The Talmud suggests using the reason of the "pursuer" only when the child is already born. The answer that the Talmud gives for not applying the reason of the "pursuer" in the case of a child already born applies just as much to the unborn child. Many of the commentators try to give answers, but they seem forced.[2] Hence, we prefer to follow the reasoning of Rashi that the whole problem revolves around the question of whether the fetus is considered a living being.

The ancients spoke of this in their idiom, e.g., the following conversation between the compiler of the Mishnah and the Roman emperor:

> **ואמר לו אנטונינוס לרבי נשמה מאימתי ניתנה באדם משעת פקידה או משעת יצירה אמר לו משעת יצירה אמר לו אפשר חתיכה של בשר עומדת שלשה ימים בלא מלח ואינה מסרחת אלא משעת פקידה אמר רבי דבר זה למדני אנטונינוס ומקרא מסייעו שנאמר ופקדתך שמרה רוחי**

> Antoninus said to Rabbi: when is the soul given unto man, at the time that the embryo is formed, or at the time of conception? He replied: at the time the embryo is already formed. The emperor objected: is it possible for a piece of meat to stay for three days without salt and not putrefy? It must therefore be at conception. Said Rabbi: this thing Antoninus taught me, and Scripture supports him, as it is said: and thy visitation has preserved my spirit, i.e., my soul (Job 10:12). (*Sanhedrin* 91b)

According to Aristotle, the rational soul is infused the fortieth day after conception in the case of a male and the eightieth day in the case of a female. The Platonic tradition was that the soul entered at conception. The Stoics believed that the soul entered at birth. Roman jurists followed the Stoics and held therefore that abortion was not murder. According to common law, too, taking a life is punishable only after there has been complete extrusion of the child from the body of the mother.

The Catholic Church evidently followed the Platonic tradition because it forbade all abortions. Even in the case of ectopic pregnancies, the official ruling of the Church issued by the Congregation of the Holy Office, 5 March 1902, is: "No, it [abortion] is not lawful. Such a removal of the fetus is a direct killing of the fetus and is forbidden." A *fatwa* of the Grand Mufti, of 25 January 1937, states that therapeutic abortions are absolutely forbidden after the embryo has "quickened." Medical science considers the fetus a living thing from the moment the ovum is fertilized.[3]

Actually, being a living thing and being a separate entity are two separate matters. Even if it is a living thing, we can say that the fetus is *pars viscera matris* or, to use the talmudic expression, *ubar yerekh imo hu*. The fetus is thus accounted as the loin of its mother. When abortion is therapeutic, there can be no objection to it because, as in any surgery, we sacrifice the part for the whole.

This is the attitude that the rabbis have taken. Abortion is forbidden. Though it is not considered murder, it does mean the destruction of potential life.[4] If, however, the purpose is therapeutic, this objection is removed. I have chosen a number of responsa dealing with the question.

Rabbi Yair Ḥayim Bachrach (1639–1702), the author of *Responsa Ḥavot Ya'ir*, had the following strange case: a married woman committed adultery and became pregnant. She had pangs of remorse and wanted to do penance. She asked whether she could swallow a drug in order to get rid of the "evil fruit" in her womb. In response, Rabbi Bachrach made it clear immediately that the question of the permissibility of abortion had nothing to do with the legitimacy of the child to be born. The only question involved was whether abortion is accounted as taking a life or not. Rabbi Bachrach drew distinctions between the various stages of the development of the fetus, e.g., forty days after conception, three months after conception. He concluded that it might be theoretically permitted at the early stages of the pregnancy, but we do not do so because of the custom adopted by both the Jewish and the general community against immorality.

Rabbi Meir Eisenstadt (1670–1744), in his *Panim Me'irot*, asked the following question: if a woman has difficulty in giving birth because the child came out feet first, is it permitted to cut up the child limb by limb in order to save the mother? This seems to be the very question explicitly answered in the Mishnah. The only problem that is introduced is a discrepancy between the Mishnah and Maimonides. Whereas the Mishnah states that if the greater part of the child has come out of the mother's body, we do not take the life of the child in order to save the mother, Maimonides says that if the head of the child or the majority thereof came out first, it is considered as born and we do not take its life in order to save the mother.

The commentators tried to resolve this contradiction by saying that the extrusion of the head or the major part thereof, or, in cases in which the head came last, the extrusion of the majority of the body, constitutes birth. The author then poses the question: if at this stage, death could result to both if we let nature take its course, is it still forbidden to take the life of the child in order to save the mother? He leaves the question unanswered.[5]

Rabbi Eliezer Deutsch (1850–1916), the author of *Responsa Peri Hasadeh,* treats the following problem: a woman who had been pregnant a few weeks began to spit blood. Expert physicians insisted that she take a drug in order to induce a miscarriage for, should she wait, it would not only become necessary to take out the child by cutting it up; it would also endanger the life of the mother. If they acted immediately, it would be possible to bring forth the child with a drug. Is it permissible to do so?

Rabbi Deutsch answered that, in this case, it is certainly permitted. He made a distinction between the various stages in the development of the fetus, *gufah aḥarina* (a separate body), *ne'ekar havelad* (the fetus has become detached); between the use of drugs and the use of surgery; and between another person [aborting the fetus] or the woman herself. The conclusion was that [taking the drug] is permitted in this case for three reasons: (a) before three months after the conception, there is not even a fetus; (b) there was no overt act involved in this case, i.e., surgery; and (c) the woman herself was doing it and it is thus an act of self-preservation.

In [more recent] literature, I found a responsum dated 5709 [1948/49]—I, *Ḥayei Sarah* by Rabbi Yitzḥak Oelbaum of Czechoslovakia, now of Canada. This is the situation: a woman had a weak child, and, according to the doctors, it would not live unless it was breast-fed by the mother. The mother had been pregnant for four weeks and had felt a change in her milk. Could she destroy the child she was carrying by means of an injection, she inquired, in order to save the child she was nursing? The author first discussed the reliability of doctors in these matters, claiming that they sometimes exaggerate, and whether a proper formula for bottle feeding could be substituted. He concluded that if there was expert evidence that danger might result if the abortion was not performed, then it is permitted. In this responsum, a new issue is introduced. Until now, we have spoken of danger to the mother. Here, there is no danger to the mother, but rather to another child. This opens new possibilities that we shall not pursue here.

An even more recent responsum on the subject is by Rabbi Gedaliah Felder of Toronto, published in *Kol Torah* (Heshvan 5719 [1958]), a rabbinic periodical published in Jerusalem. Here, the question is: a pregnant woman was afflicted with cancer of the lungs. The doctors said that if a premature birth was not effected, the cancer would spread faster and hasten her death. Is it permissible to have an abortion when the mother is saved only temporarily?

Before we sum up, it would not be out of place to bring in a comment from the medical profession. The following quotation was called to my attention by Dr. Hiram Yellen, a prominent obstetrician in Buffalo, New York:

> There is abundant evidence that the frequency of criminal induction of abortion is increasing at an alarming rate, although accurate statistics cannot be obtained. Numerous reasons may be advanced for this deplorable situation, the most probable being: (1) Twentieth-century standards of living have made children an economic liability for a large percentage of the population. This may be contrasted with more primitive rural conditions where a large family was considered an economic asset; (2) As a by-product of the women's freedom movement, a very large number of women have come to believe that pregnancy should be regulated by their personal desires; and (3) The present-day lack of religious feeling and the wide teaching that pregnancy may be controlled have contributed to a lowering of moral standards among women, with a resulting increase in the number of undesired pregnancies.[6]

Our conclusion, therefore, must be that abortion is morally wrong. It should be permitted only for therapeutic reasons.

Notes

1. Paul Titus and J. Robert Willson, *The Management of Obstetric Difficulties* [5th ed.] ([St. Louis: Mosby,] 1955), 210.

2. See *Tosefot R. Akiva Eiger* on the Mishnah in *Oholot,* and *Ḥidushei R. Ḥayim Halevi,* ad loc., and comments in some of the responsa that deal with this question.
3. See Joseph B. De Lee, [*The Principles and Practice of*] *Obstetrics,* 4th ed. [(Philadelphia: W. B. Saunders, 1924)], 274.
4. See Tosafot, *Ḥullin* 33a, s.v. *Eḥad Akum.*
5. See, however, *Melamed Leho'il* vol. 2, responsum 69.
6. Carl Henry Davis, ed., *Gynecology and Obstetrics* ([Hagerstown, Md.: W. F. Prior,] 1937), chap. 10, p. 1.

CHAPTER 13

Prenatal Testing and Abortion*

Kassel Abelson

She'eilah (Question):

The trend to later marriages has raised new questions. Women begin childbearing at a later age, increasing the risk of birth defects in children. Many physicians advise that amniocentesis and/or other prenatal tests be performed to ascertain whether there are detectable birth defects in the fetus. Such tests are also advised for younger women if there may be reason to suspect hereditary genetic defects, or if the parents may be Tay-Sachs carriers. Implicit in these prenatal tests is the assumption that should the fetus have serious defects, the parents will have to choose whether to abort the fetus. What is the Jewish view of abortion? Is it permitted to abort a defective fetus? Should we advise women who fall into categories in which there is a risk of bearing a defective fetus to have such prenatal tests?

Teshuvah (Response):

The question of abortion has long been a troubling one for religious, moral, and economic reasons. Today, the development of medical technology forces us to examine the question anew and to grapple with new aspects of this old question. Though there is no direct reference to abortion in the Torah, the status of the fetus may be inferred from the biblical law concerning injury to a pregnant woman:

*Approved by the Rabbinical Assembly Committee on Jewish Law and Standards, Aug. 1983.

וכי ינצו אנשים ונגפו אשה הרה ויצאו ילדיה ולא יהיה אסון ענוש יענש כאשר ישית עליו בעל האשה ונתן בפללים: ואם אסון יהיה ונתתה נפש תחת נפש

> When men fight, and one of them pushes a pregnant woman and a miscarriage results, but no other damage ensues, the one responsible shall be fined according as the woman's husband may exact from him, the payment to be based on reckoning. But if other damage ensues, the penalty shall be life for life. (Exod. 21:22–23)

It is obvious that the Torah considers the death of the woman a capital offense, while the death of a fetus is a lesser offense, punishable only by a fine. Hence, it seems that the act of destroying the fetus is not considered murder because the Torah does not seem to consider the fetus a person in law. This same attitude toward the status of the fetus is implied in a mishnah, which is the main rabbinic statement on abortion:

האשה שהיא מקשה לילד מחתכין את הולד במעיה ומוציאין אותו אברים אברים מפני שחייה קודמין לחייו יצא רובו אין נוגעין בו שאין דוחין נפש מפני נפש

> If a woman is having difficulty giving birth, the child must be cut in her womb and brought out limb by limb, for her life takes precedence over its life. If the greater part of the child has already come forth, he must not be touched, because one life must not be taken to save another. (*Oholot* 7:6)

An innocent person may not be killed to save the life of another person. However, the fetus in the womb may be destroyed in order to save its mother's life, for it is not a person, and the case is therefore not comparable to the case of killing one person to save the life of another. The Talmud speculates as to why the partially emerged child is spared:

יצא ראשו אין נוגעין בו לפי שאין דוחין נפש מפני נפש ואמאי רודף הוא שאני התם דמשמיא קא רדפי לה

> If the head has emerged he may not be harmed, for we do not take one life to save another. Why? Is he not a *rodeif*, a pursuer? This case is different, for she [the mother] is pursued by heaven. (*Sanhedrin* 72b)

Under normal circumstances, one person may not be killed to save another. However, it is permitted to kill a *rodeif*, a potential murderer, to save the life of the intended victim. The partially emerged child is considered a *nefesh*, a person, but not a *rodeif*, a potential murderer, for the child is innocent of any intention to harm its mother. Since the threat to the mother's life comes from natural causes, there is no reason to kill one *nefesh* to save another.

Rashi makes explicit the underlying principle in his comment on the passage:

> **דכל זמן שלא יצא לאויר העולם לאו נפש הוא וניתן להורגו ולהציל את אמו אבל יצא ראשו אין נוגעים בו להורגו דהוה ליה כילוד ואין דוחין נפש מפני נפש**
>
> Until the child has emerged into the world, it is not considered a person [*lav nefesh hu*], and it is permitted to destroy it to save the mother's life. However, once the head has emerged, it is considered as born, and one may not harm it, for one life may not be taken to save another.

Rashi states clearly that the fetus is not an independent person (*nefesh*). Rather, the fetus acquires the status of person only after it is born. Hence, feticide is not homicide and is permitted. It should be noted, however, that this does not imply blanket permission to kill the fetus. Here, we can conclude that the fetus may only be aborted for therapeutic reasons, to safeguard the mother.

Maimonides interprets the permission for therapeutic abortion in a way that leads to more restrictive conclusions than the talmudic precedents seem to require. In the *Mishneh Torah*, he writes:

> **הרי זו מצות לא תעשה שלא לחוס על נפש הרודף. לפיכך הורו חכמים שהעוברה שהיא מקשה לילד מותר לחתוך העובר במיעיה בין בסם בין ביד מפני שהוא כרודף אחריה להורגה, ואם משהוציא ראשו אין נוגעין בו שאין דוחין נפש מפני נפש וזהו טבעו של עולם**
>
> There is also a negative commandment, that we have no mercy for the life of a pursuer [*rodeif*]. Therefore, our Sages taught that if a woman is having difficulty in childbirth, the fetus may be removed by drugs or surgery, because the fetus is regarded as like a pursuer [*rodeif*] trying to kill her. Once its head has emerged, he may no longer be harmed, because we do not take

> one life to save another. What is happening is natural. (*Hilkhot Rotzeaḥ Ushmirat Nefesh* 1:9; this same position is taken by Joseph Karo in *S.A., Ḥ.M.* 425:2)

Maimonides departed from the simple meaning of the Mishnah and introduced the *rodeif* (pursuer) argument to justify therapeutic abortion. This argument implies that *only* if the mother's life is endangered by the pregnancy is there reason to perform an abortion. However, it follows that if the fetus cannot be shown to be a *rodeif* (endangering its mother's life), then abortion would not be permitted. Rabbi Isaac Klein, in his responsum on abortion, points out:

> There is a clear distinction between the reasoning of Rashi and that of Maimonides. According to Rashi, the embryo is not considered a living thing and therefore the life of the mother takes precedence. According to Maimonides, the life of the mother takes precedence because the embryo is in the position of a *rodeif,* a "pursuer." From this difference in interpretation may also result differences in legal decisions. According to Maimonides, we would permit abortion only when there is clear danger to the life of the mother. According to Rashi, there might be other adequate reasons besides the threat to the life of the mother. (See "A *Teshuvah* on Abortion," by Rabbi Isaac Klein [which appears as chapter 12 of this volume].)

The difference in the approaches of Rashi and Maimonides is reflected in the later responsa literature. Rabbi David Feldman, in his excellent book *Birth Control in Jewish Law,* traces the abortion debate and states:

> What generalizations, then, can be made about the rabbinic attitude to abortion at any time? It can best be described as bifurcating into two directions, both of which will presuppose that the fetus is not a person, yet one approach builds *down* and the other builds *up*. The first can be identified especially with Chief Rabbi Unterman, who sees any abortion as "akin to homicide," and therefore permissible only in cases of corresponding gravity, such as saving the life of the mother (Y. L. Unterman, *Shevet Miyehudah* [1955], pp. 26–30, 49, 50; *No'am* 6 [1963]: 1–11). It then builds down from this strict position to embrace a

> broader interpretation of lifesaving situations which include a threat to her health, for example, as well as a threat to her life. The other viewpoint (identifiable with the late Chief Rabbi Uziel and others, and to which we shall return) assumes no real prohibition against abortion at any time, except perhaps during the most advanced stage of pregnancy, and builds up from this lenient position to safeguard against indiscriminate abortion.[1]

There is no indication in the Mishnah that the fetus is considered a *rodeif,* and the later commentators therefore struggle to explain why Maimonides applied the term to the unborn fetus. Therefore, it appears that the original premise of the Torah, the Mishnah, and the Talmud (that the fetus is not a legal person) is more faithfully expounded by Rashi and those who begin with the premise that there is neither homicide nor even an offense in carrying out an abortion, but who build up from there, holding that an adequate reason is necessary to avoid indiscriminate abortion. However, what constitutes an adequate reason seems to depend on the judgment of the rabbi and the particular circumstances of the case.

Rabbi Feldman cites three authorities who deal with the question of whether it is permitted to abort a fetus conceived in adultery.[2] Rabbi Bachrach (seventeenth century) held that while there is no clear prohibition against abortion, nonetheless, to sanction the abortion of the fruit of adultery would open the door to immorality; therefore, he forbade it. R. Jacob Emden (eighteenth century) not only permitted abortion in such cases, but added that "with legitimate fruit, too, there is room to permit abortion for 'great need,' as long as the birth process has not yet begun, even if the reason is not to save her life—even if only to save her from the 'great pain' it causes her. But the matter requires further deliberation" (*She'eilat Ya'aveitz* no. 43). And R. Yosef Ḥayim ben Eliyahu (nineteenth century) draws the tentative conclusion that "evidently there is room to permit [abortion] when disgrace is involved, which can be called a matter of 'great need.' " However, he adds, "But I am issuing no ruling, merely placing the above before you for consultation with (another) sage" (*Responsa of Rav Pe'alim* vol. 1, *E.H.* no. 4). This trend of thought is carried to its logical conclusion by Rabbi Uziel:

> It is clear that abortion is not permitted without reason. That would be destructive and frustrative of the possibility of life.

> But for a reason, even if it is a *slim reason* [*ta'am kalush*], such as to prevent her *nivul* [disgrace], then we have precedent and authority to permit it. (*Mishpetei Uziel* vol. 3, *Ḥ.M.* no. 47; see translation from Feldman, 289–91)

Rabbi Uziel considers the woman's pain as the deciding factor in determining whether there may be an abortion. He does not differentiate between life-threatening situations and those that are detrimental to health. Even mental anguish, a sense of shame, fear of disgrace, or even a slight reason such as fear of disfigurement, would be sufficient to allow abortion.

Most authorities who follow this trend of thinking consider only the mother's physical welfare and mental well-being as determining factors in deciding whether there should be an abortion. However, there are authorities who have taken into consideration factors other than the mother's pain. Rabbi Isaac Klein quotes a responsum by Rabbi Yitzḥak Oelbaum (*Ḥayei Sarah* I, 5709), in which Rabbi Oelbaum would permit an abortion for a nursing mother if there were expert evidence that the pregnancy would affect the mother's milk and would endanger the life of the sickly child who is nursing. A new factor has been introduced here that goes beyond therapeutic abortion: the life and welfare of another child.[3] Another noted authority, Rabbi Eliezer Yehudah Waldenberg, also takes into account the future and the well-being of the fetus. He states: "If there is a substantial risk that the fetus would be born with a deformity that would cause it to suffer, it is permitted to terminate the pregnancy within the first three months."[4] Rabbi Waldenberg adds that "in circumstances where it has been conclusively proven (i.e., by amniocentesis) that the fetus will be afflicted with Tay-Sachs disease, it is permitted to perform an abortion up to the seventh month of pregnancy."[5]

New techniques of prenatal testing developed in recent years enable the testing of the fetus for life-threatening conditions and for genetic abnormalities. Most commonly used by doctors for women of all ages is ultrasound. Ultrasound employs sound waves to form live video images of some parts of the fetus that are invisible to X rays. Ultrasound can show at an early stage whether the fetus is maturing as it should, and it can reveal several different kinds of birth defects—especially malformations of the skeleton, such as some forms of dwarfism.

Amniocentesis is commonly offered to pregnant women over the age of thirty-five. A physician inserts a sharp syringe through the abdominal wall into the uterus and draws off a small quantity of the amniotic fluid that bathes the developing fetus. Cells that the fetus has cast off float in the fluid and are examined for clues to fetal well-being.

As women age, they run an increased risk of having a child with the wrong number of chromosomes. The most common chromosomal error leads to Down's syndrome, the largest single cause of severe mental retardation. Amniotic fluid can also contain high levels of AFP (alpha fetoprotein), which indicates that the fetus may be afflicted with one of two common congenital malformations—anencephaly and spina bifida, or neural tube defects. When doctors suspect that a woman may give birth to a child with a particular disorder, the amniotic fluid may be examined for other conditions, including nearly 100 rare genetic diseases, among them Tay-Sachs disease, which is a degenerative disease of the central nervous system. Tay-Sachs disease begins to manifest itself in an infant of six months with weakness, followed by progressive mental and motor deterioration, blindness, paralysis, dementia, seizures, and death, usually by three years of age. The incidence of this disease among Ashkenazic Jews is 100 times more frequent than in the non-Jewish population.

Give the horrible fate that awaits a Tay-Sachs baby, it is not surprising that Rabbi Waldenberg singles out Tay-Sachs disease, and permits abortion of the fetus, even to the seventh month. The seventh month is allowed in this case, though most abortions would be permissible only in the first trimester, because doctors do not perform amniocentesis until the end of the fourth month of pregnancy, when sufficient fluid is available. Most tests of the amniotic fluid then take three or four weeks to complete. Rabbi Waldenberg evidently permits sufficient time for the information to be gathered, a decision to be made by the parents, and the abortion to be performed. The amniocentesis test itself is safe, with few unfavorable side effects to fetus or mother (estimated at 1 percent or less).

At present, all prenatal diagnosis must be performed during the second trimester. However, new tests are being developed, among them the chorion biopsy, where a sample of tissue is taken from the trophoblast (which derives from the fertilized egg and is genetically identical with the fetus) and not from the fetus itself. These tests can be performed in the first trimester of the pregnancy, will be less expensive, and will probably be even safer than amniocentesis. The increased knowledge of the development of the fetus and the genetic defects of the fetus means that parents will have to make decisions based on information not available to previous generations, for whom there were no "windows on the womb."[6]

Conclusion

There is clear precedent in the tradition, as it has developed to our day, to permit abortion of a fetus to save a mother's life, to safeguard her health, or even for "a very thin reason," such as to spare her physical pain or mental anguish. Some recent authorities also consider the well-being of other children, and the future of the fetus itself, as reasons to permit abortion. All agree that there must be a reason to justify the destruction of the potential person the fetus will become after birth.

If there is reason to believe that the fetus may be defective, it is advisable for the mother to undergo amniocentesis and/or other prenatal tests. If the tests indicate that the child will be born with major defects that would preclude a normal life and that make the mother and the family anxious about the future, it is permitted to abort the fetus.

The rabbi should meet with the mother (and the father) and explain the approach of Jewish law to abortion. He should indicate the gravity of the act of aborting the fetus, as well as the extenuating circumstances that Jewish law considers as justification for an abortion. The rabbi should recommend a full discussion with the father and other members of the family, in consultation with a physician and a psychiatrist, to help the mother understand the impact the abortion will have on her and on other members of the family. The final decision should be made by the mother in consultation with the family.

Notes

1. David Feldman, *Marital Relations, Birth Control, and Abortion in Jewish Law* (New York: Schocken, 1974), 284 [originally published as *Birth Control in Jewish Law*].
2. Ibid., 288–89.
3. See Isaac Klein, "A *Teshuvah* on Abortion" [which appears as chap. 12 of this vol.]. See also Responsa *Ḥayim Veshalom* vol. 1, no. 40; Responsa *Beit Yehudah, E.H.* no. 14; *Tzitz Eliezer* vol. 9, no. 51:13.

4. *Tzitz Eliezer* 9:237; see also Avraham Steinberg, *Jewish Medical Law* (Jerusalem; Anaheim, Calif.: Gefen Publishing, 1980), 103.
5. In Steinberg, 103.
6. T. M. Powledge, "Windows on the Womb," *American Psychology* (June 1980): 47–53; Mitchell Golbus, "The Current Scope of Antenatal Diagnosis," *Hospital Practice* 17 (1982): 179–86.

CHAPTER 14

Abortion: Major Wrong or Basic Right?*

Robert Gordis

She'eilah (Question):

Is abortion permitted according to Jewish law? What guidance would Jewish law offer for social policy?

Teshuvah (Response):

Undoubtedly, the most highly charged issue in the area of sexual ethics in our time is abortion. The question is by no means limited to the United States. Controversy has swirled around the problem everywhere—in Catholic Italy, in the State of Israel, and in Communist China, to cite only a few countries. In Italy, the long struggle by the Roman Catholic Church against legalizing abortion proved unavailing, and the Parliament adopted a highly permissive law on the subject. In the State of Israel, one study claimed that 46.7 percent of all Israeli women had had at least one abortion by the time they reached the age of forty. Estimates of the number of abortions in the country range from 40,000 to 70,000 a year. The Orthodox rabbinate fought strenuously against legalizing the practice. Its efforts ended in failure, when the Israeli Knesset adopted an abortion law on 31 January 1977, the provisions of which will be discussed below. In Communist China, abortion is recognized not merely as legal but as an act worthy of praise as a service to the revolution.

*Approved by the Rabbinical Assembly Committee on Jewish Law and Standards, Aug. 1983. The explicit statement of the *she'eilah* (question) has been added by the editor.

In the United States, as we have seen, there has been a steady rise in the rate of *reported* abortions in recognized hospitals and by reputable physicians, ever since the practice was legalized in most of the states of the Union. The adjective in italics is important because its significance has often been overlooked in heated discussions on the subject. Available data indicate that legal abortions are on the increase among both married and unmarried women. For the former, it serves as a method of family limitation, especially after the birth of a number of children. The rate of abortion has been rising even more rapidly in the case of unmarried women, for self-evident reasons.

From a purely rational point of view, one would have imagined that abortions would have declined in popularity in view of the ready availability of contraceptive means, which do not entail the destruction of incipient life. In this connection, one would have thought that the old adage applied: "An ounce of prevention is worth a pound of cure." Nevertheless, hundreds of thousands of women—and the number is increasing—are undergoing abortions. The reason may be ignorance or negligence, or the fact that sexual intercourse had not been expected and the partners therefore were not prepared with contraceptives. One must also suspect that the rapid rise in abortions and the call for abortion on demand point to another disquieting factor—a lack of sensitivity with regard to the moral issues that may be involved.

During the past few decades, many states of the Union have legalized abortion within their borders, some with various limitations. These statutes have been challenged in the courts, but they were upheld by the Supreme Court in 1976; the Court reaffirmed the right of a woman to decide whether she would undergo an abortion. Many of the restrictions subsequently imposed by state legislatures have been declared unconstitutional on the grounds that they were basically efforts to circumvent the original Court decision.

The victories that the right-to-abortion forces have achieved in legislatures and the courts have stimulated the unfortunate tendency, to which Americans are particularly prone, of identifying the legal with the moral and concluding that what the law permits is, therefore, ethically sound. This fallacy is particularly disastrous in the area of personal morality and family ethics.

The acceptance of abortion as legitimate is far from unanimous. On the contrary, it has evoked passionate opposition from the Right to Life movement and other groups whose original impetus derived from Catholic theology but whose ranks include people of other persuasions as well. What the antiabortion movement may lack in numbers and practical influence is largely compensated for by its zeal and dedication. All Americans, including those who do not share its position, owe the movement a debt of gratitude for reminding the American people that moral issues cannot be settled merely by a majority in the legislature or by the decisions of judges.

Catholicism has been confronted by some special theological problems. For many centuries, Catholic theologians have debated the casuistic question of "ensoulment," i.e., just when the soul enters the fetus. The consensus among Catholic theologians, at least up to the present, has been that the soul enters the fetus at the moment of conception, so that the destruction of the embryo is tantamount to murder. Moreover, since Augustine, the Church has taught that an embryo must be baptized if it is not to suffer eternal damnation. These theological attitudes explain the passion with which the Catholic clergy and many of the laity react against abortion.

In view of the heat with which the issue is argued today, it is of interest to note that Catholic teaching on the subject has fluctuated through time. In the fourth century, Saint Basil condemned abortion at any stage, but the Code of Justinian in the sixth century exempted from penalty abortions during the first forty days of pregnancy. This position was reaffirmed repeatedly by papal decree for nearly ten centuries. In 1588, Pope Sistus V declared all abortions to be murder, but less than three years later, Gregory XIV rescinded his decree. Not until 1869 was the prohibition reinstituted by Pope Pius IX.[1] It is this position that is now official Catholic doctrine.

What are the facts on the attitude of Jewish tradition toward abortion? The first point to bear in mind is that Catholic theological problems such as ensoulment and baptism have no counterparts in Judaism. In Jewish sources, random speculations as to when life begins are to be encountered, but they play no significant role in connection with abortion. In fact, Jewish law has a variety of time periods applicable to different issues as to when a newborn child is *bar kayama* (independent and viable). To cite one familiar example, the *pidyon habein* (the redemption of the firstborn) does not take place until the thirty-first day of the baby's life. What is fundamental is that halakhah explicitly recognizes that the fetus is not a viable being while it is in its mother's womb, since its life cannot be sustained outside its natural shelter there.

The basic sources on abortion in the Bible and the Talmud are very sparse. In Exodus 21:22–25, we read:

> When men strive together and hurt a woman with child, so that there is a miscarriage, and yet no harm follows, the one who hurt her shall be fined, according as the woman's husband shall lay upon him; and he shall pay as the judges determine. If any harm follows, then you shall give a life for a life, an eye for an eye, a tooth for a tooth, a hand for a hand, a foot for a foot.

In other words, the Torah commands that if the woman is not injured and only the fetus is destroyed in the encounter ("no harm follows"), there is to be financial compensation to the husband for the embryo. But if the woman is killed or hurt ("if any harm follows") as a result of the quarrel, the assailant is guilty of a capital or major crime. The destruction of the fetus is clearly not treated as coequal with the death of the mother in the text of the Hebrew Bible.

However, an alleged biblical source for a prohibition of abortion has been derived from this same passage, on the basis of an enigmatic and an almost certainly erroneous translation of the Hebrew text in the Septuagint. This ancient Greek version renders the Hebrew word *ason* ("harm," "injury") inexplicably as "form," "shape," a meaning for which scholars are unable to offer a warrant or even a credible explanation.[2] The passage then emerges as "But if [the embryo] be perfectly formed, you shall give a life for a life."[3] This dubious rendering has been used in the Christian Church as a biblical support for treating abortion as murder.

The second passage bearing directly upon the subject of therapeutic abortion occurs in rabbinic literature. The Mishnah reads:

> If a woman is having difficulty in childbirth (so that her life is endangered), one cuts off the embryo, limb by limb, because her life takes precedence over its life. If most of the fetus (or the head) has emerged, it may not be hurt, for we do not set one life aside for the sake of another. (*Oholot* 7:6)

This classical passage clearly embodies the principle that the fetus is a limb of its mother.[4] In Rashi's words, "The life of the mother in childbirth takes precedence over that of the embryo to the very last moment of pregnancy."[5]

Maimonides, who summarizes this provision of the Mishnah in his code, adds an explanation that has had the practical effect of limiting the permissibility of abortion among some later authorities. He explains that the permission to destroy the embryo set forth in the Mishnah is due to the fact that the embryo is "like a pursuer seeking to kill the mother."[6] This explanation would seem to permit abortion only when and if the mother's life is in danger. This interpretation of Maimonides, which Feldman rightly calls "a surprising position,"[7] is clearly more restrictive than the talmudic provision.

I would suggest that the reason that Maimonides and other medieval codifiers diverge from the Mishnah may inhere in the same conditions that led them to disregard the clear talmudic warrants for birth control. They were leaders of a community perpetually engaged in a desperate struggle for survival against disease, expulsion, and massacre. They felt keenly the necessity for bringing many children into the world and thus preserving the Jewish people against extinction. Since group survival took precedence over individual well-being, they sought to limit such practices as abortion and birth control, or to forbid them altogether, in spite of the clear provisions in the Mishnah and the Talmud.

Many later authorities attempted to explain away Maimonides' limitation and to harmonize it with the broader principle laid down in the Mishnah, a discussion that has continued to the present.[8] While some would restrict the provision permitting abortion only to cases in which the mother's life is in danger, the majority of decisions recognize that physical injury to the mother, even if death is not involved, should also be legitimate grounds for abortion.

Other factors also command impressive rabbinic support. Some authorities explicitly permit an abortion if the pregnancy adversely affects the feeding of an existing child. The dominant attitude of the halakhah, which is derived from the mishnaic statement already quoted, is summarized by Rabbi Ben Zion Uziel, former chief rabbi of Israel, who declared that abortion is permitted even for "a very thin reason," such as avoiding pain for the mother.[9] The mother's anguish at the possibility of bearing a defective child is also admitted as grounds for abortion. So is the element of disgrace and the threat of suicide by a woman who has been raped or has become pregnant as a result of adultery. The twentieth-century authority Rabbi Yeḥiel Weinberg ruled that "the authorities who differ with Maimonides are *in the majority,*" and he therefore agreed with Rabbi Jacob Emden in permitting abortion to spare the mother pain.[10]

In spite of the luxuriant variety of views and nuances to be found in rabbinic sources, it is clear that the halakhah on abortion may be fairly described as lenient. It surely cannot be regarded as establishing a blanket prohibition. Indeed, the broad interpretation of the rabbinic attitude is entirely justified, since it is a fundamental principle of the Mishnah, amply confirmed by modern medicine, that an embryo is not an independent living being.

The rabbinic discussions on the subject are primarily concerned with therapeutic abortions. There are several types of abortion that may be described as extensions of the therapeutic category into the mental area. On these, a broad consensus of agreement probably exists in contemporary society, except possibly for some of those bound closely to Catholic dogma. Earlier Jewish authorities devote little attention to the problem of women who become pregnant as a result of incest or rape, yet undoubtedly, both these evils existed in the past. Perhaps we are more conscious of these crimes today because of a greater recognition of women as independent personalities. Whatever the reason, it will be generally agreed that the victims of such atrocities have already undergone major psychological trauma even if they did not suffer additional physical violence.

To permit such a pregnancy to run its course means to bring into the world a permanent reminder of the terror and the shame that the woman experienced at the time the crime was committed. Furthermore, the child would forever bind her to one who had viciously violated the sanctity of her person. Moreover, the child himself, who is totally free from guilt, would carry a stigma almost too heavy to bear throughout his life. Moreover, since a human being is an amalgam of spirit and body, the mental well-being of the mother is as important as her physical health.

There is warrant in rabbinic responsa for permitting abortion if the mother is deeply concerned about the health of her unborn child.[11] If, therefore, there is a possibility that the child may be born defective because the mother is a drug addict or has taken some medication with aftereffects dangerous to the offspring, the pregnant woman's worry is sufficient grounds for an abortion because of the debilitating effects psychologically or otherwise on her well-being. Under any of these circumstances, few would be disposed to oppose abortions designed to prevent a major traumatic episode from being converted into a lifetime tragedy. These instances may fairly be regarded as falling within a broadened category of therapeutic abortion.

While therapeutic abortions are by no means negligible in number, the gravamen of the struggle today lies in the area of nontherapeutic abortions, where the woman simply does not wish to have the child born—so-called abortion on demand. Her motive may be the size of her family or the fact that she is unmarried or simply a desire not to be burdened by the responsibility of child-raising.

On the one hand, it may be argued that there is no urgency to permit such nontherapeutic abortions, particularly in view of the variety of moral issues that have been raised with regard to the right to life of the unborn fetus. On the other hand, we have seen that such issues as ensoulment and the baptism of unborn infants are strictly dogmatic in character and are applicable only to believing Catholics.[12] For other elements of the population in general, and for Jews in particular, the weight of authoritative opinion, both religious and scientific, does not regard the fetus as a viable and independent human being or abortion as murder.[13]

When, therefore, a woman asks for an abortion for one of the reasons mentioned, we cannot in justice ignore several other aspects of the situation that are of valid social and ethical concern. What destiny awaits a child who cannot be properly cared for, because he is being born into a family where there are already far too many mouths to feed? What about a child who is not wanted because he is the result of extramarital intercourse? In the latter case, does the mother deserve lifelong punishment for a single indiscretion? What about the handicaps for a child growing up in a home without a father, from which the mother is often absent, with no one to supervise and guide the youngster because she must work for a living? Think what we may of a woman who does not wish to bear and raise a child simply because she consults only her own convenience and comfort, what environment awaits an unwanted child born under such circumstances? A study of the mounting tide of child abuse and child murder by parents might well disclose this attitude as a motive for crime.[14]

Finally, we cannot ignore the fact that all too often the issue is not whether an abortion is to take place, but under what circumstances. Will it be done through proper procedures by experts, or under unsanitary and dangerous conditions by incompetents or charlatans who threaten the life or health of the mother? We cannot overlook the fact that the affluent and the well-educated have always had access to abortions on demand. All that is being asked is to make the same procedures available to the poor and the underprivileged as well. In effect, opposition to legalizing properly performed abortions on demand amounts to a flagrant form of economic discrimination. Not altogether unjustly, therefore, the movement against legalizing abortion is often charged with being both hysterical and hypocritical.

It is no wonder that the liberalization of abortion laws is proceeding apace throughout the world. In 1976, a United Nations study found that two-thirds of the world's population lived in countries where legal abortion was relatively easy, as compared with only one-third five years earlier. During the last decade, thirty-three countries have liberalized their abortion laws, and twelve permit abortion on demand during the first three months of pregnancy. The record discloses that no democratic nation has ever moved to make abortion more restricted.[15]

Do these considerations effectively dispose of the case against abortion on demand and justify the practice? Such a conclusion would be premature. The alleged right of abortion on demand is generally supported by the argument that a woman has rights over her own body. This is a contention that Judaism, and indeed all high religion, must reject on both theological and ethical grounds as being essentially a pagan doctrine. It is basic Jewish teaching that no human being is master of his own body, because he did not create himself; male and female alike have been fashioned by God in His image.

This conviction lies at the heart of the Jewish insight that in addition to *mitzvot bein adam lamakom* (commandments between a person and God) and *mitzvot bein adam laḥavero* (commandments between person and person), we may posit another category, *bein adam le'atzmo* (obligations and prohibitions between person and self). These include debasing one's character through degrading habits and demeaning actions, injuring one's body through addictive drugs or excessive drinking, or other sins of the first magnitude. When the human body and the human spirit are injured, a sin is committed against the handiwork and the property of God. This is the root of the religious prohibitions of suicide and of self-mutilation.

Moreover, abortion on demand is a threat to a basic ethical principle that Judaism enunciated centuries before Albert Schweitzer. An embryo in its mother's body is not actually a living creature, but it is potential life, not to be lightly cast aside. Obviously, what is only potential must be sacrificed when necessary for saving what is actual, but where no such threat exists, potential life, too, must be safeguarded. When an embryo is aborted, we are, in the fine rabbinic phrase, "diminishing the divine image in which man is fashioned."[16]

In sum, while the law does not categorically rule out abortion, since it is not "murder," the spirit of Judaism, reinforced by a realistic understanding of human motivation, must look askance at any blanket provision for abortion on demand. Long before Albert Schweitzer enunciated his justly famous ethical doctrine, Judaism sought to inculcate in its adherents—and largely succeeded—reverence for life and hatred of violence and bloodshed.

This all-important principle is imperiled today. If the law were to remove all conditions and restrictions, the increased practice of abortion on demand would further erode reverence for life, which has already been tragically weakened in our violence-riddled society. It cannot be denied that the casual attitude toward potential life implied in the practice is one more instance among many of the cheapening of life in contemporary society.

Are we confronted once again by an insoluble dilemma? On the one hand, refusal to legalize abortion is obviously discriminatory. On the other hand, permitting abortion on demand means sanctioning a practice that at best is ethically dubious and socially corrosive. Such permission undermines what is perhaps the most sacred value in the Hebraic tradition, the sense of life as holy.

Actually, the contradiction involved in balancing opposite positions and opposing what is legally permitted is only apparent. It can be understood as an extension of the traditional rabbinic doctrine of *seyag* (a fence around the law), a "margin of protection" to safeguard a fundamental article of faith or practice. It may also be suggested that here we have another illustration of the valuable tension between law and society that has been noted in the attitude of the Jewish tradition toward divorce and birth control. The law on abortion is and should be liberal, to meet genuine cases of hardship and misery that are not soluble in any other way. But society has an obligation to educate its members to ethical standards that rise above the level of abortion on demand. In other words, abortion should be legally available but ethically restricted, to be practiced only for very good reasons. Men and women must be persuaded that though the abortion of a fetus is not equivalent to taking an actual life, it does represent the destruction of potential life and must not be undertaken lightly or flippantly.

Until the day comes when ethical standards suffice to govern the actions of men and women without the use of external restraint, how is this tension to be resolved? We must have recourse to secular law, which alone has the power to enforce its norms. Here, blanket permissibility would be almost as morally and socially catastrophic as a total ban.

On 31 January 1977, the Israeli Knesset adopted a new law on abortion that was strenuously opposed by the Orthodox rabbinate and did not please Israeli feminists. Nevertheless, the provisions of the law are both realistic and humane and might well serve as a model for other countries. Under Israeli law, abortion is permitted if carried out in a recognized medical institution, with the woman's approval, and according to one or more of the following criteria: if the birth would endanger the woman's life or injure her physical or emotional health; if it can be determined that the child would be born either physically or mentally handicapped; if the pregnancy was the result of rape, incestuous relations, or intercourse outside of marriage; if the woman is under the age of sixteen or over forty.

Obviously, there can be no totally satisfactory solution to the abortion problem, which is itself a symptom of a tragedy. The choice of the lesser of two evils must be the goal in guiding society to a rational decision. So long as we must depend upon a legal system rather than upon the human conscience to enforce an ethical code, it is clear that the best solution lies in preserving a basically liberal attitude toward abortion with conservative safeguards. That is to say, proper facilities for an abortion should be generally available to all classes of the population, while precautionary procedures must be established in special cases.

Over and above its intrinsic value, such a system of checks and balances would represent a protest against the pagan notion that human beings are absolute masters, either of the world about them or of their own persons, or of burgeoning life within them. The triumph of paganism today, as in the past, must lead to moral catastrophe and the destruction of civilization.

Notes

1. This history of the question in Catholicism is conveniently summarized in David Feldman's *Marital Relations, Birth Control, and Abortion in Jewish Law* (New York: Schocken, 1974), 269. He presents a detailed summary of the rabbinic sources in "Abortion," pt. 5 of his excellent volume, 251–94. Our approach to the issue and the conclusions we have drawn from the vast amount of often contradictory data that he has assembled are our own and diverge at times from the views he apparently holds.
2. The Hebrew words for "form," or "shape," *tzelem, demut, tzurah,* are all totally unlike the Hebrew *ason* in appearance or in sound.
3. The Septuagint interpretation is followed by Philo, as well as by the Samaritans and the Karaites. Aptowitzer regards this interpretation as a compromise between Plato, who held the fetus to be dependent upon its mother, and the Stoics, who held it to be an independent living human being. See *Jewish Quarterly Review* 15 (1924): 114, and Feldman, *Marital Relations,* 259. Actually, the

Septuagint seems to be an approximation of the Stoic position rather than a compromise.

4. *Ubar yerekh imo* (*Ḥullin* 58a; see also *Gittin* 23b). The phrase, as Feldman points out, is the equivalent of the Latin *pars viscerum matris* or *spes animati.*
5. See Rashi and Meiri on *Sanhedrin* 72b, "The fetus in the womb is not a living being [*lav nefesh hu*]."
6. *M.T., Hilkhot Rotzeaḥ Ushmirat Nefesh* 1:9.
7. Feldman, *Marital Relations,* 277.
8. In Feldman, *Marital Relations,* 284–94, a large number of varied responsa are collected and summarized.
9. *Ta'am kalush,* Feldman, *Marital Relations,* 291.
10. *No'am* 9 (1966): 193–215.
11. See responsa cited on the subject by Feldman, *Marital Relations,* 285–86.
12. See Leo Pfeffer, "Abortion and Religious Freedom," *Congress Monthly* (June 1976): 9–12.
13. A strongly negative approach to abortion is espoused by Rabbi Immanuel Jakobovits in "Jewish Views on Abortion," in David T. Smith, *Abortion and the Law* (Cleveland: Western Reserve University, 1967), chap. 6. The impulse to be more Catholic than the pope apparently continues to prove irresistible. His view is energetically rebutted by Feldman, *Marital Relations,* 294 n. 144.
14. On this growing problem, see the *New York Times,* 1 Febr. 1977.
15. According to a report by the International Planned Parenthood Federation, published in the *New York Times,* 1 Febr. 1977.
16. *Mema'atim et hademut* (*Yevamot* 63b). The phrase is applied to those who avoid procreation (without reference to abortion).

III. RESPONSIBILITIES AT THE END OF LIFE

E. MEDICAL CARE AT THE END OF LIFE

Introduction

Treatment decisions at the end of life are among the most common, and the most wrenching, issues in bioethics. In countries such as the United States, most deaths are accompanied by decisions about forgoing life-sustaining treatment. These include dramatic decisions to terminally wean a patient from a respirator, controversial decisions to forgo artificial nutrition and hydration, and simple and sometimes implicit decisions not to try yet another round of chemotherapy. Choices about forgoing treatment can be informed by values and precedents of traditional halakhic discourse. They also have generated extensive discussion in general bioethics.

Rabbis Avram I. Reisner and Elliot N. Dorff draw on both traditional halakhah and contemporary bioethics in major papers approved in 1990. For the convenience of the reader, Reisner's paper is presented here in two chapters, and Dorff's in three. What is presented here as Dorff's first essay is "Methodological Concerns for a Jewish Approach." Here he argues in favor of the legal model of traditional halakhah in addressing new ethical challenges. Such a model reflects continuity with the tradition and offers clear guidance for individuals.

At the same time, Dorff advocates a reading of the tradition that is neither literalist nor simplistic, and suggests that flexible values and policy goals (termed "principles"), rather than absolute rules, are central in formulating a halakhic stance.

Theoretical arguments of each author are presented below in chapters subtitled "Halakhic Concepts and Values." Both articulate Jewish commitments that include the value of life, the responsibility to seek healing, concern to benefit the patient and avoid suffering, and attention to the patient's autonomous judgments (pp. 241–53, 309–16). At the theoretical level, two key differences separate the authors. First, Reisner identifies the tradition's central precedents as those involving the *goseis,* a dying patient (pp. 245–47). In this, he agrees with most halakhic authorities who have discussed these issues. Dorff argues, however, that the paradigm of *tereifah,* a patient with an incurable disease, better fits contemporary clinical realities and affords welcome room for case-by-case judgments on appropriate treatment (pp. 316–25). A second difference concerns the understanding of the patient's benefit and the prolongation of life. For Dorff, a key ethical guidepost emerging from the tradition is to provide treatment that is beneficial for the patient. While life-sustaining treatment is generally beneficial, in some cases therapy could fail to offer benefit even if it is effective in prolonging life (pp. 311–14). For Reisner, traditional sources consider the prolongation of life to be inherently beneficial, and mandate the continuation of life regardless of its quality or duration. Reisner would allow impediments to the dying process to be removed in order to allow for a natural death, in accord with our best understanding of God's will (pp. 241–49, 256–57).

Each author's theoretical analysis is followed with a chapter subtitled "Practical Applications." The authors share much common ground on the guidance that halakhah offers for treatment decisions near the end of life. For both, hospice can be a legitimate option; near the end of life, a patient may choose the supportive and palliative care offered in this setting "in order to live one's remaining days in the best way possible" (pp. 251–52, 338–39). Decisions to forgo cardiopulmonary resuscitation (CPR) and respirators may be made in appropriate cases (pp. 267–69, 339–48). People while healthy may complete advance directives, such as proxy directives and living wills, to guide their treatment should need arise (assuming that the decisions are themselves consistent with halakhah) (pp. 270–72, 354–55). A patient who has irreversibly lost all brain function (including the brain stem), meeting medical whole brain death criteria, is recognized as dead by Jewish law (pp. 247–48, 278–81, 351).

Key disagreements between the authors concern the provision of medication, such as antibiotics, and artificial nutrition and hydration. For Reisner, these treatments cannot be seen as impediments to the dying process; they should be provided whenever they would be effective in prolonging life (pp. 265–67, 272–73). For Dorff, such interventions, like others, might fail to benefit a dying patient even if they are effective in prolonging life; accordingly, they may be forgone in appropriate cases for terminally ill or permanently unconscious patients (pp. 348–54).

The papers are preceded by a brief summary of some of the key differences between the authors, "*Mai Beinaihu*?: Dorff and Reisner on Medical Care for the Terminally Ill."

CHAPTER 15

Mai Beinaihu?: Dorff and Reisner on Medical Care for the Terminally Ill*

Avram I. Reisner

In the spirit of the talmudic interrogative *Mai beinaihu?* the Subcommittee on Biomedical Ethics of the CJLS undertook a careful consideration of the practical differences of law that remain between the presentations of Rabbi Reisner and Rabbi Dorff. It was felt that, although the legal reasoning differs strongly, both papers tend toward a consensus of treatment in most areas, which would perhaps obviate the need to fight it out on theoretical grounds. The following are our conclusions:

The primary difference in theory between the positions of Rabbi Reisner and Rabbi Dorff may be summarized by their key phrases: in Rabbi Reisner's words, "Neither the quality of life nor its likely short duration is admitted as a mitigating circumstance," as against Rabbi Dorff, "The fetus and the *tereifah* are both cases of human beings whose blood is indeed judged to be 'less red' than that of viable people." Rabbi Reisner insists on the inviolability of the principle of protecting even *ḥayei sha'ah*, life of short duration, whereas Rabbi Dorff feels that principle is made moot by the status of *tereifah* and the need to consider the patient's best interests (*avdinan letovato*). Rabbi Dorff might center his objection to Rabbi Reisner's paper in the comment that it is too literalist and not sufficiently alert to the real emotional needs of patients and their families. Rabbi Reisner might frame his

*A summary statement submitted to the Rabbinical Assembly Committee on Jewish Law and Standards, Dec. 1990.

objection to Rabbi Dorff's paper in the comment that it arrives at its sensitivity to patients by degrading the status of their God-given lives, which we are constrained not to do.

Nevertheless, both agree in principle and practice on the large area of autonomy that the patient holds with regard to his own treatment where risk and prognostic uncertainty exist, as they almost always do. Thus, both would allow patients to rule certain treatment options off-limits, to choose hospice care as a treatment option, and to draft advance directive documents but only within the parameters established to be in accord with Jewish law. Both permit withdrawal of mechanical life support where unsupported life has been shown to be impossible, under the primary precedent of removing impediments to the death of a *goseis*. Both are in agreement concerning the use of CPR and DNR orders, though for fundamentally different reasons. They agree that CPR need not be done when it is unlikely to succeed in restoring the patient to a meaningfully healthy life. That is perforce a medical judgment call. It is not clear that they would adjudge all cases equally, but on a case-by-case basis, this judgment will fall neither to Rabbi Dorff nor to Rabbi Reisner, but to the family's attending physician, and any member of the clergy advising the family.

The points on which Rabbis Dorff and Reisner differ are few, but significant.

A. With regard to medication to treat a terminally ill patient and with regard to artificial nutrition/hydration:

Rabbi Dorff would permit withholding or withdrawing such medication, since the patient is categorized as a *tereifah,* whose life does not require our full protection. Rabbi Dorff would assimilate artificial nutrition/hydration to medication in such a case.

Rabbi Reisner would prohibit withholding medication, nutrition, or hydration as long as they are believed to be beneficial, since we are obligated to maintain even *ḥayei sha'ah* (N.B.: and as long as the patient has not ruled out said treatment in a valid treatment directive).

B. With regard to the patient in a persistent vegetative state:

Rabbi Dorff would permit withholding/withdrawal of artificial nutrition and hydration, viewing this patient, like the *tereifah,* as an impaired life (N.B.: after due tests and time, of course).

Rabbi Reisner finds no grounds for denying even this limited life, and therefore requires full maintenance pending God's own determination.

C. With regard to pain relief:

Both Rabbis Dorff and Reisner regard treatment for pain as medical treatment to be pursued. They differ on the question of "double effect"—of whether pain medication must be capped at that point at which its probable effect would be to hasten the patient's death.

Rabbi Dorff argues that the intent to alleviate pain controls. Rabbi Reisner argues that the probable result controls. Although they do not argue this point clearly in terms of the primary premises of their papers, it appears clear that Rabbi Reisner's concern for *ḥayei sha'ah* and Rabbi Dorff's vacating of that principle inform their rulings here.

Both Rabbis Dorff and Reisner point out, however, that the best medicine available today should permit sufficient relief of pain without approaching this dilemma; both hope that it quickly recedes to a footnote about antiquated medical ethical problems.

D. A minor note:

Rabbi Dorff's reasoning and a citation of his source, Dr. Sinclair, in chapter 19, appear to permit the early termination of a terminally ill patient for purposes of saving life through organ transplants. It is clear that Rabbi Reisner would disapprove. It is unclear whether Rabbi Dorff would care to proceed, in fact, upon the logic of that position.

We note these matters in this statement of reconciliation so that both powerful attempts to deal with one of today's greatest ethical and halakhic dilemmas might be properly read and understood side by side. We believe that both represent cogent, Conservative responses to the demands of God's Torah and our times, and commend them, as such, to the attention of the full Committee on Jewish Law and Standards.

CHAPTER 16

Care for the Terminally Ill: Halakhic Concepts and Values*

Avram I. Reisner

פקוח נפש מצוה רבה היא הזריז הר"ז משובח הנשאל מגונה השואל שופך דמים וכ"ש המתיאש ואינו עושה

Saving life is a great mitzvah. Who approaches it with alacrity is praised, who hesitates is despicable, who questions it is guilty of murder, and certainly so, one who despairs and does not do it.

—*Naḥmanides, Torat Ha'adam*

She'eilah (Question):

Increasingly, modern medical progress puts us face-to-face with a terrible dilemma: How do we treat a patient who is clearly beyond our powers of healing?

Teshuvah (Response):

There was a time when the medical profession could do little in such a

*Chapters 16–17 present material that originally appeared in the form of one longer paper, "A Halakhic Ethic of Care for the Terminally Ill." This paper was approved by the Rabbinical Assembly Committee on Jewish Law and Standards, Dec. 1990.

case, beyond providing certain rudimentary comforts and companionship until the touch of the Angel of Death accomplished its mission. Today, however, medical technologies have progressed to the point where we can deflect and delay the divine decree for a time, sometimes an extended time, though we do so without any hope of returning the patient to health. The results, it must be said, are often terrible to behold. An unresponsive patient, breathing with the aid of a respirator, fed through a nasogastric feeding tube, periodically resuscitated from cardiac-arrest crises, might be so maintained for months while the family tries to juggle the demands of their lives with the demands of hospital visits and a guilty grief that cannot be relieved through any proximate consolation. A patient in an advanced stage of cancer may suffer months of pain (and the stupor induced by the pain and by the drugs to fight the pain) while the family stands by helpless. Are we, in such cases, as patients, as relatives, as Jewish physicians, to hold on as long as we can, come what may, or is there a reprieve, a dispensation to do less than we can in order to find a quicker, more merciful death—what has come to be known as "death with dignity"?

The answer to these questions must surely be placed at God's doorstep, for the essential problem, the knot that we must untie, is the nature and value of life and death and the obligations that those most remarkable of God's creations place upon us. The specifics are new, but the dilemma flows directly from mankind's eating from the Tree of Knowledge, thereby gaining our awareness of mortality, along with the ability—and the attendant responsibility—to heal. But we no longer have Abraham's easy ability to converse with God or Aaron's access through the oracle of the *Urim Vetumim*, or even a prophet's vision. How, then, do we determine God's will? As always, we seek God's direction through our understanding and through the medium of halakhah, through the unfolding texts and traditions that represent God's Torah as placed before this generation.

To apply our understanding alone to the dilemma, to allow our untutored sensitivities to direct our thinking, is to put ourselves on an even footing with the secular ethicists who abound in our day. To do so is morally upright but alienates us from the Torah. But to apply our understanding only to the texts of our tradition, without striving to set them in the context of life as we feel and live it today, is to deny God the opportunity to address us directly through His Torah, insisting instead on distance and veils. So we choose to approach our texts through life and our life through texts in order to hear God's instructions clearly so that we may carry them out.

What does our tradition teach?

A. The Value of Life

We know, first, that we are obliged to heal, and that the saving of life is of such overriding importance that it takes precedence over virtually all God's other commands.[1] We recognize human lives as the infusion of God's spirit by virtue of which we are considered made in His image, so that death is a diminution of His image in the world.[2] We begin, in short, with a preeminent concern for life, which we view as God's gift, one of the crowning achievements of creation, and with the understanding that the termination of life, like its inception, is God's domain.

How, then, can we approach the treatment of any patient, even one hopelessly ill, except with the determination to extend that life to the limits of our abilities? Indeed, until medical capabilities brought us up against the current dilemma, that was the position of secular medicine as well: that it is the physician's responsibility to do everything possible to preserve life.[3]

That orthodoxy has been ceded by doctors and ethicists, in light of the new technologies, to a new orthodoxy based on two fundamental and interdependent notions. The first of these notions is that of the absolute autonomy of the self. "The voluntary choice of a competent and informed patient should determine whether or not life-sustaining therapy will be undertaken," writes the Presidential Commission for the Study of Ethical Problems in Medicine and Biomedical and Behavioral Research.[4] The renowned Hastings Center frames the issue as follows:

> Our ethical framework draws on the value of patient autonomy or self-determination, which establishes the right of the patient to determine the nature of his or her own medical care. This value reflects our society's long-standing tradition of recognizing the unique worth of the individual. We respect human dignity by granting individuals the freedom to make choices in accordance with their own values. The principle of autonomy is

> the moral basis for the legal doctrine of informed consent, which includes the right of informed refusal.[5]

The second notion, dependent on the first, is the notion often described as the "quality of life." If life should become so troubling to an individual as to be untenable—in the key terms of this analysis, should life's burdens outweigh its benefits—then it is reasonable and not contrary to any moral claims, to seek release from the burdens of that life that no longer offers rewards. Again, the Hastings Center, which serves in many ways as the unofficial philosopher of the biomedical ethics community, best articulates the theory behind these ubiquitous terms:

> Patient well-being—benefiting more than burdening the patient: The obligation to promote the good of the patient is basic to the relationship between the health-care professional and patient. A decision about whether to use life-sustaining treatment raises the question of whether it will promote the patient's good. Extending life is usually, but not always, good—the patient's life, for example, may be full of pain or suffering and the patient may prefer to forgo the treatment even though it means an earlier death. Individual patients evaluate the benefits and burdens of a treatment and the life it offers differently. Consequently, the obligation to promote the patient's good involves identifying the benefits and burdens of the treatment from the patient's perspective. Then the question becomes: Do the burdens of the treatment outweigh its benefits from the patient's perspective? If they do, it is ethically acceptable to withhold or withdraw the treatment. When, however, the treatment provides more benefits than burdens from the patient's perspective, treatment should be provided. When it is unclear whether the burdens or benefits are greater, it is appropriate to err on the side of life.[6]

This latter notion of weighing benefits against burdens is not intended to override patient autonomy, but rather flows from it and serves as a means to approximate the decisions that a patient who is incompetent might have made and to release any surrogate of the competing claims of external value systems. Clearly, if a competent patient determines to terminate treatment, that decision most closely corresponds to a decision from the patient's perspective that life's burdens outweigh its benefits. If a surrogate must make these decisions, however, that surrogate is advised to consider the patient's own value system and not to substitute his own or any other received value system, neither religious nor traditional, for a judgment of the continuing value of life from the patient's perspective.[7]

From a Jewish religious perspective, these two notions are fundamentally flawed, and all consequent deliberations of the secular literature on biomedical ethics must be read carefully in that light. Judaism, more than most of the world's major religions (certainly more so than Christianity, in whose orbit we reside), has always respected individual autonomy. God is a creative and commanding presence in the universe, but man has perfect autonomous free will to live life as he chooses. It is through our choices and our efforts that God is served. But ethics and morality are not conditioned by our choices. Their source and direction are eternal.[8] Indeed, we experience our subservience to God's command as liberating, giving us the opportunity, since the days of Sinai and yet today, to live our lives in God's image, not enslaved by idolatry. As we shall see in detail below, our autonomy in medical decision making is not compromised by the halakhah but simply directed thereby. Ultimate choices rest squarely with us, under the mandate of God's command to choose life.

God's mandate to choose life follows from the very essence of His universe as we understand it. Life and the human soul are attributes of the divine essence; as such, these are properly outside the domain of human choice even as we exercise effective control over them. The martyr Rabbi Ḥananiah ben Teradyon, when urged that his own death in the flames be hastened, provides the classic response, "It is well that He who gave it should take it. One should not injure himself."[9] That is the basis of the Jewish and the general prohibition of suicide, a prohibition that the ethicists are loath to lose even as they function under the rubric of perfect autonomy.[10] Were this not the case, were life or death choices properly in the human domain, the halakhah should recognize a benefit calculation that would permit handing over one individual for execution to save many. It does not. Were this not the case, the basic ruling with regard to murder, *yeihareig ve'al ya'avor*—one should forfeit one's own life rather than transgress—could not stand. Self-preservation would be a compelling argument, as it is in self-defense.[11] Active euthanasia and refusing life-giving treatment with an eye to ending life are tantamount to suicide if life is seen to be God's alone to give and to take.[12]

Indeed, the Rabbis explicitly reflected on the matter of the benefits and burdens of life, and their deliberations are instructive.

> שתי שנים ומחצה נחלקו בית שמאי ובית הלל הללו אומרים נוח לו לאדם שלא נברא יותר משנברא והללו אומרים נוח לו לאדם שנברא יותר משלא נברא נמנו וגמרו נוח לו לאדם שלא נברא יותר משנברא עכשיו שנברא יפשפש במעשיו

> For two and a half years, the schools of Hillel and Shammai differed, the one saying, "It is better for a person not to have been created than to have been created," and the other saying, "It is better for a person to have been created than not to have been created." They voted and determined: "It is better for a person not to have been created than to have been created, but now that he has been created, let him examine his deeds."[13]

Life, it seemed to them, must be inherently burdensome to the divine soul, yet such is life—we are enjoined to carry on.

B. Concern for Suffering

Is there, then, no compassion in Jewish tradition for those who are suffering, no recognition of the inevitable end as it comes? Certainly, there is. Medicine and healing are obligatory. Pain relief is considered without exception as a part of the healer's brief.[14] But beyond these, the tradition early recognized that when the end comes, as it must, it is best to slip away easily. Several stories in the Talmud poignantly counsel us on the need to know and to respond to that moment. In Rabbi Yoḥanan's old age, grief over the death of his brother-in-law and closest colleague caused his "sense to slip away" (*shaf da'atei minei*). "The rabbis prayed for mercy on him and he died."[15] When Rabbi Judah Hanasi was ill, the Rabbis fasted and prayed for him. His maid prayed also, saying, "Rabbi is sought above and sought below; may the ones below prevail over those above." But when she saw his great suffering, she reversed her prayer. Seeing that the Rabbis still prayed for his life, she cast a jug from the roof, disrupting the prayers being said on his behalf, whereupon he died.[16] It is clear that these stories are cited with approval. Rabbenu Nissim of Gerondi formulates a dictum thereby: "It seems to me . . . there are times when one must pray that the sick might die, as when he suffers greatly of his illness and he cannot live."[17]

The Rabbis of the Talmud understood the need to respond mercifully in such situations. The response they proposed was prayer: the request that God offer a quick and merciful release to the sufferer. To be sure, prayer was considered efficacious, as the story of the Rabbi's maid clearly illustrates, but the final arbiter, the one who determines life and death in such a case, was God, not man.[18] No precedent for the withdrawal of medically effective treatment[19] can comfortably be derived from here.[20] No such remedy was proposed.

C. The Law of Goseis

From medieval rabbinic sources, we discover how feelings of compassion for a person's final journey played themselves out in practice. Two texts preempt the field and serve, when merged in the codes, as the predominant rule and locus of comment. The first source is the minor tractate *Eivel Rabbati* or *Semaḥot,* chapter 1,[21] which reads:

> הגוסס הרי הוא כחי לכל דבר. . . . אין קושרין את לחייו ואין פוקקין את נקביו. . . . אין מזיזין אותו ואין מדיחין אותו . . . עד שעה שימות. . . . הנוגע בו ומזיזו הרי הוא שופך דמים רבי מאיר היה מושלו לנר שהוא מטפטף כיון שנגע בו אדם מיד כיבהו

> A person on his deathbed [*goseis*] is like the living in every regard. . . . One does not bind his cheeks or stop his orifices. . . . One does not move him or wash him . . . until the moment that he dies. . . . Whoever touches and moves him, that one commits murder. Rabbi Meir would compare him to a candle that is flickering; should a person touch it, it immediately goes out.

This source serves as the primary text codified in *Shulḥan Arukh, Yoreh De'ah* 339:1. Its concern is primarily to prohibit beginning ministrations to the dead on a living person. Such ministrations, though an honor in death, are an affront to the life yet present in the dying patient. The baraita reflects on the ease with which our actions on behalf of the dying may hasten death if only by moments, and warns us that even an infinitesimally small precipitation of death is tantamount to murder—no uncertain term. Neither the quality of life nor its likely short duration is admitted as a mitigating circumstance.[22]

The second source, united with the first in *Y.D.* 339:1 through the agency of Moses Isserles' embedded commentary there, comes from *Sefer Ḥasidim* (723) via *Shiltei Hagibborim* to Alfasi. *Sefer Ḥasidim* rules that where external impediments (such as the harsh noise of wood-chopping, or salt placed upon the patient's tongue) prevent the flight of the soul, it is permissible to remove those impediments, although to move the patient to a location where he might more easily die is prohibited. Here, the countervailing concern for the merciful death of the lingering patient comes to the fore. Rabbi Joshua Boaz in *Shiltei Hagibborim* formulates this principle as a command, not simply permission, as follows:[23]

> Certainly, to do anything that would cause a dying person not to die quickly is forbidden—for instance, to chop wood in order to delay the soul's departure or to put salt on his tongue so that he not die quickly. . . . In all such matters, it is permissible to remove the causative factor.

We have, then, two competing demands codified as one—to maintain life to its utmost while not hindering death at all.[24] It is not surprising that we suffer some perplexity in walking that very delicate and cosmically important line.

Some would claim that the category of *goseis* (the patient on the deathbed) is severely limited and diagnostically unclear, not to be applied to most of today's hospitalized patients; a *goseis* is one who cannot live three days, and given today's technology, that cannot be assumed of any patient. Since the call not to hinder death is made only in the context of such a *goseis,* the rule is moot.[25] This is, however, a classic case of overreaching. That a person reported to be a *goseis* may be assumed to have died after three days is the codified ruling in *S.A., Y.D.* 339:2, because, in the words of the gloss there, *vadai kevar meit,* he has surely died. The ruling has its provenance in a case that came before Rabbi Meir of Rothenberg and is reported in *Tur* here, and in the *Rosh* to *Mo'ed Katan,* chap. 3, no. 97. It is the case of a woman who had received a report that her husband was seen on his deathbed four days before. Rabbi Meir permits her to mourn, reasoning that the Talmud indicates (*Gittin* 28a) that most persons who lie deathly ill do not recover (*rov gosesin lemitah*), and those generally pass away in three or four days. A *goseis* might indeed live longer. We are nonetheless instructed to remove impediments to his death. We are also instructed to do nothing to hasten that death and to do everything to prolong life.

Sharp as this conundrum appears, we believe that it can be construed and resolved in a way that responds to our moral and psychological needs and remains true to the intent of the sources before us, while addressing as well the medical knowledge and technologies of our day. The first key to this resolution is to recognize that whatever *goseis* may have meant specifically to our rabbinic sources, it refers in our day to all those who have been diagnosed as imminently dying. The halakhic sources ask us to define the distinction between extending life—any life, not just "quality life," for even the smallest duration—and prolonging the process of dying. That, and not the right to die, is what we seek as a Jewish response, as a God-fearing response, to these dilemmas.[26]

D. Natural Death

How are we to define, then, the natural process of life and the natural process of dying, given that we are mortal and our lives can be said, in a sense, to be a terminal disease? Earthly life, biological life, is that ordering of cells and systems such that they maintain animate life, such that they take nourishment and excrete waste, grow and multiply.[27] Should these processes cease, life is no more.

God did not create (or leave) our human bodies immortal. Death, as much as life, is a natural part of the biological system. Biological systems are designed to change and ultimately to deteriorate, with reproduction an essential part of God's creation, to replace the lives thus decommissioned.

What constitutes natural death? The cessation of the integrated biological functioning of an organism due to natural causes. Perhaps surprisingly, all deaths have one proximate cause—the deprivation of oxygen to the cells. The mechanisms that lead to a shortage of oxygen and the death of a cell may differ considerably, but whether the heart ceases to circulate the blood because of mechanical failure or whether the lungs cease to maintain the oxygen levels in the blood or whether either of these follow upon a breakdown of instructions from the brain stem (brain death as it must be defined by the halakhah), the proximate cause remains the same.[28] Yet not all deaths are the same in our moral accounting. We recognize some deaths as untimely, and others as natural.

Death by violence is culpable not because the death is intrinsically different from a natural death but because of the agent and the untimeliness. Death by famine and disease (not caused by specific human design) is intolerable but not culpable because the agent is "an act of God," but the death remains, in our minds, untimely. Death of old age is neither intolerable nor culpable since it is timely and attributable to the nature of our creation. The permission granted in the Torah for a physician to heal, according to the primary midrash of the words *rapo yerapei* (Exod. 21:19), is, in the first instance, granted with regard to injuries in the first category. Of healing in the second category, there existed some debate; perhaps these afflictions should be taken to be God's will, but Jewish law and tradition ruled firmly that here, too, we are required to act to the extent of our ability.[29] The third category was never before susceptible to our ministrations. Nor is it evident that it should be or ever will be meaningfully within our ken. This, ultimately, is God's calculation. This, it seems to me, is the theological rationale behind removing impediments to death—and not primarily the relief from pain (which is the rationale behind praying for death). We try in all our dealings, including healing and including death, to act in a way that will correspond to God's will.

The diagnostic problem remains: How do we determine that a particular death is "natural" and timely, according to God's will and plan? The answer must reside within medicine. If timely, death—the ultimate death of God's choice—will not be meaningfully affected by our ministrations. We need only see if our medicine is able or futile. Here, the law of treatment of the dying is rephrased. By doing everything possible medically and biologically to treat the life systems of the critical patient, while removing impediments to death—items or procedures that interfere with the natural shutdown of the body's major systems in death—we allow ourselves to see if God indeed has ordained the closure of this life, while we do not cede at all our roles as healers and nurturants.

This corresponds, in many ways, to what was possible before the new technologies, but it is not simple nostalgic thinking. Medical treatment has always been a biological endeavor. Medicine aimed to heal and strengthen the body by providing chemicals needed by the cells, to attack invader organisms biochemically, enhancing the body's own biological defense mechanism. Many of our most promising medical advances today are on the level of genetic manipulation to heal through the internal mechanisms of life. This, as Maimonides notes, is perfectly analogous to the elemental natural process of nutrition that is necessary for the life and well-being of any living organism.[30] Some of our more recent technologies are mechanical rather than biological, however, and do not parallel life functions. Thus, for instance, a heart-lung machine—while it has the effect of continuing to circulate and oxygenate the blood, thus providing the needs of life to the cells—does not operate as a biological system but rather circumvents one. Its function is mechanical, a holding mechanism maintaining the status quo against the deterioration and death that would follow upon cessation of heart and lung function. It has a major medical function in enabling open-heart surgery and may carry a patient over a crisis. Taken alone, however, it offers no curative potential. It is not and does not promise the return to a living, organic system. It is thus a candidate for the category "impediments to death." In this category we might place respirators, dialysis machines, and perhaps certain transfusions.[31]

We need to be very cautious before agreeing that a lifesaving procedure should be classified as a dispensable impediment to death. We need to weigh not just the mechanics, but the medical utility of any procedure and the medical situation in which it is applied. We need weigh carefully the medical uncertainties that come with any medical diagnosis or prognosis. Nevertheless, certain clear lines derive from this analysis that are, first, traditional; second, God- and life-affirming; and third, powerful aids in making the decisions that we face in the treatment of the critically ill. They are traditional in that they follow from a crisp reading of the regnant distinction in the codes. Furthermore, despite whatever claims for flexibility might be made, halakhah has not been a fluid, relativistic system (*ish hayashar be'einav ya'aseh*, "Every man did as he saw fit," is the Book of Judges' formula for godlessness, not autonomy). It has always sought comprehensive directives that might then be tailored to the specific situation under the trained eyes of the consulting authority. This runs counter to the relativistic norms of most secular ethicists today and is, in that sense, traditional. They are God- and life-affirming because they insist that we must maintain our treatment of life at all times, and leave it to God alone to determine journey's end. They are powerful because they establish fairly clear directives and directions in the treatment of the terminally ill, which it should be possible to apply even in the tension of a hospital room or an intensive care unit.

E. Patient Autonomy

We shall proceed to break these principles down into specific guidance, but first a few more words on the matter of patient autonomy and the role of surrogates in end-stage treatment of patients unable to express their will. On its face, the line of halakhic reasoning developed here seems to be leading to a rather mechanical solution of a human problem. Whereas the secular ethicists speak continually of patient autonomy and the patient's perspective and choices, there appears, so far, to be no such concern in Jewish law. Indeed, as we said, Jewish law is not generally relativist, but there are two major areas in which human autonomy can dramatically color the final result: the patient's autonomy under Jewish law to choose between competing physicians and treatments; and the fundamental element of human free will, which leaves the ultimate choice to act upon or disregard halakhic counsel in the hands of individuals and their personal reckoning with their Maker.

A physician is enjoined in Jewish law to use his skill to heal. Although piety would like to claim that a person should seek to be healed by God, not man, the definitive ruling has been that when ill, one is required to seek medical attention without delay.[32] It follows, therefore, that a patient must also heed medical directives. Yet if the doctor rules that a patient may fast on Yom Kippur and the patient claims that he cannot—even should a hundred physicians concur in the medical judgment—we listen to the patient. The Talmud claims scriptural precedent for this counterintuitive autonomy against the judgment of the experts, citing Prov. 14:10, "The heart knows its own bitterness." Yet even without a scriptural basis, this follows from the ruling *safeik nefashot lehakeil,* where there is any uncertainty we are required "to err on the side of life."[33] Unlike the absolute autonomy recommended by secular ethicists, this autonomy inheres in the patient choosing life-giving treatment. It cannot reach to the autonomous choice to seek death. But it is a powerful autonomy nonetheless.

Medical science is, by its very nature, a science full of uncertainties. The myriad variations in the constitutional makeup of individuals, in the virulence and etiology of disease, in the effectiveness of various medications together leave the art of medical prognosis just that, an art, and not a matter of scientific precision.[34] This uncertainty opens the very question of the nature of treatment, and not simply the question of whether treatment is indicated, to the autonomous determination of the patient. Thus, the Talmud reports of Rabbi (Judah Hanasi), who suffered from an eye disease. His physician, Samuel Yarḥina'ah, prescribed an injection into the eye but Rabbi waved him off, saying, "I cannot endure it." Samuel's second suggestion, a salve, was similarly rejected, and only his third proposed treatment was applied.[35] While many treatments entail some risk to the patient, and the requirement to seek healing includes the permission to undertake reasonable and commensurate risk to effect a cure, no patient is required to undergo significant risk or endure abnormal pain if an alternative treatment exists or if the efficacy of the proposed treatment is in doubt. Some rabbinic authorities have been of the opinion that all medical treatment is of such character. But without recourse to such radical distrust of medicine, it remains clear that the patient's own judgment whether to undergo risk is determinative, unless medical certainty in the efficacy and low risk of a treatment is exceedingly high and the patient's objection is clearly irrational or suicidal.[36]

This realm of patient autonomy, then, does not reach quite as far as proposed by the secular ethicists. But it effectively controls most of the significant decisions to be made in treating the critically ill. Those who are imminently threatened with death, those of whom the question of the nature of treatment comes up, are almost without exception in need of treatment that carries with it real risk, or whose efficacy is uncertain at best. Were this not the case, we could all agree that treatment is required by the accepted prohibition on suicide. The one area of exception is the quality-of-life judgment, wherein secular ethicists have accepted the patient's autonomous right to seek release from a burdensome existence, though stopping short, as a rule, from condoning euthanasia or suicide. Thus, save the decision to seek death, we function here almost exclusively within the realm of patient autonomy.

This fact is the source of Jewish legal and moral support for hospice care. Hospice care is an attempt to ease the burdens of terminal illness, that is, to address the question of the quality of life of terminally ill patients through the support of their lives, not the pursuit of their deaths. As such, it meets the aims of secular ethics while preserving the value of life, as Jewish law requires. Critics object that hospice care cannot provide the same level of critical intervention as a hospital setting, and that therefore, it should be forbidden for a Jewish patient to forgo hospitalization in favor of hospice care. Here, the uncertainty of medical effectiveness and the high risk of treatment enters. Candidates for hospice care have all been through the medical mill and have concluded that since there is no treatment available to them, even in a hospital's intensive care unit, they would choose the palliative and reassuring care that the hospice offers. They have exercised their autonomy in the realm of medical uncertainty, albeit rather broadly, to seek the treatment that they deem tolerable.[37] Again, it must be emphasized that the permission to seek hospice care is a life-affirming permission. One may not choose hospice care so as to die more quickly, but rather, only in order to live one's remaining days in the best way possible. As such, instructions to the hospice should clearly state that while only palliation is in order for the immediate incurable condition, other unrelated and curable conditions that may arise, such as infections, should be treated in line with standard medical care.[38] Jewish hospice must be an attempt to live one's best with dignity, not an attempt to speed an escape into death.

This leads us to consider the other, ultimate autonomy. No one can know for certain why patients choose one treatment over another, or why they reject hazardous treatment, whether out of fear of the risk or out of a will to die. As rabbis, we must present the case of Jewish law and ethics to those who face these situations, but it is not ours to judge whether a given decision was made well. That is ultimately a matter for God's reckoning, as is the evaluation of all our doings, for good or for ill. Ultimately, the patient has the autonomy of individual free will, including the autonomy to reject God's commands and seek death. The propriety of such a deed is exclusively subject to the individual dialogue between the affected soul and its Maker, a dialogue soon to be continued in person. This is not to say that we may sit back and counsel the moral neutrality of this decision. We must counsel the choice of life. It is to say that as we counsel that choice, we need to acknowledge our own humanity, to realize that we cannot judge others until we have ourselves been in their place, and that God may apply a different calculus in His compassion for us than He allows us to apply for ourselves.[39]

It is precisely when faced with this autonomy over the advice of our physicians that we need the direction of our faith and law. Far from the halakhah being a constraint, it serves as an anchor at a time of bewildering choices. In this context, our tradition counsels an uncompromising regard for and pursuit of life. It asks that as patients, or as counselors to patients, or as surrogates for patients, we seek to maximize life by choosing the best endurable treatment we can find. We may choose to avoid fear, risk, and pain, when we do so in the interests of the remaining moments of life. We may not do so in an attempt to attain release, to annul our final moments and travel a short route to oblivion. Withal, we are not to stand in the breach to ward off death in its time. Thus, where medicine yields to technology, we may assume the law of the *goseis,* one whose death process has begun, and withhold or withdraw such procedures in the interests of God's natural order.

Notes

1. *Bava Kamma* 85a, *S.A., Y.D.* 336:1. And see *Turei Zahav* 1 and *Bei'ur Hagra* 1 there. *S.A., O.Ḥ.* 329, *Yoma* 85a ff. For a full discussion, see Rabbi Immanuel Jakobovits, *Jewish Medical Ethics* (New York: Bloch, 1975), chaps. 1 and 3.
2. Genesis 1 and 2. M. *Sanhedrin* 4:5.
3. In the Hippocratic oath, every physician vowed, "I will use treatment to help the sick according to my ability and judgment, but never with a view to injury" (*Bartlett's Familiar Quotations,* 88). It was understood that physicians could take life as well as protect it, so the oath took care to proscribe the use of medicine against life. "I will give no deadly drug, though it be asked of me, nor will I counsel such" (cited in *Journal of the American Medical Association* 259, no. 14 [8 Apr. 88]: 2143). This commitment was translated by the American Medical Association in 1982: "The social commitment of the physician is to prolong life and relieve suffering" (President's Commission for the Study of Ethical Problems in Medicine and Biomedical and Behavioral Research, *Deciding to Forego* [*sic*] *Life-Sustaining Treatment* [Washington, D.C.: U.S. Government Printing Office, 1983], 16 n. 2). Some cite Hippocrates, from another treatise entitled *The Art,* as one who did not recognize a duty to prolong life. They refer to a passage that advises the physician to refrain from treating "those who are overmastered by their diseases, realizing that in such cases, medicine is powerless" (Pres. Comm., ibid., and see below, n. 26). This recognition of the limits of his medicine, however, should not distract from the primary message received in the Hippocratic tradition, that the physician was to use his art in the interests of life and the relief of suffering. The President's Commission offers its own formulation of this common understanding: "The individual health-care provider is likely to help dying patients most by maintaining a predisposition for sustaining life. . . . Indeed, this favoring of life is part of society's expectation regarding health-care professionals" (48).
4. Pres. Comm., 3. This Presidential Commission was made up of eleven members and an extensive staff. Among its members: Rabbi Seymour Siegel (*z"l*), and its chairman at the time of this report in Mar. 1983, Morris Abram, former president of the National Conference on Soviet Jewry.
5. The Hastings Center, *Guidelines on the Termination of Life-Sustaining Treatment and the Care of the Dying* (Briarcliff Manor, N.Y.: Hastings Center, 1987), 7.
6. Hastings Center, *Guidelines,* 19. Even the Vatican has invoked this concept of burdens, stating, "When inevitable death is imminent in spite of the means used, it is permitted in conscience to make the decision to refuse forms of treatment that would secure a precarious and burdensome prolongation of life" (cited in

Critical Care Medicine [Jan. 1984]: 61; and see *New England Journal of Medicine* [14 Apr. 1988]: 986 and n. 3).

7. This is intended expressly to overrule the old medical orthodoxy wherein the doctors must exert their lifesaving abilities and did so regularly in a paternalistic and dogmatic way, overriding patient choices in the name of their own professional obligations.
8. M. *Avot* 2:1 cites Rabbi Judah Hanasi offering advice concerning "the right course that a person should choose for himself." The commentary Midrash Shmuel by Samuel diOzeida objects: " 'The right course that a person should choose for himself?' As if it is in man's hands to choose a path according to his will! Not so. The Torah directed us on the right path, and none is straighter, as is written: 'and you shall show them the path they should follow and the deed they should do.' "
9. *Avodah Zarah* 19a.
10. Using a strict benefit/burden analysis, from the patient's perspective one could easily argue the case for suicide if one's despair so elevated the burdens of life as to offer no release. That conclusion is unacceptable to everyone. Seeking a nonreligious, theoretical justification for the prohibition of suicide and euthanasia, the Hastings Center concludes:

> Finally, under the rubric of "termination of treatment," we do not include active euthanasia or assisted suicide. These *Guidelines* have been formulated in the belief that a reasonable, if not unambiguous, line can be drawn between forgoing life-sustaining treatment on the one hand, and active euthanasia or assisted suicide on the other.

> Our society forbids assisting suicide or active euthanasia, even if the motive is compassion. This prohibition serves to sustain the societal value of respect for life and to provide some safeguards against abuse of the authority to take actions that shorten life. (*Guidelines,* 6)

11. Maimonides, *Yad Haḥazakah, Hilkhot Yesodei Hatorah,* chap. 5; M. *Terumot* 8:12 and *Yerushalmi* thereon; B. *Sanhedrin* 74a, 72a.
12. Thus *Arukh Hashulḥan, Y.D.* 339:1, simply:

> **ואע״פ שאנו רואים שמצטער הרבה בגסיסתו וטוב לו המות מ״מ אסור לנו לעשות דבר לקרב מיתתו והעולם ומלואו של הקב״ה וכך רצונו יתברך**

> Even though we see that he suffers greatly in dying, and death would be better for him, nevertheless we are forbidden to do anything to hasten his death, for the world and all it contains is God's, and such is His will, may He be praised.

13. *Eruvin* 13b.
14. Eliezer Waldenberg, *Tzitz Eliezer* 13:87.
15. *Bava Metzia* 84a.
16. *Ketubbot* 104a.
17. *Nedarim* 40a, s.v. *ein mevakeish alav raḥamim.* The last phrase, *kegon shemitz-ta'eir haḥole ve'i efshar lo sheyiḥyeh* (since the patient suffers greatly and cannot live), has some ambiguity. Does it refer to the nature of the illness, which is terminal so the patient "cannot live," or is the reference subjective, that the patient suffers such that he cannot stand it (*i efshar lo*)? Either is linguistically defensible. Is suffering a sufficient condition to warrant death, or is the objective medical prognosis material? The subject, however, is prayer, so that even the more liberal interpretation offers no dramatic turn. R. Nissim's dictum is cited by Rabbi Y. M. Epstein in his *Arukh Hashulḥan, Y.D.* 335:3 and by many modern Jewish writers on biomedical ethics. However, Rabbi J. David Bleich (in *Jewish Bioethics,* ed. Fred Rosner and J. David Bleich [New York: Sanhedrin Press, 1979], 35) points out that Rabbi Waldenberg rejects the dictum as a point of law (*Tzitz Eliezer* 9:47).
18. To attempt to blur the distinction between God's role in answering prayer and His role in our direct actions by contending that even where we act, it is God who ultimately determines whether our act will succeed or fail, is unacceptable. Such a claim reduces our free will, making God ultimately responsible for our actions, and could be used to justify any sinful conduct.
19. It goes without saying that a course of treatment that is medically worthless, lacking even a placebo effect, is not medical treatment at all. It should never knowingly have been begun and may be withdrawn at any time. The question of how to gauge medical futility is itself subject to the ethical analysis of this paper.
20. Attempts to do so (see Rabbi Moshe Feinstein, *Iggerot Moshe, Ḥ.M.* 2, 73:1; Rabbi Morris Shapiro, "To What Extent Should Life-Prolonging Means Be Extended to a Dying Person?" presented to the CJLS, Nov. 1987, not accepted) notwithstanding, the inference is not valid.
21. M. Higger, Treatise *Semaḥot,* 97ff.
22. The halakhah is clear that life should be saved even on Shabbat even if it is for a very limited duration (*ḥayei sha'ah*), *S.A., O.Ḥ.* 329:4, *Yoma* 85a. In Responsa *Beit Ya'akov* (no. 59), the author argues that a *goseis* need not be saved for a limited duration, since the death process has begun and we are not to intervene to thwart it. He argues that for a *goseis,* since we are required to remove impediments to death, any treatment undertaken solely for a temporary lengthening of life is inappropriate. This ruling is contrary to the ruling of Tosafot, *Niddah* 44a, s.v. *ihu* and many others, as cited in Waldenberg, *Tzitz Eliezer* 5, *Ramat Raḥel,* 28. Even *Beit Ya'akov* limits said ruling to a classic end-stage *goseis,* specifically exempting a longer-term *tereifah,* who must be saved in accordance with the ruling in *Yoma* above. The question of the definition or duration of *ḥayei sha'ah*

(life of short duration) is moot as long as there is no functional legal difference between treatment for the short term (*leḥayei sha'ah*) and that for the long term (*leḥayei olam*). Those who would so distinguish between these situations define *leḥayei sha'ah* (the short term) as less than one year, based on the definition of *tereifah,* collapsing categories and muddying *Beit Ya'akov*'s own distinction. See sources cited, n. 20 above.

The other major source cited to release us of concern for *ḥayei sha'ah* is a gemara on *Avodah Zarah* 27b with its related Tosafot, s.v. *leḥayei sha'ah lo ḥaishinan.* Faced with conflicting *gemarot* on whether we take *ḥayei sha'ah* into account, Tosafot concludes *hakha vehatam avdinan letovato;* in each case, we do what is best. This source is cited by Rabbi G. A. Rabinowitz in *Halakhah Urefu'ah,* 3:113ff., to suggest that we might disregard any temporary life-extending treatment for a patient in pain, where death is preferable to such a life. Thus do some propose putting the quality-of-life, benefits-and-burdens analysis into the mouth of Tosafot.

An analysis of the text source, however, does not admit of this reading of *letovato.* The mishnah and gemara there deal with the following scenario: Gentile physicians are suspect of murdering their Jewish patients. The Mishnah therefore rules that it is forbidden to accept treatment by a Gentile physician. But what, asks the Talmud, if one is deathly ill? Comes the response: If it is unclear if the patient will live or die, we do not resort to the Gentile physician—perhaps the patient will live, and the "treatment" is too dangerous. If, however, the patient will surely die, he may try the Gentile physician, for there is nothing to lose. But, objects the Gemara, there is something to lose—*ḥayei sha'ah!* Should his physician kill him, his life will have been shortened thereby. The Talmud waves off this concern, saying, *leḥayei sha'ah lo ḥaishinan,* we do not take into account life of a short duration. Note that this is no different from a standard calculation on whether to undertake risky treatment. If the risk of treatment is greater than the risk of the illness (the first case of uncertainty), do not undertake treatment. If the risk of the illness is greater, you may risk treatment even though it may fail and be fatal.

Tosafot question the dismissal of *ḥayei sha'ah* in the case of the Gentile physician, since in the case of a building collapse we *are* concerned about it. Tosafot's resolution: "In both cases, we do what is best for him." Note that in both cases, "what is best" is to live longer. In the one case, we override Sabbath restrictions so that perhaps he can live longer; in this case, we do or do not accept treatment from a Gentile based on our analysis of what is likeliest to prolong life. Thus, Tosafot in detail:

הכא והתם עבדינן לטובתו דהתם אם לא תחוש ימות והכא אם תחוש ולא יתרפא מן העובד כוכבים ודאי ימות וכאן שבקינן הודאי [שימות!] למיעבד הספק [שמא יחיה!]

In both cases, we do what is best for him. In the one case [building collapse], if you are not concerned [about life of short duration; therefore, do

> not clear the debris on Shabbat], he will die, whereas here, if you are concerned [about the possibility of his remaining life of short duration] and [if, therefore,] he does not seek medication from the Gentile, he will surely die. Therefore, here we eschew the certain result and act on a possibility.

There is no precedent here for acting on the "benefit" of an earlier death, and the phrase *leḥayei sha'ah lo ḥaishinan* does not mean that we may dispense with a life of short duration but rather, that we always trade up with regard to life. In life, a little is very much, a little more is very much better.

23. *Shiltei Hagibborim* to Alfasi, *Mo'ed Katan,* chap. 3, no. 1237.
24. It must be said that the impediments to death outlined by Isserles and *Shiltei Hagibborim* are not medical but folkloristic. One might conclude that we may do only nonphysical things (such as prayer) in hopes that they affect, inexplicably, the death of the patient. But whatever we think about the efficacy of the actions mentioned, prayer was addressed to God, who properly determines life and death, whereas these folkloristic acts are intended to affect the patient directly. Thus, the principle that is being pointed to is very much as expressed, to set aside anything that is preventing the soul's departure.
25. Rabbi J. David Bleich, "The Moribund Patient," in *Jewish Bioethics,* ed. Bleich and Rosner, 33–35; and Fred Rosner, ibid., 263, who characterizes Rabbi Immanuel Jakobovits as "quick to point out" this three-day limit. In fact, in Jakobovits, *Jewish Medical Ethics,* this goes unmentioned in the text, but appears in a footnote, n. 18 to chap. 11, as the opinion of Rabbi Joshua Falk, author of the Perishah commentary to the *Tur.* Rabbi Moshe Feinstein defends the three-day notion more plausibly as not being a physical fact, but rather a strong probability (*rov*). It is that probability that allows the legal presumption of death after three days. It is safe to say that this is the classical notion of *goseis* codified in the literature, whereas this discussion presumes a major expansion of this category to medicine's category of the terminally ill who have not days but months to live, in all probability. See next note.
26. Some general writers on medical ethics have adopted a similar stance, placing themselves at some distance from the "benefits and burdens" view, but with results distinctly different from those we propose here. Thus, Kenneth L. Vaux, a professor of ethics in medicine at the University of Illinois, cites approvingly the "classical clinical wisdom":

> In this tradition, the physician was discouraged from invading the atrium of death therapeutically or technologically. Attempts to cure were now to yield to attempts to comfort. In the Hippocratic treatise, *The Art,* the *techne iatrike* is defined as follows: "In general terms, it is (1) to do away with the sufferings of the sick, (2) to lessen the violence of their diseases, and (3) to refuse to treat those who are overmastered by their diseases, realizing that in such cases medicine is powerless." This reflects the fundamental religious and ethical genius of classical ethics: In the atrium of

> death, one's life is given over to the transcending spirit who gave it. ("The Theological Ethics of Euthanasia," *Hastings Center Report* 19 [Jan./Febr. 1989]: 20–21)

He would, on that basis, permit some cases of euthanasia. Drs. Kenneth Micetich, Patricia Steinecker, and David Thomasma, "Are Intravenous Fluids Morally Required in a Dying Patient?" *Archives of Internal Medicine* 143 [May 1983]: 977, write:

> We agree that respect for the living, regardless of their status or function, is an important value for medicine and for society. However, if no intervention we can conceive of will stave off death, then our obligations toward living beings are altered. Thus, just prior to the discussion of faithfulness toward the dying, Ramsey (Paul Ramsey, *The Patient as a Person* [New Haven: Yale University Press, 1970], 113ff.) points out that the morally significant point is that one is not obliged to prolong dying *in any way.* Once a judgment can be made that death is irreversibly imminent, the medical obligation to prolong life drastically changes. It is not now a question of prolonging life, but of postponing death [emphasis in original].

They then define their terms as follows (978): "Our suggestion about drawing the line between prolonging life and prolonging death is the criterion that death will be imminent (within two weeks) no matter what intervention we may take."

They would withhold even nutrition and hydration once the criterion of imminence is fulfilled, as represented by their arbitrary choice of a two-week limit. Thus, they take a technical position that the imminence of death releases altogether any obligation to medicate or treat other than what relieves suffering. This is akin to the objective position of *Beit Ya'akov,* who finds that the state of *gesisah* (imminent death) requires cessation of life-giving care, so that it would be inappropriate to desecrate the Sabbath to save the life of a *goseis,* even though the Talmud specifically requires doing so to save a life even temporarily and a *goseis* is emphatically protected as a living person. Teamed with a mechanical time limit of three days under the guidance of halakhic precedent (see previous note), this is a narrow approach to the rule of *gesisah* that yields an expansive result in terms of withholding treatment. But life and time are innately valuable in our tradition, even in their smallest denominations, and prevailing opinion runs counter to the position of *Beit Ya'akov* and, it follows, of Micetich, Steinecker, and Thomasma (see n. 22 above).

Rather, we need to adopt a more expansive theoretical reading of the principles espoused in the halakhot of *goseis* and follow those principles to a life-affirming, compassionate stance that recognizes the twin provinces of life and death. I believe that this expansion of the law, creating a second category of *goseis,* is warranted by the facts. In antiquity, diagnostic tools were insufficient to diagnose consumptive illnesses and to predict long-term prognoses. (See n. 34 below on the extent of our weakness in this regard even today.) Only the *tereifah*, suffering from a visible puncture wound to a vital organ, could be so diagnosed, and the one who was but moments away from death—the classical *goseis*. Anyone dying of illness but not falling into these two categories would have been classed a *shekhiv mera*—deathly ill, but who is to say what miracles God has in store in His treasury? Today, with our expanded medical knowledge, we can identify the inexorable march toward death much earlier. In that situation, it is precisely the logic of the rule of *goseis* that applies. The patient is dying by God's decree. Yet we are enjoined to treat and save even *leḥayei sha'ah*. We can only walk that line by applying these rules of *gesisah* and leaving the final judgment in the hands of the Ultimate Judge.

27. *Encyclopaedia Britannica* (1901), 3:684–85; (1982), 2:1015–16.
28. A. M. Capron and L. R. Kass, "A Statutory Definition of the Standards for Determining Human Death," *University of Pennsylvania Law Review* 121 (1972): 87–89, 100–18 n. 89:

> Life is supported by the smooth and integrated function of three principal systems: circulatory, respiratory, and nervous. . . . So long as the integrated function of these three systems continues, the individual lives. If any one of them ceases to function, failure of the other two will shortly follow, and the organism dies. In any case, it is anoxia, or deprivation of oxygen, that is the ultimate cause of death of cells: in central nervous system failure, because the impulses which maintain respiration cease; in cardiac failure, because oxygenated blood is not moved to the cells; and in respiratory failure, because the blood, although circulating, is not releasing carbon dioxide or replenishing oxygen in the lungs. Although other organs, such as the liver and kidneys, perform functions essential to life, their failure does not per se result in immediate death; it results, rather, in the eventual failure of one of the three systems described, and is thus only an indirect cause of death. (M. Houts and I. H. Haut, *Courtroom Medicine,* 1.01[2][a])
>
> It has long been known that, even when a patient loses consciousness and becomes areflexive, he may recover if heartbeat and breathing continue, but if they do not, there is no hope of recovery. Thus, death came to be equated with the absence of these two "vital signs," although what was being detected was really the permanent cessation of the integrated functioning of the circulatory, respiratory, and nervous systems. In recent years, the traditional concept of death has been departed from, or at least severely strained, in the case of persons who were dead according to the rationale underlying the traditional standards in that they had experienced a period of anoxia long enough to destroy their brain functions, but in whom respiration and circulation were artificially re-created. By recognizing that such artificial means of support may preclude reliance on the

> traditional standards of circulation and respiration, the statute proposed here merely permits the logic behind the long-existing understanding (i.e., integrated trisystemic functioning) to be served. . . . Dr. Jean Hamburger has observed, "After the guillotine has cut off a criminal's head, it is possible now to keep the heart and lungs going on for days. Do you think such a person is dead or alive?". . . .The purpose of the "new" standard is to make clear that the answer to Hamburger's question is unequivocably that the person is dead. Cf. *Gray vs. Sawyer,* 247 S.W.2d 496 (Ky. 1952), "newly discovered evidence that blood was gushing from decedent's decapitated body is significant proof that she was still alive."

Brain death may be formally new to the halakhah, but the premises required are old and were always self-evident. Cf. M. *Oholot* 1:6 and Rambam's commentary thereon, and the famed dictum *pesik reisheih velo yamut,* "should you cut off its head, will it not die?" (*Shabbat* 75a, 103a, et al.). See chap. 17 of this vol., n. 5.

29. See Jakobovits, *Jewish Medical Ethics,* chap. 1, particularly pp. 3–5.
30. Maimonides, commentary to M. *Pesaḥim* 4:9. This reference was uncovered by Rabbi Bleich, in *Jewish Bioethics,* ed. Bleich and Rosner, 270. Maimonides draws the analogy that these are both God-given for one's satisfaction and health. Bleich concludes that the analogy applies as well to lifesaving medical technology. We agree, but sense in the texture of Maimonides' passage the physical image of ingestion.
31. We are not alone in championing this distinction as the proper implication of the precedent before us in the codes. One of the stellar thinkers of this generation in matters of halakhah, science, and society, Dr. Yeshayahu Leibovitz, in a 1977 lecture at Tel Aviv University published in a collection of his essays entitled *Emuna, Historiyah Va'arakhim* (Akademon, Hebrew University, 1982), 249 [from original Hebrew, my translation], states simply:

> It appears that Rabbi Moses Isserles distinguishes between two impediments to death in cases of imminent death, i.e., inexorable death: an impediment due to a necessary factor that continues to function in the dying organism itself, in which case it is forbidden to stop the functioning of this factor; and an impediment due to an external factor, such that were it not applied artificially to the dying patient, his life would have already ended on its own. In this case, there is no requirement to prolong his life. We have before us the case of Karen Quinlan. There are *posekim* who disagree with Isserles in this regard. But it is likely that in a case such as this, it would be said—as is the norm in difficult cases—"Isserles may be relied upon when in dire straits," and there is no doubt that this is a case of dire straits: we are in both intellectual and emotional straits. It turns out, then, that were the Quinlan case to be decided not in an American court, but according to Jewish law, we would be permitted to

do the parents' bidding and stop treatment that has no hope and that we feel has an element of desecration of the dying patient and torture of living people.

Dr. Leibovitz goes on to hesitate at the boldness of his own understanding. He worries of the slippery slope and concludes: "*halakhah ve'ein morin kein.* This is the law but we do not so instruct." Withal, he proposes that doctors should function by the halakhah and not seek the judgment of the court, which, should it need to rule, would perforce need to speak the *hora'ah* (instruction) publicly and not the proper *halakhah* (law).

Nor is Leibovitz alone in proposing this distinction. Its earliest clear proponent, to my knowledge, was Rabbi Moshe Munk in an article in *She'arim* 24 in 1968. (This understanding is referred to in passing even earlier, in 1957, in a long but opaque article by Rabbi M. D. Wollner in *Hatorah Vehamedinah* 7–8 [5716/17]: 318ff.) It is supported by Rabbi Y. Rabinowitz in *Assia,* no. 3 (1971) and reported as normative by Dr. Abraham Steinberg in an excellent review of the halakhic literature pertaining to euthanasia, *Retzaḥ Mitokh Raḥamim* in *Assia* 5, no. 19: 5–38. He cites Rabbi Eliezer Waldenberg, *Tzitz Eliezer* 13:89, as arguing this case at length—and, indeed, he seems to do so. However, in the following issue, *Assia* 5, no. 20: 17ff., Rabbi Waldenberg insists in two letters that his permission to remove life support is only for one who is effectively brain-dead, and that that was the only *goseis* to which Isserles ever referred. Save, then, for that rather surprising limitation of Isserles, the case for extending Isserles' ruling to mechanical life support is made by Rabbi Waldenberg quite effectively. Similarly, Rabbi G. Rabinowitz and Dr. M. Koenigsberg (*Hadarom,* Tishri 5731) also state that mechanical life support is clearly not a vital sign, but they do so in the context of brain death. Whether they would extend that notion to the matter of *goseis* remains open to speculation. Against this understanding, see the demurral by Dr. Ya'akov Levy in *No'am* 16 (1973): 61.

32. *Berakhot* 60a with Rashi and the commentaries of Ibn Ezra (both long and short) and Naḥmanides' to Lev. 26:11 are two loci of the pietistic approach. But even Ramban did not so rule at law, as R. Eliezer Waldenberg shows definitively, *Tzitz Eliezer* 11:41. He cites Naḥmanides' *Torat Ha'adam* in the chapter on danger, addressing the very heart of the issue before us, as follows:

פקוח נפש מצוה רבה היא הזריז הר״ז משובח הנשאל מגונה השואל שופך דמים וכ״ש המתיאש ואינו עושה

Saving life is a great mitzvah. Who approaches it with alacrity is praised, who hesitates is despicable, who questions it is guilty of murder, and certainly so, one who despairs and does not do it.

And see Fred Rosner, "The Physician and the Patient in Jewish Law," in *Jewish Bioethics,* ed. Bleich and Rosner, 45ff.

33. *Yoma* 83a, codified at *S.A., O.Ḥ.* 618:1. The same ruling applies to transgressing Shabbat for treatment, *O.Ḥ.* 328:10. The phrase "to err on the side of life" appears often in the literature of biomedical ethics and is used in the *Guidelines* of the Hastings Center (see n. 5). I am unable to verify its original source. It is attributed to Judge J. Skelly Wright in his opinion in Application of the President and Directors of Georgetown College, Inc., U.S. Court of Appeals, D.C. Circuit, 1964 by J. David Bleich in *Jewish Bioethics,* ed. Bleich and Rosner, 39 n. 12. However, Judge Wright's precise words are "to act on the side of life." Whether these words are indeed the source of this citation remains unclear.
34. Pres. Comm., 176:

> [U]ncertainty affects any scientific proposition about as-yet-unobserved cases. No matter how extensive the past evidence is for an empirical generalization, it may yet be falsified by future experience. Certainty in prognosis is always a matter of degree, typically based upon the quantity of the evidence from which a prediction is made.

23 n. 37:

> When 205 physicians in one study were presented with a hypothetical case, the range of assessments was striking, with those who favored and those against aggressive treatment offering the same reasons but projecting very different views of the patient's future.

25 n. 44:

> Physicians' predictions of prognosis were relatively inaccurate, with actual survival plus or minus one month coinciding with that predicted in only 16 percent of patients. Except in patients who were very ill and had short prognosis [*sic*] of three to four months, survival was consistently underestimated.
>
> The subjective nature of prognoses affects the types of treatment that are encouraged, which in turn affects patients' outcome. In one study, physicians who preferred to intubate and artificially ventilate a patient with severe chronic lung disease projected that the patient would survive about fifteen months; other physicians who decided against artificial ventilation when presented with the same case predicted that, even with artificial life support, the patient had only six months to live.

Lo et al., " 'Do Not Resuscitate' Decisions: A Prospective Study at Three Teaching Hospitals," *Archives of Internal Medicine* 145 (June 1985): 1117:

> In six cases, a DNR (Do Not Resuscitate) order was made without the agreement of the patient or family. . . . The physicians in these cases believed that the futility of further treatment justified overriding the families' wishes. The judgment that patients 2, 3, and 4 would die despite treatment seemed incontrovertible (N.B.: But went untested given the DNR

order). However, for patients 5 and 6, the physicians' assessments of futility were incorrect, perhaps influenced by their judgment of the patient's quality of life; *patients in these cases survived to discharge* [emphasis added].

35. *Bava Metzia* 85b.
36. On this matter of hazardous and uncertain treatment, see the discussion by Rabbi Bleich, in *Jewish Bioethics,* ed. Bleich and Rosner, chap. 1, pp. 29–33, "Experimental Therapy and Hazardous Procedures." He reviews the literature, citing various rabbinic positions. Within these shades of opinion, however, two statements are unequivocal. "A patient may be compelled to submit to medically indicated therapy" (28). But "procedures which involve any significant risk factors are always discretionary rather than mandatory." Determining which of these formulations applies to any given situation is, in the nature of things, subject to medical opinion and patient discretion. Here, medical and rabbinic humility before the autonomous choice of the patient is crucial. We may advise, but the patient alone chooses. The Sephardic chief rabbi of Israel was recently taught a poignant lesson in this regard. Early in 1990, eighty-four-year-old Ruth Trabelsi lay in a hospital in Israel, refusing amputation of a gangrenous leg. Rabbi Mordecai Eliyahu, the Sephardic chief rabbi of Israel, intervened to persuade her, despite her resolve to meet her Maker whole, to accede to the surgery, because ostensibly, halakhah demanded that she act to prolong her life. But life confounded his good counsel. Having acceded to the rabbi's intercession, Trabelsi died of respiratory complications following surgical anesthesia. And see Moshe Feinstein, *Iggerot Moshe, Ḥ.M.* 2, 73:5.
37. On the uncertainty inherent in the prognosis of terminality, see n. 34 above. Given the great uncertainty affecting prognosis and treatment, there can be no assurance that a particular patient will not live longer under the care of a hospice program than in the hospital. The only possible advantage is the availability of cardiopulmonary resuscitation. This procedure, if successful, restores life immediately where it would otherwise be lost. May one forgo that possibility by placing oneself beyond the reach of critical care equipment? It is plain that we are not required to live our lives in intensive care units. Being beyond the reach of critical care equipment is within the purview of normal risk, a permission assumed in all our behavior, e.g., automobile or air travel. Only where cardiac arrest is specifically and imminently anticipated might this question arise as a serious consideration (see ahead [in chap. 17] on DNR orders).
38. [See chap. 17 of this vol.]
39. In a response to the article "It's Over, Debbie" (*JAMA* 259, no. 2 [8 Jan. 1988]), Kenneth Vaux labels a certain subset of euthanasia cases as "exceptional case euthanasia." He writes ("Debbie's Dying: Mercy Killing and the Good Death," *JAMA* 259, no. 14 [8 Apr. 1988]: 2141):

    I argue that while positive euthanasia must be proscribed in principle, in exceptional cases it may be abided in deed. There has always been a

> place, albeit carefully restricted to a limited range of cases, for voluntary euthanasia. From classical times throughout the Christian centuries and into modern secular society, this allowance has always existed alongside the dominant ethic of prolonging and sustaining life. . . . In his classic of medical ethics, *The Patient as a Person,* Paul Ramsey, Ph.D., a spokesman for traditional ethics, makes unrelenting cancer pain an exception to the dominant ethic of "doing nothing to place the dying more quickly beyond our love and care." Here, "one can hardly be held morally blameworthy if in these instances dying is directly accomplished or hastened" (163). Philosophical ethics aside, the most moving evidence I have witnessed for this viewpoint . . . is the testimony of highly ethical and humane physicians. . . . Although impeded by law and custom from giving a lethal dose to their patient, these physicians would, in fact, do so . . . for their wife or father or child. . . . Such loving acts illustrate a kind of "exception" ethic that has a place in the tradition of alleviating suffering.

This sense of the exceptional case is probably quite as Vaux has described it, except that it was never concretized as a permission for euthanasia; rather, it allowed courts and juries to mercifully acquit where the crime of euthanasia seemed humanly justified, if not legally so. This refers, then, to a special form of the ultimate autonomy of our individual accounts with God. Who knows if what was done contrary to law and custom, but out of love, finds favor or disapproval before the Lord? Who would want to ascribe guilt in such a case?

The case of Rudy Linares, the father of a two-year-old child in a technologically assisted vegetative state, who forcibly detached his child's life-support system, then held the hospital guards at bay with a gun while holding his son until he died (Chicago, 26 Apr. 1989), strikes one as such a case. The Talmud's case of the martyr Rabbi Ḥananiah ben Teradyon (*Avodah Zarah* 19a) is often cited as an example of Judaism's aversion to suicide ("One should not injure himself"), but halakhah's permission to remove impediments to death from the dying (the centurion removes the protective damp tufts). Neglected in this analysis is the fact that the centurion also stokes the flames. The approval merited by the centurion is almost certainly based on such an exceptional case understanding, and does not imply any standing permission for euthanasia.

The case of Saul's apparent suicide, much debated in the codes (*Tur* and *S.A., Y.D.* 345) and considered by some as a warrant for suicide in some circumstances, is also best viewed as an exceptional case (like a *ḥidush*) from which no warrant to follow suit can be derived. See Fred Rosner, "Suicide in Jewish Law," in *Jewish Bioethics,* ed. Bleich and Rosner, chap. 20, for more on this debate. The halakhic distinctions ultimately made between a culpable suicide, for whom we do not mourn, and an excused suicide, for whom we may, revolve around this problem of exceptional cases and our right to judge them. In a moment of humility before the depth of human emotion, on the one hand, and divine compassion on the other, we leave judgment in these cases to God's infinite wisdom.

CHAPTER 17

Care for the Terminally Ill: Practical Applications*

Avram I. Reisner

[This chapter continues a response to the *she'eilah* (question) addressed in chapter 16: Increasingly, modern medical progress puts us face-to-face with a terrible dilemma: How do we treat a patient who is clearly beyond our powers of healing? Practical applications with regard to hospice are discussed in chapter 16, pp. 251–52.]

How do we apply this in practice?

A. Nutrition, Hydration, Medication

All nutrition and medication against illness—antibiotics, insulin, intravenous fluids, and so on—organic treatments whose effectiveness is well established and that have no significant attendant risk, cannot be classified as impediments to death. These should generally be continued as long as they are effective, notwithstanding a patient's requests to discontinue, when those requests are indicative of the patient's desire to die.[1] Where that is not the case, however, that is, where those procedures or treatments entail recognized risks beyond the most minimal, or

*Chapters 16–17 present material that originally appeared in the form of one longer paper, "A Halakhic Ethic of Care for the Terminally Ill." This paper was approved by the Rabbinical Assembly Committee on Jewish Law and Standards, Dec. 1990.

where the option of another line of treatment exists, the patient should exercise choice, and Jewish law recognizes the patient's choice as the final word even against the doctor's advice, even should this ultimately hasten death. The patient must be encouraged not to choose based on a desire to die, but to live. Still, choice of treatment rests with the patient. In terminal illness, the patient is perforce in some form of very personal dialogue with God, and we are not appointed—nor are we able—to judge the resolution of a soul's accounts with God.

The area of greatest debate in this regard is the initiation (and, in some cases, the continuation) of "artificial nutrition and hydration," via intravenous fluid and feeding tube. There can be no question that intravenous fluids are medically indicated and do not entail measurable risk or unbearable discomfort, at least until veins collapse, requiring an incision to insert the IV. These must be continued. To withhold them is effectively a decision to hasten the death of the patient affected, since death by dehydration is likely to precede death from the underlying disease. Even when surgical techniques are necessary to emplace the IV, the difficulties would have to be large and the patient quite deteriorated before such basic care could be considered futile and therefore dispensable, or of significant risk, and therefore subject to the patient's choice.[2]

The same is not the case with tube feeding. Lack of interest in food to the point of substantial anorexia is normal in late-stage terminal illness. This is simply symptomatic of the decreased needs of a system engaged in shutting down, and death by starvation is a far less proximate outcome than by dehydration where fluids are not supplied. Most important, there does exist significant risk of aspiration surrounding tube feeding, a risk that requires consistent, careful attention. Furthermore, significant discomfort, often reported as unendurable, accompanies the nasogastric tube, while surgery with anesthetic, albeit simple surgery, accompanies the placing of a gastrostomy tube—unlike IV fluids, which require no surgery and can go unattended for long periods of time with only topical discomfort.[3]

Once risk and prognostic uncertainty is present, the patient retains the right to choose to accept such risk or reject it. Thus, for instance, elderly patients who eat fitfully, but do not refuse all nutrition, can be presumed to best know the needs of their own bodies. We may cajole, but should not resort to forcible tube feeding.[4] Again, the patient's right to subjectively choose between risks is substantially less for physician and surrogate. Their determination must be made more objectively in terms of their understanding of the best course of treatment.

The other side of the equation needs to be stated boldly as well. There is no obligation nor any merit on the part of the patient or the physician to continue a treatment of any sort, even nutrition and hydration, where it is clearly futile. "Futility" must be defined closely, however, in order to protect life to its last. A course of treatment that is organic and expected to extend life, and that is not rejected as untenable by the patient, cannot be considered futile solely because the prolongation of life will be minimal. However, where death is imminent, that is, anticipated from the underlying condition before the effects of the withheld treatment would threaten the patient, the treatment need not be applied (save that palliative effects must also be considered). This holds true for nutrition and hydration as for medication where imminent death is anticipated from the underlying disease and not from the withholding of the treatment. In such a case, the cessation of futile ministrations, which pretend to ward off death where it cannot be fought, is an act of *ḥesed* (an act of love) and an acknowledgment of God's domain. This is the classic *goseis* for whom non-ministration is the order of the day.

B. Life-Support Systems

Mechanical procedures that are undertaken to immunize the body from the failures of the major organs and bodily systems should be done only where there is a medical reason to hope that they will contribute to a healing, curative process or to the return of the body's systems to unaided function. Thus, heart-lung machines during bypass surgery, respirators during breathing crises that are understood to be reversible, indeed, transplants—all gross attempts to circumvent the deterioration of major bodily organs—are all proper and required (insofar as the patient does not opt for alternative treatment to avoid risk, as mentioned above). These same procedures undertaken without hope of any curative process, simply to prolong the beating of the heart or the expansion of the lungs mechanically, are unnecessary, and it would be proper to disconnect them from a patient who had initially been connected in hopes of some success in treatment when those hopes have been abandoned completely by qualified medical personnel.[5]

Where intubation alone, without attachment to a respirator, is recommended to assist a weak respiratory system to gain access to oxygen, it is the natural biological system that continues functioning. As such, this should be seen as extending life, not delaying death. However, intubation is a procedure that is invasive, debilitating, and can be very disturbing to the patient. Patients may refuse intubation as unendurable, choosing instead an oxygen tent or other less invasive means to support their normal respiratory reserve.

C. CPR

Cardiopulmonary resuscitation poses an unusual legal situation. The patient is in cardiac arrest, a condition that surely qualifies the patient as a *goseis*, for the dying process has begun. The laws of *goseis* limit our manipulation of the patient's body in the interests of allowing the patient to die. Yet we know that such patients can often be saved, not only momentarily, but for years of subsequent health. The patient may have begun to die, but we know that God's last word is not necessarily in. In seeking to determine the capacity of the natural biological system of the patient to function again, it should be obvious that, for an otherwise healthy individual, a first attempt at resuscitation must be attempted if any chance of recovery to unsupported function exists, notwithstanding specific instructions to the contrary by the patient. Here, no analysis of the risk inherent in chest compression and shocks applied to the heart muscle can activate patients' rights to direct their own treatment, since any other treatment is a choice not of treatment but of death. However, attempts at resuscitation after it has been determined that no unsupported life is possible are clearly unnecessary. (Here, we refer to a patient who is maintained on a respirator after cardiac arrest and resuscitation, for whom the determination is made that no treatment is possible and the respirator is removed as an impediment to imminent death. When cardiac arrest ensues, it is part of the dying process. CPR intervention will simply prolong that death.)[6]

For most patients, the real situation is in an intermediate category: cardiopulmonary resuscitation may restore them to unaided function for a short period, but their general condition leaves it highly unlikely that they will continue in life for an extended period. Indeed, the success rate of cardiopulmonary resuscitation is directly correlated to certain measures of frailty through age or disease.[7] Normally, we would require saving the individual even if only for *ḥayei sha'ah*, life of short duration.

In this case, however, a loophole of a sort provides the patient with an additional moment of autonomy. The patient in cardiac arrest presents a figure that is dead by standard legal criteria.[8] Our obligation to heal extends to the ill, but does not extend to reviving those of whom it may definitely be said that dying has set in. Our interest in life leads us to override that technicality when we are hopeful of our ability to restore a full measure of life. Where we are not so hopeful, it is proper to respond to a "Do Not Resuscitate" request, wherein patients assert that if death overtakes them, they would have us let it be. It should be noted, however, that nothing in the permission granted for removal of impediments to death mandates that removal if the patient expresses the wish to be saved with all available measures. Miraculous cure is unlikely, but the patient is allowed to hold out such hopes until the patient's unreasonable hopes interfere with the realistic treatment of another patient.[9]

D. Transfusions

Transfusions for loss of fluid during surgery or accident or to relieve any acute but temporary condition are akin to medicine and nutrition, in that they provide necessary biological material. Transfusions undertaken to remove toxins accumulating because of renal failure resemble more closely mechanical circumvention of system failure. In the context of awaiting transplant or of radiation or bone-marrow treatment, these procedures are clearly medical/curative and are therefore required. Taken alone in the absence of any hope of restored function, they are impediments to death that may be forgone.[10]

E. Pain Relief

Treatment of pain is considered medical treatment, even though it is not undertaken for curative purposes. It is required because of our concern for suffering and because great pain is debilitating and assumed to be antithetical to healing (unless we specifically know otherwise). As such, all agree that this is an elemental requirement until the very last.[11] The question arises, however, of a dying patient in great pain whose dosage of painkilling medication no longer suffices, while any greater amount might hasten death. Here, Catholic medical ethical thinking took the lead in the general biomedical ethics literature, defining a "doctrine of double effect," which permits medicating for the virtuous intention of achieving pain relief even though death is a foreseeable consequence of that action. This has been interpreted by many to allow "double-effect euthanasia," that is, the administering of large doses of painkilling medication with the expectation that death will follow.[12]

In Jewish precedent, such a choice would not be allowed even the competent patient, since the expectation of death overrides any apparent benefit. In this case, the physician cannot be excused from the analysis, which is his profession, and the competence of the patient is suspect in the face of great pain. For the physician, this is essentially a dilemma of medical judgment. As long as the physician can honestly say that the hastening of death is not probable, the uncertainty is sufficient to prescribe medication to relieve suffering, despite its inherent risks. When the probability turns, so must the physician's behavior, for our concern for pain must be second to the claim of life, and the physician cannot escape his medical judgment.[13]

To a large extent, however, we can hope, and demand of our physicians that the number of cases that require this judgment may be reduced to a null set. There is growing literature in the medical community arguing that the old dilemma of narcotic-induced respiratory failure can even now be successfully circumvented with the proper palliative regimen. Speaking before our Subcommittee in February 1989, Dr. Pat Hartwell, an anesthesiologist at Einstein Medical Center, former director of its critical care unit and past president of the New York State Society of Critical Care Medicine, insisted that with the newest narcotics and anesthetic techniques, the control of pain is always possible before depressing respiration and that "the fear of overdose is not real." She railed against physicians who have not kept up with the state of the art and leave their patients to suffer pain for fear of applying appropriate doses of painkilling medication at appropriate intervals.[14]

F. Advance Directives

We believe that this biological versus mechanical criterion for distinguishing the extension of life from the prolongation of death, if applied assiduously in line with the clinical discussion above and in light of patients' autonomy to direct their own treatment, can serve to direct patients, surrogates, and physicians aright in affirming life, yet recognizing death in its time. It does not differ much from the conclusion reached by Rabbi David M. Feldman in his book *Health and Medicine in the Jewish Tradition:*

> A clear distinction is thus implied between deliberate termination of life and the removal of means that artificially prolong the process of death. Jewish law codes subsequently make the teaching explicit: to "remove hindrances to the soul's departure is permitted and even mandated." While physicians, then, may not disconnect life-support systems where they shorten life thereby, they may do so to shorten the death process. . . . At the outset, the physician should connect the support systems of respiration or circulation; he should not decline to do so on the grounds that this may be prolonging death. He must give the patient every chance for life. Having connected the systems conditionally, however, he may remove them if he then determines that their function was not prolongation of life but of death.[15]

This paper [appearing as this chapter and the previous chapter] has sought to determine the parameters of the halakhah with regard to treatment of the terminally ill. Since so much of this treatment comes under the sway of our ultimate right to direct our own treatment, it follows that this paper becomes primarily an instrument to advise Jewish individuals concerning the decisions that they may have to make about their own care. Unfortunately, all too often our frailty at the latter stages of terminal illness gets in the way of a conscientious personal application of the halakhah, and it is the family or the physician who will seek this guidance.

It is immensely important, halakhically and morally, that all concerned with the treatment of an end-stage patient remember that the ultimate autonomy that undergirds patient decision making rests with the patient alone. Competent individuals can assert the interests of their souls, plausibly claiming to know God's will for themselves, or to be willing to face His judgment. No one else can fully project himself into another's soul and another's place. When patients are unable to express their wishes, however, surrogates[16] and physicians must take over. Lacking direct access to the mind and feelings of the patient, these surrogates need be even more careful to affirm life in their judgment of the best course of treatment than are the patients themselves, for to fail would be, in the baraita's words, akin to murder.[17]

Here is the area in which there is a great usefulness for the living wills or durable powers of attorney that have come into use. Surrogates or physicians armed with written indication of patients' wishes may rely on those instruments to permit what would be permitted the patients under their right of directing their treatment. Even when designated as surrogate by a patient without specific instructions, the surrogate may make necessary decisions that are normally within the realm of the individual since *sheliaḥ adam kemoto*. As surrogate, one functions as an extension of the patient. Nevertheless, as a *shaliaḥ,* a surrogate must proceed with extreme caution and humility not to presume of the patient what cannot be assumed. The surrogate can never be privy to the personal dialogue between the patient and God, the ultimate source of autonomy. Patients themselves cannot know, when they draft living wills, the precise nature of their encounter with God in their final illness. Changes of heart are not uncommon.[18] Thus, even living wills are suspect. Yet treatment decisions must be made. In the face of an incompetent patient, those who knew best the soul of the patient need to stand ready to shoulder the burden of surrogacy with a commitment to furthering the interests of the patient's life in accordance with his or her desires.

G. PVS: Persistent Vegetative State

Some cases involving surrogates pose additional problems because the very meaning of the patients' lives and desires comes into question. A special complication is posed by cases of extended, irreversible coma and PVS, persistent vegetative state. Such unconsciousness follows upon destruction of the higher brain while the brain stem remains largely intact. Patients in this condition may maintain spontaneous reflexes, including heartbeat and respiration, circadian wake/sleep rhythms, eye movements and gestures, but are altogether without consciousness and must be nourished artificially. Physicians feel confident of their ability to diagnose this state, given a flat EEG and lack of responsiveness or of any purposive action with no change over a period of one month. Certain other confirmatory tests, such as CAT scan, MRI (magnetic resonance imaging), blood-flow studies, and carbon-dioxide levels would be used to support such a diagnosis. If maintained, such patients can live for years (the longest recorded case being thirty-seven years).[19] Increasingly, the courts in this country, on the basis of the literature of biomedical ethics, have considered these cases under the rubric of benefits and burdens as cases of no conceivable life benefit to the patient, and therefore, cases in which life-sustaining treatment (including nutrition and hydration) may be withheld or withdrawn. In one noted case, that question centered on the removal of a feeding tube from PVS patient Nancy Cruzan.[20] We do not accept that burdensome life is dispensable, and such a patient is manifestly not in the process of dying.[21] Does that mean that we must maintain patients in such condition until their natural deaths?

If vegetative life is life, the answer would appear to be that we must. We have expressly rejected quality-of-life calculations, nor are such patients able to appreciate the quality of their lives. Here, it appears that we have been cast by God in the role of custodians of a life that He has harshly reined in but allowed to continue. We do not maintain the patient in hopes of some future cure, which would be too slight a hope to maintain, or against the possibility of error in the diagnosis of irreversibility, though any remediable uncertainty in the diagnosis must be pursued.[22] We maintain the patient because it is not within our domain to choose to terminate life.

But these cases remain deeply troubling. Is such a life really life? Has not the soul departed while the body, in some aberrant glitch, refuses to shut down? If so, what courtesy do we owe such a soulless body? Surely not all the reverence we accord human life. Yet when we see the body of a patient breathing and moving before us, though unconscious and, to the best of our medical and scientific knowledge, destined never to be conscious again—can we be certain that this patient's soul (a soul we cannot quantify in scientific terms) has departed? When the family of Nancy Cruzan, the principal in the case argued before the Supreme Court, spoke to her at her bedside, they said things to the effect of, "We do not know if you are there, if you can hear us." The relief they sought for their daughter was not predicated on her being dead, but on the undesirability, even horror, of living with no interaction with the human world. Their question to her was to the point, and as for the answers—we have no way of knowing. Facing an evidently living being, not knowing the state of its soul, we are left with the *ḥazakah* (the legal presumption) of life, and the requirement to treat that life as we would any other life.[23]

H. Neonates

Another area requiring special consideration is that of neonates. These fragile creatures are increasingly being rescued from the grave by extraordinary medical and technological means. They clearly have no personal opinions about their care. To what extent may they be considered sentient creatures at twenty-three weeks and at five hundred grams? Their prognosis for healthy life is often very poor; and for them, as well as for full-term but grossly abnormal babies, what is required of us in terms of treatment?

The principles may be set out in brief: on the one side, our reverence for life, our opposition to determinations based on quality of life; on the other, our awareness of the nonviability of many of these infants (a nonviability recognized by the halakhah in the area of bereavement), and our questions about the limits of medicine and God's intentions. To deal with these issues exhaustively would require a thorough classification of the genetic and medical problems being faced by neonatologists every day. We reserve that discussion for a later essay [found in this volume, chap. 24].

I. Conclusion

Judaism holds clearly and unequivocally that human life, that special presence we know as the human soul, is a divine gift. It comes from God and returns to Him. We seek to do, in our allotted stay on this earth, what He has commanded us to do, as we best understand it, through the tools offered us by revelation, tradition, and reason. We embrace medicine and science as advancing the cause of mankind without any theological hesitation. We demur, however, at that point where our earthly sojourn meets divine destiny. There we continue to apply our best science and our best sense and sensitivity, all the while looking over our shoulders so as not to miss the divine whisper. We must undertake to treat people, even *in extremis*, even to the very last, in a humane and life-affirming way. That means that we must accord the patient's wishes great respect, and our concern for the patient's total well-being must be seamless. Yet above the patient is the presence of the Almighty, closer, it would seem, than at almost any other time. His is the final medical judgment, the final intervention. We seek His guidance and test His instructions by doing all that we can to heal and treat the ill, to the last; we recognize His hand by staying ours where it seeks to overrule the very nature of His creation in favor of a new one that we have devised.

אלהים יחננו ויוציא כאור משפטינו, איום קדוש

May God favor us and broadcast our judgment like radiant light, for He is awesome and holy.

Notes

1. This follows from the value placed upon *ḥayei sha'ah* (life of short duration); see chap. 16, n. 22 of this vol. It is expressed clearly by Rabbi Eliezer Waldenberg in his conclusion to *Tzitz Eliezer* 5, *Ramat Raḥel,* 28. The same is stated by Rabbi Moshe Feinstein in *Iggerot Moshe, Ḥ.M.* 2, 74:2, as long as excessive suffering is not present. This raises the nub of the issue. As long as we are required to respect unconditionally the importance of God-given life, even *ḥayei sha'ah,* the position espoused in this paper, follows. Some respected authorities, however, have sought to resolve our dilemma by manipulating that principle in search of exemptions.

   Secular ethicists, of course, are not committed to the absolute value of life. Thus, "many medical and legal scholars hold that medical benefits should not be understood only in a narrow physiologic sense (after all, there always are some potentially achievable goals) but instead, within a broader context that is relevant to the patient's own values and proportional to their general condition and prognosis" (Dr. Michael Nevins, unpublished draft, "The Legacy of Karen Quinlan"). Colloquially, they speak of curing the person and not the individual diseases. Thus, where a patient is terminal, these voices would allow death by a subsidiary, treatable ailment, since a full cure of the primary disease is unavailable.

   Something akin to this position is argued by Rabbi Immanuel Jakobovits in *Hapardes* 31:1 and 3. He returns to the basic question of the source of the requirement to medicate [see chap. 16, n. 1 of this vol.]. He concludes, with Rambam, that the Talmud's provision permitting medication is based in the verse *verapo yerapei* (he shall surely heal) as elucidated in *Bava Kamma* 85, but that the requirement to heal follows from the rules of return of a lost object—in this case, health. But where a cure cannot be effected, health cannot be restored; therefore, all obligation to treat is removed. My discomfort with this position stems, in the first instance, from my unwillingness to grant that the requirement to heal is simply a version of returning lost objects. Healing clearly flows from the grand premise of life, not the minor premise of property. Furthermore, this position is weaker, in that it can permit only inaction (no obligation) but not withdrawal of treatments. Though there is ample halakhic warrant for the distinction in liability between active and passive involvement, where the issue is life or death this is a very thin reed, indeed. Moreover, this perception will often lead to pernicious results, for if we cannot withdraw a treatment once begun, but only withhold it *ab initio,* the pressure rapidly grows against initiating any treatment that might later prove hopeless but would nonetheless cause the patient to linger. Yet we often do not know which treatment will succeed and which patients will respond, and the pressure not to initiate treatment will certainly cause unnecessary deaths before long. Last, and quite basically, this position opens the door too wide. What is left of the clear prescription that we transgress the Sabbath to save a life, even for the shortest duration? If healing, in such a case, is impossible, the treatment, it follows, is optional—yet it overrides the Sabbath? I do not believe this to be the intent of the tradition.

A second approach, that taken by Rabbi Moshe Feinstein, was proposed before the CJLS by Rabbi Morris Shapiro [see chap. 16, n. 20 of this vol.]. Rabbis Feinstein and Shapiro propose to utilize the talmudic precedents concerning prayer for the release of a suffering soul to argue that excessive pain may make life undesirable, and therefore not to be maintained. At the extreme, this argument could admit quality-of-life considerations and even legitimize euthanasia. Feinstein and Shapiro do not go that route, being constrained by the taboo on murder to limit this policy to inaction, *sheiv ve'al ta'aseh.* As with Jakobovits, this argument only extends to withholding treatment, not withdrawal. It also applies only in cases of excessive pain, offering no leniency where pain is controlled or the patient is insensitive thereto. Indeed, Feinstein expressly reviews the rulings concerning impediments to death, asserting that they only apply in the case of extreme pain, that being the key to releasing our concern for *ḥayei sha'ah.* But no such proviso appears in those rulings, nor does that appear to be the focus of their concern. But more fundamentally, I argued above that the talmudic passages on prayer cannot serve as a precedent for effective medical steps to shorten life. Rather, the limitation of our examples to prayer and later to extraneous impediments to death argues the opposite, that effective life-shortening action (including intentional inaction) must be forbidden; therefore the resort to prayer.

A third approach, which appears in some writers, including Rabbi Shapiro, Rabbi M. D. Wollner (*Hatorah Vehamedinah* 7–8 [5716/17]: 315ff.), and Rabbi G. A. Rabinowicz and Dr. M. Koenigsberg (*Hadarom* [Tishri 5731]: 75), attempts to mitigate the demands of protecting life by questioning the status of the life of the terminally ill patient. Utilizing sources concerning a *tereifah*—that is, a person so wounded in a major organ that he cannot live—which sources rule that the murder of such a person is not punishable (Maimonides, *M.T., Hilkhot Rotzeaḥ* 2:8 et al.), or sources that rule that certain catastrophically broken accident victims are considered "as dead" for purposes of imparting impurity (Maimonides, *M.T., Hilkhot Tum'at Meit* 1:15), these authors argue that given the virtual death of terminally ill patients, they lose their claim to maintenance *leḥayei sha'ah* (for the short term). Technically, these arguments open themselves to great problems in determining which of our patients, diagnosed as terminally ill, fit the much more restrictive criteria of *tereifah* (fatally wounded) or *nikra kadag* (mangled). Thus, Wollner, for instance, using the more stringent purity source, sets criteria that might apply to accident victims but not to end-stage cancer patients.

But much more important is my fundamental objection to taking this tack—that to do so is to permit hastening the death of patients, albeit based on a humanitarian impulse, because we vacate their lives in advance. This is (a) pernicious, (b) unseemly, (c) wrong. Yes, such precedent exists in the literature, but always about incidental results. If you kill a *tereifah,* can you be found guilty, given the stringency applied to capital punishment? No. But there is no implication that such murder is permissible. Do badly injured accident victims defile? Perhaps, but this does not override the requirement to transgress the Sabbath for an accident victim. Should it?

Rabbi Elliot Dorff [in his essay that appears in this vol., chap. 19], basing himself on the work of Dr. Daniel B. Sinclair (*Tradition and the Biological Revolution: The Application of Jewish Law to the Treatment of the Critically Ill* [Edinburgh: Edinburgh University Press, 1989]), has argued this case elegantly. Notwithstanding the persuasiveness of his prose, the fundamental flaw remains. It devalues life in order to attain its end. The approach taken herein to the contrary, I believe, is consistent, precedented, godly, and life-affirming. The other attempts, though all well-intentioned, it seems to me, are deeply flawed.

2. Many secular ethicists have drawn the line at artificial nutrition and hydration, seeing these as normal care and, therefore, not dispensable. But increasingly, the secular ethical consensus in favor of the "right to die" has affected this area, too. Thus, for instance, in an article on hydration (Kenneth Micetich, Patricia Steinecker, and David Thomasma, "Are Intravenous Fluids Morally Required in a Dying Patient?" *Archives of Internal Medicine* 143 [May 1983]: 977), the authors argue that in comatose patients, who will not suffer from thirst and whose death is imminent (less than two weeks), it is permissible to withdraw IV fluids, though not a respirator. They argue:

> We are aware of the irony of withdrawing IV fluids but maintaining the respirator. While there is no normal obligation to continue to use the respirator after the patient's condition is stabilized, nevertheless its withdrawal would precipitate immediate death. Withdrawal of the respirator, while normally possible, creates an immediate consequence of death for which we must take responsibility. It represents an extreme form of abandonment. Letting the patient die of later dehydration or other complications permits the family time to reconcile themselves to death.

Death, to these thinkers, once imminent, may be morally effected by any means, so long as they are not too sudden or jarring.

3. President's Commission for the Study of Ethical Problems in Medicine and Biomedical and Behavioral Research, *Deciding to Forego [sic] Life-Sustaining Treatment* (Washington, D.C.: U.S. Government Printing Office, 1983), 288. The Hastings Center, *Guidelines on the Termination of Life-Sustaining Treatment and the Care of the Dying* (Briarcliff Manor, N.Y.: Hastings Center, 1987), 60. In a presentation to the Subcommittee on Biomedical Ethics of the CJLS on 30 Mar. 1989 and in a subsequent telephone conversation, Dr. Michael Nevins, a cardiologist at Pascack Valley Hospital in Westwood, N.J., and a member of the New Jersey Bioethics Commission, emphatically made the point that artificial feeding is not benign and carries significant risk of its own, because of aspiration, whether by nasogastric tube or gastrostomy (direct to intestine). He reports that according to a study of twenty-nine patients with gastrostomy tubes, within days 50 percent suffered episodes of aspiration pneumonia and half of those died of pneumonia rather than of their underlying conditions.
4. That oral feeding is preferable to any artificial feeding procedures is obvious. Yet both the President's Commission (288) and the Hastings Center (*Guidelines,* 62) felt the need to say so, so powerfully are we drawn to our technological toys (and see comments by Feinstein, *Iggerot Moshe, Ḥ.M.* 2, 74:3). The problem of patient choice with regard to feeding tubes is exacerbated by problems of patient competence that often accompany conditions requiring feeding tubes. Surrogates and physicians need to maintain life wherever possible when the patient's choice is unknown. However, they may choose to see the recurrent removal of a nasogastric tube by a patient who is not otherwise violent as indication of a desire not to suffer the tube.

   Dr. Nevins suggests that in line with the distinction that we have established between medicine (which is the support and enhancement of the body's systems) and the circumvention of major organs and bodily systems, it follows that in advanced Alzheimer's disease and similar degenerative neurological disorders, the failure of the swallowing reflex should be seen as a system failure that the feeding tube seeks to circumvent. This is less obvious a proposition than that concerning mechanical life support. While we do not endorse this view, it appears cogent, and one could be justified in applying the method of this paper in that way. If so, feeding tubes would be dispensable even without patient approval, in such cases where no hope of a return to unaided function is possible. These cases would not include PVS where no dying process is in evidence and where the swallowing reflex may be in place but the lack of patient consciousness makes oral feeding virtually impossible.
5. This is an area where the question of the status of brain death under Jewish law becomes highly relevant. The question is often raised whether patients who are being maintained on respirators may be removed from the respirator, and whether other treatment may be discontinued when they show signs of brain

death. This differs somewhat from the termination of treatment questions addressed here, since a finding of brain death, should it be acceptable to halakhah, would show the patient to be already dead, and therefore not a candidate for further treatment. To continue the trappings of treatment in such a case by mechanically maintaining the operation of the lifeless body must surely be forbidden as a particularly morbid form of *nivul hameit.*

Two types of brain death have been proposed: the cessation of function of the cerebral brain, which controls thought and language, an effective definition of a vegetative state or irreversible coma (see ahead, on PVS); and the cessation of function of the whole brain inclusive of the brain stem, which controls reflex functions, including breathing and heartbeat. The courts and medical community have, to date, taken the more conservative measure of brain death. The Uniform Determination of Death Act proposed jointly by the American Medical Association and the American Bar Association states: "An individual who has sustained either (1) irreversible cessation of circulatory and respiratory functions, or (2) irreversible cessation of all functions of the entire brain, including the brain stem, is dead" (Pres. Comm., 9 n. 7).

Halakhah has as its established criterion of death the cessation of breathing and heartbeat, viz. respiration and circulation (*Yoma* 85a). This is the age-old form of recognizing death codified as the first criterion in the UDDA. It may be noted that this criterion has often proven problematic. Thus, Isserles required a waiting period after apparent cessation of respiration for fear that we are insufficiently expert at recognizing the true moment that breathing finally stops (*S.A., O.Ḥ.* 330:5). Against this stricture, it has been cogently argued that medical technology has progressed to a point where even the most minimal respiratory and circulatory activity can be measured, such that, in their absence, no further waiting period need apply (J. Levy, *Hama'ayan,* Tammuz 5731; on all this, see Rabbis J. David Bleich and Aaron Soloveitchik, in *Jewish Bioethics,* ed. Fred Rosner and J. David Bleich [New York: Sanhedrin Press, 1979], chaps. 17–19, pp. 277–316). On the other hand, modern advances in resuscitation techniques have rendered the cessation of respiration and heartbeat no longer the final word. This does not affect the definition of death—thus, for instance, a patient in whom resuscitation efforts fail is considered to have died at the original cessation of heartbeat, even though some sporadic activity may have been elicited in the attempt. It does, however, require efforts at resuscitation, unless such efforts are known to be futile (Jakobovits, *Jewish Medical Ethics* [New York: Bloch, 1975], 278; and see ahead, CPR).

Using a respirator or heart-lung machine, it may be impossible to tell if circulation and respiration are naturally continuing. Here, the second criterion of the UDDA comes into play: the brain is no longer able to support independent respiration and circulation, so that it may be said that the ongoing processes are purely mechanical, but that the organism is no longer functioning. As noted previously (chap. 16, n. 28), M. *Oholot* 1:6 and Maimonides' commentary thereon, along with the principle of *pesik reisheih* (a legal doctrine concerning effects that follow inexorably upon their cause), establish clearly that when the integrated function of mind and body is irreversibly destroyed, death is established. It is but a small and necessary step from there to the comparable ruling that where we are able to determine that there is no brain activity, even of the brain stem, with elevated carbon-dioxide levels and no perfusion of blood into the tissue of the brain, no communication of brain to body is possible, and the irreversible atrophy of the body known as death has begun. This determination must be made with adequate and redundant testing to guard against human and equipment failure, and accounting for factors such as trauma, hypothermia, or drugs, which might have a temporary effect on the adequacy of such tests, since the determination is of such moment, but whole brain death, as opposed to higher brain criteria, is acceptable according to halakhah.

Rabbi Bleich, in particular, has argued vehemently against this possibility, basing himself on the decapitation model of M. *Oholot*. He writes (308):

> The currently proposed criteria differ significantly from decapitation as described in the Mishnah. Decapitation involves destruction of the entire brain. It might be argued cogently that total cessation of circulation of blood to the brain will result in destruction of brain tissue. Total destruction of the brain might then be equated with decapitation and the patient pronounced dead after total destruction has occurred.

He renews that thesis in *Tradition* 24, no. 3 (spring 1989): 44–66:

> Decapitation . . . involves physical severance of the entire brain from the body. Physiological decapitation, then, must also be defined as physiological destruction of the entire brain. That phenomenon has simply never been observed. To be sure, autopsies performed on patients pronounced dead on the basis of neurological criteria reveal that the brain has become a spongy, liquidy mass. In colloquial medical parlance, this phenomenon is categorized as "respirator brain" because the condition is found in patients sustained on a respirator for a lengthy period of time and is the result of lysis or liquefaction of the brain. However, total lysis apparently does not occur.

This analysis is untenable. Decapitation does not signal total destruction of the tissue of the brain, but only its loss of contact with the organism. Destruction of the brain tissue will surely follow, but only at some unspecified later time. It is precisely the irreversible cessation of the integrated function of brain and body that is modeled by decapitation. Indeed, Bleich's rather lurid description of the deterioration of the brain of respirator patients may be the most eloquent testimony that death has indeed set in, despite the apparent maintenance of life signs through mechanical means. Furthermore, in nn. 4–6, Bleich admits that death follows rapidly upon total brain dysfunction, even where mechanical life support is continued. He expresses puzzlement as to why this should be so, but ignores the obvious message that life is not meant to be prolonged in such cases. He seeks refuge in medieval halakhic argumentation concerning incomplete decapitation, arguments that are not compelling, given the different physiological problem and the difference in medical knowledge.

Bleich does cast some doubt on the efficacy of presently available tests of total cessation of brain-stem activity. However, he defends the right of experts to make final determinations about the cessation of respiration despite the potential for error, yet will not apply similar standards to a determination of brain death. For our purposes, these fine points are close to irrelevant, since even where brain-stem death cannot be conclusively shown, the use of mechanical life support is dispensable as an impediment to impending death.

Standing against Rabbi Bleich has been Rabbi Moshe Tendler, who in July 1986 supported the halakhic acceptability of brain-stem death and reported the same in the name of his father-in-law, Rabbi Moshe Feinstein (*Teḥumin* 7 [5746]: 187ff.; *Tradition* 24, no. 4 [summer 1989]: 9 n. 9; and see back and forth by Rabbi Aaron Soloveitchik and Rabbi Tendler on this in *JAMA* 240 [14 July 1978]: 109). This position effectively became the norm when the Chief Rabbinate Council in Israel cautiously endorsed brain death criteria for the purposes of transplants in Israel in 1987. These criteria are laid out in detail in the Chief Rabbinate Council's report that appeared in *Assia* 42–43 (Nissan 5747): 70–81 (*Sefer Assia,* 6:27–40) and in English with notes by Dr. Yoel Jakobovits in *Tradition* 24, no. 4 (summer 1989): 1–14. These operating instructions are essential for any medical team evaluating a patient for a diagnosis of brain death, but they are not carved in stone. They will certainly change over time.

Bleich, who strongly endorses the views of Israeli authorities who oppose the new criteria, attempts to cast even those criteria as not truly related to brain death, but to the proven expectation that independent respiration can never be restored. There is a tautology here. The total brain death criteria were never intended to do other than establish a neurological analog to the traditional definitions of death.

Thus, the UDDA definition of death is acceptable under halakhah. When these criteria are present, no further treatment of any kind is necessary, or indeed, permitted, and organ donation is then possible. Even without the fulfillment of these criteria, a patient exclusively and irreversibly reliant on life-support equipment, though yet alive, has begun the dying process, and it is appropriate to remove all impediments to death, though patients may continue them if they wish.

6. See previous note.
7. Taffet et al., *JAMA* 260, no. 14 (4 Oct. 1988): 2069f., "In-Hospital Cardiopulmonary Resuscitation": "Of the 77 CPR efforts in patients seventy years of age or older (N.B.: males) who had arrests, 24 (31%) were successful, and in 22 (92%), patients were alive after twenty-four hours. None lived to discharge.

There were 322 CPR efforts in the younger cohort: 137 (43%) were successful, in 124 (91%) of these 137 efforts, patients were alive after 24 hours, and in 22 (16%), patients were discharged alive. . . . When a multivariate analysis was used, the presence of sepsis, cancer, increased age, increased number of medication doses administered and absence of witness were all 'predictive' of poor outcome."

8. While it is true that Isserles rejects this conclusion until an hour has passed without heartbeat or respiration lest it be a faint with heartbeat and respiration imperceptibly maintained, our diagnostic and monitoring abilities are significantly improved and may be relied upon. See n. 5 above, and see Rabbi I. Untermann's classification, obiter dictum, in *No'am* 13, no. 1: 3–4.
9. The question of triage, which goes beyond the scope of this paper, deserves separate treatment. The general principles with regard to lifesaving treatment would appear to be the well-known dictum *ein doḥin nefesh mipenei nefesh* (M. *Oholot* 7:6, the famed abortion text) and the rules of personal priority derived from the desert stories in *Bava Metzia* 62a. But the level of danger and prognosis, as well as certain broad enactments for the sake of society, should enter into the picture. Some attention is given these problems by Dr. Fred Rosner in *Modern Medicine and Jewish Ethics* (New York: Ktav, 1986), chap. 23. And see Dr. Elliot Dorff's suggestive arguments in his paper [that appears in this vol.]; and Dr. Moshe Sokol, "The Allocation of Scarce Medical Resources," *AJS Review* 15, no. 1 (spring 1990): 63ff.
10. This implies that patients on dialysis could choose to cease treatment without incurring the full severity of the sin of suicide. This may indeed be a necessary corollary of the analysis herein. Where an active life is possible, however, the patient must certainly be advised to choose life, much as any patient facing a choice of treatments is advised to maximize life. In the event of willful death, however, this would be a mitigating circumstance that would allow us to treat the deceased with full honor. This provision will effectively apply, as well, to any new mechanical devices that may be devised, such as artificial hearts and lungs. These are clearly mechanical means circumventing system failure. However, their efficacy at restoring meaningful life argues powerfully for their use, even though rejecting them would not constitute suicide. The provisions here permitting the removal of impediments to death do not mandate doing so, nor do they grant permission to do so when restoration to an active life can be effected by their use.
11. R. Immanuel Jakobovits, *Jewish Medical Ethics,* chap. 8; Feinstein, *Iggerot Moshe, Ḥ.M.* 2, 73:9. As Feinstein suggests, pain treatment can have some effect on longevity. "The relief and comfort given an aged patient often affects the prolongation of life if only by restoring the willingness to live" (Pres. Comm., 77 n. 100). Similarly, Dr. Pat Hartwell reported before the Subcommittee (Febr. 1989) that pain can interfere with a patient's sleep and ability to heal, as well as lead to depression, which can further aggravate many conditions. Such pain relief is, in

almost all cases, organic and could not be considered an impediment to death. Moreover, it is undertaken to relieve suffering, not to extend life, a separate justification that stands on its own.

12. Pres. Comm., 80 n. 110. Kenneth Vaux, "The Theological Ethics of Euthanasia," *Hastings Center Report* 19 (Jan./Febr. 1989): 20.
13. Rabbi Immanuel Jakobovits refers both to intent and probability of effect in his description of the situation in which painkilling medication is permitted. He writes (*Jewish Medical Ethics*, 276): "Analgesics may be administered, even at the risk of possibly shortening the patient's life, so long as they are given solely for the purpose of rendering him insensitive to acute pain." Clearly, proper intent is necessary, but it is unclear how great a risk Rabbi Jakobovits had in mind. He does not use words such as "likelihood" or "expectation" of death, as do the representatives of the doctrine of "double effect," but rather refers to "risk" and "possibly." I am not convinced that proper intent can be claimed when flying in the face of legitimate expectations. Therefore the criterion proposed here.

   The role of legitimate expectations is highlighted in a ruling by Radbaz, as cited in *Magen Avraham, O.Ḥ.* 328:8, who states clearly:

   חולה אומר צריך אני לתרופה פלונית ורופא אומר א״צ שומעין לחולה ואם הרופא אומר שאותו תרופה יזיקהו שומעין לרופא

   The patient says, "I need a certain medication," and the physician says, "He doesn't need [it]"; one listens to the patient. But if the physician says the medication will harm him, one listens to the physician.

   Even the patient is limited by the physician's knowledge. Oddly, Radbaz is cited by *Magen Avraham* elsewhere in a seemingly contradictory ruling that *afilu harofe'im omerim shehama'akhal yazikeihu shome'in laḥole.* Even where the physician says the food will harm him, one listens to the patient (*Magen Avraham, O.Ḥ.* 618:3). See *Levushei Serad* there, that the distinction has to do with the relative competences of doctor and patient. With regard to medication, as against food, a patient may exercise autonomy only within accepted medical wisdom. (But see Wollner, who tries to derive a further leniency based on the contradiction. His argument fails to convince.)

   Essentially, this becomes a problem of *pesik reisheih,* wherein the high probability or expected aftereffect cannot be divorced from the action, and intent is no defense, wherefore the ruling *pesik reisheih dela niḥa leih asur.* Where the effect is certain, even though it is not pleasing to him, it [the causative action] is forbidden. Where ill effect is less certain, there is no *pesik reisheih,* and intent governs. Interestingly, the President's Commission, though it proposes to permit use of potentially lethal painkillers when the benefit/burden ratio so indicates, nevertheless criticizes the use of intent to immunize physicians from the foreseeable consequences of their treatment. They write (77–82 and n. 101):

> The question arises as to whether physicians should be able to administer a symptom-relieving drug—such as a painkiller—knowing that the drug may cause or accelerate the patient's death, even though death is not an outcome the physician seeks. The usual answer to this question . . . is often said to rest on a distinction between the goals physicians seek to achieve or the means they use, on the one hand, and the unintended but foreseeable consequences of their actions on the other (Note: The customary use of "foreseeable" is for those things that would be predicted as possible outcomes by a person exercising reasonable foresight; it is not limited to consequences that are certain or nearly certain to occur.). . . . However, health care professionals cannot use it to justify a failure to consider all the consequences of their choices. By choosing a course of action, a person knowingly brings about certain effects. . . . The law . . . holds people to be equally responsible for all the reasonably foreseeable results of their actions and not just for the results that they acknowledge having intended to achieve.
>
> For the use of morphine, or other pain-relieving medication that can lead to death, to be socially and legally acceptable, physicians must act . . . in a professionally skillful fashion (for example, by not taking a step that is riskier than necessary), [and with] sufficiently weighty reasons to run the risk of the patient dying.

Of course, the commission's judgment regarding "sufficiently weighty reasons" and our own differ.

In an interesting turn, Rabbi Moshe Feinstein, writing in *Bishvilei Harefu'ah* (a journal published by the Kiryat Sanz/Laniado Hospital) no. 6 (Sivan 5744 [June 1984]): 35, permits withholding medicines that would extend the life of a patient in severe pain even before that patient is classified as *goseis,* but does not permit pain-relief medication that would shorten life even for a moment, relying on the difference between action (*asei*) and inaction (*sheiv ve'al ta'aseh*). He does not address uncertain effect, but clearly holds any life-threatening action as precluded even to release a patient from a pain that he considers sufficiently important to allow the remedy of conscious and intentional passive hastening of death. His ruling, like this whole discussion, is born of a pessimism and frustration concerning the possibility of continuing life and controlling pain. On this, see directly ahead.

14. Dr. Pat Hartwell, at a meeting of the Subcommittee on Biomedical Ethics of the CJLS of the RA, Febr. 1989. In the aftermath of the controversy in the *Journal of the American Medical Association* in 1988 over a physician's confession to administering painkilling medication with the intent of putting an end-stage patient permanently beyond the reach of suffering, known by the name of the original article ("It's Over, Debbie," *JAMA* 259, no. 2 [8 Jan. 1988]), Dr. Porter Storey reports of his hospice training:

> During the past five years I have treated some 2,000 terminally ill patients to the times of their deaths, mostly in their own homes. . . . I have learned that patients like Debbie do not need to be killed by their physicians to be relieved of their shortness of breath. . . . Shortness of breath, like pain, can be effectively palliated by administering narcotic analgesics . . . [that] can be used safely in people who have very poor respiratory function if the dose is carefully titrated against the symptom. (*JAMA* 259, no. 14 [8 Apr. 1988]: 2095)

Even the President's Commission, which exerts much effort articulating its position in the event of conflict between painkilling and maintenance of life (see previous note), expends greater efforts directing physicians as to the proper treatment of pain, a discussion that virtually precludes the problem at the heart of the prior discussion. One gets the impression that the classical dilemma need no longer exist if physicians only performed up to the best standards of medical science. They write (278ff.):

> Only a minority of dying patients . . . have substantial problems with pain. . . . Fortunately, the chronic pain of dying patients is almost always fairly easy to control. First, the caregivers should seek a remediable cause. . . . Second, anxiety and fear must be mitigated. . . . A nurse or physician who can say with assurance that a patient need never (or never again) feel overwhelmed by pain, and who proceeds to demonstrate the truth of the assertion, greatly eases the patient's mind and reduces his or her attentiveness to pain. Conversely, the most potent stimulus to fear of pain, and thus to increased pain, is inadequately treated pain. Patients who obtain short periods of relief with a narcotic followed by periods of pain while waiting for a next dose become trained to fear the expected onset of pain while pain-free. . . . Adequate treatment for the pain can break this cycle. . . . Control of pain with narcotics involves continual experimentation to keep the dose in the zone between oversedation on the one hand and recurrence of pain on the other, so that the patient stays fairly alert but pain-free. Most patients have a substantial "therapeutic window," though what doses achieve it and at what frequency do change over time. For a few patients, especially when death is close, there is no such zone and the physician, with the patient's or family's concurrence, must be willing to accept sedation if pain is to be avoided.

As described by the President's Commission, the dilemma may only exist with regard to "agonal respiratory insufficiency" in "the last few hours and minutes" (see their description, 294–95). Is this the classical symptom of *gesisah* (imminent death), the noise or liquid in the throat that is referred to by Maimonides in the commentary to M. *Arakhin* 1:3 and codified in a gloss to *S.A.*,

E.H. 121:7 and *Ḥ.M.* 211:2? But Dr. Storey expressly refers to this situation as did Dr. Hartwell, and both insist that the dilemma is moot with proper care.

15. Rabbi David M. Feldman, *Health and Medicine in the Jewish Tradition* (New York: Crossroad, 1986), 95. Closest to our approach, across the board, among the writers and speakers on biomedical ethics, appears to be Dr. C. Everett Koop, former surgeon general of the United States. He writes ("The Challenge of Definition," *Hastings Center Report* 19, no. 1 [Jan./Febr. 1989]: 2–3):

> Tradition . . . places a consistent and primary emphasis on the supreme value of human life. . . . Each one of us must choose for himself or herself. And we're enjoined to choose life. . . . I've been in medicine for a half century, and . . . I have no idea what anyone else's "quality of life" was, is, or will be. . . . If "Granny Doe" appears on my watch, I will want her to receive whatever medical treatment is indicated. . . . I will pay special attention to her receiving the best possible regimen for the management of pain. . . . That does not mean prolonging the act of dying. But it does at least mean providing her with the nutrition and fluids needed to sustain life at most basic levels. And if indeed she were in the final stages of a terminal illness . . . I would prescribe basic nutrition and fluids and then stand back to let nature take its course.

On a public television broadcast on 13 Dec. 1989, part of the *Frontline* series, Dr. Koop, sitting in a panel discussing the Cruzan case, repeatedly distinguished between nutrition and hydration, on the one hand, and respirators on the other, based on the fact that "[respirators] are machines."

16. The qualifications for serving as a surrogate are not subject to halakhic review, being determined by the courts, and are properly subsumed, as a matter of Jewish law, under the principle of *dina demalkhuta dina,* that the law of the land controls. The natural surrogate empowered by courts and legislatures in this country, through whatever mechanism, will tend to be a family member, though not necessarily the closest member, because of problems of emotional involvement. Jewish law is aware of reasons to suspect the emotional motivations of close relatives and would tend, rather, toward rabbinic decisors. This is impractical, in many cases, and will certainly run counter to the law of the land. Rabbis should make themselves available to the family, however, in an advisory capacity.
17. This means, in effect, that surrogates must be cautious never to assume the autonomy of the patient and make treatment decisions according to their own predilections. Wherever possible, the surrogate must decide based on the known predilections of the incompetent patient. Indeed, it is for possessing that knowledge that a given surrogate is usually designated. Absent that knowledge, the surrogate or physician should presume the preference for life that our tradition assumes and not substitute any personally held preferences.

18. An eloquent testimony to the fact of a patient's changing perceptions and to the pitfalls often encountered in family surrogate situations appeared in *JAMA* 251, no. 24 (22/29 June 1984), entitled "Three Worlds," by Dr. Carl Kjellstrand:

    > Her husband left her with us. He refused to dialyze her at home; lately she saw things that weren't there, was up all night and slept at odd hours. They quarreled, and he wanted her treatment discontinued. . . . A family conference was called. . . . A daughter was there, too, and she agreed with her father. "No, I can't do it any more. She is no longer what I was married to. She is crazy. . . . Quarrels, accusations, wandering around at night. Insanity! Better off dead!". . . . I left them and went in to see my patient. . . . "Ann, do you know you are on dialysis, on the artificial kidney?" "Yeah, I've been on for four years." "What would happen if we stopped treatment?" "I would croak." "Some time ago you said you would rather be dead than to go to a nursing home. Lars cannot care for you at home any longer." . . . "Doc, death is scary. I'll make friends in the nursing home, we'll play cards and talk. . . . Lars and I used to love each other so . . . maybe we still do. Something has come up and it pushes us around." . . . We, of course, continued the treatment. She lived on in her three worlds, the grim real one that we shared, her world of memories, softened by time, and a world of frightening hallucinations. Lars never returned to see her.

19. Pres. Comm., chap. 5, pp. 170ff.; Dr. Pat Hartwell, presentation to the Subcommittee, 12 Dec. 1988.
20. *Quinlan,* N.J., 1976; *Leach,* Ohio, 1980; *Severn,* Del., 1980; *Jobes,* N.J., 1987. However, in the State of Missouri case before the Supreme Court, the lower court held that the state has an absolute interest in protecting life and refused to permit withdrawal of her feeding tube. Interestingly, Missouri state attorney general Webster, whose office argued the case, when pressed during a televised symposium on the Cruzan case aired 13 Dec. 1989 as part of public television's *Frontline* series, admitted that had the patient's family objected to the insertion of a feeding tube initially, when her condition had not yet stabilized into long-term PVS, that request would in all probability have been honored. His answer was not perfectly clear, but he appeared to justify this with the standard distinction between withholding treatment and withdrawing it. It was noted, however, that in the early context when the patient's prognosis was not yet known, it would be medically most unusual not to emplace any mechanism that might aid in producing a cure. Only later, when PVS is finally diagnosed confidently, is the question of sustaining the patient indefinitely in a vegetative state likely to surface. So if the family could reject the feeding tube earlier, it was asked again, why can they not now? No answer was forthcoming.

It should be noted that the halakhic criteria established in this paper produce a similar split, but offer a rationale that was not available to the attorney general of Missouri. If a patient, through a living will or other manner, had made known an objection to being sustained on a feeding tube, said patient's right to direct treatment would permit a surrogate to refuse the feeding tube. This refusal, however, must be predicated on the patient's concern about the method of treatment. Without direction from the patient, the surrogate alone would not inherit the patient's autonomy, and must offer the medically indicated treatment. Furthermore, were the patient's living will so worded as to indicate, for instance, "I do not wish to be maintained in a persistent vegetative state. Should it be determined, after a reasonable period of observation, that my consciousness is irreversibly impaired, I would wish all treatment discontinued, including provision of nutrition and hydration," it would be null, for the message contained in that statement of the patient's will is not a legitimate choice between different modalities of treatment, but rather the illegitimate choice of death over life. (Save any contrary considerations raised in the body of this paper directly ahead.) This distinction would quite obviously apply in the matter of the Cruzans. In its ruling on the Cruzan case in the summer of 1990, the U.S. Supreme Court allowed that a state may demand great certainty of the patient's specific wishes, as Missouri did, and therefore found for the state that had prohibited the removal of nutrition and hydration. This left open the possibility of state review of the instant case and the likelihood that permission to withdraw these treatments would eventually pass muster in some state, if not, ultimately, in Missouri itself. Indeed, in Dec. 1990, the court in Missouri approved, and Cruzan's feeding tubes were removed; she died several weeks later.

21. Former surgeon general C. Everett Koop, PBS, *Frontline,* aired 13 Dec. 1989, characterized Nancy Cruzan's condition as follows: "This young lady is severely impaired. She is not terminally ill." Koop opposed removal of the feeding tube and took a position strikingly similar to that of this paper. Another physician, Dr. Joanne Lynn of George Washington University Medical Center, herself favoring removal of the feeding tubes, when asked if Cruzan was dying, answered, "Yes. She's dying like you or I are dying." (N.B.: Gist of remarks, not a true transcript)
22. Although physicians insist on the high level of certainty that can be obtained with proper testing and observation over time, the possibility of error always remains [see chap. 16, n. 34 of this vol.] because of the inherent uncertainties of medicine and because of human errors and inattention that lead, from time to time, to half-baked determinations. Halakhah recognizes the real, but expects maximum attention to detail in arriving at the judgment upon which actions are based. The following frightening scenario was recently played out in New York State, as reported in Bonnie Steinbock, "Recovery from Persistent Vegetative

State?: The Case of Carrie Coons," in *Hastings Center Report* 19, no. 4 (July/Aug. 1989): 14–15.

Carrie Coons, age eighty-six, had a massive stroke in late Oct. 1988 and entered a vegetative state in November of that year. She was unresponsive, and CAT scan and EEG (electroencephalogram) supported the diagnosis of PVS. In late Jan., her sister, with whom she lived, asked that the feeding tube be removed, since her sister would not want to be maintained in that condition. A specialist was consulted and recommended a second CAT scan, but the family refused, since the diagnosis appeared settled. On 4 Apr. 1989, a state supreme court judge granted the petition for removal of the feeding tube, "the first New Yorker for whom a right-to-die petition was approved since the state's highest court, the Court of Appeals, authorized in 1988 the removal of feeding tubes in cases in which the prior wishes of an incompetent patient could be proved." On 9 Apr., she regained consciousness, took food by mouth, and on 10 Apr. engaged in conversation. On 11 Apr., the judge vacated his order. She remained alive and alert as of the published report, and her court-appointed lawyer found her "lucid and able to speak," though she continued to be classed incompetent since, among other things, the neurologist does not find her lucid, but rather "more or less communicative" though "inconsistent." Asked about removal of the feeding tube, she has been ambivalent.

In a similar vein, *Time* magazine, 19 Mar. 1990, reports the case of Rev. Harry Cole, whose comatose wife he sought to detach from a respirator, only to have her regain consciousness and return to a full, active life. "I thought my decision was well planned," said Cole.

Although halakhah allows action on the basis of our best knowledge, cases such as that of Carrie Coons and Jackie Cole must give pause to those who would push for a standard that allows the removal of feeding tubes from PVS patients, given our present state of knowledge (see ahead). As Professor Steinbock (philosophy and public policy, SUNY Albany) observes, the court in the Quinlan case argued that there was no doubt that Karen Quinlan would seek to have her respirator removed were she to become "miraculously lucid" yet know that she would soon return to a permanent vegetative state. There is, in fact, no way to project what "miraculously lucid" PVS patients might choose, given their new and radically altered perception of life during and after an episode of PVS. *Caveat decisor.*

23. Some voices in the medical ethics community would define brain death as the irreversible cessation of the function of the cerebral brain, rather than of the whole brain, so as to declare such permanently unconscious patients for whom there appears to be no hope of ever regaining sentient function as, in fact, dead. This position was taken, during the PBS *Frontline* broadcast of 13 Dec. 1989, by Dr. Fred Plum, a neurologist at Cornell University Medical College. It is argued forcefully by Drs. Stuart J. Youngner and Edward T. Bartlett in "Human

Death and High Technology: The Failure of the Whole-Brain Formulations," *Annals of Internal Medicine* 99 (1983): 252–58. Our halakhic descriptions of death clearly preclude such a definition. The President's Commission likewise found that "permanently unconscious patients are not dead" (173). However, there may be room to consider a more lenient ruling in this regard based on Maimonides' description of ensoulment, for he claims to know what we do not otherwise know of the soul. Maimonides writes:

נפש כל בשר היא צורתו שנתן לו האל והדעת היתרה המצויה בנפשו של אדם היא צורת האדם השלם בדעתו, ועל צורה זו נאמר בתורה נעשה אדם בצלמנו כדמותנו כלומר שתהיה לו צורה היודעת. . . . ואינה הנפש המצויה לכל נפש חיה שבה אוכל ושותה ומוליד ומרגיש ומהרהר, אלא הדעה שהיא צורת הנפש ובצורת הנפש הכתוב מדבר בצלמנו כדמותנו

> The vital principle of all flesh is the form that God has given it. The superior intelligence in the human soul is the specific form of the mentally normal human being. To this form the Torah refers in the text, "Let us make man in our image, after our likeness" (Gen. 1:26). That means that man should have a form that knows. . . . Nor does (this) refer to the vital principle in every animal by which it eats, drinks, reproduces, feels, and broods. It is the intellect that is the human soul's specific form. And to this specific form of the soul, the scriptural phrase "in our image, after our likeness" alludes. (Maimonides, *Yad Haḥazakah, Hilkhot Yesodei Hatorah* 4:8; English, Moses Hyamson, *The Book of Knowledge,* 39b)

A similar bifurcation of the brain into the subcortical brain, the equivalent in humans of the brain of animals, and the neocortex, the seat of humanness, is described in evolutionary terms by Dr. Carl Sagan in his book *Dragons of Eden* (New York: Random House, 1977). If we were to seek to elevate this description to practical halakhah, it would seem possible to conclude that patients with irreversible loss of consciousness have already lost their human life, having been reduced to their former state of animal life. As such, our obligations to such life might be adjudicated under the rules of *tza'ar ba'alei ḥayim* (concern for the pain of living creatures), and generally under a lower level of sanctity. We are loath to consider this option. We do not share Maimonides' certainty about the life of the soul. Furthermore, while this may help solve the particular moral dilemma described here, it does so by demeaning the sanctity of a vessel that carried God's image. To do so carries grave risk of opening the door to the warehousing of cadavers for research and a continuous supply of biological products, and the risk, as well, of extension to the mentally ill. Thus an anonymous marginal commentary to Maimonides. Nor is it clear that this rethinking would resolve the dilemma, since the patient is not in any recognizable pain. The cost of maintaining such creatures might then prove to be the decisive halakhic factor in a decision to discontinue care. I believe that this would be repugnant. Rather, as in antiquity, this is a case that allows us no recourse but to pray for God's compassion, upon the patient and upon us.

CHAPTER 18

End-Stage Medical Care: Methodological Concerns for a Jewish Approach*

Elliot N. Dorff

She'eilah (Question):

In view of modern medicine's technological ability to sustain biological life, how should we treat the terminally ill?

Teshuvah (Response):

The ability of medicine to sustain people in conditions that would have been unquestionably fatal just a decade or two ago is, in some cases, a clear blessing and, in others, the source of physical pain for the patient and of agonizing decisions for all concerned. As I try to address the latter situations here, it is with full appreciation of their inherent moral ambiguity and a renewed sense of my own limitations as a human being and as a Jew in being able to discern the right and the good. Not to face these situations, however, is to make Conservative Jewish law irrelevant to some of the most crucial cases confronting us today, and so one must try.

Rabbi Morris Shapiro first presented a responsum on many of these issues in May 1988. After a full session of discussion, the Com-

*Chapters 18–20 present material that originally appeared in the form of one longer paper, "A Jewish Approach to End-Stage Medical Care." This paper was approved by the Rabbinical Assembly Committee on Jewish Law and Standards, Dec. 1990.

mittee on Jewish Law and Standards decided to ask the chair to appoint the Subcommittee on Bioethics to discuss these complex matters at greater length before the full Committee took action on them. After the Subcommittee had the benefit of hearing from a number of physicians on the relevant medical data, Rabbi Avram Reisner, Chair of the Subcommittee, wrote a responsum. In further discussion and correspondence, it became clear that the Subcommittee was evenly divided on how to conceive of these issues, and so I wrote this responsum to articulate the alternative position of the Subcommittee. In doing so, I have found myself largely agreeing with one of the suggestions in Rabbi Shapiro's original responsum. In this responsum, then, I have supported that proposal, providing the relevant argumentation and spelling out its implications.

To make sure that the reader can distinguish the forest from the trees in the rather lengthy essays that Rabbi Reisner and I have produced, let me briefly state at the outset the similarities and differences in our approaches. Rabbi Reisner and I share a common Conservative methodology, and we share the strong reverence for life at the heart of the Jewish tradition. This leads us to agree on most of the practical questions. We have, however, chosen different legal categories in which to construe many of the issues at the end of life. He prefers to treat most of them as instances of *goseis*, a person in the very last stages of life, while I think that the category of *tereifah* (a terminally ill person) better describes the medical realities and the legal status of the people about whom we are most troubled, the ones whose cases raise difficult moral questions. This leads us to disagree on some matters now, and our disparate approaches will undoubtedly mean that there will be some differences in future issues as well. From beginning to end, though, this is definitely a *maḥloket lesheim shamayim*, a dispute in the name of Heaven.

Several methodological convictions define my approach to matters in medical ethics—and, indeed, to Jewish law generally. In a recent insightful article, Professor Louis Newman pointed out how crucial matters of method are in deciding contemporary issues on the basis of Jewish sources.[1] I accept that as an admonition. Furthermore, since those who part company with me on points of method may well take another tack on the practical matters as well, simply to understand my current decisions it is important to spell out the principles of my methodology at the outset. Moreover, since the medical technology at our disposal and the questions that accompany it change almost daily, only if the parameters of a general approach are delineated clearly can one hope to have the tools to make sound, reasoned judgments on future issues.

A. A Legal, Rather than a Nonlegal, Approach

Jewish tradition has had a long love affair with medicine. It has not flinched from exploring and applying whatever could help people overcome illness, seeing this process not as an infringement upon God's prerogatives, but as aiding God in the process of creation. In doing this, it has been remarkably open to seeking and using new discoveries. Indeed, medieval rabbi-physicians largely ignored expressed talmudic passages detailing specific cures that they found to be ineffective.[2] They saw their overarching duty in this area to be the healing of the sick, even when that required deviating from precedents encased in legal sources.

I mention this because when we turn to the difficult issues that we are now considering, we are confronted with the fact that precedents within the tradition dealing with extending the life of the dying are very few and, more significant, are not on point. Some commonly used sources are not even properly medical; one, for example, recounts Rabbi Ḥananiah ben Teradyon's responses to his students while being burned at the stake, and another describes Rabbi Judah Hanasi's handmaiden interrupting the prayers of her master's students to permit the rabbi to die. Others, while medical, assume far less human ability than we now have to affect the condition of the dying. They speak, for example, of the efficacy of salt on the tongue or a knocking noise coming through an open window to extend life. This is hardly the world of respirators and gastrointestinal tubes.

Rabbi David Ellenson, an important Reform ideologue at Hebrew Union College in Los Angeles, has pointed out that, largely because of the wide disparity between contemporary medical conditions and those of times past, but also for other reasons, some rabbis in all three major movements have suggested abandoning legal methodology altogether. They claim that applying legal methods to earlier sources is playing fast and loose with the sources and is simultaneously not doing justice to current issues. Instead, these writers are individually developing an alternative, nonlegal approach, which Ellenson, following Rabbi Irving Greenberg, calls "covenantal."

> This approach is marked by the dialectical, personal model of relationship between God and humanity found in the Bible. It affirms the belief that "humankind is created so as to be God's partner in completing creation." This means that God's covenant with Israel does not restrict human freedom, but presupposes it. . . . This means that one must search out the tradition for those precedents relevant to the making of an ethical decision. Not to do so would provide an unwarranted break with a huge dimension of the tradition and would deny Jews the wisdom such precedents have to offer. However, this theory also affirms that since human beings are created in the image of God, they share in God's power. . . . In short, human autonomy—the ability of individual persons to make and to act upon their own ethical decisions—derives from the freedom that God has given persons. The affirmation of human autonomy is not the product of Enlightenment thought. Rather, it receives a divine, religious warrant.[3]

In this approach, the rabbi, while certainly a resource for the patient, family, and health care personnel, is not the ultimate arbiter of what is moral in any given case; the individual patient is. As a result, if the patient so chooses, quality-of-life considerations can enter directly into medical decisions, contrary to the bulk of rabbinic opinion to date.

I understand the allure of this approach; as Ellenson says, it "empowers" individuals to make their own decisions, and who does not want to do that? Moreover, the realities of contemporary medicine are indeed very different from those of our ancestors—so much so that one sometimes wonders whether any reading of the sources can properly give guidance to our decisions. Greenberg also claims that the Holocaust has shown us what terrible things can happen when individuals do not take responsibility for their own decisions.

Nevertheless, I think that this approach is wrongheaded. My view ultimately rests upon three factors: (a) my appreciation of the strengths of a legal approach to the moral issues in life and the corresponding weaknesses of the suggested alternative; (b) my conviction that personal responsibility can be retained in a properly understood halakhic system; and (c) my confidence that, when properly understood and applied, legal methods can enable Jewish law to treat realities as new as contemporary medical phenomena. I shall explain the first two assertions in this section, and the third in the next.

Over the course of history, human beings have decided moral issues in a variety of ways, each with its strengths and weaknesses. Some religions and secular systems depend upon the decision of a specific person, chosen for any of a variety of reasons (e.g., Catholicism). Others ask individuals to exercise their own consciences to resolve moral dilemmas (e.g., Protestantism). Some secular systems decide these matters by majority vote, at least in theory. Judaism, however, has historically depended upon a judicial mode, blending exegeses of the Torah and later rabbinic literature, precedents, and customs to arrive at a decision. No method is a foolproof path to moral sensitivity and wisdom, and each one can be abused. Nevertheless, the features inherent in these various procedures give us grounds for analyzing and predicting their respective strengths and weaknesses.

In contrast to the other methods mentioned, the judicial way of deciding moral issues, used by Judaism, has the distinct advantage of continuity, for the determinative parties in the other procedures—a specific person, each individual, or a majority of a society—can switch gears at any moment. A judge may innovate as well but must justify the innovation in terms of the past tradition. This does not ensure a good decision, and it does not even guarantee that the present decision will be a clear-cut copy of past policies; but it does ensure that the tradition will be taken seriously into account and that a thoughtful rationale may be demanded of a judge who deviates from it. Jews have historically adopted this method because they believed that this was the only way to preserve the divine authority of the tradition, but such continuity is also crucial to preserve the identity of a people as widely scattered as Jews are. Moreover, the inherent conservatism of the judicial mode enables it to bring to bear the wisdom of the past without being enslaved to it—at least if judges are adept at judicial methods of stretching the law when necessary. Judgment calls are clearly central to this method, and not everyone will agree with any given decision; but the continuity, authority, and coherence that this method produces, together with its ability to balance the past with the needs of the present, are clear advantages that should not be lightly discarded.

In contrast, a method that seeks to determine morality on the basis of each individual's interaction with God poses a severe danger of anarchy. One wonders how community is supposed to be maintained under such a system. Reform thinkers such as Rabbi Eugene Borowitz have claimed that Jews are identified by their common commitment to the Covenant, but I, for one, doubt whether that has any meaning in practice without specification of authoritative norms under the Covenant.

Moreover, this method ironically robs individuals of precisely what they seek when they turn to religion for guidance in these matters, for it tells them to seek God and decide for themselves. The Reform movement, committed to this kind of autonomy, has even produced a body of responsa in an attempt to inform people of how some rabbis, at least, understand the tradition, but ultimately these responsa cannot relieve individuals of any of the responsibility of such decisions, for on this model everyone bears the full weight of moral culpability for the decisions that are made.

In one sense, of course, this is right and proper, which brings me to my second point. For Rabbi Irving Greenberg, one lesson of the Holocaust is that people should not depend upon the law to tell them what is right and proper, for the legal mode carries with it the ultimate danger of legitimating morally atrocious acts. He is clearly right in his warning, but even he must admit that the Nazis' use of law constituted an abuse of it. The correct lesson to learn from that event is not that because of this danger, the law should be abandoned as a way of determining moral decisions, but rather that individuals retain the obligation to examine any law for its morality and to disobey any ruling that is immoral on its face. Once again, this is not an easy criterion to use, especially in morally complex matters such as those posed by contemporary medicine, for one person's judgment about these issues may well differ from another's. If a legal system is working properly, however, those adhering to it should be able to depend on it to guide them through morally murky waters, and they would need to disobey the law only in cases of obvious and gross moral perversion. Jewish law clearly assumes both elements of this methodology: it asserts that God's law is just and good, and it bids us obey the rabbis' interpretation of that law in each generation; but it also requires that we go beyond the letter of the law and even disobey it when it—or a given interpretation of it—is mean-spirited or downright immoral.[4] Thus, personal responsibility can and would be retained in a properly understood halakhic system, but the burden of moral responsibility would not fully and exclusively devolve upon the individual.

B. Weighing the Applicability of Precedents

How, though, should we apply Jewish law to contemporary medical questions? Orthodox rabbis have generally taken their customary literalist approach. Some have indeed been ingenious in making the few precedents available seem to determine the outcome of contemporary questions; Basil Herring's *Jewish Ethics and Halakhah for Our Time* is an especially thorough and fair presentation of their various attempts to do this on many issues.[5] This procedure, however, ignores the historical context of past medical decisions and the crucial differences between medical conditions then and now. In Arthur Danto's felicitous phrase, such responses to the issues are paradigm examples of "misplaced slyness." The source simply did not contemplate the realities of modern medicine; neither, for that matter, do American legal sources from as recently as the 1940s. Consequently, reading such laws and precedents closely to arrive at decisions about contemporary medical therapies all too often amounts to sheer sophistry. The texts themselves, in such attempts, are not providing clear guidance but are being twisted to mean whatever a particular rabbi or judge wants them to mean.

In a different form, in truth, this is simply legal method. To bring new situations under the umbrella of the law, judges in any legal system must often stretch precedents to make them relevant to new circumstances. Indeed, for a legal system to retain continuity and authority in current decisions, this must be done. Thus, if a decision is going to be Jewish in some recognizable way, it must invoke the tradition in a serious, and not a perfunctory, way. One can do this without being devious or anachronistic if one does not pretend that one's own interpretation is its originally intended meaning (its *peshat*) or its only possible reading. The Conservative objection to many Orthodox readings of texts is thus both to tone and method: not only do many Orthodox responsa make such pretenses (often with an air of dogmatic certainty), but they do so with blatant disregard for the effects of historical and literary context on the meaning of texts and for the multitude of meanings that writings can often legitimately have.

Even if we set aside such matters of intellectual honesty, on a purely practical basis, literalist efforts to arrive at contemporary medical decisions seem to be misguided. Even if we presume that our ancestors were consummately wise and divinely inspired in making the decisions they did, there is no reason to suppose that their decisions would bear those qualities in our own setting. On the contrary, I am sure that they themselves would have insisted, as the Talmud did, that each rabbi now take a good look at "what his eyes see"[6] to be sure that his application of the tradition is deserving of the godly qualities of wisdom and kindness that we ascribe to Jewish law.

In our topic, "what his eyes see" means, in my view, just what it meant for medieval Jewish physicians and rabbis. Specifically, we should apply the general theological and legal concepts that emerge out of our heritage to the conditions at hand, even if this means deviating from the specific directions given in a specific precedent. We want to root our decisions as strongly as possible in the tradition, but not at the cost of ignoring the significant differences between the medical circumstances of our own time and those of the past. To carry out this program, we must first determine whether medical practice has changed significantly in the area of medicine that we are considering. This is in itself a judgment that depends on a substantial understanding of the history of medicine, among other factors. If medicine in this area is more or less the same as it was in the past, we can proceed in a fairly straightforward, legal manner. If, on the other hand, we find that innovations in medical practice have made conditions relevantly different from what they had previously been, we will have to stretch some halakhic and aggadic sources beyond their original meanings. We should do this in order to retain clear connections to the tradition—not only in spirit and concept, but in expression. At the same time, we should openly state what we are doing: namely, that we are choosing the texts to apply as well as the interpretations of those texts to develop a Jewish medical ethic that carries traditional Jewish concerns effectively into the contemporary setting.

In insisting that we retain the legal form and substance of past Jewish law, I am disagreeing with Reform positions such as that articulated by Matthew Maibaum. He claims that the radical individualism and secularism of contemporary American Jews mean that "to an increasing degree, trying to talk about Jewish medical ethics from a traditionalist point of view will impress no one."[7] He objects not only to using the precedents of the past, but even to many of the concepts that underlie those precedents—concepts such as God's ownership of our bodies.

It seems that this makes one's claim to articulate a Jewish position all too tenuous. With such an approach, how does one rule out anything as being contrary to Judaism? Why, indeed, would one be interested in developing a specifically Jewish approach to medical matters in the first place?

From one perspective, then, there is a methodological spectrum, in which positions are differentiated according to the degree to which individual Jewish sources are held to be determinative of specific, contemporary medical practices. For most Orthodox rabbis, who read the classical texts of the Jewish tradition in a literalist way, such texts are totally determinative; thus, the only substantive question is how you are going to read your decision out of, or into, those sources. For at least a segment of the Reform movement, the goal, as Maibaum says, is to show secular Jews that a given Jewish position "also happens to be immediately and centrally good for them." If this cannot be shown, then the whole tradition is "like a fine fossil or an elegant piece of cracked statuary; it is venerable, but is not relevant today."[8] I am taking a methodological position between these two poles, affirming the necessity to root a contemporary Jewish medical ethic in the Jewish conceptual and legal structure of the past, but recognizing that to do so honestly and wisely we will have to make difficult judgments as to when and how to apply that material to substantially new settings.

The Conservative position, however—in these matters, as in all others—is not defined solely by what it denies or by its comparison with others; on the contrary, central to its identity is its positive position on the proper way to understand and apply Jewish sources. In brief, it affirms that an accurate assessment of Jewish conceptual and legal sources—both early texts and their later interpolations throughout history—requires studying them in their historical contexts. Once one has done that, one can identify the relevant similarities and differences between previous settings and our own. Only then can one hope to apply traditional sources authentically and perhaps even wisely to contemporary conditions.

C. Rules versus Principles and Policies

Ronald Dworkin, an eminent legal philosopher of our time, has made a distinction that is important for our purposes. He points out that some standards that judges invoke are rules that "are applicable in an all-or-nothing fashion." If the rule describes facts that exist, then the rule is either valid or not. The rule is valid if we agree that it governs the situation that we are considering, in which case the answer that the rule supplies must be accepted. If the rule is not valid—that is, we decide that it does not govern the situation—it contributes nothing to the decision. Rules play a central role in domains such as games, military procedure, and diplomatic protocol much more than they do in legal decisions, so the use of rules is probably best illustrated in one of the former settings. To use Dworkin's example, in baseball an umpire cannot consistently acknowledge that a batter who has had three strikes is nevertheless not out. There may be exceptions to the rule (e.g., if the catcher drops the third strike), but then an accurate statement of the rule would stipulate that exception. Once the conditions of the rule have been met, however—in this case, three strikes that the catcher has caught—the result that the batter is out follows inexorably.

In contrast, principles and policies do not automatically determine consequences when the conditions stipulated are met. Dworkin defines principles and policies as follows:

> Most often I shall use the term "principle" generically, to refer to the whole set of . . . standards other than rules; occasionally, however, I shall be more precise, and distinguish between principles and policies. . . . I call a "policy" that kind of standard that sets out a goal to be reached, generally an improvement in some economic, political, or social feature of the community (though some goals are negative, in that they stipulate that some present feature is to be protected from adverse change). I call a "principle" a standard that is to be observed, not because it will advance or secure an economic, political, or social situation deemed desirable, but because it is a requirement of justice or fairness or some other dimension of morality.[9]

Legal decisions use principles and policies extensively, but the latter never totally determine the outcome of a case. One principle of U.S. law, for example, is that people should not profit from their legal wrongs, but there are clear cases in which the law allows them to do just that. For example, the law recognizes that adverse possession (that is, when I trespass on your land unchallenged long enough) ultimately establishes my right to cross whenever I please, and, while it may punish my breach of contract with civil damages, I can still break my contract to take one that is much more lucrative. In these instances, we do not say that the principle needs to be amended to stipulate exceptions to it because we cannot hope to capture all the situations in which we would want judges to decide contrary to the principle. They are not treated, as rules are, in an "all or nothing" fashion. Instead, we ask judges to weigh principles and policies against each other in every case to which they reasonably apply. In that way, principles and policies establish important considerations that courts must address in cases to which they are relevant, but they do not determine outcomes without exception. (There is no weighing of one rule against another; when rules conflict, some second-order rule must stipulate which takes precedence—e.g., a second-order rule that prefers a rule enacted by a higher authority, or a rule enacted later, or the more specific rule.)

In law, though, it is not always clear whether a standard is to function as a rule or a principle (or policy). Does the first amendment to the United States Constitution ban Congress from any impediment to freedom of speech (that is, is it a rule?), or does it establish a policy that Congress may not ban freedom of speech unless there is some important social reason to do so? The amendment is not clear on its face as to that issue; only later court decisions determine how the law is going to be construed and used.[10]

It is precisely this issue that applies to much of what we will have to say about end-of-life issues. Orthodox responsa generally treat the sanctity of human life and the consequent need to preserve even small moments of it (*ḥayei sha'ah*), whatever its quality, as an overarching axiom—a rule, in Dworkin's terminology. In an immensely insightful doctoral thesis at the Hebrew University, however, Rabbi Daniel Sinclair has pointed out that, while Judaism certainly cherishes human life, it does not include a duty to preserve all human life under all circumstances at whatever cost. On the contrary, in some situations we are actually commanded to take a human life (e.g., when execution is mandated by law, or when killing another in self-defense). In others, we are obligated to give up our own lives (specifically, when the alternative is that we ourselves must commit murder, idolatry, or incest).[11] Although Sinclair does not mention this, it is important to point out, along these lines, that the biblical phrase "and you shall live by them" (Lev. 18:5) is a divine promise in the Torah, not a command, and in Jewish law it functions as the ground to justify overriding other commandments in order to save a life; it is not meant, either in the Bible or in later rabbinic literature, as a general command to save all human life in all cases. Instead, Jewish law, based upon that verse and others, establishes a general policy to preserve life, but, like all other policies, this one is open to being supplanted in given circumstances by specific considerations.

It was Maimonides, Sinclair suggests, who was the quintessential exemplar, in the Jewish tradition, of the method of creating rules to derive specific laws deductively from them. This followed from Maimonides' general distrust of analogical, legal reasoning. One of the principle criticisms leveled against his code, in fact, was that if Jewish law amounted to a series of unexceptional rules, there was no need for rabbinic adjudication. The overwhelming preponderance of rabbis, however, did not follow Maimonides in articulating general rules and deducing specific rulings from them; most rabbis instead reasoned analogically from individual precedents. The latter method might admit of generalizing commonly held policies with regard to a given matter, but not of creating inviolable rules.[12]

Whether or not one agrees with Sinclair's ascription of this method to Maimonides, it can certainly be said that historically some rabbis have tried to establish rules and to deduce their rulings in specific cases from them, while others—the vast majority—have understood generalizations in the law as summaries of some decisions but not as determinative instructions for others. The former, deductive approach was undoubtedly influenced by the medieval penchant for systematics in both thought and law, and it produced the genre of codes; the latter, casuistic method has its roots in the Bible and the Babylonian Talmud, and it has led to the genre of responsa.[13] While many rabbis in the last millennium have used both methods at various times, some have tried as much as possible to fit their decisions under the rubric of a well-defined rule, while most have preferred to reason analogically from a variety of precedents.

In any case, this distinction in method is crucial in cases such as those treated in this responsum for two reasons. First, a rule that seems unexceptional in one era may be subject to serious criticism in another when circumstances have changed. The use of rules to determine law would then require the wrenching task of either discarding the long-standing rule, radically reconceptualizing its meaning and application, or bearing the guilt of making exceptions to it. Any of those alternatives would amount to a disorienting departure in what one had assumed to be a fixed rule. Normal legal reasoning, however, simply sets one on a search for other precedents within the law that seem to be more appropriate to the case at hand. One may not always find such precedents—and then some serious revision of the law may be necessary even when using this approach—but the chances of extending the law aptly by using this method are considerably greater than when invoking hard and fast rules. Second, arguing analogically from precedents is the standard method in Jewish law; therefore, following it is actually adhering to the more traditional approach.[14]

D. Balancing General Rules and Individual Cases

One other methodological point. Through the good efforts of our chair, Rabbi Avram Reisner, the Subcommittee on Bioethics of the Committee on Jewish Law and Standards has had the immense benefit of talking with a number of physicians who deal with various aspects of end-stage care on a regular basis. One of our consultants was Dr. Michael Nevins, who, in addition to having medical expertise, is an observant and active Conservative Jew. In a written response to an earlier draft of Rabbi Reisner's responsum, Dr. Nevins pointed out how important the context of a specific medical decision is. He urged us to use not only what Harvard psychologist Carol Gilligan has called the "masculine voice" in ethics—that voice concerned primarily with abstract principles—but also what she calls the "feminine voice," which pays more attention to the specific human situation in which the decision is made, the relationships of the people involved, and the question of how a course of action will help or hurt.[15] Dr. Nevins also invokes another model to make the same point:

> In these cases, perhaps we do best when we emulate the Hasidim, who followed their emotions, rather than the Mitnaggedim, who relied excessively on their intellect. Yes, we must be cognizant of standards, both secular and religious, but we should not lose sight of the human tragedies of patient and family, and our first responsibility is to them.

I agree with his concern, as my discussion below [in the next two chapters] will demonstrate. I must say, though, that this approach is neither distinctly feminine nor distinctly Hasidic. The first story I heard about Jewish law, in fact, came from my father. My grandparents and their children lived across the street from a large Orthodox synagogue, of which they were members. Because of the proximity, my grandparents often hosted guests of the congregation for Shabbat. One Friday afternoon, my grandmother sent my father, then a lad of fifteen or so, to ask Rabbi Solomon Scheinfeld when the guests for that week were expected. (Rabbi Scheinfeld served that congregation from 1902 to 1943 and, according to the *Encyclopaedia Judaica*, "was the recognized head of the city's Orthodox congregations during his tenure."[16] The *Encyclopaedia* clearly refers to the camp of the Mitnaggedim, for the Twersky family was firmly in charge of Milwaukee's Hasidim.) When my father entered the rabbi's office, he was in the process of deciding whether a chicken was kosher. As Rabbi Scheinfeld turned the chicken over in his hands, he asked the woman who had brought it many questions about the physical and economic health of her husband and family. After he pronounced the chicken kosher and the woman left the room, my father asked him why he had asked so many questions about her family. The rabbi replied, "If you think that the kosher status of chickens depends only on their physical state, you understand nothing about Jewish law!"

This, of course, attests only to the attitude of one rabbi in one instance, but it does bespeak the Jewish tradition's insistence that law and morality are, and must be, intertwined.[17] In any case, I cannot help but think that Rabbi Scheinfeld was right about how Jewish law should be applied to chickens and, all the more so, to human beings.

Even Drs. Nevins and Gilligan, though, acknowledge the importance of articulating general standards—that is, commonly used policies; one must just know when and how to use them. In the technical terms of contemporary ethicists, I am arguing neither for an exclusively situational ethic nor for a solely rule-based one (regardless of whether the rules are seen as deontological or consequentialist); I am suggesting instead a character-based ethic, in which both rules and contexts play a part, along with moral moorings in philosophical/religious perspectives and narratives, and moral education to produce moral sensitivity in the first place.[18] This is a much richer—and, I think, a much more realistic—view of how moral norms evolve and operate than is the traditional attention exclusively to rules and specific decisions taken under them.

This approach does include principles and policies, though, as important components of how we make moral decisions. Let us turn [in the next chapter] to some basic policies that come out of the Jewish tradition and that, at least in many cases, can and should inform our decisions on medical matters at the end of life.

Notes

1. Louis E. Newman, "Woodchoppers and Respirators: The Problem of Interpretation in Contemporary Jewish Ethics," *Modern Judaism* 10, no. 1 (Febr. 1990): 17–42; reprinted in *Contemporary Jewish Ethics and Morality: A Reader,* ed. Elliot N. Dorff and Louis E. Newman (New York: Oxford University Press, 1995), 140–60.
2. Tosafot, *Mo'ed Katan* 11a; Jacob ben Moses Mollin, *Yalkutei Maharil* (Segal), cited in Fred Rosner, *Medicine in the Bible and the Talmud* (New York: Ktav,

1977), 21; Solomon Luria, *Yam Shel Shelomo,* "Kol Basar," sec. 12; Joseph Karo, *Kesef Mishneh* commentary to *M.T., Hilkhot De'ot* (Laws of Ethics), 4:18; Abraham Gombiner, *Magen Avraham* commentary to *S.A., O.Ḥ.* 173.

3. David Ellenson, "Religious Approaches to Mortal Choices: How to Draw Guidance from a Heritage," in Dorff and Newman, 129–39. The articles that he cites as articulating one form or another of this approach are: Daniel H. Gordis [a Conservative rabbi], "Wanted—The Ethical in Jewish Bio-Ethics," *Judaism* 38, no. 1 (winter 1989): 28–40; Irving Greenberg [an Orthodox rabbi], "Toward a Covenantal Ethic of Medicine," in *Jewish Values in Bioethics,* ed. Levi Meier (New York: Human Sciences Press, 1986), 124–49; David Hartman [an Orthodox rabbi], "Moral Uncertainties in the Practice of Medicine," *The Journal of Medicine and Philosophy* 4 (1979): 100ff.; and Eugene B. Borowitz [a Reform rabbi], *Choices in Modern Jewish Thought* (New York: Behrman House, 1983), esp. 367–68, and "The Autonomous Self and the Commanding Community," *Theological Studies* 45 (1984): 48–49.
4. See my article "The Interaction of Jewish Law with Morality," *Judaism* 26, no. 4 (fall 1977): 455–66.
5. Basil Herring, *Jewish Ethics and Halakhah for Our Time* (New York: Ktav, 1984).
6. B. *Bava Batra* 131a. To see how this text and others like it were used in the Middle Ages, cf. Elliot N. Dorff and Arthur Rosett, *A Living Tree: The Roots and Growth of Jewish Law* (Albany: State University of New York Press; and New York: Jewish Theological Seminary of America, 1988), 383–95.
7. Matthew (Menachem) Maibaum, "A 'Progressive' Jewish Medical Ethics: Notes for an Agenda," *Journal of Reform Judaism* 33, no. 3 (summer 1986): 29. He is definitely correct, though, in his call for Conservative, Reconstructionist, and Reform rabbis to articulate their respective views on medical matters in written form and to anthologize them into easily accessible collections so that lay Jews do not mistakenly think that the only Jewish views on these matters are those of the Orthodox, simply because they are the only ones in print. (The Orthodox, who publish books with titles such as "Jewish Bioethics," certainly do not let on that there are other possible Jewish approaches.)
8. Ibid., 29.
9. Ronald Dworkin, *Taking Rights Seriously* (Cambridge, Mass.: Harvard University Press, 1977), 22. His characterization of the distinctions among rules, principles, and policies appears on 22–31. (This chapter of his book originally appeared in the *University of Chicago Law Review,* 1967.)
10. As Dworkin points out, sometimes courts muddy the waters yet further by interpreting rules with words such as "reasonable," "significant," and "just," which invoke the principles or policies that led the legislature to enact the rule in the first place. "But they do not quite turn the rule into a principle, because even the least confining of these terms restricts the kind of other principles and policies on which the rule depends." Ibid., 28.

11. The Torah mandates executing people for a long list of offenses. Largely through specifying stringent evidentiary rules, the Rabbis narrowed the scope of this punishment considerably (cf. M. *Makkot* 1:10), but they retained it, at least in theory. The Talmud (if not the Bible) requires that, even at the cost of killing the attacker, we defend both ourselves (Exod. 22:1; B. *Berakhot* 58a; *Yoma* 85b; *Sanhedrin* 72a) and even others (the law of *rodeif,* B. *Sanhedrin* 72b–73a; *M.T., Laws of Murder* 1:6–7; *S.A., Ḥ.M.* 425:1). The duty to give up one's own life when the alternative is to commit murder, idolatry, or incest is specified in B. *Sanhedrin* 74a.
12. Daniel B. Sinclair, *Tradition and the Biological Revolution: The Application of Jewish Law to the Treatment of the Critically Ill* (Edinburgh: Edinburgh University Press, 1989), 80–81, 88–89. This distinction is parallel to one commonly cited in Anglo-American law between absolute and rebuttable assumptions of the law.
13. Umberto Cassuto has made this point with reference to biblical law codes, which, he says, "should not be regarded as a code of laws, or even as a number of codes, but only as separate instructions on given matters." See his *A Commentary on the Book of Exodus* (Jerusalem: Magnes Press [Hebrew University], 1967), 260–64. The Babylonian Talmud in B. *Eruvin* 27a and B. *Kiddushin* 34a expressly objects to treating the Mishnah's general rules as inviolable principles; moreover, in practice it routinely interprets general principles announced in the Mishnah (with phrases such as *zeh hakelal*) not as generalizations at all but rather as additions of further specific cases. See Jacob Eliyahu Efrati, *Tekufat Hasabora'im Vesifrutah* (Petaḥ Tikvah: Agudat Benei Asher [New York and Jerusalem: Philipp Feldheim, Inc., distributors], 1973), pt. 2, pp. 157–278 (Hebrew), who demonstrates this with regard to the eighty-five unrepeated instances in the Mishnah where this expression occurs and who claims that these discussions, limited to the Babylonian Talmud, are Saboraic in origin (i.e., from 500–689 C.E.). (I thank my colleague at the University of Judaism, Dr. Elieser Slomovic, for this reference.) See also Dov Zlotnick, *The Iron Pillar—Mishnah: Redaction, Form and Intent* (Jerusalem: Bialik Institute, 1988), for a shorter, but sufficient, discussion of this in English. With regard to the genre of Jewish codes, its methodological pros and cons, and its origins in medieval systematics, see Dorff and Rosett, 366–401.
14. The more radical option of instituting revisions in the law (*takanot*) is also an available alternative within the methods of classical Jewish law, and, given the radically new realities of contemporary medical practice, one might reasonably argue that such revisions can be more easily justified in this area than in most others. I would agree, but I share the tradition's reticence to employ this method unless absolutely necessary (cf. Dorff and Rosett, ibid., 402–20). We do not have much experience in dealing with many of the morally excruciating questions posed by modern medicine, so at this point we have not yet had time to see if instituting revisions is required. I think that the classical methods of legal

exegesis and analogizing, if used creatively and sensitively, are fully capable of producing appropriate guidelines to modern Jewish medical decisions, and we owe it to the tradition to try to use these more conservative methods for a period of time before resorting to *takanot*.

15. Carol Gilligan, *In a Different Voice* (Cambridge, Mass.: Harvard University Press, 1982).
16. *Encyclopaedia Judaica* 11:1590, s.v. "Milwaukee."
17. Cf. my article "The Interaction of Jewish Law with Morality."
18. Stanley Hauerwas has probably been the preeminent exponent of this in the Christian world; cf. his *Character and the Christian Life: A Study in Theological Ethics* (San Antonio: Trinity University Press, 1975); *Vision and Virtue* (Notre Dame, Ind.: Fides Publishers, 1974); *Truthfulness and Tragedy* (Notre Dame, Ind.: University of Notre Dame Press, 1977); and *A Community of Character: Towards a Constructive Christian Social Ethic* (Notre Dame, Ind.: University of Notre Dame Press, 1981). Cf. also Alasdair MacIntyre, *After Virtue* (Notre Dame, Ind.: University of Notre Dame Press, 1981); James William McClendon, Jr., *Ethics* (Nashville: Abingdon, 1987); and Paul Lauritzen, "Emotions and Religious Ethics," *The Journal of Religious Ethics* 16, no. 2 (fall 1988): 307–24. I am indebted to Professor Louis Newman for this last reference.

CHAPTER 19

End-Stage Medical Care: Halakhic Concepts and Values*

Elliot N. Dorff

[This chapter continues the discussion of chapter 18 in addressing the following question: In view of modern medicine's technological ability to sustain biological life, how should we treat the terminally ill?]

The relevant Jewish concepts and rules in cases [of end-stage medical care] can be summarized as follows:

A. The Duty to Maintain Our Life and Health

Our bodies are not our own to do with as we will; they are, rather, God's property, on loan to us throughout our lives. We therefore bear a responsibility to God to take reasonable care of them through proper diet, exercise, sleep, and hygiene, and we have a clear-cut duty to avoid endangering them. Although the Talmud does not explicitly establish a duty for each Jew, when ill, to seek medical care, it does permit physicians to heal (despite God's role in inflicting sickness and healing it), and it does require that Jews live only in a community that has a physician. These and other provisions of talmudic law—as, for example, the

*Chapters 18–20 present material that originally appeared in the form of one longer paper, "A Jewish Approach to End-Stage Medical Care." This paper was approved by the Rabbinical Assembly Committee on Jewish Law and Standards, Dec. 1990.

mandate to violate the Sabbath to save a life—were seen in later Jewish legal literature as the basis for a positive duty on the part of each Jew to seek professional medical help in regaining health. It is important to note that, for the tradition, this is not simply good advice, as it is for adults in American law, but a legal duty, which we must do. Even though it took some time for the tradition to articulate this as such, it follows naturally from the theological presupposition underlying all of Jewish medical ethics, that our bodies belong to God.[1]

B. The Role of the Patient in Determining Therapy

What constitutes appropriate care depends, of course, upon objective medical data concerning the status of the patient and the outcome of possible therapies, but it also depends upon the patient's will. Individual Jews do not, under Jewish law, have the same degree of autonomy that they increasingly enjoy under American law. They do not, for example, have the right to refuse medical care altogether, and under Jewish law women do not have nearly the scope of discretion to abort a fetus as they currently do under American law.

Nevertheless, as Rabbi Avram Reisner has aptly demonstrated, individual Jews do determine considerable elements of their health care. Specifically, if individuals feel that they cannot bear the treatment that the physician prescribes, they may refuse such treatment. Indeed, the Talmud specifies that patients may choose their physician, when there is more than one available (the basis for the penchant of Jews, more than others, to seek a second opinion?) as well as their therapy, when several courses of action are medically justifiable. Ultimately, people have the freedom of will and the physical ability—although not the sanction—to disregard Jewish law entirely, and this includes the directives of the physician to carry out the halakhic mandate to preserve one's health.[2]

In practice, this means that a dramatic confrontation between physician and patient should be avoided in the first place. Instead, in prescribing a therapy, the physician should explain to the patient the facts and the alternative modes of treatment, each with its benefits and drawbacks, and then the physician and patient should together decide what to do. As contemporary ethicists have pointed out, this process is immensely complex, for patients and physicians may not share the same values, goals, sensitivities, or lifestyles, and physicians may be so unaware of these differences in perspective that they never even bother to explore or explain alternative approaches to treating a disease. They simply assume that what they think is right is what the patient wants. This approach, however, is futile, for the best of prescribed treatments, if not endorsed and followed by the patient, is useless. Thus, while classical Jewish sources put the decision as to the course of therapy in the hands of the physician, every sensible doctor will discuss the proposed form of therapy with the patient and will ultimately decide on one that will enlist the patient's agreement and cooperation.

C. The Distinction between Sustaining Life and Prolonging Dying

For the last eight hundred years or so, traditional Jewish sources have drawn a line between sustaining a person's life, on the one hand, and prolonging the process of dying, on the other. The former we are obliged to do, the latter we are not.[3] In many contemporary instances, medical technology has made this distinction harder to draw. Nevertheless, we must try to preserve the tradition's intent in differentiating these activities—namely, that we do nothing to hasten death and thereby coopt the prerogative of God to determine such matters and, along the same lines, that we openly recognize that physicians are not, and should not be expected to be, omnipotent in effecting cure. In the words of Kohelet (Eccles. 3:1–2), "A season is set for everything, a time for every experience under heaven; a time for being born and a time for dying. . . . "

D. Effective versus Beneficial Therapies

The line that the tradition draws between sustaining a person's life and prolonging his or her death also bespeaks another of its concerns. In times past, choosing an appropriate course of care with this distinction in mind was relatively straightforward, since nothing much could be done to keep the patient alive, anyway. In our time, this is no longer true. We can now keep people alive long past what would have been their natural life spans. In some cases—as, for example, the prescription of antibiotics to cure pneumonia in an otherwise healthy patient—there is no question that we should use the medical means available in an attempt to restore a person's health. We have, however, effective means to prolong the functioning of vital organs, even when most other functions of the body have shut down. This leads to the independent issue of whether a given therapy is not only effective, but beneficial to the patient.

This question demands a difficult judgment call on the part of the patient (or, when the patient cannot make a decision, the surrogate) and the physician. Orthodox responsa have closed off all discussion of these issues on the grounds that, according to their interpretation, Jewish law establishes an inviolate rule that all life is sacred and must be preserved under all circumstances. As I have indicated above [in the previous chapter], that is a mistaken reading of the tradition, for there are cases in which Jewish law expressly requires that we take a life or give up our own. Jewish law does embody a strong push for life as a consistent policy (or, perhaps, principle), but *not* an unexceptional rule. In my view, the later tradition's distinction between sustaining life and prolonging dying establishes the minimization of pain, for example, as one factor that, under specific circumstances, can be used to set aside the tradition's general policy to preserve life with all possible effort.

Other sources in the tradition argue that we should use the benefit to the patient as the primary criterion in determining a course of action rather than our ability to accomplish a limited medical goal (such as keeping one or more organs functioning). *Avodah Zarah* 27b specifically states that one need not be concerned for "the life of the hour" (*ḥayei sha'ah*). The context is a discussion of an opinion by Rabbi Yoḥanan that "where it is doubtful whether [a patient] will live or die, we must not allow them [Gentiles] to heal [since non-Jewish healers were suspected of killing Jewish patients], but if he will certainly die, we may allow them to heal." It is clear, then, that the Gemara defines "the life of the hour" as the time a person lives after having being diagnosed as having a terminal illness. After that time, we need not try to cure a person who, as far as we know, cannot be cured. (An objection to this is raised in the name of Rabbi Ishmael, but it is deflected.) In our setting, this means that we may relinquish aggressive medical treatment, even if it is effective in prolonging vital organs, if the patient is dying of a terminal disease. We then may, and probably should, concentrate instead on relieving pain.

In commenting on this talmudic passage, Tosafot ask how the Gemara can say here that we need not be concerned about "the life of the hour" and yet state in *Yoma* that we should violate the Sabbath to remove debris from a person buried under it in an attempt to try to save the person, presumably even when we have little hope that he is alive (for otherwise, there would be no question). This latter precedent assumes that we do indeed care about "the life of the hour." Tosafot reconcile these sources as follows:

> There are grounds to say that in both sources we should act *for his benefit,* for there [in *Yoma*] if you do not care [about "the life of the hour"], he will die, and here, if you do care [about "the life of the hour" and therefore prohibit the Gentile physician from treating him], he will not be healed by the Gentile and will certainly die. So here and there, we abandon the certain [course of action] to do that which is doubt[fully appropriate].[4]

Jewish vitalists—if I may call them that—seize upon the specific therapy that Tosafot prescribe here and claim that they always want us to act to sustain life, that they always think that that is "for his good." Such an interpretation, however, confuses examples with rules. It is, in fact, to use the examples to create a rule in direct contradiction to the principle for which the examples were adduced in the first place. In these two cases, acting for the victims' good amounts to trying to preserve their lives, despite the grounds in each instance for thinking that we should not do so; that, however, does not mean that in every case such a goal would be appropriate. On the contrary, Tosafot articulated a *general principle* on the basis of this case—namely, that the proper objective of the medical care of a patient is to act *for the patient's benefit.* The very fact that they generalized in this way indicates that the patient's benefit is the relevant criterion. When we apply that standard to some contemporary cases, we may have to abandon the attempt to save a life—that certain course of action that presents us with the least moral risk—and adopt the therapy fraught with moral doubt, just as Tosafot describe the situation here.[5]

The Subcommittee on Bioethics was, in part, launched by a responsum by Rabbi Morris Shapiro to these issues. In that responsum, he listed a number of other sources that support his contention, and mine, that it is the patient's benefit that should be our paramount concern in determining a course of therapy, and that the pain of the patient can, in some circumstances, be sufficient warrant to decide that it is not in the patient's best interests to continue aggressive treatment.[6] This would definitely not justify active euthanasia, even in cases where the homicide would clearly be a "mercy killing"; absent the excuse of self-defense or a court order, we never, in Jewish law, have the right to hasten our own death or that of another person. Moreover, when there is a reasonable chance that medical intervention can redeem the person from a terminal illness (that is, from being a *tereifah*) or a state of morbidity (*gesisah*), we must do everything in our power to do so, even if it means that the patient must suffer pain. When there is little or no chance of doing that, however, and when aggressive treatment will involve considerable pain to the patient (as it usually does), we need not follow that course of therapy.

It is legally and morally much easier, of course, to ignore all such considerations. One can then take what appears to be the moral high ground by insisting that we expend every effort to save any human life, no matter how tenuous or painful. With the development of more and more means to sustain vital organs, however, what may once have been the high moral position has ceased to be that. Aggressive medical treatment comes at considerable cost in pain to the patient (let alone the monetary cost to both the patient and the society) and, as discussed below, other considerations also may mitigate against such therapy. Like it or not, we can no longer rely alone on what we *can do* to sustain a patient but must face the difficult decisions that must be made concerning what *benefits* the patient. This will inevitably involve decisions about quality-of-life issues, and there is always the danger of a slippery slope in that. The danger should not be exaggerated, however, for we certainly can discern at least some cases in which treatment is clearly in the patient's interest and some cases in which it is not. Moreover, the essence of moral sensitivity is not the evasion of life's complexities, but the ability to make distinctions within them.

E. Hazardous Therapies

In making their joint decisions, physicians and patients may, according to Jewish law, try a risky therapy if it has a chance of curing the disease. (It is not, however, a sin of omission to choose not to employ such therapies.) The decision to employ high-risk procedures must always be justified in terms of the benefit that the patient may be expected to gain if it works. A physician may not suggest them on the grounds of "one chance in a million," and a patient may not use them on the grounds of "what do I have to lose?" for, when the chances really are one in a million, doctors do not honestly expect that the therapy will work, and they are, in the meantime, hastening the person's death.

In general, minimum risk may be assumed for minimum benefits, maximum risk only for maximum benefits. Thus, if a therapy presents a reasonable chance of actually curing a patient's life-threatening disease, it may be employed even if it simultaneously poses the risk—if it fails—of hastening the patient's death. The patient and the physician may decide to engage in such treatment as long as the motive is to try to cure the patient.

On the other hand, if a disease is incurable and the only hope is to reduce pain, only the risks that need to be assumed to accomplish that goal may be undertaken. One may take those risks, however. This applies even in cases in which a person is suffering from a nonterminal disease and, all the more so, when such a disease is present.[7] Thus, for example, in an attempt to alleviate the severe pain of a person in the last stages of dying, morphine and other pain medications may be administered in doses sufficient to dull the pain, even if this simultaneously hastens the person's death. The intent to treat is the crucial factor.

In applying this principle, we must recognize three important variables. First, people have differing thresholds of pain and differing tolerances of risk. Consequently, in judging what is a "reasonable" risk to take to cure a disease or to dull pain, the patient, if possible, must make the decision on the basis of the information that the physician supplies. Patients (and, if they are incapable of making the decision, the family and physician) should not be second-guessed in this; the variation in people's assessment of pain and risk is real, and the relevant factors in deciding whether to use hazardous therapies are the depth of this particular patient's experience of pain and the strength of his or her hope for recovery.

Second, medical science is excruciatingly uncertain in predictions of death; there will always be a small number of unexpected results—e.g., recoveries from apparently permanent comas and longer survival than anticipated in specific patients with a given disease. Jewish law cannot be properly interpreted, however, to oblige us to be omniscient; what counts in a decision to use dangerous drugs or surgeries (or not to use them) is the judgment of the attending physicians based on what their knowledge and experience have taught them to expect.

Third, in these areas, as in many others, human motivations are often multiple and, indeed, conflicting. What is required, then, is simply that the intent to help the patient live as comfortably as possible is the predominant motive in administering a treatment.[8]

As we learn more about pain management (hospital teams focused exclusively on pain management have come into existence only in the last decades), we may no longer need this "double-effect" argument, for it appears that new techniques of pain control actually lengthen life.[9] This is understandable, for people can be expected to fight for their lives harder and longer if they are not racked with pain. As our abilities to manage pain improve, we certainly are under a Jewish mandate to mitigate it as much as possible; pain is not seen as an independent good in the Jewish tradition, as it is in some others.[10]

F. Ineffective Therapies

On the other hand, patients and physicians need not engage in a therapy that lacks a reasonable chance of effecting a cure. We have previously asserted that even if a mode of treatment is effective, we may not use it if it is judged not to be beneficial to the patient; we certainly do not need to employ medical means that are not even expected to be effective. Moreover, if a mode of therapy is tried and proves to be ineffective, it may, and probably should, be removed.[11] These principles may seem obvious—Jewish law, no matter how interpreted on specific issues, surely could not require us to do what in all probability will not work—but they must be reiterated in the context of modern medicine, for they hold the key to restraining us from treatment that is well-intentioned but overzealous and, ultimately, misguided.

G. Tereifah, rather than Goseis, as the Operative Category

Before we proceed to some applications of the above policies, we must consider one conceptual matter. Almost all discussions in Jewish circles of the terminally ill have relied on what Jewish law does with the category of *goseis*, a moribund person. As indicated above, during the last eight hundred years, Jewish law has continued to prohibit hastening a person's death but has permitted (or, in some versions, required) removal of anything that impedes the death of a moribund person. This distinction originates in the thirteenth-century work *Sefer Ḥasidim,* and in the sixteenth century it is incorporated, with some modification, in Isserles' authoritative comments on the *Shulḥan Arukh.*[12]

The case in both sources is one of a person on his deathbed. In our time, however, people can be "on their deathbeds," as it were, almost indefinitely, sustained by heart and lung machines as well as by other medical paraphernalia. Thus, definitions of "mortally ill" (*goseis*) in terms of a specific number of hours (commonly held to be within seventy-two hours of death)[13] are inappropriate to today's medical realities, such as our ability to maintain artificial respiration. Even if one restricts the use of such a definition to the expectation of one's remaining life unaided by medicine, one still must face the problem that this definition has always entailed—namely, how can one know ahead of time the moment of a patient's impending death with such certainty? Moreover, the distinction between direct and indirect means of letting people die has become increasingly difficult to recognize and maintain and, according to some contemporary ethicists, it can easily mask highly immoral activities.[14]

Because we can maintain people on life-support systems, and because we still cannot accurately predict the moment of a person's death, the only way to use the category of *goseis* at all in these matters is to define a *goseis* not in terms of the remaining hours of his life, but rather as anyone who has been adjudged by the attending physicians to have an irreversible, terminal illness. Some Orthodox and Conservative rabbis in recent years have moved in this direction.[15] (In a very broad sense, life itself is an "irreversible, terminal illness," but that stretches the term "illness" beyond recognition—and, more important, beyond the experiences that we intend to denote by using the term "illness" in contrast to the term "life.")

While I am in sympathy with those who want to broaden the meaning of *goseis* to address the difficult medical decisions that we face, it is really playing fast and loose with the category. Rabbinic sources commonly compare the life of a *goseis* to a flickering flame,[16] and therefore, for fear of extinguishing the flame, one must not even move such a person. This describes neither the condition of, nor proper medical treatment for, a terminally ill patient, who may have many months or even years to live after correctly being diagnosed as having an irreversible, terminal illness.

If there were not other ways to respond adequately to modern medical conditions, I would nevertheless be willing to stretch the category of *goseis* to include everyone with a terminal illness—and indeed, in an earlier writing of mine, I suggested just that.[17] There is, however, a better way in Jewish law to conceive of most of the cases with which we are concerned. As Rabbi Daniel B. Sinclair has pointed out, however we define the category of *gesisah,* all agree that the person in that category is still considered alive. Therefore, any withholding or withdrawing of treatment from such people always comes with not a small amount of ambivalence and guilt. The halakhic category that describes these situations much more accurately and appropriately, he suggests, is that of *tereifah,* a person with an incurable disease. Such a person is, according to medieval authorities, a *gavra ketila,* an already dead person, and consequently one who kills him is exempt from human punishment although subject to divine and extralegal penalties.[18]

When applied to animals other than human beings, the term *tereifah* refers to one suffering from a fatal organic defect, such as a pierced windpipe or gullet.[19] It is presumed that a *tereifah* animal will die within twelve months.[20] A human *tereifah* is also defined on the basis of medical evidence—specifically, as Maimonides says, "It is known for certain that he had a fatal organic disease and physicians say that his disease is incurable by human agency and that he would have died of it even if he had not been killed in another way."[21] Since the death of a *tereifah* is inevitable, evidence of *tarfut* is equivalent to evidence of death, and therefore, according to the Talmud, the deserted wife of a *tereifah* may remarry.[22] According to most authorities, twelve months must elapse before permission to remarry may be granted, analogous to the presumption regarding animal *tereifot.*[23] Tosafot, however, argue that fundamental physiological differences between humans and other animals (and, I would add, the expenditure of considerably more human energy and resources in caring for sick humans) often enable people to survive for longer periods.[24] These factors underscore the fact that for all these authorities, the twelve-month period with regard to humans is only an estimate, and the crucial factor in the definition of *tereifah* is the medical diagnosis of incurability. As Sinclair says:

> The outstanding feature of the category of human *tarfut* for the current debate concerning the treatment of the critically ill is the exemption of the killer of a *tereifah* from the death penalty. This feature focuses attention upon the fact that a fatal disease does detract from the legal status of a person, and also introduces a measure of flexibility into the issue of terminating such a life.

> This is in direct contrast to the category of *goseis*, which is based on the premise that a *goseis* is like a living person in all respects. Indeed, almost all the laws of the *goseis* confirm his living status and, as already observed, can only be appreciated against the background of the domestic deathbed. The *tereifah* category adopts a different perspective (the effects of the critical illness upon a person's legal status), and as such, it is much closer to the current debate on the termination of the life of a critically ill patient.[25]

This is not, of course, to say that an incurably ill person is entirely equivalent to a dead person. On the same page of the Talmud on which Rava says that "all admit" that the killer of a *tereifah* is exempt from human legal proceedings, he also asserts that one who has illicit sex with a terminally ill person is liable. As the Talmud goes on to explain, the liability derives from the fact that the sexual act performed with an incurably ill person will still produce pleasure, while the same act with a dead person would not do so since, as Rashi says, all of a dead person's warmth and moisture (humors) have been lost.[26] One must also note that the exemption from prosecution stems from two converging reasons, only one of which is relevant to our concerns. The factor discussed in the Talmud is that the expected death of the person makes his testimony irrefutable (*edut she'i atah yakhol lehazimah*); it is only explanations in Rashi and other medieval sources that add the consideration that the incurably ill person is considered as if already dead (*gavra ketila*).

Moreover, while one may be exempt from punishment (*patur*) for intentionally killing an incurably ill person, one is still forbidden to do so (it is not *mutar*); indeed, one is still, according to Maimonides, subject to divine sanction and to extralegal sanctions by the court or king. With regard to all people guilty of bloodshed who, for some reason, cannot be convicted of a capital crime under the usual rules, the king may, if it is necessary to reinforce the moral standards of the society, execute them on his own authority. If he chooses not to do so, he should, says Maimonides, "flog them almost to the point of death, imprison them in a fortress or a prison for many years, or inflict [some other] severe punishment on them in order to frighten and terrify other wicked persons" who specifically plot to commit bloodshed in a way not subject to court action.[27]

In sum, as Rashi is careful to say, the *tereifah* is *considered* a dead person (*gavra ketila ḥashiv lei*); that is, the incurably ill person is made *analogous* to a dead person, not *equated* to one. This makes the entire category of *tereifah* exactly parallel to the state of health that concerns us. The Talmud records a disagreement as to whether an incurably sick animal can or cannot live for another twelve months, and this resembles the ambiguity of the situation each moment with regard to incurably sick humans as well. Interestingly, in one place in the Talmud, it is Rava who claims that the *tereifah* can live a year, and in another the selfsame Rava is identified with the reverse position. Tosafot therefore describe this as one of several discussions in the Talmud in which names have been reversed when recorded in different places, and they claim that the correct version is the one in which Rava claims that a *tereifah* can live an additional year.[28] Critical students of the Talmud might have yet another answer. For me, though, the very existence of this confusion in the Talmud concerning the status of the *tereifah* is just right: we are confused as to how to think of an incurably ill person, especially in the last stages of life, now more than ever.

The parallel case is that of the fetus. Since the fetus is not considered a full human being (*nefesh*) with the attendant legal protection against murder, Jewish law carries no criminal sanction for feticide.[29] Consequently, a Jew who kills a fetus is exempt (*patur*) from normal legal sanctions. Non-Jews, however, according to Jewish law, are governed by the seven laws given to all descendants of Noah. While the general assumption of rabbis over the centuries has been that Jews are held by God to a standard higher than that for non-Jews by virtue of the many additional obligations in the Covenant of Sinai, there are a few cases in which the Noahide laws governing non-Jews were at least initially interpreted to be more stringent than Jewish laws governing Jews. This is one of those cases, for feticide is, according to the Rabbis, prohibited as a capital offense under the Noahide prohibition of bloodshed, based on Gen. 9:6. Embarrassed by this, some authorities assert that Jews who commit feticide are subject to a range of extralegal penalties similar to what Maimonides prescribes for killing an incurably ill person.[30]

With regard to abortion, though, there are many who see clear-cut grounds to override this general prohibition and its extralegal penalties to permit, or even require, feticide. The intriguing question is whether there might also be grounds to override the general prohibition against killing an incurably ill person to permit withholding or withdrawal of lifesaving machines or medications, at least in some cases.

The law of siege may well provide such a precedent. The Tosefta describes a case of a group of travelers threatened by brigands. The latter demand that the travelers give up a specific person in their group to be killed. The Tosefta permits the group to hand over the individual.[31] Later sources understandably qualify this provision. According to one view, the specified individual may be delivered only if the whole group is otherwise faced with certain death.[32] Another interpretation maintains that the designated person may only be handed over if that person is guilty of a capital crime. Maimonides and most commentators after him rule according to the latter reading.[33]

What if the designated person was a tereifah? Rabbi Menahem Meiri says: "It goes without saying that in the case of a group of travelers, if one of them was a *tereifah,* he may be surrendered in order to save the lives of the rest, since the killer of a *tereifah* is exempt from the death penalty."[34]

Meiri does not extend this to a *goseis*. This is surprising, for a *goseis* is typically closer to death than is a person who has just been diagnosed as having an incurable illness. Nevertheless, one can understand Meiri's reasoning: the *goseis* is a living person in all respects, and hence any complicity in his death would be tantamount to murder. The *tereifah,* on the other hand, is, as it were, already dead, and hence, killing a *tereifah* does not entail capital punishment. These facts mean, for Meiri, that in a case in which many lives might be saved as a result of the death of a *tereifah,* the latter's life does not possess the same value as that of the other, viable persons.

Put another way, the Talmud establishes the general principle of the sanctity of each and every human life by posing the rhetorical question, "How do you know that your blood is redder? Perhaps the blood of the other person is redder!"[35] As Rabbi Joseph Babad says, the Meiri is effectively asserting that a *tereifah* is one exception to this tenet of the equality of all human lives; that is, a *tereifah*'s blood is "less red" than that of a viable human being.[36]

This is in keeping with a passage in the Talmud. That passage refers to animals, so it is not directly on point, but it compares a *tereifah* to a fetus, and it discusses whether a *tereifah* continues to belong to its own species. Specifically, *Shabbat* 136a records a dispute between Rabbi Eliezer and the Rabbis as to whether a calf born after eight months of gestation, rather than the usual nine, is to be considered a *tereifah.* Rabbi Eliezer says that it is, while the Rabbis claim that it is not. The reason for the Rabbis' position is that a *tereifah* had a period of fitness for slaughter before it contracted the disease that made it a *tereifah,* while a calf did not. Thus, a *tereifah* from birth is, for the Rabbis, not considered ever to have attained the status of being a calf; it has never been "of its kind," its species. Similarly, the Meiri is suggesting that a doomed person is no longer considered a full member of its category of being.

In light of the gravity of the subject of this ruling, it is not at all surprising that later authorities variously agreed and disagreed with it. Probably the sharpest demurral came from Rabbi Ezekiel Landau, who, in a case involving embryotomy to save the life of the mother, said, "Who was permitted to kill a *tereifah* to preserve a viable life? We have never heard of such a thing."[37] Even though I shall side with the Meiri against Landau here, notice that Landau also equates the case of a fetus with that of a *tereifah* and rightly concludes that whatever one says about the former has direct implications for what one says about the latter.

Following a number of modern authorities in Jewish law, Sinclair suggests that the Meiri and Landau may possibly be reconciled. Landau, after all, is dealing with a case of actively taking the life of the fetus; Meiri, on the other hand, is talking about handing over a *tereifah* for others to kill. It is not at all obvious that Landau himself would object to the indirect homicide involved in the case of the travelers when the lives of the rest of the group are at stake.[38] Even if he does, the Mishnah, the Talmud, and the vast majority of rabbis after them permit, and even require, abortion to save the life of the mother.[39]

The case of the fetus and the *tereifah* are, however, dissimilar in several ways. A *tereifah* may presumably be killed, even for the Meiri, only in an indirect fashion, while the fetus must (may) be actively killed when threatening the life of its mother.[40] On the other hand, while a *tereifah* may be sacrificed for the sake of any viable life, the fetus is generally killed only to preserve its mother's life.[41]

Even so, the fetus and the *tereifah* are both cases of human beings whose blood is indeed judged to be "less red" than that of viable people. This led to specific rulings during the Holocaust that permitted people to smother crying infants if that was necessary to preserve the lives of adults who were trying to escape—not only on the grounds that the babies were pursuers, but also because those less than thirty days old were not yet indubitably viable. In a parallel way, rabbis permitted Jews to acquiesce to Nazi commands to throw victims of the gas chambers into crematoria rather than be shot themselves, despite the fact that the gassed people still exhibited some signs of life. As people with terminal illnesses, the lives of the gassed could be sacrificed for others who were not.[42] Notice that in this last case, the distinction between active and passive action was blurred, and, as mentioned above, as medical technologies become more complex, it may increasingly become a distinction without a clear technical or moral difference.

H. The Concept of Tereifah and Contemporary Policy

None of the above considerations, of course, permits us to kill either fetuses or terminally ill people on whim; the prohibition of bloodshed applies to both categories and may not be lightly ignored. Certainly, anyone who wants to do so bears the burden of proof that it is justified in this particular case—and the burden is as heavy as they come. Maimonides, remember, spoke of extralegal and divine penalties for the killer of the *tereifah*.

In our own time, the institutions have changed, but American society has, over the years, developed several institutional frameworks to ensure that these actions are not taken lightly. The courts are one; there have been court cases on these issues in virtually all states, with widely publicized higher court rulings in California, Connecticut, Massachusetts, Missouri, New Jersey, and New York. In addition, in June 1990, the United States Supreme Court ruled on one aspect of this complex of issues in the Cruzan case, on appeal from Missouri.

Courts have the advantage of being able to apply the sanctions of the law against homicide and malpractice, and they are seen as the ultimately authoritative bodies to resolve disputes, but there are real drawbacks in using them. If all such cases threaten litigation, physicians will increasingly refuse to treat such patients or will choose other specialties entirely—a phenomenon that we are already witnessing with obstetrics. Moreover, it is not at all clear that courts have the required expertise in these matters to make proper decisions. Some court decisions on these issues, in fact, have been roundly criticized by the medical community, the legal community, and experts in bioethics.[43] The standards that courts set are often the minimum of what will be accepted by the legal system; one would hope, though, that medical practice would follow the higher standard of what is appropriate medical care, and the definition of that probably must come from some other forum. One wants the best decision for the patient and society, not just a minimally justifiable one. The time frame of courts is also not helpful: courts often take months or years to make decisions that are needed for specific patients in hours or days.

The legislative arena offers the opportunity to take more time and to involve more professional experts in formulating policy in these areas. It also, however, poses the danger of directing medical practice on the basis of the political advantages that politicians can reap from taking highly public, but medically ill-advised, stances on these issues. In practice, state legislatures have largely left these matters to the courts, probably sensing that the complexity of these cases and the wide range of opinion on them do not lend themselves well to the form of legislation as a remedy and the processes of political compromise necessary to achieve it.

For all these reasons, the medical profession itself has sought to formulate appropriate standards in these difficult areas, to be applied to specific cases at the discretion of the attending physicians. As early as 1983, the President's Commission for the Study of Ethical Problems in Medicine and Biomedical and Behavioral Research published its report, *Deciding to Forego* [*sic*] *Life-Sustaining Treatment*.[44] The Commission consisted primarily of physicians, but also included lawyers and ethicists. Subsequently, regions of the American Medical Association have made their own recommendations in these areas. In light of the substantial effects of the law on medicine nowadays, sometimes these efforts have included official participation by the legal community. For example, "Principles and Guidelines Concerning the Foregoing [*sic*] of Life-Sustaining Treatment for Adult Patients," a report of their joint Committee on Bioethics, was adopted on 13 December 1985 by the Board of Trustees of the Los Angeles County Bar Association and on 6 January 1986 by the Council of the Los Angeles Medical Association. Hospital ethics committees, which usually include representatives of the broader community, ethicists, and lawyers as well as physicians, have assumed an increasingly significant role in shaping policy in these matters. Their varying policies bespeak a healthy pluralism in approaching these difficult matters. We hope that greater experience with many alternatives in caring for the dying will gradually provide us with the moral wisdom we need.

In the meantime, no forum is totally satisfactory; the high stakes and excruciating vagaries of these issues will inevitably leave many dissatisfied, no matter who decides an issue and no matter what the decision may be. The point, though, is that the kind of extralegal agencies that Maimonides envisaged have evolved, although not specifically in the form that he knew at his time.

As a result, with proper precautions to ensure that such decisions are taken seriously, and with the institutions in place to shape appropriate policies and to punish those who kill fetuses or terminally ill people without appropriate justification, a decision to remove modes of medical intervention from such people in given cases may be taken in good conscience and in consonance with Jewish law, even though such action will lead to their deaths. The diminished status of these categories of people, coupled with the precedents on siege, justifies the conclusion that the lives of the terminally ill may be—and, in some cases, must be—sacrificed to preserve the lives of others. As Sinclair puts it:

> It would appear that where the indirect termination of the life of a critically ill patient would result in the saving of a viable life, as in the case of organ transplants or the allocation of scarce medical resources, Jewish law would, in principle, legitimate such an act, provided that an institutional framework existed for assessing the effect of such a deed upon the moral fabric of society and for administering discretionary punishments. In all cases involving the killing, either directly or indirectly, of a *tereifah,* the killer would be exempt from the death penalty and his fate would be decided by extrajudicial bodies. These bodies would have at their disposal a whole range of sanctions, including death. Presumably, where proof was brought to the effect that the death of the *tereifah* had been brought about in an indirect fashion for the sake of saving viable life, those involved in the relevant acts would not be subject to any sanction.[45]

As indicated above, life-support systems may also be removed to relieve a terminally ill person of excruciating pain. I will detail [in the following chapter] when and how each of these justifications becomes operative.

Notes

1. God's creation and ownership of all creation, including our bodies: Gen. 14:19, 22 (where the Hebrew word for "Creator" [*koneh*] also means "Possessor," and

where "heaven and earth" is a merism for those and everything in between); Exod. 20:11; Deut. 10:14; cf. also Lev. 25:23, 42, 55; Deut. 4:35, 39; 32:6. The resultant duty to take care of oneself through proper hygiene, diet, exercise, and sleep is summarized best in *M.T., Hilkhot De'ot* (Laws of Ethics), chaps. 3–5, but it derives from many talmudic precedents that mandate specific measures to prevent illness. A discussion of those, and of this first principle of my list generally, can be found in my article "The Jewish Tradition," in *Caring and Curing: Health and Medicine in the Western Religious Traditions,* ed. Ronald L. Numbers and Darrel W. Amundsen (New York: Macmillan, 1986), 20–23 on this point, and 9–20 on the general principle.

The general principle that "endangering oneself is more stringently [prohibited] than the [explicit] prohibitions [of the law]" is in B. *Ḥullin* 10a (*ḥamira sakanta mei'isurah*), and the Talmud includes many injunctions that apply that principle in practice, as, for example, the command not to go out alone at night (B. *Pesaḥim* 112b) and the many medical measures enjoined to prevent illness, noted above. (Many, but not all, contemporary rabbis have used this to prohibit smoking or hallucinatory drugs.) That the physician both may and must heal: B. *Bava Kamma* 85a; B. *Sanhedrin* 73a; *S.A.,Y.D.* 336:1. That Jews may live only in communities where physicians are available: J. *Kiddushin* 66d; B. *Sanhedrin* 17b. The mandate to violate the Sabbath to save a life: M. *Yoma* 8:6 (83a); B. *Avodah Zarah* 28b.

These and other sources clearly establish that one may avail oneself of medical care, but that one must do so is only implicit in the Talmud. As Dr. Fred Rosner summarizes, "From these and other Talmudic passages, it seems evident that an individual is undoubtedly permitted and probably required to seek medical attention when he is ill" (Fred Rosner, "The Physician and the Patient in Jewish Law," in *Jewish Bioethics,* ed. Fred Rosner and J. David Bleich [New York: Sanhedrin Press, 1979], 54). Rabbi J. David Bleich provides an extensive list of medieval and modern rabbis who affirm that duty, but that very list indicates that he, too, fails to find the duty explicitly established earlier; cf. his *Judaism and Healing: Halakhic Perspectives* (New York: Ktav, 1981), 9–10 n. 9. Some of these later authorities attach it to their interpretation of Deut. 4:9, 15, first interpreted metaphorically in B. *Berakhot* 32b, but, as the Maharshah notes on that passage, neither the biblical text nor the rabbinic interpretation there institutes the rule.

On these matters generally, cf. also Rabbi Immanuel Jakobovits, *Jewish Medical Ethics* (New York: Bloch, 1959, 1975), chaps. 1 and 3.

In American law, adults do not have a duty to avail themselves of medical care, but they do have a legal obligation to provide such care for their children. The Supreme Court has even mandated some specific forms of care for children, as, for example, its insistence that Jehovah's Witnesses allow their children to receive blood transfusions when medically necessary, despite the parents' belief that that is prohibited as an act of eating blood. Along these lines, the duty in

Jewish law for adults to seek medical care can also be seen—if one will pardon a little modern midrash here—as an implication of the fact that we are all God's children.

2. Rabbi Avram Reisner, "A Halakhic Ethic of Care for the Terminally Ill" [chap. 16, pp. 250–53 of this vol.]. He draws upon B. *Bava Metzia* 85b, where Rabbi Judah Hanasi, suffering from an eye disease, refused two medications proposed by his physicians, saying "I cannot endure it," and ultimately accepted only their third prescription. As Rabbi Reisner emphasizes, this source legitimates the patient's refusal to undergo a given therapy only when another, medically viable, alternative is available; the patient does not have the right to refuse a course of therapy when it constitutes the only, or by far the best, chance to cure the disease.

   The permission to choose among physicians is clearly stated in B. *Bava Kamma* 85a. Naḥmanides, however, asserts a duty to choose the most competent physician available (see his *Sefer Torat Ha'adam* [B'nei Brak, Israel: Mif'al Hasefer, 1979], *Sha'ar Hasakanah* [although this edition may have mistakenly combined this section with the one previous to it, such that it should be *Sha'ar Harefu'ah*], 18), and Joseph Karo (*S.A., Y.D.* 336:1) also rules that a person "should not engage in medicine unless he is expert and there is nobody there [in that location] greater than he, for if this is not the case, he spills blood [murders!]." These rulings are apparently based on J. *Nedarim* 4:2 (38c), which is cited approvingly by Rabbenu Asher (the Rosh) in his comment to B. *Nedarim* 41b. Those sources, however, seem to be saying the opposite, namely, that it is a mitzvah for a physician to tend to a patient, even if there is someone else available to heal him, "for not from everyone does a person merit to be healed"—i.e., people can be healed most effectively by specific physicians (presumably, ones they know and trust), even if other available physicians are as skilled or even more so. Thus, it certainly is mandatory that physicians become expert in their art before practicing and even gain the permission of the court to practice (the early equivalent of licensure), but it is not clear that a Jew must use the most competent physician at all times. Indeed, if that were so, a few physicians would be very busy, and others would have very little to do.

   The recognition that people have free will to disobey the law is embedded in the very nature of the Jewish doctrines of sin and return (*teshuvah*).

3. *Sefer Ḥasidim* (attributed to Rabbi Judah the Pious), nos. 723, 234; *S.A., Y.D.* 339:1, gloss. The story of Rabbi Ḥananiah ben Teradyon in the Talmud (B. *Avodah Zarah* 18a) also suggests this distinction (since Rabbi Ḥananiah refuses actively to hasten his own death, but both he and the Voice from Heaven approve the removal of impediments to death), but that is not in a medical context, and these latter sources are.

4. Tosafot, B. *Avodah Zarah* 27b, s.v. *leḥayei sha'ah lo ḥaishinan.*

5. I can imagine someone arguing that I should construe this comment of the Tosafot according to the hermeneutical rule of *kelal uferat* (a generalization fol-

lowed by a specification), where one is to interpret the generalization as being limited by the specific example. I would point out, however, that Tosafot follow their discussion of the two examples with another generalization—namely, that we abandon the certain and adopt the uncertain course of action (in order to act for the patient's benefit). Thus, this is actually an instance of *kelal uferat ukelal* (a generalization followed by a specification followed, in turn, by another generalization), and then the generalizations, rather than the examples, determine the scope of the author's meaning.

6. The sources he cites—some of which clearly support this position, while some do only if one accepts Rabbi Shapiro's reading of them—are these (in the order he discusses them): Responsa *Avnei Neizer, Ḥ.M.,* no. 193; Reponsa *Maharsham,* pt. 1, sec. 54; B. *Ketubbot* 33b (with the commentaries of Tosafot [s.v. *ilmalei*] and Rabbi Jacob Emden); Num. 11:15 and the commentary of the Ramban thereon; 1 Kings 19:4; Jon. 4:3; the Ran on B. *Nedarim* 40a; the story in B. *Gittin* 56b of the woman who threw herself off the roof after seeing her seven sons die, followed by the approbation of her act by a heavenly voice, even though her suffering was solely psychological and not physical; the story of Rabbi Shimon and Rabbi Ishmael in the Yom Kippur martyrology, in which each pleads "Kill me first" in order not to witness the execution of his colleague; *Yalkut Shimoni, Eikev,* no. 871; Rabbi Moshe Hershler, *Halakhah Urefu'ah* 2:32–33. Another important contemporary authority who supports using the benefit of the patient as the criterion of appropriate medical care is Rabbi I. Jakobovits (in his article in *No'am* 6: 271ff.).

   Rabbi Shapiro also suggests using the *tereifah* category in these cases; I shall discuss that at some length and apply it below. The sources that Rabbi Shapiro adduces in regard to that category are *M.T., Laws of Murder* 2:8; *Minḥat Ḥinukh,* mitzvot no. 34 and no. 296. Rabbi Shapiro notes that Ezekiel Landau (*Noda bi-Yehudah, Ḥ.M.* no. 59), the author of *Tif'eret Tzevi, O.Ḥ.* no. 14, and others cited by Rabbi Eliezer Waldenberg in *Tzitz Eliezer* 5:28 (and the Tosafot in B. *Niddah* 44a–b, as Rabbi Reisner points out in chap. 16, n. 22 of his responsum) all dispute the ruling of the *Minḥat Ḥinukh* (and that of the Meiri, which Rabbi Shapiro does not mention but which I shall discuss below), but he claims that B. *Nedarim* 22a and the Rosh's comment thereon support the former, permissive opinion, as do the *O.Ḥ.* on Exod. 31:16; Responsa *Beit Ya'akov,* no. 59; and, in our own time, Rabbi G. A. Rabinowitz (*Halakhah Urefu'ah* 3:113) and Rabbi N. Goldberg (cf. Rabinowitz, ibid., 2:146–47).

7. I think that it can be fairly said that, among contemporary Orthodox rabbis, J. David Bleich usually articulates the most extremely conservative positions in medical ethics. Nevertheless, even he permits the use of hazardous drugs and other therapies for the alleviation of pain, and he specifically includes in this permission cases that do not involve a terminal illness. Part of his argument is based upon what is, in our present state of knowledge regarding pain therapies,

a weak argument—namely, the statements of Naḥmanides and Rabbenu Nissim Gerondi that all medications are hazardous, and so once the Torah permits medical treatment, the degree of hazard makes no difference. He also invokes, however, precedents by Rabbis Meiri and Isserles, which speak more directly to this issue. Despite the Torah's prohibition of children wounding their parents (Exod. 21:15), when there is no other physician available, a child may perform an amputation or bloodletting to ameliorate the condition of a father who is "in pain" (Meiri on B. *Sanhedrin* 84b; *S.A., Y.D.* 241:13, gloss). See J. David Bleich, "The Obligation to Heal in the Judaic Tradition: A Comparative Analysis," in *Jewish Bioethics,* ed. Fred Rosner and J. David Bleich, 32 and 28–33 generally; reprinted in a somewhat different form (but with no substantive changes on this issue) in his *Judaism and Healing,* 116–22; cf. also 137–38 there. Rabbi Immanuel Jakobovits agrees, and so do the rabbis he cites, e.g., I. Y. Unterman and M. D. Wollner. Cf. Jakobovits, *Jewish Medical Ethics,* 276. My treatment of hazardous therapies closely follows that of David M. Feldman and Fred Rosner, *A Compendium on Medical Ethics: Jewish Moral, Ethical and Religious Principles in Medical Practice* (New York: Federation of Jewish Philanthropies of New York, 1984), 94–103.

8. All responsible ethicists want to prevent cases in which family members seek to discontinue treatment for selfish, immoral reasons ("We want Granny dead so that we can inherit her fortune"). Even when such malevolence and malfeasance are not at issue, however, the uncertainties of medicine make it difficult for the most loving and responsible of relatives to make an appropriate decision in these matters. An emotionally compelling instance of this was reported by Nancy Gibbs in "Love and Let Die," *Time,* 19 Mar. 1990, 70–71. Rev. Harry Cole, a Presbyterian minister, faced a dilemma when his wife fell into a coma after a massive stroke. Rev. Cole, not the state, would have to pay the bills for continued care. "If she were to go on that way," he is quoted as saying, "our family faced not only the incredible pain of watching her vegetate, but we also faced harsh practical realities." The cost of nursing-home care was likely to exceed $30,000 a year. "How could I continue to send three kids to college with the additional financial strain?" Under advice from physicians that Jackie Cole would never recover, and after consulting his three college-age children, Rev. Cole went to court, seeking to have her respirator removed. The court agreed, but since Mrs. Cole had been in a coma for too short a time to diagnose her coma as permanent, the court stayed its order for a period of time, and six days later, Jackie, against all expectations, woke up with minimal brain damage. According to the article, she does not blame Harry for wanting to pull the plug. "I know he loves me. I know he was never trying to do away with me." But the story highlights the dilemma that family members and judges face. "I thought my decision was well planned, well thought out, responsible," said Rev. Cole. "It was what Jackie asked me to do."
9. Cf. Dallas M. High, "Quality of Life and Care of the Dying Person," in *Medical*

Treatment of the Dying: Moral Issues, ed. Michael D. Bayles and Dallas M. High (Cambridge, Mass.: Schenkman, 1983), 101.

10. The closest Judaism gets to advocating subjecting oneself to pain is on the Day of Atonement and, by rabbinic extension, on historical fasts such as the Ninth of Av. (Some pietistic Jewish communities encouraged personal fasts for specific reasons as well.) According to the Torah, God commands Jews to "afflict your souls" on Yom Kippur, which was understood in the tradition to involve fasting, sexual abstinence, and other forms of physical self-denial. These were abstentions from pleasures otherwise enjoyed, however, and not submission to positive pain; the latter was reserved for the court's punishments for violations of the law. Moreover, in each case, abstinence is restricted to the given day and is designed to call attention to the theme of the day; it is not invoked with the idea that pain itself effects atonement or historical memory. Thus, if a person's life is medically endangered on Yom Kippur, the most restrictive day of the Jewish year, the law itself requires that abstinence cease and appropriate measures be taken to assure life and health (Lev. 23:32; M. *Yoma* 8).

    The Rabbis do speak of "punishments out of love" (*yisurim shel ahavah*) (cf. B. *Berakhot* 5a), but that is only to justify God when a person's suffering seems to be undeserved; it is certainly not used to advocate pain as a religious desideratum. On the contrary, the Rabbis also say that suffering only comes from sin (B. *Shabbat* 55a), which is certainly not a goal of the rabbinic tradition. Moreover, the very mandate to engage in medicine is, in essence, a command to relieve suffering.

    Most forms of Christianity saw suffering as either penalties for sin or as a way of God's teaching us humility and other important religious lessons. Some, however, actively sought suffering as a means to salvation (cf. *Caring and Curing: Health and Medicine in the Western Religious Traditions,* ed. Numbers and Amundsen, 53, 59–60, 96–97, 121–22), and the Inquisition was justified, in part, as a way of inflicting pain in this world so as to attain salvation in the next.

11. Cf. Jakobovits, ibid. In 1985, when Rabbi Jakobovits addressed a large group of physicians and rabbis at Cedars-Sinai Medical Center in Los Angeles, he said that physicians need feel no compunctions in removing machines or medications that have not effected the hoped-for medical results. If they do feel such compunctions, however, he recommended setting such machines on timers so that the therapy will automatically be terminated unless the physician makes a conscious decision to renew it.

12. See n. 3 above.

13. Cf. Bleich, *Jewish Bioethics,* 34, and the contemporary rabbis he cites in n. 120; Bleich, *Judaism and Healing,* 141–42. His main classical sources for this ruling are *Perishah, Tur, Y.D.* 339:5 and the ruling in *S.A., Y.D.* 339:2 that one must begin observing the laws of mourning three days after the onset of *gesisah.*

14. Cf. J. Rachels, "Active and Passive Euthanasia," *New England Journal of Medi-*

cine 292 (1975): 79ff.; I. Kennedy, "Switching Off Life Support Machines: The Legal Implications," *Criminal Law Journal* (1977): 443ff.; G. Williams, "Euthanasia," *Medico-Legal Journal* 14 (1973): 14ff.; R. Veatch, *Death, Dying and the Biological Revolution* (New Haven: Yale University Press, 1976), 93ff.; J. Glover, *Causing Death and Saving Lives* (New York: Penguin, 1982), 109, 112; J. Harris, *Violence and Responsibility* (London: Oxford University Press, 1980), chap. 4.

15. [For Avram Reisner's development of this view, see chap. 16.] I first suggested this in print in my article " 'Choose Life': A Jewish Perspective on Medical Ethics," in *University Papers* (Los Angeles: University of Judaism, 1985), 19–21. The section of that article on issues at the end of life was reprinted in a somewhat different form in my article "Rabbi, I'm Dying," *Conservative Judaism* 37, no. 4 (summer 1984): 37–51, esp. 45–48.

    In light of our contemporary ability to keep people breathing and palpitating artificially, Rabbi Eliezer Waldenberg of Jerusalem has reinterpreted *gesisah* to make it independent of its traditional symptoms. Instead, a "final-phase *goseis,*" according to him, is a person who has lost all capacity for basic physiological functioning where the loss is irreversible. In that state, Rabbi Waldenberg argues, all forms of life support, including mechanical aids to respiration and heartbeat as well as artificial nutrition and hydration, constitute impediments to the person's dying and may be removed. It is also unnecessary, according to him, to resuscitate a clinically dead person. Cf. *Tzitz Eliezer* 13:89 and 14:80.

    Cf. also Jakobovits, *Jewish Medical Ethics,* 124 and n. 46; Daniel C. Goldfarb, "The Definition of Death," *Conservative Judaism* 30, no. 2 (winter 1976): 10–22; Seymour Siegel, "Updating the Criteria of Death," ibid., 23–30; and their discussion, ibid., 31–39.

16. M. *Semaḥot* 1:4, cited in many later sources, including *Siftei Kohein* and *Ba'eir Heiteiv* to *S.A., Y.D.* 339:1.
17. Dorff, " 'Choose Life': A Jewish Perspective on Medical Ethics," 19–20.
18. B. *Sanhedrin* 78a; *M.T., Hilkhot Rotzeaḥ* 2:8. Cf. also B. *Bava Kamma* 41a, according to which the owner of an ox that kills a person who has a fatal organic disease is not considered forewarned (*mu'ad*) in regard to the animal's likelihood to kill healthy persons and need not be put to death; and B. *Shevuot* 34a, which repeats that a person who kills a *tereifah* is exempt from human penalties. Daniel B. Sinclair, *Tradition and the Biological Revolution: The Application of Jewish Law to the Treatment of the Critically Ill* (Edinburgh: Edinburgh University Press, 1989).

    The term *gavra ketila* occurs four times in the Babylonian Talmud. According to *Sanhedrin* 71a, once a person has been sentenced to death, he is immediately a *gavra ketila,* a killed man. Because of that, *Sanhedrin* 81a deals with the possibility that one might think that a person sentenced to one of the more lenient forms of execution, since immediately presumed dead, could not subsequently be sentenced to a harsher form of execution for another crime. It rejects that conclusion, but in the meantime reaffirms the description of a doomed person as a dead one. *Sanhedrin* 85a adds the consideration that one sentenced to death, since considered an already killed person, is no longer "abiding among your people" in the terms of Exod. 22:27. And, perhaps most relevant to our purposes, *Pesaḥim* 110b says that a person who drinks more than sixteen cups of wine is a *gavra ketila.* There, it is medical, rather than judicial, factors that make the person thought of as dead.

Rabbis who explicitly call a *tereifah* person a *gavra ketila* (or the Hebrew equivalent, *kemeit*) include Rashi, B. *Sanhedrin* 78a, s.v. *shehu patur; Hokhmat Shelomoh* on B. *Sanhedrin* 78a, s.v. *mai ta'ama ḥayav; Minḥat Ḥinukh,* nos. 34 and 296; and *Mitzpeih Eitan* on *Sanhedrin* 78a. In addition, the midrash, in *Canticles Rabbah* 4:1, translates *taraf* in Gen. 8:11 as *katil,* comparing it with Gen. 37:33, Jacob's shriek that "Joseph has surely been mangled [torn up]."

Rabbi Morris Shapiro also suggests, at one point in his responsum, using the category of *tereifah* to deal with these cases, and he lists a number of people who do so (cf. n. 6 above), but he does not develop the argument further. We are, however, clearly thinking along the same lines.

19. M. *Ḥullin* 3:1; B. *Ḥullin* 42a; *M.T., Hilkhot Sheḥitah* 10:9; *S.A., Y.D., Hilkhot Tereifot* generally.
20. B. *Ḥullin* 58a; *M.T., Hilkhot Sheḥitah* 11:1; *Tur, Y.D.* 57; *S.A., Y.D.* 57:18; *Siftei Kohein, S.A., Y.D.* 57:48.
21. *M.T., Hilkhot Rotzeaḥ* 2:8.
22. B. *Yevamot* 120b–121a; *M.T., Hilkhot Gerushin* 13:16–18; *Tur, E.H.* 17; *S.A., E.H.* 17:3–32.
23. Cf. M. *Yevamot* 16:4; Ramban, *Yevamot* 120b, s.v. *umi matzit;* Rashba, *Yevamot* 230, s.v. *umi matzit; Maggid Mishneh, Hilkhot Gerushin* 13:16, s.v. *vekhakh nir'eh; Kesef Mishneh, Hilkhot Gerushin* 13:16, s.v. *vekhein im; Tur, E.H.* 17; *S.A., E.H.* 17:32. Also see Responsa *Mishpetei Uziel, E.H.* no. 79; *Tzitz Eliezer* 1:23.
24. Tosafot *Gittin* 57b, s.v. *venikar bemokho;* Tosafot *Eruvin* 7a, s.v. *kegon shidra.* Cf. also *Kesef Mishneh,* ibid.; Tosafot *Yom Tov,* M. *Yevamot* 16:4.
25. Sinclair, *Tradition and the Biological Revolution,* 22. Cf. also 71–75.
26. B. *Sanhedrin* 78a. Cf. Rashi there, s.v. *hayuv* and *veha it lei hana'ah.*
27. *M.T., Hilkhot Rotzeaḥ Ushmirat Haguf* (Laws of Murder and Care of the Body) 2:8; cf. 2:2–5; *Hilkhot Melakhim* (Laws of Kings) 9:4. Cf. also *Mekhilta Derabbi Yishmael,* "Massekhta D'Nezikin," 4, ed. H. Horowitz, I. Rabin, 263; and R. Moshe Feinstein, *Iggerot Moshe, Y.D.* no. 36. As Maimonides explains, homicides that cannot be classified as murder for some reason (specifically, the evidentiary rules are not satisfied, the perpetrator committed the act through an agent, the victim is the killer himself [suicide], or the victim is a *tereifah*) are nevertheless prohibited as acts of bloodshed under Gen. 9:6. Sinclair discusses at

length why such offenses are punished as a capital offense for non-Jews under Noahide law while the remedy is left to God for Jews; cf. Sinclair, *Tradition and the Biological Revolution,* 22–35.

Sinclair also points out that the midrash (*Genesis Rabbah* 34:14) only includes the first three cases mentioned above as subject to divine penalty as bloodshed. Maimonides, though, includes killing the *tereifah* also because bloodshed is one of the Noahide laws, all of which, for him, are based on reason, and consequently any act that can reasonably be identified as the shedding of blood should come under the sanctions of the Noahide laws, even if there is no formal source for doing so. This also follows from the general talmudic principle that there is nothing permitted to an Israelite that is prohibited to a Noahide (B. *Sanhedrin* 59a; cf. Tosafot there, s.v. *mi ika,* and Tosafot, B. *Ḥullin* 33a, s.v. *eḥad oveid kokhavim*).

The extralegal penalties specified by Maimonides are not mandated by the law for all such cases; rather, God, the human court, and the king, in applying such punishments, have considerably greater latitude in deciding whether to punish at all and, if so, how; in the case of the human court and the king, their decision must be based on how this one act affects the general moral standing of the society. As Rabbi Solomon Duran, a fifteenth-century Algerian authority, noted in a polemic defense of Jewish law, this approach is preferable to the usual method by which legal systems deal with this problem—i.e., making the perpetrator liable under the law but eligible for judicial or executive pardon—because the latter approach obscures the true grounds for not administering capital punishment and leaves the public believing that justice was simply not done. The halakhic approach, on the other hand, excludes the death penalty in this type of case from the very outset, so that the public can know that the law has been upheld in court, but it affords society the ability to rid itself of such behavior if it needs to do so. Cf. R. Solomon Duran, *Milḥemet Mitzvah* 32b, s.v. *od heishiv,* and p. 35. Sinclair makes a similar point in comparing Jewish law with Anglo-American law; cf. Sinclair, *Tradition and the Biological Revolution,* 57–59.

28. The dispute is recorded in B. *Ḥullin* 42a. Rava claims that the *tereifah* can live a year in B. *Temurah* 11b (and cf. Tosafot, s.v. *Rav Ḥisda* there), while in B. *Bekhorot* 3a he claims the reverse. Tosafot, s.v. *Rav Ḥisda,* on this last page argue that the version associating Rava with the position that the *tereifah* can live a year is the correct one. Tosafot on B. *Sanhedrin* 78a, s.v. *hahoreig et hatereifah patur,* suggest substituting Rabbah for Rava in these passages since Rabbah, not Rava, is the contemporary and the common sparring partner of Rav Ḥisda, but this would still leave the conflict in the other two sources intact.
29. It does, however, provide for civil penalties for the injury to the mother, in accordance with its usual laws of tort. Cf. Exod. 21:22–25; M. *Bava Kamma* 8:1.
30. That feticide is a capital crime under Noahide law for non-Jews: B. *Sanhedrin* 57b; cf. *Genesis Rabbah* 34:13. That Jewish law does not provide an indepen-

dent criminal sanction for feticide: Rashi, B. *Sanhedrin* 72b, s.v. *yatza; Yad Rema, Sanhedrin* 57a, 72b; Meiri to *Sanhedrin* 72b; Ramban, *Ḥiddushim* to B. *Niddah* 44b; see David M. Feldman, *Birth Control in Jewish Law* (New York: New York University Press, 1968) [subsequently published under the title *Marital Relations, Birth Control, and Abortion in Jewish Law*], 251–94, esp. 254ff. That feticide nevertheless bears civil penalties: Exod. 21:22; B. *Arakhin* 7a; *Tzitz Eliezer* 9, 51:3. That therapeutic abortion is permitted to, and, in some cases, even required of, Jews: M. *Oholot* 7:6; *M.T., Hilkhot Rotzeaḥ* (Laws of Murder) 1:9; *S.A., Ḥ.M.* 452:2; and cf. Feldman, *Birth Control,* 275–84. That abortion unjustified by therapeutic concerns, despite the lack of specific criminal penalties, is forbidden to Jews: Tosafot, B. *Sanhedrin* 59a, s.v. *mi ika;* B. *Ḥullin* 33a, s.v. *eḥad oved kokhavim;* cf. Feldman, *Birth Control,* 284–94. That it carries divine penalties (and perhaps extralegal ones) similar to killing the *tereifah*: R. Meir Cohen, *Or Sameaḥ* on *M.T., Hilkhot Issurei Bi'ah* 3:2; *Meshekh Ḥokhmah, Parashat Vayakhel,* s.v. *shabat shabaton.* Also note the words of R. Menahem Meiri (B. *Sanhedrin* 57b) to the effect that Israelites are exempt from capital punishment for bloodshed "since the king can punish them." Cf. also J. David Bleich, *Contemporary Halakhic Problems* (New York: Ktav, 1977), 331, 367.

31. T. *Terumah* 7:20; cf. S. Lieberman, *Tosefta Kifshutah, Terumah* 7:148. Cf. J. *Terumah* 8:4; *Genesis Rabbah* 94:9; and *Leviticus Rabbah* 19:6. For a general discussion of these sources, see David Daube, *Collaboration with Tyranny in Rabbinic Law* (London: Oxford University Press, 1965), and for a discussion of how Rabbi Joel Sirkes (the *Baḥ*) used them in 1620 in a specific case, cf. Elijah Judah Schochet, *A Responsum of Surrender* (Los Angeles: University of Judaism Press, 1973). The main legal distinctions arising out of these sources are discussed by Shmuel Shiloh, "Sacrificing One Life for the Sake of Saving Many Lives," in *Ḥevrah Vehistoriah,* ed. Yehezkel Cohen (Jerusalem: World Zionist Organization [Office of Education and Culture], 5740 [1970]), 57–62.
32. J. *Terumah* 8:4. Cf. Daube, ibid., and Shilo, ibid.
33. *M.T., Hilkhot Yesodei Hatorah* 5:5. The basis for this ruling is discussed in *Kesef Mishneh* there; Responsa *Habaḥ Hayeshanot,* no. 43; Responsa *Seridei Eish* 2, no. 78. Those who rule with Maimonides include *Baḥ, Tur, Y.D.* 153; *Taz, S.A., Y.D.* 157:7; *Noda bi-Yehudah* 2, *Y.D.* no. 74. The Tosefta and its variations were used also in responsa to determine how a Jewish community should supply men for the army; cf. Schochet, *A Responsum of Surrender,* 47–48.
34. Meiri, *Sanhedrin* 74a, s.v. *yera'eh li* (p. 271). Also see Tiferet Yisrael, *Yoma* 8:7, s.v. *venireh li,* and Ḥayyim Benviniste, *Sheyarei Knesset Hagedolah* on *S.A., Y.D.* 156, no. 36.
35. B. *Sanhedrin* 74a.
36. *Minḥat Ḥinukh* no. 296, s.v. *vehinei af de'ubar.*

37. *Noda bi-Yehudah, Tinyana, Ḥ.M.* no. 59. Landau is reacting to a statement *She'eilot Uteshuvot Binyamin Ze'ev,* no. 403, which justifies embryotomy on the grounds that one may push aside a doubtful life, i.e., that of the fetus, in order to preserve an established life, i.e., that of the mother.
38. Sinclair, *Tradition and the Biological Revolution,* 49–51. Among those he cites who suggest this differentiation between Meiri's case and Landau's are Responsa *Yabia Omer* 4, *E.H.* no. 1 and R. Benjamin Rabinowitz-Teumim, "Extradition to Non-Jewish Authorities," *No'am* 17 (5734): 357 (Hebrew). He also notes a number of other Jewish legalists who draw this distinction independent of the Meiri-Landau context, including *Levush Mordekhai, Y.D.* 157:1; Tiferet Yisrael, *Yoma* 3:3; Shilo, "Sacrificing One Life," 60; A. Enker, "Homicide Committed in Circumstances of Duress and Necessity in Jewish Law," *Shenaton Hamishpat Ha'ivri* 2 (5737): 171 (Hebrew); and E. Ben-Zimra, "Bloodshed by Necessity in Jewish Law and Israeli Law," *Shenaton Hamishpat Ha'ivri* 3–4 (5736/37): 142 (Hebrew).
39. M. *Oholot* 7:6; B. *Sanhedrin* 72b; and cf. T. *Arakhin* 1:4; T. *Yevamot* 9:5; B. *Niddah* 29a; J. *Sanhedrin* 8:9; *S.A., Ḥ.M.* 425:2; and, more generally, David M. Feldman, *Birth Control,* 251–94. That the rationale for justifying abortion is that the fetus is not a person: Rashi, B. *Sanhedrin* 72b, s.v. *yatza;* Ramban on B. *Niddah* 44b, s.v. *veha ditnan;* Ramban, *Torat Ha'adam,* "Inyan Hasakanah," s.v. *uvahalakhot;* Meiri on B. *Sanhedrin* 72b, s.v. *ubarah;* Ran, B. *Ḥullin,* chap. 3 (19a), s.v. *ule'inyan; Yad Rema, Sanhedrin* 72b, s.v. *aval kol zeman.*

    Maimonides (*M.T., Hilkhot Rotzeaḥ* 1:9) justifies the Mishnah's instructions to abort a fetus endangering the life of its mother on the grounds that the fetus is a pursuer (*rodeif*) of the life of the mother, but many commentators have pointed out, among other objections to this theory, that the pursuer principle applies to full human beings who are being threatened by others, while the Mishnah's permission to abort is specifically restricted to the stage prior to birth. To rescue Maimonides (and Landau) from this objection, some suggest that even Maimonides was suggesting the pursuer principle as only a second, additional reason to permit (require) an abortion, but even for him the primary reason is that the fetus is not yet a viable human being while the mother is.

    As Sinclair suggests, the indirectness of killing the *tereifah* is parallel to the pursuer argument with regard to the fetus: both are secondary justifications for the permission to commit bloodshed or indirectly abet it, while the primary justification is the medical status of the fetus or *tereifah* as "less red" than a viable human being. See Sinclair, *Tradition and the Biological Revolution,* 73.
40. Given that both the fetus and the *tereifah* are considered to have "less red" blood, one might argue that direct killing of the *tereifah* ("active euthanasia") should be permitted. There are specific biblical and mishnaic texts permitting (mandating) the active killing of the fetus, however, and that is not true for the *tereifah*. Moreover, as Sinclair suggests, "the effect upon society of the direct killing of a *tereifah* who is capable of 'eating, drinking, and walking about on

the streets' is much more traumatic than that of directly destroying a fetus that is threatening its mother's life" (Sinclair, ibid., 52).

41. This is normally the situation in which the possibility of an abortion arises. During the First World War, however, Rabbi Isser Unterman permitted a Jewish doctor to commit feticide rather than be killed by the Germans ordering him to do so on the grounds that the absence of a biblical prohibition against feticide makes martyrdom unnecessary. See R. Unterman, *Shevet mi-Yehudah* (Jerusalem, 5715), 29; and R. Michael Stern, *Harefu'ah Le'or Hahalakhah* (Jerusalem, 5740), pt. 1, sec. 1, chap. 3. The fetus, like the *tereifah,* therefore consistently is considered to have "less red" blood.

42. R. Simon Efrati, Responsa *Migei Hahareigah,* no. 1 (where he permits taking the infant's life but says that one who chooses martyrdom instead is a "holy person"); E. Ben-Zimra, "Halakhic Decisions Relating to the Sanctity of Life and Martyrdom in the Holocaust Period," *Sinai* 80 (5737): 151 (Hebrew).

    These heartrending cases are instances of broader precedents within Jewish law. The questionable viability of newly born infants, due, at least in part, to doubts as to whether they were premature or full-term, led Jewish law to exempt one who kills a child less than thirty days old from human prosecution, just as it treats the person who kills the *tereifah.* [T. *Shabbat* 15:7; B. *Shabbat* 135b; B. *Niddah* 44b; Tosafot, *Shabbat* 136a, s.v. *mimhal.* The mishnah that subjects the killer of a day-old baby to the death penalty was taken by later halakhists as a theoretical rule only since whether the child was premature or full-term could never be conclusively known; cf. M. *Niddah* 5:3; *Noda bi-Yehudah* 2, *Ḥ.M.* no. 59.] According to R. David Hoffman, one may even intentionally sacrifice a newly born infant to preserve the life of its mother (Responsa *Melameid Leho'il* no. 69). Here again, in the infant less than thirty days old, we have a category of human being whose questionable viability makes it subject to bloodshed if—but only if—another person's life could be saved by doing so.

    Sinclair also points out that Jewish law treats both the fetus and the *tereifah* in a parallel manner with regard to the Sabbath laws: in both cases, saving the life of the fetus or the *tereifah* at the cost of violating the Sabbath is a moot point, with opinions going in both directions. Since this is never a question with regard to other people, these Sabbath laws further demonstrate that the lives of both the fetus and the *tereifah* are "less red" than those of viable people.

    On all this, cf. Sinclair, *Tradition and the Biological Revolution,* 53–57.

43. This has occurred with regard to several decisions, but perhaps most vociferously in reaction to the decision of the Massachusetts Supreme Court in the case of *Superintendent of Belchertown State School v. Saikewicz* (1977) 373 Mass. 728, 370 NE 2d. 417, in which the judges attempted to define the criteria by which physicians should determine the quality of life. The decision was sharply attacked by the medical profession; e.g., W. Curran, "The Saikewicz Decision," *New England Journal of Medicine* 270 (1978): 500 ff.; A. Relman, "The

Saikewicz Decision: Judges as Physicians," *New England Journal of Medicine* 270 (1978): 509ff.; cf. C. Baron, "Medical Paternalism and the Rule of Law," *American Journal of Law and Medicine* 4 (1979): 337 ff.

44. New York: U.S. Government Printing Office, 1983.
45. Sinclair, *Tradition and the Biological Revolution,* 62–63.

CHAPTER 20

End-Stage Medical Care: Practical Applications*

Elliot N. Dorff

[This chapter continues the discussion of chapters 18 and 19 in addressing the following question: In view of modern medicine's technological ability to sustain biological life, how should we treat the terminally ill?]

A. Hospice Care

One clear consequence of the policy described above [in chapter 19, section F] is that hospice care is Jewishly legitimate. "Hospice care" is a mode of medical care for those with an irreversible, terminal illness in which the goal is not to do what has been deemed to be medically impossible—that is, to reverse the progress of the primary, terminal illness and cure the patient—but rather to enable the patient to be as active and as free of pain as possible in the remaining days, months, or years of his or her life. Since it is a form of medical care, Jews who choose this option are fulfilling their obligation to avail themselves of such care; it is just that the goal of the treatment has changed. Instead of spending days on end in the hospital undergoing painful and deforming treatments, the patient remains at home, amid family and friends, doing

*Chapters 18–20 present material that originally appeared in the form of one longer paper, "A Jewish Approach to End-Stage Medical Care." This paper was approved by the Rabbinical Assembly Committee on Jewish Law and Standards, Dec. 1990.

as much of what he or she can do for as long as possible. As indicated above [in the previous chapter], one *may,* according to Jewish law, exert every effort in seeking a cure—including those with low probability and high risks—but one *need not* do so.

As we learn more about the dying process, hospice care becomes not only a permissible option, but in most cases, the Jewishly preferable one. As a result of research on the psychology of dying and increasing experience with modes of dying outside hospital settings over the last several decades, it has become widely known that dying patients usually do not fear death as much as they fear pain, isolation, physical deterioration, and infantilization. Therefore hospice care, which keeps the patient at home and in other familiar settings as long as possible and does not impose the burden of long, frequent, and often painful visits to the hospital, has a much better chance than a hospital does of addressing the real needs of the dying. In hospice care, the patient is more likely to know the people surrounding him, thus affording a sense of familiarity, security, and comfort. They, in turn, are more likely to know the patient's likes and dislikes, style of life, and values, and they are also more invested in ensuring that the patient's social, emotional, and religious needs are met. Even the patient's physical needs are probably better served through hospice care. One enters a hospice program fully aware that death cannot be avoided; therefore, the goal of both the patient and the attending health care personnel is no longer confused by unrealistic wishes but is focused on pain management. Since Judaism generally is interested in the whole person and not just the body, and since care of the body is greatly influenced by a person's psychological well-being, rabbis should explore [the option of hospice care] with the terminally ill and their families, and where appropriate, recommend it.

B. Withholding or Removing Medicine and Other Forms of Medical Intervention from the Terminally Ill

Another clear implication of these principles is that when the patient has an irreversible, terminal illness, medications and other forms of therapy may be withheld or withdrawn. Because withdrawing treatment requires a positive act, some physicians are more morally queasy about that than they are about withholding treatment in the first place, but it is easier to justify withdrawing a treatment that has proven not beneficial than not to try a possibly beneficial therapy at all. Moreover, since the physical condition of patients may change over time, the goals of treatment and the methods used to attain those goals need to be continually reassessed, and that may easily involve discontinuing some therapy and beginning another. Only if little or no chance exists that a treatment will benefit the patient—or, as explained below, triage issues require that a treatment not be provided—may it properly be withheld. When the patient has an irreversible, terminal illness, however, even withholding treatments is justified: we need not do what the attending physicians judge to be medically futile.

Even when a decision is made to withhold or withdraw aggressive modes of therapy, the patient may not be abandoned. All appropriate forms of pain therapy and all relevant humanitarian support systems must be maintained.

If the *goseis* category is to be used to regulate care of the terminally ill, this policy permitting the withdrawal and withholding of aggressive treatments from such patients invokes the Jewish tradition's distinction between sustaining the life and prolonging the death of the moribund (chapter 19, section C). The definition of the person to whom it applies (the *goseis*), however, is broader than most Orthodox rabbis make it—but more in keeping with the intent of the tradition, as discussed above.

If the *tereifah* category is to be used to guide our thinking on these issues—and that category does more accurately describe the vast majority of situations in which questions arise nowadays—withholding or withdrawing treatment from the terminally ill represents a permissible failure to act, in the case of withholding treatment, or a permissible act of bloodshed, in the case of withdrawing treatment, in order to save the life and health of the viable or to alleviate the pain of the dying. The justification for this ruling in each of the last two cases follows.

1. Scarce resources. Scarcity involves two related, but different, issues: rationing, where there are effective, beneficial therapies that cannot be given to everyone and that must therefore be allocated according to some formula; and allocation of resources, where there are questions as to the effectiveness or benefit of a given therapy for a specific person or group of people and therefore doubts as to whether to spend time, energy, and money on it for those people or whether to assign those limited resources to other health care needs—or to other matters altogether. Dealing with both these limitations on our ability to do all that we want to do is often emotionally wrenching for us, and no matter what we do, we shall have pangs of conscience.

In the first case, when a given therapy would benefit two or more persons but there is only enough for one, physicians must first decide whether it would benefit all the possible recipients more or less equally. If not, those who are likely to benefit most from the treatment should have first priority to receive it. If all potential recipients would benefit roughly equally from the therapy, then one should determine the recipient on the basis of "first come, first served," by random lottery among those who need it, or by any other procedure that similarly preserves the theological and moral equality of all human beings.[1]

In the cases that concern us here, this means that when one patient has an irreversible, terminal illness, and other, viable lives are at stake, the traditional sources on siege, coupled with the terminal status of a *tereifah*, provide a warrant, and perhaps even a demand, for switching scarce resources from those dying of an irreversible, terminal illness to those for whom the treatment may lead to recovery. It is as if all of us are besieged by the Angel of Death, who calls specific ones of us (those who have irreversible, terminal illnesses) to be sacrificed for the rest of us. Since terminally ill people are already "under a sentence of death" (albeit a medical one, not a legal one), it is permissible, although often heartrending, to suspend our efforts to prolong their lives in order to preserve the lives and health of others.

Similar remarks apply to the second of our situations, the allocation of scarce resources to the various needs of society. Recent statistics on American health care clearly indicate that comparing our medical situation to a siege is not stretching matters much. Americans spend over $600 billion annually on health care—that is, 50 percent more than we spend on education, many times more than we spend on other social-welfare programs, and even double the amount we spend on defense. Even so, infants die at a higher rate in America than in twenty-one other countries, and American life expectancy ranks only sixteenth in the world. Medical experts estimate that up to one-third of all medical services now performed are of questionable value. Most of these are performed on the terminally ill. Of heart-bypass operations, for example, the Rand Corporation has determined that 14 percent were totally inappropriate and another 30 percent were of equivocal value.[2] If we were instead to spend our time and money on preventive measures and health care education for the viable, we would preserve the lives and health of many more people, thereby carrying out much more effectively our mandate to be God's partners in healing. In fact, we would be even more successful in preserving people's lives and health if, instead of engaging in any specific health care measures, we would assure people food, clothing, and shelter.

The figures are even more startling if we look worldwide. According to a report of the World Health Organization, annual health care expenditures in the poorest countries average about $5 per person, compared with $460 in Western Europe and $1,900 in the United States. Many of the 40 million people who die annually from disease "could be saved by shifting a small amount of resources to health care." For example, more than 8,000 children die each day from diseases that could have been prevented by immunization, and almost 11,000 die each day of dehydration caused by diarrhea, according to the report. Further, an additional 8,000 die every day of pneumonia. Approximately $2.5 billion spent annually to immunize all children and provide medication for dehydration and pneumonia would save the lives of an estimated 7.5 million children annually. Changes in lifestyle could eliminate at least half of the 12 million deaths annually associated with cardiovascular disease, including the 3 million who die from diseases associated with tobacco. Educational programs to prevent smoking and wean people from the habit will not only save lives, but cost considerably less than the expensive operations that we try later to reverse the results.[3]

This is not simply a numbers game, or a suggestion that the old and infirm are somehow less valuable to God than the young and healthy; it is a recognition of the reality that allocation of resources for expensive and often futile treatment for the terminally ill in preference to providing basic health care, food, clothing, and shelter for the viable is a direct threat to the latters' lives. The social and political problem is that money saved in restricting expensive operations and the like will not necessarily be allocated for improved health and living standards for the masses. Indeed, we Americans as individuals spend inordinate amounts of money each year on cosmetics, alcohol, and junk food. Nations might allocate money from elsewhere in their budgets for health purposes (defense budgets are the usually mentioned target), but we must remember that states will inevitably—and often properly—balance their health-related expenses with those for other desires and needs. The money spent on saving lives may increase somewhat, but ultimately there will be a limit.

In these circumstances, we are at least permitted, if not commanded, by the sources on siege to desist from aggressively treating those whose lives we have little chance to save (specifically, the terminally ill) so that we can turn our energies and resources to saving those we can. Specifically, if we were to order our health priorities according to the Jewish demand to afford health to as many of society as possible, the order of services that a community should provide would probably be something like this, in descending order of importance: (1) sufficient food, clothing, and shelter for everyone; (2) preventive care in the form of immunizations and health education; (3) treatment of acute and life-threatening, but reversible, illnesses; (4) medical care for illnesses, whether acute or chronic, which are treatable and not life-threatening; and (5) treatment of irreversible, life-threatening illnesses.

It is not fair to ask physicians to make these decisions; they must focus on benefiting the individual patients for whom they are responsible. Moreover, the burden of giving up access to scarce therapies cannot legitimately be put on the shoulders of individual patients; society as a whole must determine when it will provide a given type of medical care and when not. Indeed, Jewish sources indicate that while individuals may devote all their own resources to an attempt to save their lives, however unlikely the chances of success, a community must be more circumspect in its allocations, taking into account the welfare of all its members.[4]

Americans, with a "can do" attitude toward medicine as well as toward most other things, find it extremely difficult to acquiesce to the inevitable, and our medicine is therefore considerably more aggressive than the medical practices in other Western countries such as France and England.[5] The Jewish penchant to "fix the world" makes American Jews even more reticent than other Americans to let nature take its course. While such aggressiveness may generally promote the progress of medical research and may often be in the best interests of patients as well, we may not have, or may not be able or willing to mobilize, the resources to treat everyone to the maximum—even when such treatment has some chance of benefiting a given individual. In such conditions of scarcity, we as a society must make difficult triage decisions.

We should make these difficult allocation decisions with forethought about the totality of social needs rather than on the basis of emotional reactions to individual cases, and we hope that these decisions will be determined by a calculation of how we can best carry out our social and religious mandate to maintain the health of the members of our society. Certainly, the potential success of treatment would be a more ethically, and therefore halakhically, acceptable criterion than others, such as social worth or the ability to pay. Ultimately, a careful consideration of these decisions is not only a social, medical, and legal necessity, but a theological one: we must face the fact that we are not God, but human beings, with limited medical abilities and limited resources.

2. *Pain.* The argument for withholding or withdrawing treatment from a terminally ill patient does not rest exclusively on concern for the health and welfare of others; even attention to the best interests of the patient would sometimes permit (maybe even require) removal of life-support systems from the terminally ill. If a person with an irreversible, terminal illness is experiencing severe pain, it should be considered permissible not only to manage the pain with whatever medications are necessary, but also to withhold or remove life-support systems so as to allow the person to die. The warrant for this comes from our compassionate attention to the best interests of the patient and from precedents in Jewish law on abortion.

Above [in chapter 19, section D], I presented the case for using the best interests of the patient as the criterion for selecting appropriate therapy. "Best interests" are, in each case, to be defined by the patient, if possible—presumably in consultation with others, such as the patient's physician, family, and rabbi—or otherwise, by the physician together with the patient's family or surrogate. In the latter case, all parties involved should take into consideration the patient's sensitivities and values as applied to his or her current medical condition. If the best interests of the patient are accepted as the grounds for making Jewish decisions on medical care, we have a relatively clear criterion for making decisions in many of the agonizing cases that face us today. Difficult judgment calls will still have to be made in every case, and the danger of making a decision on the basis of incorrect medical assessment or inappropriate motives always remains, but at least the standard that should be applied is clear, humane, and Jewishly grounded.

Rabbi Avram Reisner and many others, however, think that the obligation to be compassionate, the duty to love others as ourselves, and the patient's right to refuse a mode of treatment that he or she cannot tolerate all pale in the face of the prohibition against suicide; they think, in other words, that life, even if it is excruciatingly painful, is better than no life. I do not agree, but I certainly appreciate the gravity of the decision to withdraw life-support systems and how that may lead people with moral sensitivity and Jewish commitment to take this stand firmly. Even those who take this position, however, might permit withdrawal and even withholding of life-support systems from the terminally ill on the basis of another justification that I embrace, coming from precedents in Jewish law on abortion.

The reader will remember that the closest analogy in Jewish law to the terminally ill patient is the fetus. The lives of both are protected by the sanctions of Jewish law. In the case of all human beings, however, under some circumstances homicide is permitted or actually required (e.g., as an act of self-defense, in war, or upon the decree of a court). The burden of proof that must be borne to justify the killing of a fetus or a terminally ill person, while certainly heavy, is somewhat lighter than that required for killing other persons; as we have seen, their status as a fetus or a terminally ill person (*tereifah*) makes their blood "less red" than that of other people. With regard to abortion, this has meant that feticide is justifiable not only to maintain the physical life and health of the mother, but, since the eighteenth century, her mental health as well. Rabbi Eliezer Waldenberg and others have permitted aborting a fetus stricken with Tay-Sachs disease on the grounds of the mental anguish of the mother.[6] This precedent and the others based on the mother's mental health could reasonably be extended to justify the withholding or withdrawal of life-support systems from the terminally ill in cases where the pain, even with all the drugs, is unbearable: just as a mother may, under such circumstances, injure herself and take the life of the fetus within her, so may any adult, when in unbearable agony with no reasonable hope of recovery, direct that life-support systems be discontinued, and those who oblige commit a justifiable homicide.[7]

Those who find either or both justifications for this ruling convincing must nevertheless use the permission it provides with extreme caution. First, efforts must be redoubled to ensure that the patient's request to withhold or remove life-support mechanisms is not a result of abnormal, psychological depression or a misplaced desire not to be a burden on others. Clearly, people in this condition often have good reason to be depressed, and their care is, in fact, a burden on others; but one must try to buoy up the patient's spirits through visits and perhaps even with antidepressant drugs, and one must assure the patient that the burden of care is being willingly borne. The last thing we want to do is to rob people of reasonable hope. If the patient, in asking that life-support systems be removed, is honestly responding to the pain of his or her existence, then the patient's status as a *tereifah*, coupled with a desire to accommodate his or her "great need," would justify removal of life-support mechanisms. (The same considerations and procedures would apply if a surrogate were making the decision for a mentally incompetent patient, but then one must additionally ensure that a morally responsible and sensitive process to make the decision is in place.)

Finally, a word on the distinction between action and inaction (or "negative acts"). Philosophical discussions in contemporary theory of action increasingly challenge the reasonableness of distinguishing between actively causing a result and passively letting it happen—including the matter of withdrawing and withholding treatment.[8] We commonly hold people accountable for their failure to act in situations in which they could reasonably be held responsible to do something—as, for example, rich people who do not give charity commensurate to their wealth, or a physician who fails to treat a disease of his patient that clearly should have been treated. Ethicists therefore sometimes suggest that there is no difference between withholding treatment and withdrawing it. Some go further, suggesting that active euthanasia be allowed, at least in those cases in which the patient has an irreversible, terminal illness, and perhaps also in those cases in which the patient is not suffering from a physically terminal illness but is leading a degrading life because of Alzheimer's disease or the like.

It is true that inaction sometimes is morally blameworthy. Nevertheless, inaction usually brings less culpability than action. We say, for example, that those who oppress the poor verbally or financially are more blameworthy than those who avoid them and give them nothing. The latter surely have failed in their responsibility to do something, but the former bear greater guilt. Therefore, the Talmud's advice to remain passive (*sheiv ve'al ta'aseh*) in morally impossible situations still makes good sense.

This means that we would still assert a morally relevant distinction between withholding and withdrawing treatment. On the one hand, it is, as we asserted before, more difficult to justify withholding a possibly effective therapy than it is to withdraw it once tried, for in the former case one has done what one can and has not relied on one's estimate of what will happen. On the other hand, once a therapy has been tried, there is a moral repugnance and a psychological burden in removing it, for one then actively disconnects what is sustaining a person. Thus, Rabbi Jakobovits's advice to physicians to use timers with treatments that they are not sure will work in specific cases (such as intravenous drips or machines) so that they will be discontinued automatically if they prove ineffective, while generally mocked by physicians, does diminish the moral onus of stopping the treatment. Even if this is not done, however, it may also be justifiable to withdraw a form of therapy—and indeed, it is so, according to Jewish law—if it is not effective in achieving the desired medical result or if conditions of scarcity require that it be transferred to another patient.

C. Cardiopulmonary Resuscitation

These considerations would also be relevant to cardiopulmonary resuscitation applied to those with a terminal, irreversible illness. CPR was originally intended for heart-attack victims who are otherwise in good health, and it has the greatest chance of effectiveness with them. Even then, in one study, 80 percent of all those who suffered heart attacks, regardless of age, died of the arrest, either immediately or while under the subsequent intensive hospital care. Another 10 percent died during follow-up care, and only 10 percent survived beyond three years. Among those seventy years of age or older, figures for surviving to hospital discharge range in various studies from 0 to 15 percent, and the prognosis is even more dismal for those over eighty-five.[9] Other studies have produced somewhat more hopeful results, but even they make clear that our ability to resuscitate patients in cardiac arrest through CPR is severely limited. Moreover, one must recognize that CPR, especially in the elderly, commonly requires breaking ribs as well as other untoward results, each with its attendant pain and risks.

Those who advocate trying CPR under all circumstances point out that all pain and risks undertaken in the process are in the name of trying to save the person's life, and that certainly is true. Nevertheless, since the success rate of CPR is sufficiently less than 50 percent in all patients, it is considerably more probable that it will not work than that it will. Consequently, it should be considered halakhically optional to administer it, since no patient need undergo a medical procedure that is more likely to fail than to succeed. This is especially true for patients in categories where CPR's success rate approaches zero—specifically, those in whom the cardiac arrest occurred outside a hospital setting, unwitnessed, or associated with asystole or electromechanical dissociation, sepsis, cancer, or advanced age.[10]

In line with the discussion above, one may choose to ask for CPR in the event of cardiac arrest, just as one may ask for other therapies whose effectiveness is unproven or even unlikely, but one need not do so. Thus, when treating people in advanced stages of cancer or heart disease, for example, who mercifully suffer a heart attack, we may let nature take its course, and "Do Not Resuscitate" orders may properly be written for such people.

D. Removal of Nutrition and Hydration from the Terminally Ill

Applying these principles to two other cases [involving artificial nutrition and hydration] is harder and more controversial, but we must address them. While most would agree that, at least at some stage, withdrawing or withholding medications from the terminally ill is halakhically justifiable, there is considerably more debate concerning artificial nutrition and hydration. Every person must be afforded normal food and liquids. This is an obligation of the community with regard to the poor,[11] and if a sick person cannot afford normal food and liquids, it becomes part of the duty of the community and its agent, the physician, to provide them as part of the individual's medical care.

When the person cannot or will not ingest food and liquids through the mouth, however, may the community—or must it—feed the patient through tubes? In the *Cruzan* case, the United States Supreme Court determined that it did not have enough evidence of how Ms. Cruzan would want to be treated if comatose. That was relevant because if there were a sufficiently clear expression of her will, the justices needed to balance the American values of personal autonomy and liberty against the state's rights to assure the welfare of its citizens. The Jewish question, however, is somewhat different: In light of the individual's duty to take care of God's property (chapter 19, section A), may an individual, or a person acting on his or her behalf, refuse to ingest nutrition or hydration intravenously or enterally (that is, through the intestines) when it is not possible to do so orally?

Most rabbis who have written on this issue have answered negatively, even if the patient is terminally ill. They draw a distinction between medications, on the one hand, and nutrition and hydration, on the other, permitting the withdrawal or withholding of the former but not the latter. They reason that medications are, by definition, an unusual substance introduced into the person's system to cure an illness, and therefore they may be removed or withheld if they have little chance of functioning in that way. Nutrition and hydration, however, are needed by everyone. Therefore, the burden of proof shifts: one needs to justify the *use* of medications, but one needs to justify the *failure* to provide nutrition and hydration.

I accept this analysis, but I think that its burden can be met in one of three ways:

(1) First, one should note that what we are calling "nutrition and hydration" fulfills the function of normal food and water, but in form and administration it is much closer to medication. We are, after all, talking about inserting tubes into a patient and running liquids through them into the patient—just as we introduce medications when the patient cannot swallow. This would argue for assimilating nutrition and hydration, administered intravenously or enterally, to medications rather than to normal food and water.

Furthermore, there are halakhic grounds for such an analogy. The Torah expressly forbids us several times from eating blood (e.g., Gen. 9:4; Deut.12:16), but we are nevertheless permitted to accept blood transfusions because from the Talmud on, we, in contrast to Jehovah's Witnesses, do not consider the insertion of blood through tubes to be a case of "eating" interdicted by the law.[12] (Even if it were, of course, we would permit eating blood to save a life, but we do not need to use that justification, because our tradition has already restricted "eating" to what we swallow orally.) Similarly, intravenous or enteral administration of nutrition and hydration is essentially different from providing food and water in the usual sense, which we must do. If the patient cannot swallow normal food and water, however, we may, but also may not, administer such nutrition and hydration intravenously. The decision is a medical one, based upon the likelihood of the patient to be cured or at least to benefit—just as it is with all other medications.

(2) Even if one does not want to accept the above line of reasoning, one could still argue for withholding or withdrawing nutrition and hydration from a terminally ill patient on the grounds of the elevated risks of infection to the patient. Starvation is a much more certain and severe risk than the aspiration and infections that gastrointestinal and other tubes may cause, but we would still offer normal food and liquids to the patient (even though, by hypothesis, the patient is not in a state to in-

gest them). The question is only whether we must also offer a form of nutrition and hydration that, by its very nature, exposes the patient to elevated risks of life-threatening illness.

When thought of this way, the issue reduces to the risk-benefit calculus in many critical care medical decisions, where the crucial question is whether there is a reasonable goal for which the patient should be exposed to the elevated risk. All such decisions, including this one, are properly and justifiably left to those involved, who alone can know the patient's threshold of pain and danger, can accurately assess all other relevant aspects of the particular situation, and can then apply the patient's understanding of "reasonable risk" and "benefit" under such circumstances to the situation at hand. Such people would include, first and foremost, the patient (presumably by a previous expression of his or her will in some form) or surrogate, but it should also include consultations with the physician, family, rabbi, and other relevant parties.

Some forms of injecting nutrition and hydration bear greater risks than others. As a result, this argument will vary in its strength, depending upon the degree of risk that the patient must assume to be fed in a particular way.

(3) We are being more than a little disingenuous in offering the patient food and liquids that we know he or she cannot ingest and then treating artificial nutrition and hydration as a strictly medical decision to be determined by a risk-benefit calculus. It would be neater if the physician's decision could be based straightforwardly on the criterion of what is in the patient's best interests (*letovato*). We have discussed above [chapter 19, section D] the talmudic, medieval, and modern sources that support using that standard, together with its problems and advantages.

Patients for whom removing nutrition and hydration is a question usually can no longer make decisions on their own, and therefore determining the patient's best interests in such cases is especially difficult. We must rely on previous expressions of the patient's will or on the interpretations of his or her will by surrogates or family. Provisions can be made to guard against abuses in making this judgment, but even so, this remains a major worry.

On the other hand, this approach does not require, as the previous one did, that one be sly in applying the categories of the legal theory to the case at hand. Moreover, it would empower one to make decisions even in cases in which there is no shortage of facilities and in which the patient feels no pain—Alzheimer's patients or unconscious patients in the last stage of life, for example. All such cases will clearly involve decisions and dangers of utmost gravity, but medical care of the terminally ill often requires that such decisions be made, and we can, in fact, make at least some relatively confident moral judgments in these cases.

(4) If all the above arguments prove unacceptable, physicians, in fulfilling their role of saving lives, would be required by Jewish law to prescribe artificial nutrition and hydration when the patient can no longer swallow. As Rabbi Reisner points out, however, ultimately all Jews must decide whether they will follow the law. Under the hypothesis that none of the above arguments justifies withholding or removing artificial feeding tubes, obeying Jewish law in this case amounts to following the physician's directions to use them. Patients for whom this is prescribed, however, are often already unconscious, and therefore, it would have to be the surrogate or family member who would be refusing the therapy on the patient's behalf. If the patient had been sufficiently clear about his or her wishes while conscious, such a third party might properly make such a decision as the patient's representative. It would be for the delegate, however, as it would be for the patient if conscious, a decision that the decisor had the power to make, but not the legal sanction to make—again, under the assumption that none of the above arguments is effective to alter the substance of the law. I think that one or more of them—in particular, (3)—should be accepted as grounds to permit removal or withholding of artificial nutrition and hydration, thereby making such disobedience unnecessary.

E. Removal of Nutrition and Hydration from Those in a Persistent Vegetative State

All the above is with regard to a person with a terminal, irreversible illness. A much harder case is the person in a persistent vegetative state (PVS). If the patient meets the criteria for neurological death, we can, on good authority, consider the person dead within the terms of Jewish law. There is by no means unified opinion to accept the neurological standard, but no less than the chief rabbinate of Israel has approved heart transplants on this basis, and many others agree, including some of our own colleagues who have written on this issue.[13]

In many cases, however—especially after accidents or strokes—some brain-wave activity persists, but little else. Since the patient in these instances does not have a terminal illness, the permission to withhold or withdraw treatment so as not to prolong death does not apply. The patient may be sustained through the use of heart and lung machines, but many, like Karen Ann Quinlan and Nancy Cruzan, manage to survive even when such machines are removed. Since these patients clearly cannot ingest food and liquids orally, the question quickly turns on whether we must administer artificial nutrition and hydration and, if so, for how long.

This case is complicated in Jewish law by virtue of our strong stance against making judgments on the basis of the quality of a given life. Every life is precious in God's eyes, we aptly say; therefore we may not decide to remove or withhold treatment from people just because we would prefer not to continue living under such circumstances. This principle serves the crucial role of reminding us that people handicapped in some way must be treated with the full respect that their divine image warrants, and that, indeed, we must bless God for such variations among creatures, even if—or, especially if—we would much prefer not to be like them.[14]

When it comes to the person in a persistent vegetative state, however, this principle is tested in the extreme. Arguments based upon minimizing pain to the patient become less plausible, since the patient has lost all neocortical function and thus, by definition, is incapable of experiencing pain. Similarly, with regard to a nonterminal patient, it would be hard to make the case that, because of the elevated risks of infection involved, intravenous feeding effectively hastens the patient's death rather than extending his or her life [D.(2) above]; since the patient is not in the process of imminently dying, we cannot plausibly talk of hastening his or her death. Triage considerations would apply to heart and lung machines and other advanced technology, but the tubes necessary for nutrition and hydration per se are generally not in short supply.

There are, then, only two arguments that I can see to justify removal of nutrition and hydration from such patients. One is a version of [D.(1)] above. That is, if nutrition and hydration are to be categorized as medicine, one might argue that, since they are not curing the patient, they may be removed, as long as we offer normal food and water to the patient, even though we know that he or she cannot possibly ingest them.

Dr. Nevins, the Subcommittee's consultant whom I mentioned above [in chapter 18], urged us to take this line. We should recognize, he told us orally and in writing, that in all cases of people in a persistent vegetative state, it is the underlying disease that causes the death rather than the withholding or removal of treatment—even though the latter action would, of course, be the proximate cause of death. The same is true for people with advanced Alzheimer's disease. In such patients, the failure of the swallowing reflex should be seen as a system failure that the feeding tube seeks to circumvent. Thus, even though such a person is not dead by the standards of either cessation of respiration and circulation or cessation of whole-brain function, he or she should be allowed to die. Treatment of such a person, then, including artificial nutrition and hydration, should, in his opinion, be considered optional.

The other possibility is to follow those in the medical community who would define brain death as the irreversible cessation of the functions of the neocortex (the upper brain) rather than of the whole brain. Permanently unconscious people would then be classified as dead, and nutrition and hydration tubes could be removed.[15] As Rabbi Reisner points out in his paper on these issues, Maimonides may provide a basis for this line of reasoning through his concept of ensoulment. Maimonides writes:

> The vital principle of all flesh is the form that God has given it. The superior intelligence in the human soul is the specific form of the mentally normal human being. To this form the Torah refers in the text, "Let us make a human being in Our image, after Our likeness" (Gen. 1:26). This means that the human being should have a form that knows. . . . Nor does [this] refer to the vital principle in every animal by which it eats, drinks, reproduces, feels, and broods. It is the intellect that is the human soul's specific form. And to this specific form of the soul, the scriptural phrase "in Our image, after Our likeness" alludes.[16]

Rabbi Reisner argues against this line of reasoning, pointing out that this would impugn the sanctity of the vessel that carried God's image. Moreover, he points out the risk inherent in this theology of medicine, as it were, for if followed, one could easily argue that one should discontinue treatment of the mentally ill, who do not exhibit the rational soul of which Maimonides spoke. I agree with Rabbi Reisner's objections to this approach.

Like Dr. Nevins, however, I think that the first analysis of this situation (that tubes are medication and therefore may be removed as an inappropriate medical intervention in some cases, even when the patient is not terminal) should make it unnecessary to use nutrition and hydration tubes to treat PVS and advanced Alzheimer's patients. I, too, think that the slippery slope can be contained; indeed, as I have stated previously, the essence of developing moral sensitivity is to recognize that moral principles cannot be applied indiscriminately, that acute moral judgment must be used in deciding when and how to apply and balance our moral concerns. Such careful balancing of goods is, in fact, essentially our understanding of the nature of the halakhic process—at least when the halakhah is addressing predominantly moral issues.

I recognize that there is something that is, minimally, highly unaesthetic in removing feeding tubes from such patients. Since their brain stems are intact, they are, by hypothesis, still breathing on their own. Clearly, then, in line with current practice, PVS patients should be maintained on nutrition and hydration at least for some time—especially if they need no scarce resources—to guard against the possibility that they were misdiagnosed as being PVS patients and were instead in a reversible coma. Triage considerations apply to the other machinery necessary to sustain such patients; but, like many physicians, I would give up on such patients only reluctantly and after trying to revive them for some time. I am, in any case, comforted by Dr. Nevins's point that these cases are extremely rare, and that in twenty-five years of practice [to that point] he had never had one and that he knew of only one in his hospital.

F. Living Wills and Durable Powers of Attorney

Finally, let me address the issue that brought us to this point. Once we determine our position on the matters above, it seems that instructing physicians and surrogates to follow a person's desires through one or the other of these written instruments is perfectly acceptable halakhically in those areas in which we determine that a person may choose among forms of therapy. The fact that these instructions are given in advance of the illness, or that they are in written form, does not affect their legitimacy. As Rabbi Seymour Siegel, may his memory be for a blessing, said some time ago:

It is clear that where death is imminent and where the procedure cannot bring a cure or even a significant amelioration of pain, what is best for the individual (especially if he expresses his opinion through a will) is to allow him to die naturally. . . . What the Living Will makes possible is the giving of the privilege to the patient himself to stop those things "that delay the soul's leaving the body." The developments of medical technology have caused problems that our ancestors could hardly have foreseen. We must not forget, in our loyalty to tradition, the welfare of the suffering patient who, when the Giver of Life has proclaimed the end of his earthly existence, should be allowed to die in spite of our machines.[17, 18]

Notes

1. For general, ethical discussions on this, cf. Daniel Callahan, *Setting Limits: Medical Goals in an Aging Society* (New York: Simon and Schuster, 1987); N. Rescher, "The Allocation of Exotic Medical Lifesaving Therapy," *Ethics* 79 (1969): 173–86; J. Childress, "Who Shall Live When Not All Can Live?" *Soundings* 53 (1970): 339–55.

   In accepting the criterion, used by most ethicists, that physicians first determine which patients can benefit from a treatment most, I am disagreeing with David M. Feldman and Fred Rosner (see their *Compendium on Medical Ethics: Jewish Moral, Ethical, and Religious Principles in Medical Practice* [New York: Federation of Jewish Philanthropies of New York, 1984], 105), who claim that "since, in Judaism, all human life is equally sacred, including each moment of an individual's life ('Is your blood redder than your brother's?'—Talmud *Pesaḥim* 25b), therefore no selection is justifiable among those with the need for, and the possibility, however slim, of cure." In cases of people with irreversible, terminal diseases, their blood is indeed less red according to Jewish law, as we have demonstrated. Even in cases in which all the potential patients involved are not terminally ill, however, Jewish law must surely allow (actually, require) physicians to apply scarce therapies to those who can benefit from them most. To say otherwise would make Jewish law require that treatment that is of questionable medical value to one person be given to that person while denying it to another person for whom its value is quite certain. All living people without terminal illnesses certainly do have lives that are equally sacred, but that does not mean that we should do what is medically inappropriate in securing those lives. I am agreeing with Feldman and Rosner, however, on how the triage decision should be made if there is no difference in the expected benefits among the potential patients—namely, with respect to the ultimate equality of all human beings—at least, those without a terminal illness.

The Mishnah records an order of triage based upon social worth (M. *Horayot* 3:7–8). The Talmud and codes, however, limit this to people whom one can save in addition to oneself, for one must first save oneself (B. *Horayot* 13a; *Tur/S.A., Y.D.* 242 and 252). In the context of medicine, of course, the assumption is that the health care personnel are in no danger themselves. Nevertheless, the Mishnah is singularly unhelpful. Even if one has no objections to the ruling of the Mishnah itself (and one certainly might), one must reckon with the fact that it does not address what one should do if some of the people on its list had a better chance of survival than others. I have therefore ruled here without taking this mishnah into account, choosing instead to invoke the principles of effectiveness and fairness embedded in Jewish law generally and in Jewish medical law in particular. (Cf., in addition, the article by Dr. Fred Rosner in n. 4 below.)

2. See, for example, "America's Scandalous Health Care," *U.S. News and World Report,* 12 Mar. 1990, 24–30, esp. 25 and 27. [Since this article was written, costs have continued to increase, further strengthening the argument in the text.]
3. Marlene Cimons, "Premature Deaths Held Preventable," *Los Angeles Times,* 30 Apr. 1990, A-6.
4. Cf. Fred Rosner, "The Allocation of Scarce Medical Resources," in his *Modern Medicine and Jewish Ethics* (Hoboken, N.J.: Ktav, 1986), 339–54.
5. Cf. Lynn Payer, *Medicine and Culture* (New York: Henry Holt, 1988).
6. *Tzitz Eliezer* 13:89 and 14:80. Cf. Responsa *Rav Pe'alim, E.H.* no. 4 and Responsa *She'eilat Ya'aveitz* no. 43 for some of his sources for permitting an abortion when the woman would have "great shame" if she were to deliver the baby or when she has "great need" of it. Rabbi Moshe Feinstein disagreed strongly with Rabbi Waldenberg's position; cf. R. Moshe Feinstein, "On the Law Concerning the Killing of a Fetus," in *Rabbi Ezekiel Abramski Memorial Volume,* ed. M. Hirschler (Hebrew) (Jerusalem, 5735), 461–69. For a point-by-point analysis of the two positions, cf. Sinclair, *Tradition and the Biological Revolution: The Application of Jewish Law to the Treatment of the Critically Ill* (Edinburgh: Edinburgh University Press, 1989), 93–98.
7. Sinclair (ibid., 76–79) has suggested this line of reasoning, although he says that the question must "be left open in the hope that it will eventually be addressed by halakhic authorities." I move that we address this.

There are those who justify the abortion of a deformed or genetically diseased child, not on the basis of the mother's reaction to the child's condition, but directly on the grounds of the child's medical condition. For those who hold that position, the analogy of taking the life of a fetus and a terminally ill patient would be even stronger. Those who take this position on aborting diseased children include: E. Waldenberg, *Tzitz Eliezer* 9: 51 (1967) and 13: 102 (1978); S. Israeli, *Amud Hayemini,* no. 35, cited in *No'am* 16 (new series) 27 (note); L.

Grossnass, Responsa *Leiv Aryeh* 2:205; cf. Alex J. Goldman, *Judaism Confronts Contemporary Issues* (New York: Ktav, 1978), chap. 3, esp. pp. 52–62.

8. See, for example, John Casey, "Actions and Consequences," in *Morality and Moral Reasoning,* ed. John Casey (London: Methuen, 1971), 165ff.; James Rachels, "Active and Passive Euthanasia," *New England Journal of Medicine* 292 (1975): 78–80; J. J. Thomson, "Killing, Letting Die, and the Trolley Problem," *The Monist* 59 (1976): 204–17; John Ladd, "Positive and Negative Euthanasia," in *Medical Treatment of the Dying: Moral Issues,* ed. Michael D. Bayles and Dallas M. High (Cambridge, Mass.: Schenkman, 1983), 105–27.
9. Donald D. Tresch et al., "Should the Elderly Be Resuscitated following Out-of-Hospital Cardiac Arrest?" *The American Journal of Medicine* 86 (Febr. 1989): 145–50. Cf. also the editorial by William R. Hazzard on 143–44 of that issue. In another study, none of the patients over seventy years of age survived to hospital discharge; cf. George E. Taffet, Thomas A. Teasdale, and Robert J. Luchi, "In-Hospital Cardiopulmonary Resuscitation," *Journal of the American Medical Association* 260, no. 14 (14 Oct. 1988): 2069–72 (and see footnotes for other studies); cf. also commentaries on the results beginning on pp. 2094, 2096, and 2098 of that issue. For studies of the old-old (over eighty-five years of age), cf. Gary E. Applebaum, Joyce E. King, and Thomas E. Finucane, "The Outcome of CPR Initiated in Nursing Homes," *Journal of the American Geriatrics Society* 38, no. 3 (Mar. 1990): 197–200 (and see nn. 1–8 there for other studies); Donald J. Murphy et al., "Outcomes of Cardiopulmonary Resuscitation in the Elderly," *Annals of Internal Medicine* 111, no. 3 (1 Aug. 1989): 199–205 (and see footnotes there for thirty other studies).
10. Murphy et al., ibid., 199; Taffet et al., ibid., 2069.
11. Cf. my article "Jewish Perspectives on the Poor," in *The Poor Among Us,* ed. Gary Rubin (New York: American Jewish Committee, 1986), 21–55, esp. 33–44; reprinted in a somewhat different form as *"You Shall Strengthen Them": A Rabbinic Letter on the Poor* (New York: Rabbinical Assembly and United Synagogue of Conservative Judaism, 1999), esp. 16–27.
12. B. *Sanhedrin* 63a.
13. See Daniel C. Goldfarb, "The Definition of Death," *Conservative Judaism* 30, no. 2 (winter 1976): 10–22; Seymour Siegel, "Updating the Criteria of Death," ibid., 23–30, and "Discussion," ibid., 31–39.
14. Cf. Carl Astor, . . . *Who Makes People Different: Jewish Perspectives on the Disabled* (New York: United Synagogue of America, 1985).
15. Stuart J. Youngner and Edward T. Bartlett, "Human Death and High Technology: The Failure of the Whole-Brain Formulations," *Annals of Internal Medicine* 99 (1983): 252–58. I owe this citation and the next, together with the suggestion of this line of reasoning, to Rabbi Avram Reisner. While he articulates it, he is not willing to endorse it. I am certainly not eager to permit removal of nutrition and hydration tubes from PVS and advanced Alzheimer's patients—such cases are always tragic, no matter what one does—but I do think that,

after trying to revive such patients for some time, it is permissible and probably appropriate to do so.

16. *M.T., Hilkhot Yesodei Hatorah* (Laws of the Fundamental Principles of the Torah) 4:8.
17. Seymour Siegel, "Jewish Law Permits Natural Death," *Sh'ma* 7, no. 132 (15 Apr. 1977): 96–97.
18. I would like to thank Professors Arthur Rosett, Louis Newman, and Judith Wilson Ross; Rabbis Daniel Gordis and David Gordis; and Drs. Michael Grodin and Michael Nevins, in addition to the other members of the Subcommittee on Bioethics (Rabbis Kassel Abelson, Amy Eilberg, David M. Feldman, Avram Reisner, and Joel Roth), for their helpful criticism of earlier drafts of this responsum. Their willingness to do this, of course, does not imply agreement with what I say here or responsibility for it.

F. MEDICAL CARE AT THE END OF LIFE: ADDITIONAL REFLECTIONS

Introduction

All the material in this section draws upon the papers by Rabbis Elliot N. Dorff and Avram I. Reisner found above in section E. Two brief papers present responses to the papers in section E; each is entitled simply, "On Halakhic Approaches to Medical Care for the Terminally Ill: A Response." Rabbi Amy Eilberg expresses her admiration for both papers. She especially appreciates what she characterizes as the boldness and creativity of Dorff's work, as well as his discussion of halakhic teachings as flexible "principles" rather than as absolute "rules." Rabbi Joel Roth opposes Dorff's use of the category of *tereifah* in formulating halakhic guidance, and so agrees with Reisner on this central theoretical point. In terms of practical applications, however, Roth agrees with and finds textual support for Dorff's understanding of patient benefit (*letovato*) as offering more flexibility in treatment decisions than Reisner would support.

"Jewish Medical Directives for Health Care" presents an advance directive developed and edited by Rabbi Aaron L. Mackler, on the basis of the papers of Rabbis Reisner and Dorff. An introduction offers a brief statement on Jewish teachings about health care, as well as practical information about advance directives. The document includes both a proxy directive, authorizing a family member or another individual to make decisions on one's behalf should one lose the capacity to decide or communicate; and an instruction directive, offering evidence of one's wishes regarding some types of treatment decisions in such a situation.

The section concludes with a paper by Rabbi Reisner, "Peri- and Neonatology: The Matter of Limiting Treatment." Reisner first considers the status of the fetus. He affirms the acceptability of abortion for maternal cause throughout pregnancy, but urges that special consideration be given to the fetus after it reaches thirty-one weeks of development. Newborns generally should be treated as all other patients. The most severely compromised newborns, however, such as those with anencephaly (but not those with Down's syndrome), may be understood to be "born dying." In appropriate cases, treatment intended to promote the survival of these nonviable newborns may be forgone.

CHAPTER 21

On Halakhic Approaches to Medical Care for the Terminally Ill: A Response*

Amy Eilberg

It has been a privilege and an extraordinary learning opportunity to serve on the Law Committee's Subcommittee on Biomedical Ethics. Most especially, it has been a deeply rewarding experience to sit as one of the midwives attending the birth of these two superb papers on halakhic approaches to medical care for the terminally ill, the one by Rabbi Avram Reisner and the other by Rabbi Elliot Dorff. Now that both papers have been birthed, although I must say that I favor one over the other, I have deep appreciation for both.

Rabbi Reisner's paper is surely one of the finest statements in the field, combining the strictest articulation of halakhic principles surrounding the sanctity of life with keen awareness of the clinical issues at the bedside. This is no view from the ivory tower, no empty proclamation of bookish teachings regarding the sanctity of life. Rabbi Reisner, as well informed on the medical issues as a layperson can be, wrestles honestly with the day-to-day realities of the intensive care unit and still, with his eyes open to the contemporary medical scene, maintains a very traditional stance in terms of the basic halakhic principles surrounding care for the terminally ill. His distinction between mechanical and biological intervention is helpful, if slippery (as are all such distinctions in

*A response submitted to the Rabbinical Assembly Committee on Jewish Law and Standards, Dec. 1990.

the literature of medical ethics!), and he uses it deftly to soften in practice the harsh conservatism of his basic philosophical stance.

Most important, Rabbi Reisner adds a unique spiritual view to the voluminous literature on these issues by suggesting an image of the patient's internal dialogue with God. For Rabbi Reisner, in the final analysis, one must remember that decisions on termination of treatment are ultimately governed by the conversation between the dying person and his or her Creator, at the moment when the two are soon to meet, and no doctor, clergyperson, or even family member has full access to this final, intimate, spiritual conversation. It would have been worthwhile for Rabbi Reisner's paper to have been written for the sake of this insight alone, not to mention its general erudition, incisiveness, and eloquence.

However, I must cast my vote for Rabbi Dorff's paper, for a number of reasons. What was extraordinary about Rabbi Reisner's paper is his ability to apply the absolutist teachings of the *goseis* case to contemporary reality, coping seriously with the medical and psychosocial context in which these teachings are applied today. Rabbi Dorff takes a very different approach, which I wholeheartedly support, working his way free of the shackles of a basically anachronistic approach. For Dorff, halakhic teachings on the sanctity of life, no less binding than they are for Reisner, are no longer rules to be applied automatically to cases unimaginable to the framers of the halakhah. Rather, halakhic "rules" become "principles" to be applied with intellectual and spiritual rigor, given an understanding that contemporary medical realities defy the more simple categorization that was possible in an earlier time. Dorff offers an approach based in the philosophy of law that allows us, as Conservative Jews, to hold fast to halakhic integrity without pretending that the Rabbis could have imagined the cases we grapple with, and without violating an emerging social consensus that, in some cases, to prolong life is a sacrilege rather than a sanctification of life.

In a way that is immensely compelling for me, Dorff rehabilitates a number of halakhic categories not typically a part of the biomedical ethical discourse, in an effort to preserve halakhah's intent in a radically changed milieu. Dorff's bold use of the *tereifah* as the operative category for the terminally ill patient; his emphasis on the principle of *leto-vato,* halakhah's most direct analogue, I think, to contemporary convictions about patient autonomy; his important application of siege legislation for medical triage questions; his stunning introduction of the mental-anguish category, borrowed from halakhic abortion law; his willingness to speak of Maimonides' definition of rational human life out loud, where it can be used as part of the dialogue regarding the PVS patient—all these specifics enable Dorff to articulate a halakhically authentic ethic that affirms what everyone who walks in the world of the tertiary care treatment center knows to be true: sometimes death is a friend, and sometimes the only sanctity lies in letting go.

I appreciate Rabbi Reisner's erudition and eloquence, his flexibility in bending a rigidly conservative philosophical stance to complex realities, and I am deeply moved by the spiritual context in which he places the dialogue. And so I am grateful that his paper was written, for it stands as an important contribution to the field. But I must stand with Rabbi Dorff's boldness in challenging the myth that there is only one way to think halakhically. I must stand with his openness to radically changed realities and convictions, with his deep concern for social justice, and with his overriding concern for the intent of the law in this baffling and anguishing arena.

Finally, I stand with Rabbi Dorff's paper because of something I once learned from a nun with whom I served on a clergy panel on biomedical ethics. I lectured, I thought, with clarity and conviction, about Judaism's absolute concern for the sanctity of life. She asked, with less certainty, and with more realism, what a life-affirming tradition must say about death in the intensive care unit, about the mindless application of technology to save one organ residing in a hopelessly ill patient, about contemporary culture's distorted view that death is a failure, and that everything that can be done must be done. That day, some years ago, that nun forever informed my thinking about how to read halakhah on biomedical ethical issues. The question is not: Are we being rigorous enough, in every case, about the prolongation of life? Rather, the question for the contemporary halakhist, as for my Catholic friend, is: What is the intent of a life-affirming, life-sanctifying tradition in the world of the hopelessly ill patient? That question brings me firmly in agreement with Rabbi Dorff's paper, and I rejoice that it was written.

CHAPTER 22

On Halakhic Approaches to Medical Care for the Terminally Ill: A Response*

Joel Roth

I find myself in a very unusual position. On the theoretical differences between Rabbis Reisner and Dorff, I am in greater sympathy with Rabbi Reisner's position. On the practical differences between the two, I find myself aligned more with Rabbi Dorff. A brief explanation is in order.

As I see one of the central differences between the two, Rabbi Reisner presents the category of *goseis* as the exclusively governing category, and Rabbi Dorff presents the possibility that *tereifah* may be an applicable category, though he does not preclude seeing *goseis* as the primarily applicable category. In this dispute, I agree with Rabbi Reisner.

The centrality of *goseis* as the governing category, however, is not the only critical factor from which his entire analysis flows. As he himself states in *Mai Beinaihu*? [chapter 15 of this volume], Rabbi Reisner insists on the inviolability of the principle of protecting even *ḥayei sha'ah*. Rabbi Reisner rejects putting "the quality-of-life, benefits-and-burdens analysis into the mouth of the Tosafot" on the basis of their claim in *Avodah Zarah* 27b [chapter 16, note 22 of this volume].

Rabbi Reisner must reject that possible reading of the Tosafot because he understands *ḥayei sha'ah* to be inviolable. He argues the posi-

*A response submitted to the Rabbinical Assembly Committee on Jewish Law and Standards, Dec. 1990.

tion eloquently and quite persuasively, but, I think, incorrectly. Rabbi Reisner himself refers us to the *Tzitz Eliezer* on this subject, but highlights only his apparent conclusion. In *Ramat Raḥel,* siman 28 and in vol. 8, siman 15, chap. 3, Waldenberg quotes many sources that intimate that the principle of *ḥayei sha'ah* may not be as inviolable as Rabbi Reisner holds.

I fully understand wanting to hold *ḥayei sha'ah* absolutely inviolable. It appeals to us theologically and ethically. Even more, affirming it prevents concern for the slippery slope. In truth, though, it cannot be affirmed with such certainty as Rabbi Reisner does. Once that fact is recognized, the claim of the Tosafot on *Avodah Zarah* 27b becomes more and more tenable.

In the specific instances to which the Tosafot refer, the benefit of the individual is for life. But only the a priori assertion that *ḥayei sha'ah* is always inviolable makes Rabbi Reisner's deduction that the Tosafot cannot be intimating a benefits-and-burdens analysis necessary.

Rabbi Dorff, in fact, recognizes this fallacy. Indeed, later in his paper Rabbi Dorff actually prefers the *letovato* [acting for the patient's benefit] argument as the basis for one of his positions. My objection to Rabbi Dorff's theoretical stance lies in his willingness to consider *tereifah* as an operative category for this discussion.

CHAPTER 23

Jewish Medical Directives for Health Care*

Aaron L. Mackler, Editor

A. Introduction

Modern advances in medicine have raised many new questions. Normally, we make decisions about our own health care as the situation arises, but in some circumstances we lose the ability to make such decisions. It is therefore important for us to indicate our wishes in advance so that those who care for us can know what we want. In doing this, we should be guided by our commitment to Judaism, to its law (halakhah), and to its moral values.

This [chapter presents] a two-part document that will affect health care decisions made on your behalf should you lose the capacity to decide for yourself. A *proxy directive,* or durable power of attorney for health care, allows you to designate a health care agent to make decisions on your behalf. An *instruction directive,* or "living will," asks you to state your preferences regarding types of treatment decisions that may arise. Together, these directives can help to ensure that treatment choices reflect your wishes and interests. Furthermore, the directives have been constructed in accordance with Jewish law and values, as interpreted within Conservative Judaism.

*Approved by the Rabbinical Assembly Committee on Jewish Law and Standards, Oct. 1993. This document was published by the Rabbinical Assembly in 1994 and is currently available through the United Synagogue Book Service.

The guidance you offer in these directives can help provide clarity for your physicians and family members, and avoid conflict or confusion. The directives would help ensure that appropriate decisions are made on your behalf if you temporarily lose consciousness or the ability to communicate as the result of an accident, a surgical procedure, or an illness. They also would supply guidance should you become unable to express your choices during the last stages of life. You can use these forms to request the medical treatments that you would want to receive and to express preferences among different types of treatment. You also may indicate those treatments that you would judge inappropriate should you become terminally ill or permanently unconscious.

These directives would only be used to guide medical treatment if you lose the ability to make decisions and communicate your wishes. If you regain this ability, you would resume making your own decisions directly. Even if you never lose decision-making capacity, filling out these directives could help you gain a sense of Jewish teachings concerning medical decisions and give you the opportunity to think about some of the choices people must make about their health care. If you need to make decisions in a stressful situation in the future, your experience in completing this document will serve as a resource to inform your decisions. You may revoke or amend these directives at any time.

1. *Jewish teachings about health care.* Jewish tradition as understood by Conservative Judaism teaches that life is a blessing and a gift from God. Each human being is valued as created *betzelem Elohim,* in God's image. Whatever the level of our physical and mental abilities, whatever the extent of our dependence on others, each person has intrinsic dignity and value in God's eyes. Judaism values life and respects our bodies as the creation of God. We have the responsibility to care for ourselves and seek medical treatment needed for our recovery—we owe that to ourselves, to our loved ones, and to God. In accordance with our tradition's respect for the life that God has given us and its consequent bans on murder and suicide, Judaism rejects any form of active euthanasia ("mercy killing") or assisted suicide.

Within these broad guidelines, decisions may be required about which treatment would best promote recovery and would offer the greatest benefit. Accordingly, each patient may face important choices concerning what mode of treatment he or she feels would be both beneficial and tolerable.

The breadth of the Conservative movement and its intellectual vitality have produced two differing positions, put forward by Rabbis Avram Israel Reisner and Elliot N. Dorff, both approved by the Conservative movement's Committee on Jewish Law and Standards. Both positions agree on the value of life and the individual's responsibility to protect his or her life and seek healing. Both agree on a large area of autonomy in which a patient can make decisions about treatment when risk or uncertainty is involved. Both would allow terminally ill patients to rule out certain treatment options (such as those with significant side effects), to forgo mechanical life support, and to choose hospice care as a treatment option.

Nevertheless, important differences between the two positions may be found regarding both theoretical commitments and practical applications. Rabbi Reisner affirms the supreme value of protecting all life. Even the most difficult life and that of the shortest duration is yet God-given, purposeful, and ours to nurture and protect. All nutrition, hydration, and medication should be provided whenever these are understood to be effective measures for sustaining life. Some medical interventions, however, do not sustain life so much as they prolong the dying process. These interventions are not required. The distinction may best be judged by our intent. We may choose to avoid treatments causing us fear or entailing risk or pain, in the interest of the remaining moments of life. We may not avoid treatment in an attempt to speed an escape into death.

Rabbi Dorff finds basis in Jewish law to grant greater latitude to the patient who wishes to reject life-sustaining measures. He sees a life under the siege of a terminal illness as an impaired life. In such a circumstance, a patient might be justified in deciding that a treatment that extends life without hope for cure would not benefit the patient, and may be forgone.

Papers by Rabbis Dorff and Reisner that explain the reasons supporting their views and the practical implications of their positions appear [as chapters 16–20 of this volume].

2. *Understanding the advance directives.* Before completing this document, you must determine which stance best fits your understanding of Jewish law and ethics. Any of the choices listed in this document would

be acceptable following Rabbi Dorff's understanding of Jewish law and ethics. *However, the options that appear as italicized would not be consistent with Rabbi Reisner's position. Thus, if you choose to follow Rabbi Reisner's position, you should not mark any of the options that appear in italic print.*

Both Rabbis Dorff and Reisner agree that advance directives should only be used to indicate preferences within the range allowed by Jewish law. Space has been provided in this directive for you to add your personal comments. This allows you to explain how you understand the choices that you indicate. Before making any substantive change in the document, you should consult with your rabbi and carefully ascertain that your statement is consistent with Jewish law and ethics.

In completing these directives, you should consult with your rabbi to discuss the values and norms of Jewish ethics and halakhah. You also may wish to talk with your physician to learn about the medical significance of these choices—in particular, any decisions that your physician feels are likely to be faced in light of your medical circumstances. You may find it helpful to discuss these concerns with family members. Finally, you may wish to speak with an attorney or another person familiar with your state's laws to determine the legal requirements needed to realize your health care choices. Some states provide a simple standard proxy directive form for appointing a health care agent. You may wish to use that form in conjunction with the *instruction directive* provided in this chapter.

Filling out both a *proxy directive* and an *instruction directive* can help ensure that treatment choices are made in accord with your wishes and interests. The *instruction directive* can offer important evidence of your wishes regarding some types of treatment and give a general sense of your values and goals. At the same time, it is impossible to anticipate what your medical condition will be, what future developments will occur in medical practice, and what particular health care decisions will need to be made on your behalf. Without a health care proxy, an instruction directive may be misleading, may be open to alternative interpretations, and may not cover all contingencies.

A proxy agent can talk with your physicians about the details of your medical condition and the treatment options that are available at the time. Your agent can interpret your wishes as medical circumstances change and can make decisions you could not have known would have to be made. At the same time, the more your agent knows about your wishes and values, the better he or she will be able to make decisions that reflect your wishes and values. Even if your agent knows you well, it would be helpful for your agent to have a written expression of your desires regarding some treatments. You should go over this document with your agent so that he or she can ask questions and get a sense from your demeanor as to how you want to approach these issues.

Experts in Jewish law and in medical ethics agree that you can best guide treatment decisions by completing both a proxy directive and an instruction directive. Nevertheless, conflicts could arise in the future between what your agent judges that your wishes would be and the way in which someone else interprets the instruction directive. In most cases, discussion among those involved would help clarify your wishes. Some experts, including Rabbi Reisner, suggest that if a conflict persists, the instruction directive should be decisive. Other experts, including Rabbi Dorff, believe that the agent should have ultimate authority in interpreting your wishes. Both directives allow you to specify which should be decisive in case of conflict. *Please be sure that you are consistent in specifying the priority.*

3. *Completing the forms.* Both directives should be signed by two witnesses over the age of eighteen, neither of whom is your agent or alternate agent. In some states, additional requirements may apply. For example, your state may require that one or both witnesses would not inherit any of your property. In some states, a directive may need to be notarized. The proxy directive allows for the appointment of alternate agents in case the agent you choose is unable or unwilling to serve. You should talk with the people you want to appoint as agent or alternate agent to make sure that they are willing to serve in that capacity, and to give them a sense of your wishes.

You should keep a copy of both directives and give copies to the agent and alternate agents. You should give a copy of the *proxy directive* to your physician and to family members. You may want to give a copy of the *instruction directive* to your physician as well, especially if you want that document rather than your agent to be the primary guide in decision making. Because medical technology and your own desires may change over time, it is a good idea to review your advance directive from time to time. Finally, you may want to carry a card in your wallet that indicates that you have completed an advanced directive, the name of your proxy agent, and how he or she can be reached.

B. Proxy Directive (Durable Power of Attorney for Health Care)

1. I, ____, hereby appoint:
(name) ____
(address) ____
(phone number[s])____ as my health care agent to make health care decisions for me. This proxy shall take effect when and if I become unable to make or communicate my own health care decisions, due to physical or mental incapacity, and shall remain effective during the period of incapacity.

My agent should make decisions in accord with my wishes. If my wishes are not known and cannot with reasonable diligence be ascertained, my agent should decide in accord with my best interests. In either case, decisions should to the extent reasonably possible reflect my beliefs and values, including my commitment to Jewish teachings as understood within Conservative Judaism.

My agent should consult with one or more health care professionals before making health care decisions for me. I want my agent to be able to receive all medical information and records necessary to make informed decisions regarding my health care.

2. Instructions for agent (Please mark one statement):

___In an associated *instruction directive,* I have expressed some of my preferences concerning health care decisions that may arise. I want my agent strictly to follow that document, and only to rely on other sources of knowledge about my wishes and values in situations not covered therein.

___In an associated *instruction directive,* I have expressed some of my preferences concerning health care decisions that may arise. I realize, however, that I cannot fully anticipate what will happen to me in years to come, future developments in medical practice, or the particular health care decisions that will have to be made on my behalf. I want my agent to draw on all sources of knowledge about my wishes and values and to have ultimate authority to make decisions for me if I cannot do so for myself.

___I have not completed any document expressing preferences with regard to health care decisions. My agent should consider all sources of knowledge about my wishes and values.

Other instructions ____

____

3. Recommended but not required
First Alternate Agent:

Should the person appointed above as my agent be unavailable, unable, or unwilling for any reason to serve in that capacity, I would have
(name) ____
(address) ____
(phone number[s])______________________________serve instead.

Recommended but not required
Second Alternate Agent:

Should both the person appointed above as my agent and the person appointed as my first alternate agent be unavailable, unable, or unwilling for any reason to serve in that capacity, I would have
(name) ____
(address) ____
(phone number[s])______________________________serve instead.

4. I make these instructions, being of sound mind and age eighteen or older, and understanding fully the consequences of these appointments.

Signature: ____
Name: ____
Date: ____
Address: ____
City and State: ____

5. I declare that the person who signed this document, or asked another to sign this document on his or her behalf, did so in my presence, that I know him or her to be the person named as the subject of this document, and that he or she appears to be of sound mind and acting of his or her free will, free of duress or undue influence. I am eighteen years of age or older, and I am not designated by this or any other document as the person's health care agent or alternate health care agent.

Witness 1:	Witness 2:
Signature ________________	Signature________________
Name____________________	Name ____________________
Date _____________________	Date _____________________
Address __________________	Address __________________
City & State ______________	City & State______________

Notarization is not necessary unless required by your state law.

C. Instruction Directive to Guide Health Care Decisions

NAME

____

I am a Jew. I express that affiliation in a variety of ways in my life, and I want Jewish teachings and values to guide and inform the way in which I live through all times in my life, including times when I may be temporarily unable to communicate, seriously ill, or in the final stages of my life. I know that at some point, I may not be able to make decisions about my health care, so I have completed this form to help make my wishes known.

Judaism values life and demands that we seek medical care. I share Judaism's respect for my body, the creation and possession of God, and I consequently wish that all prudent medical treatment be extended to me with the aim of effecting my recovery. Nothing in this directive should be construed as a wish to die, but rather as a wish to live in accordance with the traditions of Judaism and God's desires. In accordance with the Jewish tradition's respect for the life that God has given us and its consequent bans on murder and suicide, I unequivocally reject any form of active euthanasia ("mercy killing") or assisted suicide.

I ask that my health care agent, and anyone else participating in the making of medical decisions on my behalf, consider carefully my wishes as reflected in this document or otherwise ascertainable. This document should not be understood as a rejection of care, but as an indication of my preferences about medical care, including desires to have specific types of treatments administered. I understand that my wishes as expressed in this document, or as articulated by my health care agent or another surrogate deciding on my behalf, will not have greater power to compel treatment than would be the case if I could contemporaneously state my views.

I intend this document to help guide my medical care in a variety of situations, including the last period of my life. Let me say in advance that I fully appreciate the loving care given to me by my family and friends and by members of the health care professions. If I cannot thank you personally at that time, I wish to do so now from the depths of my heart. You are performing a true act of *ḥesed,* an act of devotion and love. If the pain I suffer at that time makes me cranky and hard to tolerate, please forgive me. Please understand that I may not be in control of my reactions at that time and that, no matter what I say or do, I deeply appreciate the many kindnesses you have bestowed upon me throughout life and especially at that critical stage. In the tradition of our people, I ask that the spirit, strength, and comfort of God abide with us always.

General Views

1. Goals of treatment *(Please mark one statement):*

Approved by all:*

_____ It is my wish that all prudent medical treatment should be extended to me with the aim of effecting my recovery. Should that be deemed impossible, **all nutrition, hydration, medication, and necessary surgical procedures should be continued where these are understood to be effective measures for extending my life.** Medical knowledge, however, may find itself at a loss as to which form of treatment is best for me, or whether a given treatment will be helpful or harmful. In such circumstances, I would want a course of action that protects me from unnecessary pain and degradation while pursuing the goal of life.

*Inconsistent with Rabbi Reisner's opinion:**

_____ *It is my wish that all prudent medical treatment should be extended to me with the aim of effecting my recovery. Should that be deemed impossible, I want those caring for me to act for my benefit, interpreting that value in light of the choices I have made below and any other knowledge you have of me. In some cases in which I am terminally ill or permanently unconscious, choices to withhold or stop life-sustaining treatment may be consistent with my wishes and my understanding of Jewish teachings.*

*See introduction for explanation.

Comments:____

____

2. Knowledge of my condition *(Please mark one statement):*

___ I wish to know all relevant facts of my condition. I can cope better with a known threat than with the unknown.

___ I do not wish to know all the details of my condition, especially if the news is bad. I fear that such knowledge will diminish my will to live and will cast a shadow over the time left to me.

Comments:____

____

3. Health care agent *(Please mark one statement):*

___ In an associated proxy directive, I have appointed ____________ as my health care agent to make decisions on my behalf. I want my agent strictly to follow this document, and only to rely on other sources of knowledge about my wishes and values in situations not covered by this document.

___ In an associated proxy directive, I have appointed ____________ as my health care agent to make decisions on my behalf. I cannot fully anticipate what will happen to me in years to come, future developments in medical practice, or the particular health care decisions that will have to be made on my behalf. While I am filling out this document to educate myself and give my agent some idea of my attitudes in these matters, my agent should draw on all sources of knowledge about my wishes and values. It is not this document, but my agent, who has ultimate authority to make decisions for me if I cannot do so for myself.

___ I have not appointed a health care agent. I would want those making decisions on my behalf to rely on this document in determining my wishes and values.

Comments:____

____

4. Rabbinic consultation *(Please mark one statement):*

___ If I can make my own decisions about my health care when critical decisions must be made, I intend to consult my rabbi for further advice about the specific issues that arise in the medical situation in which I actually find myself. If I cannot make my own decisions regarding my care, I would ask that those making decisions for me likewise review them with my rabbi:
(rabbi's name) ________________________________
(address)________________________________
(phone number[s])________________________________

Should my rabbi be unavailable, it is my wish that some other Conservative rabbi be consulted. If no Conservative rabbi is readily available, the Rabbinical Assembly (3080 Broadway, New York, NY 10027; [212] 280–6000) should be contacted for an appropriate referral.

___ I would leave the decision about rabbinic consultation to the discretion of those deciding on my behalf.

Comments:________________________________

____

Irreversible, Terminal Illness

If I am diagnosed with an irreversible terminal illness, such that death is expected within six months no matter what treatment is provided, and if that diagnosis is confirmed by more than one physician, the following statements should assist my agent or other decision maker in deciding on my behalf.

1. Diagnostic tests if I am terminally ill *(Please mark one statement):*

___ I wish to have available all possible information concerning my condition. Should I be unable to understand such information at the time, I wish my agent, family members, and physicians to have such information available. Even if my condition is medically hopeless, further analysis of my disease may someday help doctors help someone else, including members of my own family who may be prone to the same disease.

___ I do not wish to have diagnostic tests performed on me unless they are clearly related to the effort to make me well.

Comments:____

____

2. Surgery if I am terminally ill *(Please mark one statement):*

Approved by all:

___ I would consent to reasonable surgery as proposed by my physicians.

___ All surgery carries an implicit risk through anesthesia, the increased possibility of infection, and trauma to the body. I do not consent to such risk except if it is required to extend my life, to restore me to health, or to free me from unbearable pain.

Inconsistent with Rabbi Reisner's opinion:

___ *All surgery carries an implicit risk through anesthesia, the increased possibility of infection, and trauma to the body. I do not consent to such risk except if it is required to restore me to health or to free me from unbearable pain. I would not accept such risk if it would merely prolong my life.*

Comments:____

____

3. Amputation if I am terminally ill *(Please mark one statement):*

___ I desire above all to live. I am prepared to lose a limb if, in the best medical judgment of my physicians, this is necessary in order to prolong my life.

___ There may come a time when my physicians believe that my life is threatened by infection, and that the most effective defense lies in amputation of the affected limb. I find the notion of amputation unbearable, and the risk of such an operation intolerable. I prefer all other treatments to fight the infection, even if they are significantly less likely to prolong my life.

Comments:____

____

4. Modes of feeding if I am terminally ill: if I am not able to feed myself or to eat and drink through the mouth even with the help of others, the following would represent my wishes *(Please mark one statement):*

Approved by all:

___ I would want to receive artificial nutrition and hydration (food and water delivered through a tube) when this would help to strengthen my body, improve my well-being, or prolong my life. I understand that this procedure may at some point require restraint so that I do not dislodge the tubes (in the case of nasogastric tubes), or require surgery to place a tube in my stomach or intestine.

___ I would not want to be fed through feeding tubes at all. I fear the risks that such procedures entail. Whatever nourishment can be provided intravenously should be provided.

Inconsistent with Rabbi Reisner's opinion:

___ *I would want to receive artificial nutrition and hydration on a trial basis. A decision about continuing treatment should depend on its effectiveness in helping to strengthen my body, improve my well-being, or prolong my life; and on the degree of pain or severe discomfort that the treatment appears to impose.*

___ *I would not want to be fed by artificial means at all. I fear the risks that such procedures entail. I prefer to eat normally for as long as I can, and when I can no longer do that, to let nature take its course.*

Comments:____

____

5. Aggressive medical or surgical procedures if I am terminally ill *(Please mark one statement):*

___ I wish above all to live. To that end I would undertake any regimen, however difficult, that stands a reasonable chance of helping me.

___ Aggressive medical or surgical procedures, such as aggressive radiation and chemotherapy, can be most debilitating and destructive. While I desire to fight my disease with all effective tools at my command, I do not wish to undertake treatments that have not been shown to offer meaningful, measurable results. If my physician determines that a given mode of therapy will probably not produce remission or recovery, I prefer to engage in hospice care, accepting the inevitability of my impending death, curbing pain as much as possible, and living out the remainder of my life to the fullest.

Comments:____

____

6. Mechanical life support if I am terminally ill *(Please mark one statement):*

___ I consider that as long as my brain is still active, even if I must breathe with the aid of life-support equipment, my God-given life has not yet been called back. These technologies should therefore be maintained. I recognize, however, that if the total absence of brain activity can be verified, I will be considered dead despite mechanically induced respiration and heartbeat.

___ If mechanical means of life support cannot contribute to my recovery, I consider them to be impediments to my death at God's behest, even though they may prolong biological function. Therefore, I wish that they be forgone or withdrawn when my agent or designated representative, in conjunction with my physicians, concludes that they offer me no reasonable chance of return to unaided functioning.

Comments:____

____

7. Cardiopulmonary resuscitation if I am terminally ill *(Please mark one statement):*

___ Should my cardiopulmonary system fail for any reason, in every case I would like the utmost done in my behalf.

___If my heart has stopped beating and my condition is such that there is no reasonable expectation of my recovery, I would consider cardiopulmonary resuscitation, by whatever means, to be contrary to God's will, and therefore ask that my body not be subjected to such handling. In such a case, I would consider a Do Not Resuscitate order to be appropriate.

Comments:____

____

8. Pain relief and risk if I am terminally ill *(Please mark one statement):*

Approved by all:

___ If I am in pain or significant discomfort, I desire that I be given appropriate medication and other care to relieve my pain and make me as comfortable as possible. However, I do not want any treatment that would impose a risk of greater than 50 percent of hastening my death.

Inconsistent with Rabbi Reisner's opinion:

___ *If I am in pain or significant discomfort, I desire that I be given appropriate medication and other care to relieve my pain and make me as comfortable as possible. In the unlikely event that no alternative measures could adequately reduce my symptoms, I would want sufficiently large dosages of medication to avoid pain even if such dosages may entail great risk of the side effect of indirectly shortening my life.*

Comments:____

____

9. Pain relief and sedation if I am terminally ill *(Please mark one statement):*

___ I will accept considerable periods of sedation to avoid pain.

___ If I remain alert, I am prepared to accept a reasonable amount of pain in order to maintain my awareness.

Comments:____

____

10. Hospital or home care if I am terminally ill *(Please mark one statement):*

___ I prefer to be supported by the best medical technology. To that end, if my death is not sudden, I wish that it occur in the confines of a hospital.

___ To the extent that it is practicable and not an undue hardship upon my family, I would prefer to die at home or in a congenial supportive care facility such as a hospice rather than in a hospital. When hospital care is no longer able with confidence to effect my recovery, I would prefer such comfort-oriented care, with the clear understanding that all essential medical care that would accord with my wishes would be continued.

Comments:____

____

Permanent Loss of Consciousness

If I am diagnosed to be permanently unconscious—a diagnosis tested over a reasonable period of time and confirmed by more than one physician with appropriate training and expertise—but I am not terminally ill, the following statements should assist my agent or other decision maker in deciding on my behalf.

1. Cardiopulmonary resuscitation if I am permanently unconscious *(Please mark one statement):*

___ Should my cardiopulmonary system fail for any reason, and there is a reasonable likelihood that cardiopulmonary resuscitation would be effective in extending my life, I would like the utmost done in my behalf.

___ If my heart has stopped beating and my condition is such that there is no reasonable expectation of my recovery of consciousness, I would consider cardiopulmonary resuscitation, by whatever means, to be contrary to God's will, and therefore ask that my body not be subjected to such handling. In such a case, I would consider a Do Not Resuscitate order to be appropriate.

Comments:____

____

2. Other treatments if I am permanently unconscious (*Please mark one statement*):

Approved by all:

___ I would want to receive all treatments that would be effective in extending my life, including mechanical interventions such as respirators, even if there is no reasonable hope of my regaining consciousness.

___ All nutrition, hydration, medication, and necessary surgical procedures should be continued where these are understood to be effective measures for extending my life, even if there is no reasonable hope of my regaining consciousness. I would consider mechanical means of life support to be an impediment to my death, and would want them withheld or withdrawn.

Inconsistent with Rabbi Reisner's opinion:

___ *All means of nutrition and hydration should be continued where these are understood to be effective measures for extending my life, even if there is no reasonable hope of my regaining consciousness. I would want any machines or medications (including antibiotics) used to keep me alive to be withheld or withdrawn.*

___ *If there is no reasonable hope of my regaining consciousness, I would want to forgo all treatments and interventions extending my life, including artificial provision of nutrition and hydration, which I consider to be medications. If artificial means of providing nutrition and hydration were used during the period in which my diagnosis was being formed and tested, I hereby ask that the feeding tubes (wherever they are attached to my body) be removed once the diagnosis is confirmed, just as other medications and machines that have proven to be ineffective in effecting my cure may be removed.*

Comments:____

____

Wishes in Case of Death

1. Organ donation *(Please mark one statement):*

___ I am aware that Jewish law permits and commends the donation of organs and other body parts for transplantation. Accordingly, I desire that when I die, any or all of my vital organs and other body parts be donated for the purpose of transplantation. The rest of my remains should then be buried in a Jewish cemetery in accordance with Jewish law and custom.

___ I would want my organs and other body parts to be donated for transplantation only if there is someone who needs them at, or shortly after, the time of my death. The rest of my remains should then be buried in a Jewish cemetery in accord with Jewish law and custom.

___ I would want the following body parts to be donated for purposes of transplantation:
___Kidneys ___Heart ___Skin ___Corneas ___Liver ___Pancreas
Other_________________

The rest of my remains should then be buried in a Jewish cemetery in accord with Jewish law and custom.

___ I do not wish that any part of my body be used for purpose of transplantation.

Comments:____

____

2. Autopsy *(Please mark one statement):*

Approved by all:

___ I do not want an autopsy performed unless it is absolutely required by government authorities. If such an autopsy is performed, I ask that it be conducted with all possible respect and that all my body parts subsequently be buried in a Jewish cemetery in accordance with Jewish law and custom.

___ I would allow an autopsy to be performed if necessary to provide information that would help save the life of a family member or other identifiable patient. If any autopsy is performed, I ask that it be conducted with all possible respect and that all my body parts subsequently be buried in a Jewish cemetery in accordance with Jewish law and custom.

Inconsistent with Rabbi Reisner's opinion:

___ *I would allow an autopsy to be performed either to help save the life of a patient or if it would enable physicians to learn more about my disease because my case is not routine. If any autopsy is performed, I ask that it be conducted with all possible respect and that all my body parts subsequently be buried in a Jewish cemetery in accordance with Jewish law and custom.*

Comments:____

____

As God is my rock and my fortress and my deliverer, so may God be my refuge, my shield and my salvation, forever.

Signature: ____

Name: ____

Date: ____

Address: ____

City & State: ____

I declare that the person who signed this document, or asked another to sign this document on his or her behalf, did so in my presence, that I know him or her to be the person named as the subject of this document, and that he or she appears to be of sound mind and acting of his or her free will, free of duress or undue influence. I am eighteen years of age or older, and I am not designated by this or any other document as the person's health care agent or alternate health care agent.

Witness 1:	Witness 2:
Signature ______________________	Signature ______________________
Name ______________________	Name ______________________
Date ______________________	Date ______________________
Address ______________________	Address ______________________
City & State ______________________	City & State ______________________

Notarization is not necessary unless required by your state law.

CHAPTER 24

Peri- and Neonatology: The Matter of Limiting Treatment*

Avram I. Reisner

She'eilah (Question):

When are we justified, if ever, to allow a malformed newborn to die without applying maximum technological efforts to save that child or to extend its life?

Teshuvah (Response):

Developments in the field of peri- and neonatology are coming apace, and nothing written today can hope to digest developments on the morrow. This said, there are certain general judgments that can be made.

First, some terminological matters. For some time, the field of treating high-risk babies was known as *neonatology* and consisted of the treatment of damaged, premature, and low-birth-weight infants. In the last decade, however, the fields of genetic testing, intrauterine diagnosis, and microsurgery have all expanded dramatically, offering the possibility of diagnosing fetal flaws in the womb and intervening in that environment to correct them.[1] Consequently, a new term has entered the field to describe treatment of an infant both before and after birth. That term, *perinatology,* has been added to the older term in the literature.[2] As a result, it is necessary today to speak of treatment of the fetus as well as of the newborn.

*Approved by the Rabbinical Assembly Committee on Jewish Law and Standards, Sept. 1995.

A. The Status of the Fetus

As David Feldman sets out in his magnificent *Birth Control in Jewish Law*,[3] the unborn child is not seen as a separate and full life under Jewish law. It is protected, however, as potential life and may be aborted only for maternal causes. Concern for potential pain and burden on the unborn child cannot be a reason to choose abortion not because that would be murder, but because to do so would be to meddle in God's domain, whereas treatment of the mother is in ours. Nevertheless, any and all acts that we might undertake to heal or strengthen the potential life of the fetus are in order. As with human life, we are enjoined to heal. That is part of the divine mandate.

Often, however, the mother's interests intervene in any calculations regarding the fetus. Unlike the potential life of the fetus, the mother's life is established. As such, it takes clear precedence under Jewish law. The Mishnah in *Oholot* (7:6) clearly permits abortion, even at a very late date, to save the mother's life. No calculation of viability is material here—only birth. With this as the primary precedent, Jewish legal sources include the health and even the mental well-being of the mother as potential reason to permit abortion. Some have argued that these precedents may be stretched to include the child's own disabilities when they would severely and negatively affect the mother's mental composure, her family situation, or even the economics thereof.[4] The upshot of this literature is to permit abortion for cause, but not simply by unsupported choice. What constitutes sufficient cause is a decision to be made on a case-by-case basis by the parents and their rabbi. This position is stated clearly in the definitive rulings by the CJLS on this subject on 23 August 1983.[5]

Much more can be done for the fetus in utero today, however, than in the past, and even more will be possible in the future. Are we required to offer medical assistance to this fetus even when we do not recognize the fetus as a fully vested life and could conceivably abort it? The upshot of these permissive (but not pro-choice) rulings is that when aiding the fetus could have negative ramifications for the mother, any and all medical assistance for the fetus may be forgone. Any manipulation of the fetus, whether surgical or medicinal, would, in fact, entail some risk to the mother. Whereas the results are uncertain and the risks are real, it is appropriate to forgo endeavors to aid the fetus.

But forgoing medical treatment of the fetus in utero, while permissible, is not required. The mother's desire to undertake some risk for her child and the true extent of that risk must be considered in every case. We would, without much hesitation, permit a kidney donation to a relative, although life with only one kidney is clearly more precarious than with two. We would encourage sea rescues, despite the risk of drowning, because we understand that the risk is small when measured against what may be gained. The desire to aid the fetus is very real and should be considered. Action to save a life, even a potential one, is meritorious, and proceeds even at the cost of Shabbat transgressions.[6] But fetal life is just that, potential life not yet actualized, not, as the tradition claims, within the category of *nefesh adam,* a human life. Efforts to aid are subject to that inequality between the mother's status and that of the fetus. It should be noted that even when other human lives are at stake, there is a point at which rescuers are restrained from reentering a burning building although they had done so before because, assessing the situation, we determine that the risk has grown too great. All the more so here.

There is a second issue that enters here, the issue of viability.[7] It appears to me that a viability standard at the end of the seventh month (thirty-one to thirty-two weeks),[8] when survival approaches 85 percent, must be extended to the fetus if we speak of the presumption of life potential for medical purposes. That correlates well with the abilities of perinatology today. This is not to say that a late-term fetus has attained the status of a full life, but that greater concern for the potential life of the fetus is in order. Rabbi Waldenberg, at least, seems to hint at such a standard when he writes of abortion on account of Tay-Sachs disease:

> יש לדעתי להתיר הפסקת הריון כזה לפחות עד שבעה חדשים
>
> It appears to me that such an abortion may be permitted at least through the seventh month.[9]

Surgical and medical treatment of the fetus in utero, at this late date, should be encouraged if there is a good chance of curing the fetus and little risk to the mother.

This is not in conflict with the permission that we have granted abortion for cause. Thirty-one to thirty-two weeks is the end of the seventh month by obstetrical count, or well into the third trimester. Abortion at that late date is exceedingly rare and will not be performed except when the mother's health is endangered, or in cases of rape or incest when the mother's mental well-being is at issue, or where there are genetic indications that occasion it (where, again, we would permit abortion readily based on the mother's well-being). Indeed, the law of the land supports such a distinction, ruling in *Roe v. Wade* that states may not prohibit abortion in the first two trimesters, but that they may do so in the third.

Nor do we prohibit abortion even in the eighth and ninth months. But it is correct that the claim on life of the fetus should grow closer to that of its mother in these latter days, and treatment questions as well as abortion questions should be weighed in that light.[10]

B. The Status of the Newborn

Birth is the defining moment with regard to the status of the infant. Nevertheless, there are substantial misgivings in the halakhic literature even concerning the viability of newborns. The Talmud accepts as a given that a seven- or nine-month child may live, but that an eight-month child will not. Thus, Shabbat circumcision is required of a seven- and nine-month child, but prohibited for an eight-month child or for one about whom we hold a significant question. The same would not be true of a doubtful eight-month birth with regard to medical treatment, wherein health needs override Shabbat regulations even in the event of uncertainty. But it would be true, according to the classical halakhah, that even medical treatment could not be given on Shabbat to a verified eight-month baby, of whom the Tosefta writes:

הרי הוא כאבן ואין מטלטלין אותו אבל אמו שוחה עליו ומניקתו

> He is like a stone. One does not move him (on Shabbat), but his mother may bend over him to suckle him.

(The commentators are quick to add: *mipenei tza'ar heḥalav shemetza'arah*, "due to her pain of engorgement,"[11] not due to our concern for that infant's life.) Indeed, Rabban Shimon ben Gamaliel's dictum that a child is not considered to be viable until the thirty-first day[12] after birth is itself apparently predicated on this uncertainty.

The notion that an eight-month baby cannot live and therefore does not merit our attention is profoundly disturbing (yet it is indicative of our options to withhold care from hopeless cases, to which we will return in a moment). It is disturbing because it does not correlate with our best science and would ask us to withhold critical care from those infants we might save. Furthermore, the eight-month infant in question is in his ninth month by obstetrical count, since this is a count of months completed.[13] Yet viability in the ninth month, today, approaches 100 percent!

Candor would have us simply state that the Talmud's eight-month rule cannot stand in light of current understanding. Indeed, the well-respected sage Avraham Karelitz, known as the Ḥazon Ish, argued tentatively:

> כמדומה דעכשיו נשתנה הטבע וכפי בחינת הרופאים
>
> It seems that now nature has changed and we follow the discernment of the doctors.

While this opinion was not yet current in the early literature,[14] it seems to have gained current assent.[15] Concerning the laws of mourning, the Committee on Jewish Law and Standards has opted to waive Rabban Shimon ben Gamaliel's argument [against considering a newborn under thirty-one days viable] in favor of the more subjective standard of *aviv ve'imo,* that parental bonding that begins at birth. With regard to medical treatment, we should waive it as well, in order to correspond to the reality that greets us.[16]

Medical treatment of a viable newborn should therefore proceed as strenuously as it would for an adult. Those treatments that would be appropriate for an adult must be provided a newborn (save where the medical requirements of a newborn dictate otherwise). Where it is appropriate to withhold or withdraw treatment from an adult, it would be appropriate also to do so for a newborn.[17]

C. Genetic Abnormalities and Severe Prematurity

With regard to the fetus, we have already said that abortion is permitted for cause. Clearly, genetic factors affecting that fetus can and will have an effect on the mother's emotional well-being and will factor into any abortion decision that may be made. It is when a child is born with unexpected genetic deficiencies or is severely premature that we are faced with the awful choice of whether and to what extent to extend treatment. May we consider the viability of that child in making treatment decisions and forgo treatments when they are considered unlikely to promote the child's long-term survival? Both Rabbi Waldenberg and Dr. Jakobovits, writing on this precise question, assume that the newborn should be treated exactly as would be any patient.[18] Yet in light of the Talmud's treatment of the eight-month birth and in light of the extended discussion in the Gemara of the third chapter of *Niddah* concerning the status of varying types of concepti, there might be room to consider the basic nature of the infants in question. In the words of the Mishnah:

חכמים אומרים כל שאין בו מצורת אדם אינו ולד

> The sages say: Whatever does not have the aspect of a human being is not (considered) a birth.[19]

On its face, this would appear to describe "monstrosities": as delineated by the Mishnah, this would include "fish-like creatures," "insect-like creatures," "animal-like creatures," and so on, and would exclude apparently normal children. But baraitot and amoraic dicta in the Gemara extend this category to include one whose "forehead, eyebrows, eyes, cheeks, and chin [or jaw?] are not of a piece," and establish a further extension that rests on nonviability.[20] Thus, a woman who miscarries an infant whose esophagus is sealed (but not where it is simply perforated), whose (lower?) body is closed,[21] whose skull is malformed,[22] whose face is crushed, is considered not to have given birth to a child. These extensions, it seems me, permit the question: Is there some level of nonviability at which the defective newborn should be permitted to expire?

The problem before us in relying upon this talmudic material is the generic problem of scientific knowledge. We do not know precisely what situations the Talmud sought to describe, nor do we know the extent of their medical discernment. To say that of the Talmud is, of course, not generally allowed. But the commentators and decisors were not at all unwilling to say that of themselves. Thus, this material does not appear in codified law, not because it is inappropriate to include it, but because the decisors did not feel that they could draw practical conclusions therefrom. In the relevant section of *Shulḥan Arukh* (Y.D. 194:3), we read:

עכשיו שאין אנו בקיאין בצורות חוששת לולד

> Now, when we are not expert in the formation [of the fetus], [the birthing mother] must consider these births.

But to be fair to the extraordinary advances of medicine in our day, it might precisely be said that today, as never before, we are expert in this area.

With much trepidation, I conclude that there are, in fact, such situations. Anyone who works in the field of neonatology can confirm episodes in which, in the judgment of the medical team, an infant was too severely malformed to attempt any rescue.[23] Similarly, in the case of anencephaly, a neural tube defect by which the conceptus is born without a developed brain, in which case the infant does not have a life expectancy of beyond one month, the child should be considered akin to the Talmud's conceptus with the malformed skull. In such a case, there seems to me to be no requirement on the part of the physician to engage in attempts to save the child. Similarly, the major chromosomal abnormalities of trisomy 13, wherein the infant suffers severe abnormalities of brain and facial features and most often cannot support breathing on its own, and of trisomy 18, wherein the infants almost always succumb to respiratory difficulties within the first year, may be seen as indications of the nonviability of the infant. Although, fully supported, such children may live a year,[24] upon diagnosis within the first days after birth, it is correct to classify these infants as nonviable and end their support. I am unwilling, however, to follow the logic of these talmudic positions to the extreme conclusion that such children are altogether not considered live births. Were we to do so, there would be no impediment to treating such infants as donors while yet alive. If only because of our humility, but even more so because of our extreme reverence for life, it is unacceptable to do so. Rather, we should classify such newborn infants as born dying, and allow the latitude of nontreatment that we would consider appropriate at the end of life.[25] Given the reality of scientific advance, I believe that this ruling grants the needed flexibility.

With regard to severely premature newborns, the medical ground is shifting particularly fast. Lung development now seems to determine the earliest possible survivability, but opinion differs as to whether that is a real boundary, or whether it might be overcome by increasing medical innovations.[26] Experimentation with a pseudo-womb environment continues. Therefore, it is prudent to leave the assessment of severely premature newborns to the medical experts. When a child is found to be so severely premature as to preclude any realistic chance of survival, it may be classed with defective newborns, and aggressive efforts to save the life of the child may be forgone. But when a realistic chance of survival exists, all efforts to achieve that result should proceed.[27]

Other abnormalities, including trisomy 21 (Down's syndrome), do not affect the newborn as severely, and the infant should be treated as are all other newborns.[28] As it is impossible to categorize every neonatal possibility, it remains for the doctors and the family's rabbi to determine the appropriate category for the case before them.[29]

D. Conclusions

1. Abortion of the fetus is permitted throughout pregnancy for cause.

2. The claim of the potential life of the fetus to our ministrations is greater upon attaining viability, that is, after seven months (thirty-one to thirty-two weeks by obstetrical count).

3. Standardly, newborns must be cared for as we would care for any adult.

4. Severely deformed and compromised newborns are classified as born dying, and treatments aimed at their survival may be discontinued. Severe deformity refers to anencephaly, trisomies 13 and 18, or other similar large-scale genetic deformities. Jewish law does not insist on aggressive treatment in such cases. The term does not apply to lesser deformities, such as trisomy 21 (Down's syndrome).

5. Prematurity is generally to be considered part of the category of lesser deformities. In cases of severe prematurity, the rabbi, in consultation with the family and physician, may conclude that the infant should be classified as unable to survive.

6. In fact, everything said here is said as guidance to the rabbi, who must carefully assess the case in consultation with the family and physicians in order to determine the proper course in the instant case.

E. Addendum concerning Mourning Practices

The following is not within the purview of this paper; nevertheless, I would suggest:

1. A defective newborn who dies within Rabban Shimon ben Gamaliel's thirty-day period should not require mourning, since the parent did not reasonably expect that child to live. If the parents wish to observe mourning voluntarily, they may do so, just as one may voluntarily observe mourning for an in-law.

2. Full mourning should be accepted as a voluntary observance for stillborn children and late-term miscarriages (eighth and ninth month).

Notes

1. A particularly striking example is at the heart of the popular book *The Baby Doctors,* by Gina Kolata (New York: Delacorte Press, 1990), reporting on some of the pioneering attempts at fetal surgery. Many newborns were dying, with little hope of successful intervention, because of respiratory insufficiency. No respirator or incubator therapy could replace the lung maturity that was lacking. Stunningly, a significant subset of these children were found to be suffering from diaphragmatic hernias, wherein the diaphragm had failed to close properly in early fetal development and the intestinal organs had migrated up through the hole, effectively preventing the later developing lungs from forming in the cavity that they now filled. By learning to operate in utero to draw down the migrating intestines and close the hole in the diaphragm, the perinatal surgeons were able to forge room for the lungs to develop and the children would be born healthy. Effectively, a small mechanical problem was killing large numbers of babies, and a comparatively simple procedure could be devised to save them (although nothing is truly simple in intrauterine surgery because of the size and speed of growth of the fetus).
2. *The Random House College Dictionary* (1982), 892, defines *neonatology* as

"the branch of medicine that specializes in care of newborn children, esp. those that are premature," and a *neonate* as "a newborn child, or one in its first 28 days." (Note the similarities to Rabban Gamaliel's thirty-day measure in T. *Shabbat* 15:7.) That dictionary does not yet attest "perinatology," although it is clearly built on the Greek root *peri,* meaning "around." Thus, the new term "perinatology" connotes treatment around birth, before as well as after.

The introduction to the first chapter of *Behrman's Neonatal-Perinatal Medicine* (3d ed., ed. Richard E. Behrman et al. [St. Louis: Mosby, 1983]) defines the field as follows: "The term 'perinatal' is used to designate the period from the twelfth week of gestation through the twenty-eighth day after birth. The 'neonatal period' is defined as the first four weeks of life and is the period of the greatest mortality in childhood." In practice, an active neonatologist offers this definition: "The perinatal period extends from the beginning of the third trimester until the end of the first postnatal week. The neonatal period begins immediately after birth and extends until the end of the fourth postnatal week. A perinatologist is an obstetrician with added subspecialty training who cares for the mother and fetus. A neonatologist is a pediatrician with added subspecialty training who cares for high-risk newborns" (personal letter from Dr. Charles Paley to R. Stephanie Dickstein, 6 Sept. 1995).

3. For the details of this position, see David M. Feldman, *Birth Control in Jewish Law* (New York and London: New York University Press, 1968), chaps. 14 and 15, and infra. Schocken published a paperback reprint in 1987 under the new (and more accurate) title: *Marital Relations, Birth Control, and Abortion in Jewish Law.*
4. See R. Eliezer Waldenberg, *Tzitz Eliezer,* 2d ed. (Jerusalem: n.p., 1985), vol. 9, no. 51:3; vol. 13, no. 102; vol. 15, no. 43. His positions are summarized in A. Steinberg, *Hilkhot Rofe'im Urefu'ah* (Jerusalem: Mossad Harav Kook, 1978), 30–46. And see Feldman, n. 3 above.
5. *Proceedings of the Committee on Jewish Law and Standards 1980–1985* (New York: Rabbinical Assembly, 1988), 1–37 [reprinted as chaps. 10–14 of this vol.].
6. This conclusion is based primarily on the notion

חלל עליו שבת אחד כדי שישמור שבתות הרבה

One should transgress this one Shabbat in order that he may observe many. (*Shabbat* 151b)

This would apply well to a fetus, even though the fetus is not yet alive. See Feldman, 264, and Waldenberg, vol. 13, no. 102, sec. 3.

7. On 3 June 1992, the CJLS approved a paper by Rabbi Stephanie Dickstein, "Mourning Practices for Infants Who Die Prior to the Thirty-first Day of Life." The CJLS approved an alteration of the law of mourning from the cautious view of Rabban Shimon ben Gamaliel that mourning is not required of an infant that

dies in those first thirty days (*Shabbat* 135b), in favor of the more subjective measure of the Mishnah in *Niddah* 5:3:

תנוק בן יום אחד . . . הרי הוא לאביו ולאמו ולכל קרוביו כחתן שלם

(Even) a day-old infant is considered by his father and mother and all his relatives as a full bridegroom.

In "*Kim Li*: A Dissenting Concurrence," I argued that the measure was incorrect. If we seek to measure the subjective considerations of the parents, it is more realistic to try to measure their expectations than their hopes. Not all children born are, in fact, expected to live, even by their parents. In fact, a likelihood that the child would live is not established by a fifty-fifty chance but by some significant preponderance of the chances that the child would live. I proposed a thirty-one- to thirty-two-week threshold, corresponding to the end of the seventh month by obstetrical count. I remain convinced of that position.

8. The vagueness inherent in establishing a thirty-one- to thirty-two-week threshold rather than a date certain is intended to convey that obstetrical count is itself notoriously fallible (although with ultrasound measurements, it is much firmer than it has historically been) and that we always are bound to the best judgment of the physician. Said flexibility should be permitted to push the date back as far as the beginning of the third trimester (twenty-seven to twenty-eight weeks) when the doctor feels that his neonatal unit reaches 85 percent viability that early.
9. Waldenberg, vol. 13, no. 102, sec. 5; and see sec. 1.
10. Dr. Charles Paley, in his correspondence with R. Stephanie Dickstein, notes that this is largely a theoretical permission of abortion. In reality, he notes, a fetus of this age would have a substantial potential for survival. Consequently, most crises related to the mother's ability to proceed with the pregnancy would be resolved not by abortion but by cesarean section.
11. T. *Shabbat* 15:5–7, B. *Shabbat* 135a, J. *Yevamot* 4:2, *S.A., O.Ḥ.* 330:5ff. And see the lengthy *pilpul* in this regard by R. Yitzḥak Ya'akov Weiss, *Minḥat Yitzḥak,* 123.
12. *Shabbat* 135b. See n. 7 above.
13. That the count is of completed months is clear from the Tosefta's definition (15:7):

אי זהו בן שמונה כל שלא יצאו לו חדשיו

Which is an eight-month infant? One who has not completed his months.

and by the Talmud's use, on *Shabbat* 136a, of

קים לי ביה שכלו לו חדשיו

I am certain that he has completed his months.

as a synonym for a viable, full-term baby. Otherwise, he would need assert only that the baby had reached the ninth month. Many modern halakhic writings refer to the eighth month by obstetrical convention and assume the nonviability of the eight-month child to refer to that. (See, for instance, R. Neria Gutal, "Hapagut Le'or Hahalakhah," *Assia* 11, no. 44 [vol. 11, no. 4]: 5–30, and in nn. 1–2 to his second installment of that article, *Assia* 12, nos. 45–46 [vol. 12, nos. 1–2]: 97.) This appears to me to be insupportable. But Dr. Steinberg, ever reasonable, understands the count to be of completed months and thus cites the Talmud, "A baby born *after* [emphasis mine] eight months of gestation is nonviable" (Dr. Abraham Steinberg, "The Defective Newborn: Halachic Considerations," in Dr. Fred Rosner, *Medicine and Jewish Law II* [Northvale, N.J.: Jason Aronson, 1993], 125).

It is further the case that obstetric and Jewish count are discrepant month by month. Obstetrical count assumes a beginning at the last menses and an extent of 40 weeks, or 280 days. These amount to 9 months and one week of the secular calendar's 30/31-day months (to wit: every 3 months is, on average, 91 days; $3 \times 91 + 7 = 280$).

The rabbinic count begins at conception, roughly 2 weeks later than the obstetrical count, and is just 271 days. This extent is determined by the Talmud, *Niddah* 38b, on the basis of the numerical value of the word *heirayon* (pregnancy). Months, however, are lunar, set for this purpose at 30 days each. Nine months equals 270 days, with the birth presumed to be on the following day. The ninth month thus differs a bit accordingly.

This is the traditional rabbinic count. I prefer to believe that the Rabbis, who knew quite well that the lunar month approximates 29.5, not 30, days, and who consequently alternated months of 29 and 30 days on their calendar, knew 9 months to be somewhat shorter (to wit: $9 \times 29.5 = 265.5$), which would better match the obstetrical count of 280 days, which begins 14 days earlier. That they allowed 271 days to stand, I think, was in light of the gematria and their certain knowledge that any number here is a gross approximation of a number quite variable, in fact.

14. Thus *Magen Avraham, S.A., O.Ḥ.* 330:16 represents those who obviated the Talmud's ruling by finding all but the most certain of cases [of nonviability due to being born in the eighth month of pregnancy] to be uncertain, therefore to be treated even on Shabbat. Indeed, even in a case similar to the one he finds certain, it would be possible to adjudge the infant of uncertain gestational age, (a) because it is possible that the infant was formed in order to be born after seven months and he tarried (see Lieberman, *Tosefta Kifshutah, Shabbat,* 249), or (b) because the mother might have been mysteriously impregnated (*nitabera be'ambati*—see *Ḥagiga* 15a).
15. Ḥazon Ish, *Y.D.* 155:4. I have not seen the original, but have seen Ḥazon Ish cited in *Sefer Assia* 4:44, and in *Assia* nos. 45–46 [vol. 12, nos. 1–2]: 108 n. 37, and again in *Bishvilei Harefu'ah,* no. 9 (Tevet 5749): 84; and see Steinberg, 125 n. 7, and the other citations there.

16. Rabban Shimon ben Gamaliel's opinion is not so easily dismissed. What differentiates a newborn from an older child, he claims, is that *ḥezkat ḥayim,* a presumption of life, does not yet inhere in a newborn. But the mishnah of abortion, in *Oholot* 7:6, which forbids abortion the moment the head or majority of the body has exited the birth canal, is explicit in arguing that the presumption of life does apply immediately upon birth, "and we do not set aside one life for another."

    Certain other areas of halakhah stand to be affected by our desire to waive Rabban Shimon ben Gamaliel's ruling, were we to do so across the board as the realia dictate that we do. These are discussed by R. Yitzhak Zilberstein in "Pagim Unefalim Beyeḥidah Letipul Nimratz," *Sefer Assia* 6:42–45. Regarding *yibum* and *ḥalitzah* (levirate marriage and its ceremonial rejection), waiving the thirty-day rule would be salutory, as it would exempt more women from these requirements. Regarding *pidyon habein* (redemption of the firstborn), however, it might require redemption of the parents of an infant that died prior to thirty days (if not in our most extreme category of disability), whereas present regulations exempt. One could, however, rule with Tosafot that the thirty-day limit regarding redemption is established by Scripture independent of viability and thereby hold on to the simple ruling of exemption if any infant dies prior to thirty days. In any case, the exemption of further births is not dependent on the viability of that first infant, for any infant, even a stillbirth, would exempt future children from redemption. Nor would it affect inheritance. See Zilberstein for further detail.
17. See R. Avram Reisner, "A Halakhic Ethic of Care for the Terminally Ill," *Conservative Judaism* 43, no. 3 (spring 1991) [which appears as chaps. 16–17 of this vol.]. See also R. Elliot Dorff, "A Jewish Approach to End-Stage Medical Care," ibid. [which appears as chaps. 18–20 of this vol.].

    It is, of course, impossible to speak of the patient's autonomous will in the case of newborn infants. Family and physicians function under the constraints of unappointed surrogates, seeking the best course of treatment. That a dying newborn whose situation is futile would be treated as would an adult in a similarly futile state is stated clearly, most recently in Steinberg, "The Defective Newborn," 123.
18. Waldenberg, *Tzitz Eliezer* 13, no. 88. Dr. Yoel Jakobovits, *Tradition* 22, no. 3 (fall 1986): 13–30.
19. M. *Niddah* 3:2.
20. *Niddah* 23b.

    אמר רבא . . . ושטו אטום אמו טהורה. ת"ר: המפלת גוף אטום אין אמו טמאה לידה ואיזהו גוף אטום רבי אומר כדי שינטל מן החי וימות . . . וכן אמר רב גידל אמר רבי יוחנן: המפלת את שגולגלתו אטומה אמו טהורה

    Rava says: If his esophagus is sealed, his mother is pure (i.e., it is not considered a birth). The Rabbis taught: She who miscarries a sealed (lower?)

body, its mother is not impure the impurity of birth. Which is a "sealed body"? Rabbi says: Such that were (that portion) taken from the living, he would die.

Thus does Rav Gidal say in the name of R. Yoḥanan: She who miscarries one whose skull is sealed, its mother is pure.

21. Maimonides, *M.T., Isurei Bi'ah* 10:11. (He includes this full Gemara passage in that chap.) Precisely what these conditions refer to is debated by the amoraim there. This appears to refer to an improperly developed gastrointestinal tract. As to why the other codes do not include this material, see ahead.
22. The word translated here as "malformed" is *atum* in the Hebrew, the same word as is used with regard to the closing of the esophagus and, if I am correct, the intestinal tract. Rashi here, however, translates "missing" under the influence of the prior gemara and, I suspect, his inability to imagine the situation being described. That the reference is to a "collapsed" skull, rather than a missing one, seems to me more likely. See n. 20 above.
23. This area has occasioned much debate. See the excellent popular study *Playing God in the Nursery* by Jeff Lyon (New York: W. W. Norton, 1985), particularly the chapter "Sanctity of Life vs. Quality of Life" and the report of the President's Commission for the Study of Ethical Problems in Medicine and Biochemical and Behavioral Research, *Deciding to Forego [sic] Life-Sustaining Treatment* (Washington, D.C.: U.S. Government Printing Office, 1983).
24. Presentation by Alan Fleischman, director of the Division of Neonatology at Weiller Hospital of Albert Einstein College, to the Subcommittee on Biomedical Ethics of the CJLS, 13 Sept. 1989. And see, in detail, D. W. Smith, *Recognizable Patterns of Human Malformation* (vol. 7 in W. B. Saunders, *Major Problems in Clinical Pediatrics,* 3d ed. [Philadelphia: Saunders, 1982]). Another such case would be chromosomal triploidy, a very rare occurrence in which there is no survival (indeed, most such births miscarry).

    As our intervention in the womb grows, we must anticipate larger numbers of malformed concepti that were destined to miscarry early in their gestation but that we shall reach [while they are still] alive. While abortion of such flawed concepti is permitted for maternal causes, it is not permitted to abort a fetus because of considerations of its own infirmities or suffering. Whereas, once born, we would countenance withholding of mechanical life support, the fetus's life support is within the natural realm. It cannot be aborted but by an aggressive act on our part, which is permissible only in the context of saving another. But see nn. 5 and 6 above.
25. See n. 17 above. Thus, the use of a respirator or heart-lung machine, or extensive use of dialysis beyond immediate hope of repair of the kidneys or holding toward transplant would be counterindicated. An incubator should be required, however, as the function of an incubator is to enhance the biological functioning of the newborn and not to replace those functions mechanically. It goes without

saying that once brain death has been declared, such an infant may serve as an organ donor, as may any adult. The same criteria of brain death apply.

This responsum runs counter to the one direct early precedent known to me in this matter. R. Eleazar Fleckeles, in his responsum *Teshuvah Mei'ahavah* no. 53 (Prague, 1800), is asked about leaving monstrous newborns unattended, even to permit them to starve to death. The questioner, R. David Ber Cohen, effectively sets out the case based on these Talmud texts that monstrous newborns should not be considered human, for which reason, *yeish kan tzad heteir lesabeiv hamitah* [there is room for leniency here to bring about death]. R. Fleckeles dismisses this opinion out of hand, arguing that the Gemara deals in matters of impurity, not life and death, and that none of the subhuman monsters included could possibly survive to birth. Furthermore, we do not consider ourselves capable of making this determination. And even if we could make that determination, that conceptus would be classed a *tereifah* or a *goseis,* neither of whom may be put to death, or, at the very least, the equivalent of an animal, which may also not be caused gratuitous pain.

Were we to cite this responsum as the controlling precedent, as does *Pitḥei Teshuvah* to *S.A., Y.D.* 194, no. 5, or as do R. David Bleich in his *Contemporary Halakhic Problems I* (New York: Ktav, 1977): 366, and R. Immanuel Jakobovits, *Tradition* 5 (spring 1963): 268, then we would be bound by precedent to rule more restrictively. But a case-by-case consideration of his arguments yields a different result.

As I have said, the extent of our expertise has risen considerably in the two centuries since R. Fleckeles wrote, and he himself was suitably tentative about an opinion offered without substantial support. More important, however, the questioner seeks to rule that said defective newborns are subhuman and to permit their death by starvation on that basis. We have been more cautious. If the Talmud's presentation, in theory, posits subhuman defectives, then out of uncertainty we will certainly not entertain actively killing same, but only classify these as dying and apply those rules to them. We only allow that that categorization may color our thinking on treatment decisions. In every case, we do not draw ultimate conclusions from somewhat strained halakhic argumentation, but only allow it to move us a notch along the spectrum. This is, I believe, a thoroughly traditional model of halakhic decision making. In the instant case, it resolves the rest of R. Fleckeles' concerns, for it permits neither the killing of a *tereifah* nor the equivalent of cruelty to animals but only a measured response to the situation as we understand it.

In *Be'or Hatorah* no. 8 (English, 1993): 10, R. Yitzhak Zilberstein also cites this source and adds two other very contemporary views that, like that of R. Fleckeles, prohibit euthanizing said creatures but do not seem to address clearly this more cautious approach.

In a related matter, R. Zilberstein himself, in a responsum in *Bishvilei Harefu'ah* 9 (Dec. 1988): 81ff. (citing R. Eliezer Waldenberg for support), cannot find a true prohibition against leaving untreated extremely premature newborns, but nevertheless recommends their treatment. He defines extreme prematurity as prior to 24 weeks, viz., the end of the sixth month, understanding the "seven-month infant" of the Talmud as "in the seventh month" (see n. 13 above). Similarly, we treat the extremely premature infant as a subset of all patients, believing it appropriate to give even the tiniest ones the best chance we can. Uncertainty (*safeik*) is not sufficient ground for retreating. When uncertainty is replaced by futility, then we would back off. But that is true of any patient, if, perhaps, more likely true of the extremely premature newborn.

Most recently, Dr. Abraham Steinberg, in "The Defective Newborn," 125, seems to follow along a similar track, citing talmudic rulings that are not in effect to justify present-day leniencies. Though he cites recent rabbinic decisors as ruling the talmudic ruling of eight-month babies inapplicable, he goes on to state that "the determining factor in the decision as to whether to treat or not to treat a defective newborn depends on its chances of viability, in accordance with the scientific knowledge and technical capabilities at the time. From the pure halakhic standpoint, it might be forbidden to desecrate the Sabbath nowadays for any severely handicapped newborn who is expected to die within a few days. An anencephalic newborn falls into this category, since such a baby has the same halakhic status as a baby born after eight months of gestation as described in the Talmud." I have preferred to extrapolate from a ruling that was not applied explicitly because of lack of expertise rather than from a ruling voided because of "changed nature." In either case, however, what has really changed is precisely our medical expertise.

26. New York State Task Force on Life and the Law, *Fetal Extrauterine Survivability* (New York: New York State Task Force on Life and the Law, 1988), 9.
27. What constitutes "realistic" remains the province of the rabbi to determine. No percentage can be substituted for a judgmental ruling, here. As Dr. Steinberg notes in "The Defective Newborn," 131, "There are uncertainties as to the extent of morbidity and its severity. Moreover, there are still very few early prognostic markers for survival and for significant morbidity in individual babies. . . . Even the definition of futility is variable. Therefore, in Jewish law, an individual baby who has a chance for survival should be treated as vigorously as needed."

    It may be asked why our viability measure does not come into play here. The answer is apparent. Concerning a fetus, we need a preponderant chance for that fetus to rise near the level of a presumption of life. But a newborn has, in fact, gained a *ḥezkat ḥayim,* a presumption of life, by virtue of having been born. Henceforth we would need more than even a preponderant likelihood that that child would die to declare further ministrations futile. See n. 16 above.
28. Even a "closed" intestinal tract, specified in the Talmud as a nonviable birth (see n. 20 above), might today be susceptible to surgical correctives, which should therefore be undertaken where possible.

29. Many cases will not fall clearly into one category or another. In cases of microcephaly, encephalocele, and many other genetic abnormalities that may range in their severity, a medical judgment must be made concerning the extent of disability and the rabbi must judge if the weight of the nonviable category is met. See conclusion 6 below.

G. ASSISTED SUICIDE AND EUTHANASIA

Introduction

This section addresses one of the most controversial issues in Western societies today, that of assisted suicide. In assisted suicide, one person contributes to another person's actively ending his or her own life, with the person whose life ends taking the final action. Euthanasia (or "active euthanasia") is similar, but the final action is performed by a person other than the one whose life ends. Both assisted suicide and euthanasia are distinct from the appropriate forgoing of life-sustaining treatment, as discussed in the above sections.

Rabbi Elliot N. Dorff begins his paper "Physician-Assisted Suicide and Euthanasia" with a brief discussion of the contemporary medical and legal contexts for considering suicide and assisted suicide. He then presents key theological values and halakhic considerations that have supported a prohibition of suicide and assisted suicide. A number of contemporary circumstances add new grounds for maintaining this traditional prohibition. These include a disparity between common American views, and Judaism's theological appreciation of the intrinsic worth of humans and our responsibilities to God for maintaining life. Contemporary health care offers the capacity to treat pain effectively, but often, in fact, fails to provide needed treatment, and often imposes burdensome treatments that patients should be able to refuse. An attitude of cost containment, together with other societal developments, is likely to turn any legal right to commit suicide into a perceived duty to end one's life.

In addition to affirming the prohibition of assisted suicide, Dorff presents a number of positive responsibilities of health care professionals and members of society generally toward the severely ill. These include improved pain relief and supportive care, recognition of patients' rights to refuse interventions that have become impediments to the dying process, and fulfillment of the mitzvah of *bikur ḥolim,* visiting the sick. Dorff's paper is preceded by the brief "Statement on Assisted Suicide," summarizing its central conclusions and recommendations.

CHAPTER 25

Statement on Assisted Suicide*

Elliot N. Dorff

Since God infuses each human life with inherent meaning by creating each of us in the divine image, thereby guaranteeing ultimate value regardless of a person's abilities or quality of life; and

Since Judaism views life as sacred and understands human beings to have life on trust from God; and

Since God's creation and ownership of our bodies puts the decision of when life is to end in God's hands; and

Since we nonetheless have both the right and the duty to seek to cure, to relieve pain, and to provide comfort care, including social, emotional, and psychological support to all who are ill; and

Since current efforts to rein in costs for medical care threaten to transform any permission to aid a suicide into a perceived duty to commit suicide, shifting the burden of proof to the one who wants to remain alive;

The Conservative Movement's Committee on Jewish Law and Standards has adopted a rabbinic ruling (*teshuvah*) by Rabbi Elliot N. Dorff affirming that:

*Approved by the Rabbinical Assembly Committee on Jewish Law and Standards, Mar. 1997.

1. Suicide is a violation of Jewish law and of the sacred trust of our lives given us by God.

2. Assisting a suicide is also a violation of Jewish law and God's sacred trust of life. No human being may take his or her own life, ask others to help [him or her] do so, or assist in such an effort.

3. Patients and their caregivers nevertheless have the tradition's permission to withhold or withdraw impediments to the natural process of dying, as described in two responsa by Rabbis Elliot N. Dorff and Avram Israel Reisner, [respectively,] previously adopted by the Committee and published in the spring 1991 edition of the journal *Conservative Judaism* [as well as chapters 16–20 of this volume], and as applied in the Committee's *[Jewish] Medical Directive[s] for Health Care,* written by Rabbi Aaron Mackler on the basis of those responsa [chapter 23 of this volume].

4. Physicians must assure that patients are given sufficient pain medication as part of their duty to provide medical care, as mandated in Jewish law.

5. In the context of nuclear families, divorce, and far-flung families, the mitzvah of *bikur ḥolim* (visiting the sick) becomes all the more imperative in our day than it was in times past to counteract the loneliness that terminally ill patients often face. Individual Jews and synagogues should see this as an important priority of their Jewish commitment.

6. Requests for assistance in suicide are often an expression of the patient's extreme suffering, despair, psychiatric depression, and loneliness. The Jewish tradition bids us to express our compassion in ways that effectively respond to the patient's suffering while adhering to our mandate to respect the divine trust of life. Among such options is final care at home, with the help of palliative ministrations, including hospice care, to provide the social and emotional support [that] severely sick people need. The approach of death can provide an opportunity for the patient, family, and friends to have meaningful closure and final reconciliation.

CHAPTER 26

Physician-Assisted Suicide and Euthanasia*

Elliot N. Dorff

She'eilah (Question):

May Jews assist others in committing suicide or request that others assist them in their own suicides?

Teshuvah (Response):

A. The Medical and Legal Contexts for This Question

Killing oneself and murdering others have always been technically possible but forbidden in Jewish law. In our time, the matter has taken on new dimensions. On the one hand, while people in the past had no choice but to endure the pain of dying, with minimal medication available to ease their suffering, now we have sophisticated ways to diagnose levels of pain and to calibrate pain medication to need. We also have developed hospice care, where the patient is supported physically, psychologically, and socially by a whole team of people, including family and friends. These factors should diminish the number of people who seek to take their own lives.

Since, on the other hand, we can now sustain bodily functions al-

*Approved by the Rabbinical Assembly Committee on Jewish Law and Standards, Mar. 1997.

most indefinitely, dying people may live through a long period of disability. Moreover, the drive to save money in health care has limited medical services for the dying, and in the future even less money will be spent on the care of each dying person as more and more of the baby boomers call upon whatever resources exist and as the need to contain health care costs becomes even more critical. This is especially problematic in our age of protracted life spans, where people generally die of chronic rather than acute illnesses. Moreover, since we can now predict the course of a disease with greater accuracy, people have less room for unrealistic hope. We now also have the means to bring about a quick, virtually painless death. These last factors have prompted some people faced with an incurable disease to take their own lives, sometimes asking others to assist them.

Those who commit suicide and those who aid others in doing so act out of a plethora of motives. Some of the motives are less than noble, involving, for example, children's desires for Mom or Dad to die with dispatch so as not to squander their inheritance on "futile" health care, or the desire of insurance companies to spend as little money as possible on the terminally ill.[1] The morally hard cases are those in which the primary intention is the benign desire to stop the pain of a dying patient. Indeed, some have claimed that mercy killing is the only moral path, that keeping a person alive under excruciating or hopeless circumstances is itself immoral.

The Ninth Circuit Court of Appeals and the Second Circuit Court of Appeals have both recently affirmed that under the Fourteenth Amendment it is an American's right to commit suicide and to request others to assist in that process. The Ninth Circuit based its argument on the amendment's clause that forbids states from depriving liberty to any person without due process of law. The Second Circuit, noting that people with terminal illnesses can legally request to be disconnected from life-support systems but other people are denied aid in dying, based its argument on the amendment's clause forbidding states from denying any person the equal protection of the laws.[2] Both appellate court decisions were overturned by the Supreme Court in June 1997, with the matter left to the states to decide.

These new medical and legal realities require us to reexamine and reevaluate Judaism's stance on suicide and assisted suicide so that Jews in the United States and other contemporary nations will know their tradition's views of these issues and the reasons for those views.

B. Jewish Theological and Legal Grounds for Opposing Suicide and Assisted Suicide

1. Suicide. Judaism's stance on suicide and assisted suicide is rooted in its understanding of the body as God's possession. God created and owns everything in the universe.[3] God has granted us the normal use of our bodies during our lifetimes, and that inevitably involves some dangers and risks; but God, as Owner, imposes specific requirements and prohibitions intended to preserve our life and health as much as possible.[4]

One such provision relevant to our topic is that Jews may not even injure themselves, let alone kill themselves.[5] To do either of those things would be to harm or destroy what belongs to God. Since we do not own our bodies, we do not have the right to expose ourselves to injury or death beyond the requirements of normal living and must instead seek to preserve our lives and health. The only three times, in fact, when a Jew is supposed to prefer death to violating the law—namely, when the choice is death or being forced to commit murder, idolatry, or adultery/incest[6]—are all choices of death for the sake of God, not for oneself.

When the Romans burned Rabbi Ḥananiah ben Teradyon at the stake for teaching Torah, he refused to inhale the flames to bring about his death more quickly, saying, "Better that God who gave life should take it; a person may not injure himself [or herself]." The Romans had attached tufts of wool soaked with water to his chest to make his dying slower and more painful, and Rabbi Ḥananiah allowed his students to bribe the executioner to detach them. From this and other sources, later Jewish authorities deduced that one may remove impediments to the natural process of dying but not actively cause one's own death, much less someone else's.[7] Indeed, based on the biblical story of Ahitofel's suicide, medieval sources maintain that "he who commits suicide while of sound mind has no share in the World to Come" and is to be buried outside the Jewish cemetery or at its edge.[8]

Saul's suicide (1 Sam. 31:3–5), though, is recorded in the Bible without objection, and the Talmud, apparently approvingly, records the case of children who take their own lives to avoid being sexually violated.[9] These cases undoubtedly served as the backdrop for Jewish law's justification of suicide when done as an act of martyrdom in defense of Judaism[10] or as a way of avoiding the temptation to convert under torture.[11] Later

Jewish laws have taken this yet further: by narrowing the definition of a suicide to those who took their lives with competence of mind and freedom of will, modern authorities have maintained that those who suffered, or could be presumed to have suffered, from temporary insanity do not fall into the category of willfully committing suicide and are therefore permitted a normal Jewish burial.[12]

This distinction between the status of suicide itself and what one does with the body of a suicide has important implications for assisted suicide. As our colleague on the Committee on Jewish Law and Standards, Mr. Frederick Lawrence, has pointed out, one must distinguish justification from excuse. If suicide is permissible, as it is in U.S. law, a person who committed suicide would be justified in doing so, and an accomplice might or might not share in that justification; hence the current debate over assisted suicide in the U.S. courts and in state referendums.

In Jewish law, though, suicide is a criminal act except for the specific situations mentioned above. It is only in those exceptional cases that a justification for suicide exists; in all others, the principal can at best have an excuse that does not render the act permissible but may mitigate punishment. The accomplice may suffer, too. The aide's duress, however, is separate and apart from the principal's suffering, and so the aide's excuse to mitigate punishment must be judged independently. Indeed, while sometimes that excuse may be compelling, as in cases in which the aide acted at the patient's express request to end his or her own suffering despite having the advantages of full medical and social support, in cases at the other end of the spectrum the aide may have acted to stop the medical bills and the need to care for the patient, perhaps even contrary to the desires of the patient. In no case does the accomplice have a justification for assisting in the suicide. Even if the principal had a valid justification for committing suicide, the aide does not share in that justification and is therefore fully liable for the violations committed by assisting the suicide.

Suicide itself, then, remains forbidden by Jewish law except in the dire circumstances of martyrdom. Even then, a poignant ruling from the Holocaust indicates that suicide is to be avoided if at all possible. Rabbi Ephraim Oshry permitted a man who was to be tortured by the Nazis to force him to identify the whereabouts of other Jews to commit suicide lest he betray those other Jews, but Rabbi Oshry did not permit this ruling to be published for fear that it would undermine the commitment to life of the other Jews of the Kovno ghetto. Other authors, both during and after the Holocaust, have taken pride in the small number of Eastern European Jews who committed suicide in the midst of the Nazi terror.[13] Moreover, Rabbi Oshry was ruling in a case in which the person, were he not to commit suicide, faced the prospect of endangering the lives of others; those are not the circumstances in the vast majority of cases in which the contemporary question is being raised.[14]

In sum, the tradition prohibits suicide except as an act of martyrdom. Contemporary medical cases that raise the question anew clearly do not fit into that exception: the people involved ask to die in response to the excruciating pain of their illnesses, not in fear of being tortured by interrogators or forced to convert to another religion. Their suicides would not be justified, even if people who violate this law would retroactively be permitted a traditional Jewish burial.

2. Assisted suicide. Since suicide itself is prohibited, aiding a suicide is also forbidden. The grounds for that prohibition depend upon how the assistance is administered. Sometimes the aide provides the means for the patient to commit suicide but is not involved in any other way. In some typical cases, the assistant hands an overdose of pills to the patient or sets up a machine so that the patient can administer a lethal substance intravenously. Once supplied the means to commit suicide, the patient acts completely on his or her own.

In such cases, the helper minimally violates Lev. 19:14, "Do not put a stumbling block before the blind," for the Rabbis interpreted that verse to prohibit moral stumbling blocks as well as physical ones.[15] The aide is guilty at least of misleading the patient to think that a forbidden act is permissible, of placing a stumbling block before a patient who is morally blinded by his or her medical condition to be able to see the authority and importance of the Jewish norm prohibiting suicide.[16]

Worse, the aide in such circumstances makes it possible for the patient to do what is forbidden. In talmudic terminology, the aide is "strengthening those who commit a sin" or "aiding those who commit a sin," both of which are forbidden.[17] Such a person is even more culpable than the one who simply misleads a person into thinking that the act is permissible because the culprit in this case actively makes it possible for a person to commit the sin. The aide in such cases might also be construed to be liable for injuring the patient indirectly (*grama*). One who does that is retroactively free of monetary liability for any harm done, but *ab initio* no one may deliberately cause harm to another, even indirectly.[18]

Furthermore, one who harms another indirectly, while free of liability in human courts, is culpable in the judgments of Heaven. In fact, one specific case that the Talmud includes in this category concerns a person who placed deadly poison before the animal of a neighbor; if divine retribution is to be meted out to a person who threatens the life of an animal in that way, God would undoubtedly be even more upset with someone who puts the life of a human being at risk in that way.[19]

If the assistant not only provides the patient with the means to kill himself or herself, but also participates in the process, the liability of the assistant depends upon how the help is given. If the aide directly causes the wound that eventuates in the patient's death, then he or she violates Jewish laws prohibiting the deliberate injury of another. Even if the victim asks to be injured, others may not do that, and they are fully liable for the injury.[20] This would be true even if the patient willingly took part in the act. So, for example, if a physician compromises the life of a patient by administering a given dose of medication or poison intravenously but leaves it to the patient to push a lever to insert the rest of the dose necessary to bring about death, the physician is liable both for misleading the patient morally and for injuring him or her.

Finally, some forms of assisted suicide amount to murder. For example, if the aide shoots the victim with a gun or knowingly administers a lethal dose of a medication or poison with the intent of bringing about the person's death, that clearly constitutes murder, even though the motive was, by hypothesis, benign.

Note that these Jewish arguments against suicide and assisted suicide differ radically from the reasons invoked by many Christian opponents of euthanasia. Some Christians base their opposition on the redemptive character of suffering. Euthanasia is unwarranted, the argument goes, because pain is itself salvational, symbolized most graphically by the crucifixion of Jesus. Other Christian voices oppose any medical intervention, including those intended to reduce pain, as an improper human intrusion onto God's prerogatives of deciding when to inflict illness and when to bring healing.[21]

Judaism's opposition to euthanasia cannot be grounded in either of these lines of argument. For Judaism, the pain of disease is not in and of itself a good thing to be sustained for its own sake. Retroactively, when trying to explain how God could be just and yet innocent people suffer, the Rabbis suggested, among other approaches, that the pain of the innocent may be "afflictions of love" (*yisurim shel ahavah*) designed by God either to teach the person virtues of patience and faith or to punish the person in this life for his or her small number of sins so as to make his or her reward in the next life pure and all the greater,[22] but that doctrine was never used before the fact to justify withholding pain medication from the suffering. On the contrary, the Talmud records that Rabbi Ḥiyya bar Abba, Rabbi Yoḥanan, and Rabbi Eleazar all say that neither their sufferings nor the reward promised in the World to Come for enduring them are welcome—that is, they would rather live without the suffering as well as the anticipated reward.[23] Moreover, from its earliest sources, Judaism has both permitted and required us to act as God's agents in bringing healing or, failing that, in reducing pain.

I sympathize enormously with patients going through an agonizing process of dying, and in cases of irreversible, terminal illness, I have taken a very liberal stance on withholding or withdrawing life-support systems, including artificial nutrition and hydration, to enable nature to take its course. I would also permit the use of any amount of medication necessary to relieve pain, even if that is the same amount that will hasten a person's death, as long as the intention is to alleviate pain.[24] The Committee on Jewish Law and Standards has validated that stance as well as that of Rabbi Avram Reisner, who permits withdrawing machines and medications from the patient but not withholding or withdrawing artificial nutrition and hydration, and who permits using large doses of morphine to relieve pain up to, but not including, the amount that poses a risk to the patient's life.[25]

Since the Jewish tradition takes mental illness seriously as illness,[26] some might ask: What is the difference between administering a large dose of morphine for reducing physical pain and using that same dosage in response to a person saying, "I want to end this"? In other words, why is it the case that physical pain counts as sufficient grounds to justify doses of morphine that may risk death while mental distress does not? The answer is that in these cases, physical pain occurs against the will of the patient and the morphine is therefore a therapeutic response sanctioned by Jewish law and theology, while "I want to end this" is an expression of the individual's will, a desire that it is illegitimate to fulfill according to Jewish law and theology. We do need to respond to the patient's mental distress, but our response must be in the form of supplying sufficient pain medication, treating clinical depression if that is present, and, most important, providing the personal and social support that patients in these circumstances direly need.

Even though Jewish law, then, goes quite far in permitting terminally ill patients to die with whatever palliative care they need and without any further medical interference, it does not permit suicide or assisted suicide. The tradition bids us instead to maintain a firm line separating permissible withholding and withdrawal of medical efforts, on the one hand, and illegitimately helping a person actively to take his or her own life, on the other. To fail to do that would be to violate Jewish law and to destroy creatures belonging to God.

C. The Contemporary Circumstances That Sully Arguments for Euthanasia

We have expounded express Jewish law on the issues involved in assisted suicide. Sometimes contemporary circumstances or values argue for changing the stated law as it has come down to us, and we in the Conservative movement are open to considering such challenges. In this case, though, several aspects of the current situation instead present additional arguments for retaining the traditional position prohibiting assisted suicide. All these factors invoke parts of Jewish law or the broader Jewish tradition. These are not simply general concerns, but Jewish ones, and hence they are part of what should be our understanding and articulation of Jewish law on this issue.

1. *Theological:* First and foremost, as indicated above, theological concerns underlie the Jewish legal position forbidding assisted suicide. The entire discussion of assisted suicide in U.S. courts, in fact, calls into play two of the sharpest differences between American secular perspectives and Jewish views.

America's ideology, as expressed in its economic system, in its philosophy (especially the distinctly American school of pragmatism), in the media (where it is almost always the young and the able-bodied who are pictured), and even in contemporary reforms in U.S. welfare legislation, would have us think of ourselves in utilitarian terms, where our worth is a function of what we can do for ourselves and others. American attitudes and laws thus permit suicide, especially when one can no longer do anything useful for oneself or others. Judaism, in contrast, requires us to evaluate our lives in light of the ultimate value inherent in us because we were created in God's image. Jewish ideology and law therefore strongly oppose committing suicide or assisting others in doing so, for life is sacred regardless of its quality or usefulness.

Second, according to U.S. law and ideology, as expressed in the Declaration of Independence and in U.S. constitutional law and court rulings, each of us owns his or her own body, and, short of harming someone else, we all inherit the liberty to do with our bodies what we will. This tenet, according to the interpretation of the Ninth Circuit Court of Appeals, has made it part of every American's liberty to determine the course of his or her medical care, even to the point of committing suicide and asking others to assist him or her in doing so. Suicide itself is a legal act in all fifty states.[27]

In sharp contrast, according to Judaism, God created and therefore owns the entire universe,[28] including each person's body, and each of us therefore has a fiduciary responsibility to God to preserve our life and health. We do not have the right unnecessarily to destroy or damage God's property, including even God's vegetation and inanimate property.[29] This makes suicide an act of theft from God, a violation of God's prerogatives, and, indeed, a trespass of the proper boundaries between God and human beings.[30] Rabbi Yeḥiel M. Tuchinski, in his restatement of the laws of death and mourning entitled *Gesher Haḥayim* (Bridge of Life), puts these points starkly:

> The sin of one who murders himself is greater than that of one who murders someone else, for several reasons. First, through this murder he has left no possibility for any remorse and repentance. Second, death (according to B. *Yoma* 86, etc.) is the greatest form of repentance, but he, on the contrary, has committed through his death the greatest sin, namely, murder. Third, through his act he has made clear his repudiation of his Creator's ownership of his life, his body, and his soul: he has denied the simple idea that he did not participate in his creation at all, but [thinks] rather [that] his entire identity is exclusively within his power to sustain, to reproduce his existence or to destroy it. He is like one who actively [and intentionally] burns a scroll of the Torah, for our Sages, may their memory be blessed, compared the creation of the soul to a scroll of the Torah that [now] has been burned and he must therefore face judgment in the future for this as well.
>
> He is also among the unequivocal deniers of the continued existence of the soul and of the existence of the Creator, may His name be blessed, and of the future judgment after the departure of the soul [from the body].[31]

Contemporary Jews may not share all of Rabbi Tuchinski's traditional beliefs about life after death enumerated here, but even a comparatively liberal view of Judaism must, in order to remain recognizably Jewish, begin with the tenet that the body belongs to God.[32]

The American and Jewish traditions, then, begin with radically disparate assumptions about the worth and ownership of our bodies. These variances sometimes lead the two traditions to different prescriptions for the care of the dying. Even when the two traditions agree on a given course of action, they often arrive at their respective positions using different arguments with different burdens of proof.

Specifically, since the American tradition of pragmatism and hedonism leads us, as Americans, to value life only if we can do things and enjoy life, a physically or mentally compromised life is not considered worth living. Moreover, each person has the right to determine the fate of his or her own body. It is this perspective that undergirds requests for suicide in America, the legal grounding for those requests as expressions of autonomy and liberty, and the sense of compassion that those who assist in a suicide feel.

The Jewish tradition, in contrast, calls upon us to evaluate life from God's perspective. That means that the value of life does not depend on the level of one's abilities; it derives from the image of God embedded in us. The tradition thus strongly affirms the divine quality of the life of disabled people, even though everyone would undoubtedly prefer not to be disabled. Indeed, our tradition demands that, upon seeing a disabled person, we bless God for making people different, thus boldly reasserting the divine quality of such lives.[33] We must do everything in our power to dissuade anyone thinking of committing suicide because of disability from doing so. Embedded in the arguments for assisted suicide, though, is an assumption frighteningly close to an assertion of the worthlessness of disabled people, for the terminally ill are also disabled. In line with its view of the disabled, the Jewish tradition requires that we recognize the divine quality of people in the last stages of life, regardless of the quality of their lives.

Even when life is not ideal and we question its divine dignity and its character as a gift, we lack the authority to destroy it because the body belongs to God, who alone has the right to terminate it. In other words, in the American setting, arguments for permitting assisted suicide on the basis of autonomy have been taken very seriously, and in its worst forms these arguments are based on a culture of selfishness that diminishes human life by valuing only those who can be productive and enjoy life fully. The clear stance of Judaism, on the other hand, sets strict limits to the autonomy we have in this arena, given that we are God's creatures and agents, and it strongly affirms the value of human life regardless of its usefulness or quality. We might ask why a compassionate God would deny us the authority to take our own lives when we can no longer function. Moreover, according to Maimonides, we must keep our bodies in good health so that we may serve God,[34] and if we cannot do that any longer, it would seem that God should allow us to curtail our lives. While we can challenge God by posing such questions, the tradition is unanimous in asserting that God does not give us that authority, and that even when a person is incapacitated by, say, a stroke, God forbids him or her to commit suicide and forbids others to assist in one.[35]

In Judaism's perspective, then, it is not a compassionate act to assist a person in taking his or her own life because doing that would make both oneself and the person committing suicide violators of some of the most fundamental values and laws of Judaism, namely, those insisting that we not murder and that, on the contrary, we set aside virtually all of Jewish law in order to save lives.[36] We all sin, of course, but these are the most serious sorts of sin, ones that it is anything but compassionate to help someone commit.

2. *Social/economic:* Several aspects of the current social and economic contexts make the prospect of permitting assisted suicide all the more troubling than it is inherently. One element lurking in the background of this discussion is the history of condoned assisted suicide in Holland, where there has been a wide range of rationales that have prompted physicians to help people end their lives. In the United States, Dr. Jack Kevorkian has similarly assisted people in all sorts of physical conditions to commit suicide, most recently in response to a person's chronic fatigue syndrome. He has admittedly sensationalized the whole subject, and it is not wise or fair to judge the issue on the basis of his actions alone. I am not usually convinced by slippery-slope arguments, for the essence of moral discernment is that we learn to distinguish cases.[37] Nevertheless, the experience in Holland and Dr. Kevorkian's cases have clearly demonstrated just how slippery this particular slope is. Even though there are undoubtedly some situations where the case for assisting a suicide may seem compelling, we must prohibit assisted suicide altogether in order to prevent diminishing the value of life in the public eye and in public policy.

Another current factor that makes any opening to assisted suicide dangerous is the push to save money in health care. Motivated largely by how that economic agenda will affect care at the end of life, the American Medical Association, in briefs to the Supreme Court, strongly opposed legalizing assisted suicide. They were justifiably worried about what such action would do to both the patient and the physician, for, especially under conditions of managed care, *permission* to take one's own life and to enlist the aid of others in doing so will quickly become all but an *obligation* to end the lives of those who have no reasonable hope for cure. Physicians, in the worst scenario, will be pressured by hospitals or health-insurance companies to convince their patients that suicide is the best option, not only because it will end the patient's pain and thus serve the best interests of the patient, but also (and perhaps primarily) because it will save the hospital or insurer money. The role of the physician as the patient's advocate thus becomes severely compromised.

The same considerations apply to the patient's family. If assisted suicide becomes a guaranteed constitutional right in U.S. law, patients will feel all the more pressed by their families to end their lives rather than drain the family's finances in keeping them alive. If Jewish law is also interpreted to permit assisted suicide, both the social and the religious setting in which American Jews will be making these decisions will argue for the legitimacy of such pressure, to the point that patients or family members who resist the suicide option will eventually feel that they are being unreasonably obstinate, that "normal" people would just end their lives once they cannot be cured. Indeed, in the context of such changed social expectations, even when family members do not want the patient to commit suicide and say that as clearly as they can, patients may feel that their families want them to end their lives; my relatives, the patient may think, are just trying to be nice, but they really want me to end my own agony and theirs. Legitimating assisted suicide thus dangerously shifts the burden of proof: currently, those who want to take a life must justify that course of action, but if assisted suicide becomes legal, those who refuse it will need to show why.

The economic arguments in support of assisted suicide are not completely frivolous. In the United States, people spend more on their health care in the last six months of life than they do throughout the rest of their lives. About 2.5 million Americans die each year, and over 50 percent of those deaths occur in an acute-care hospital.[38] Surely the money could be better spent, the argument goes, if people were given the choice and aid to die.

While the economic factor is real, assisted suicide is not the appropriate response. Hospice care is. In hospice care, all concerned recognize that the patient's disease is incurable, and the course of medical care is therefore not directed to aggressively and invasively trying to prolong life, but rather to the goal of providing comfort and pain relief. In hospice care, patients spend most of their last months of life at home, with some outpatient visits along the way. That form of care is not only more medically realistic and inexpensive, but more humane. Hospital care puts the patient in a strange, antiseptic setting where he or she is subjected to the hospital schedule, to repeated and possibly painful medical procedures, and to the loneliness of having the company of only occasional visitors. Hospice care, by contrast, puts the patient at home among family and friends, where pain medication can be administered when and how the patient feels most comfortable.

Hospice care should be suggested to most people afflicted with terminal, irreversible illnesses. Moreover, contrary to current practice, patients need not first endure initial stays in intensive care units where improbably successful or knowingly futile aggressive care is attempted; rather, they should be provided hospice care as soon as it becomes clear that the odds of curing them are slim to nil.

Along with hospice care for the patient, respite care can and should be provided for family caregivers. The bill for hospice and respite care combined will pale by comparison with what we are spending for people's last weeks and months now, and the patient will gain in dignity and comfort in the bargain.

3. Medical: Possibly the most common and compelling grounds suggested for justifying assisted suicide are to relieve a patient of racking pain. This would be both understandable and compassionate if there were no other alternative, but doctors today have ample means for controlling almost all physical pain. A very small number of patients (perhaps one in 10,000) need dosages of morphine that will make them unconscious, and in those cases patients may have to choose between some amount of pain with consciousness or losing consciousness as all pain is quelled. That is a legitimate choice that should be offered to patients.

American physicians often do not offer or employ sufficient pain medication. Reasons for this vary. Sometimes doctors do not know how much morphine to administer, for people differ in size and in their thresholds of pain. That is an understandable reason for failing to employ enough pain medication. Some doctors, though, say that they minimize pain medication for fear of inducing drug addiction. That is a proper concern in general, but a truly bizarre one in the case of terminally ill patients. Other doctors have a "John Wayne" attitude toward pain, claiming that good, morally worthy patients grin and bear their pain rather than complaining about it and requesting medication to quell it. Even worse, some of this is socioeconomic: centers that treat primarily white patients provide pain relief more adequately than those treating minority patients, producing, on a percentage basis, many more requests for assisted suicide among the latter.

Perhaps the most pervasive root of this refusal to control pain is the American culture of medicine itself. American medicine, far more than medicine in other Western countries, is based on technological cures,[39] and when those do not work, doctors consciously or subconsciously avoid the patient who symbolizes the failure of their methods. They also do not bother to administer pain relief, for that is either not one of their goals (the "John Wayne" attitude) or a secondary goal to be invoked only when they have failed to cure. Whatever the basis for this pattern of supplying insufficient pain medication, physicians should certainly seek to control pain rather than acquiesce to a request to die.[40]

Requests for aid in committing suicide stem from another medical phenomenon as well: far too many people with irreversible, terminal illnesses are subjected to futile, aggressive treatment. As indicated earlier, about 2.5 million Americans die each year, and over 50 percent of those deaths occur in an acute-care hospital. That high level of "hospitalized death," researchers say, suggests that too few terminally ill patients are taking advantage of hospice care. Moreover, as an editorial in the *Annals of Internal Medicine* maintained, far too many people are finding that their express desire for life support to be withheld or withdrawn, as stated in their living wills, is being ignored by "physicians who are so preoccupied with the preservation of life that they can no longer see the broader human context of their work." Similarly, the largest study to address the human context of dying, known by the acronym SUPPORT, involves more than 10,000 seriously ill people at five medical centers in five cities. A chief finding of that study was that about half of all patients spent the end of life in what the researchers termed "an undesirable state," including a week or so in an intensive care unit, having a physician who was unaware of wishes not to be resuscitated, or being in serious, insufficiently treated pain. "I believe the enthusiasm for physician-assisted suicide is driven, in part, by the fear that we will receive overly aggressive care at the end of life and that our suffering may be prolonged," said Dr. William Knaus, an internal medicine specialist at the University of Virginia Medical School and a coordinator of SUPPORT.[41] Clearly, if that is what is prompting a request for assistance in suicide, the appropriate response is for physicians conscientiously to make themselves aware of their patients' advance directives and to adhere to a patient's desire to remove impediments to the natural process of dying.

4. *Psychological:* While some requests for assistance in dying are based on the patient's excruciating pain, others are rooted in the hopelessness of the situation. We are, after all, mortal, and some diseases cannot be cured. When afflicted with such diseases, patients cannot realistically hope to return to the life they knew. They instead face the prospect of continued suffering and debilitation until death, and some would prefer to end things quickly to avoid the suffering and degradation of the last stages of their illnesses.

Such cases are precisely the ones that have produced the term "mercy killing" to describe active euthanasia, and, indeed, the hopelessness embedded in the medical situation of such people often makes their requests for assistance in dying emotionally compelling. Nevertheless, we should respond to such cases by doing things other than assisting people to commit suicide.

Physicians or others asked to assist in dying should recognize that people contemplating suicide are often alone, without anyone who takes an interest in their continued living. Rather than assist the patient in dying, the proper response to such circumstances is to provide the patient with a group of people who clearly and repeatedly reaffirm their interest in the patient's continued life.

My mother once had a roommate in a nursing home who literally was visited by no one. She had one son who lived on the other side of the country and who called from time to time, but she had no other family or friends. To make matters worse, some clothes that her son sent her as a birthday gift were stolen by the night staff. Under such conditions of abandonment (and, in this case, violation), one can understand why people would wonder why they should continue to fight to live—indeed, why they should get up in the morning at all.

Requests to die, then, must be evaluated in terms of the degree of social support the patient has, for such requests are often withdrawn as soon as someone shows an interest in the patient's staying alive. In this age of individualism and broken and scattered families, and in the antiseptic environment of hospitals, where dying people usually find themselves, the mitzvah of visiting the sick (*bikur ḥolim*) becomes all the more crucial in sustaining the will to live, for, as the tradition recognized, visitors aid the person psychologically, physically, and religiously. The Talmud says:

> Rabbi Abba son of Rabbi Ḥanina said: He who visits an invalid takes away a sixtieth of his pain [or, in another version, a sixtieth of his illness]. . . .
>
> When Rabbi Dimi came [from Palestine], he said: He who visits the sick causes him to live, while he who does not causes him to die. How does he cause this? . . . He who visits the sick prays that he may live, . . . [while] he who does not visit the sick prays neither that he may live nor die.[42]

The Talmud here is asserting two aspects of the spiritual elements of coping with illness. On a social plane, those who visit the sick help to shift the patient's focus from the pain and degradation of the illness to the joy of the company of friends and family. They thus take away a sixtieth of the pain of the illness. Visitors also reassure the patient that family and friends are keenly interested in his or her recovery or, if recovery is impossible, in his or her comfort. They also remind the patient of life outside the sickroom and thereby reinforce the patient's determination to live. Visitors are thus instrumental in motivating the patient to follow a medical regimen of healing or palliation, however tedious or painful it may be; accordingly, in the Talmud's alternate reading, they effectively take away a sixtieth of the patient's illness itself.

As discussed above, hospice care, endorsed by both Rabbi Reisner and me, recommends itself for economic and medical reasons. It is perhaps best in responding to the psychological pressures of the dying process. Much of the loneliness inherent in being confined to a hospital is eliminated when the patient instead is cared for at home. Family members cannot be expected to shoulder all this burden; *bikur ḥolim* remains an important imperative for friends, even when the patient is living at home. The very familiarity of the home setting, together with the increased chances it offers of providing the companionship of family and friends, makes hospice care clearly preferable to hospitalization when doctors cannot realistically expect to cure.

Visitors can affect the physical quality of patients' lives not only by buoying up their will to live, but also by attending to their physical needs. Thus the Talmud tells this story:

> Rabbi Helbo fell ill. Rabbi Kahana then went [to the house of study] and proclaimed, "Rabbi Helbo is ill." Nobody, however, visited him. Rabbi Kahana rebuked [the disciples], saying, "Did it ever happen that one of Rabbi Akiba's students fell ill, and the [rest of the] disciples did not visit him?" So Rabbi Akiba himself entered [Rabbi Helbo's house] to visit him, and because they swept and sprinkled the ground before him [i.e., cleaned the house and put it in order], Rabbi Helbo recovered. Rabbi Akiba then went forth and lectured: He who does not visit the sick is like one who sheds blood.[43]

Taking physical care of the sick can include not only cleaning house, but shopping for groceries, doing laundry, taking over carpool duties, and seeing to the other needs of the patient's children. Depending upon the circumstances, it can also include more direct physical interventions, such as taking the patient for a ride in a wheelchair (if medically permitted), feeding the patient (if necessary), and attending to the patient's other physical needs.

Visitors affect the patient on a more religious plane as well. By praying for and with the patient, and by indicating that prayers are being offered in the synagogue on his or her behalf, visitors invoke the aid of God, the ultimate Healer. Jewish prayer is traditionally done in community, in part because Jewish sources maintain that communal prayer persuades God to grant a request more effectively than private prayer does.[44] Praying with the patient at bedside and for the patient in the synagogue thus throws the weight of the entire community behind the patient's own plea to God for recovery or, failing that, for comfort.

The medical hopelessness of people with terminal, irreversible illnesses remains, and it violates our duty to tell the truth to try to deceive patients into believing otherwise. While some sources in our tradition justify such behavior in the name of buoying up a patient's spirits,[45] deception is generally not the way to do that. Patients usually have a sense of their medical prognosis, so they generally do not believe those who tell them otherwise, anyway. Moreover, lies can only lead to distrust, anger, and feelings of disrespect and abandonment. The last thing one wants to do is to infantilize patients: they already feel diminished in stature by their illness, and deception makes them feel further diminished, as if they were being treated as children (who, by the way, should also not be misled). Family and friends should not appear at bedside with sullen faces, dwelling on the terrible prognosis. At the same time, they should not pretend that the medical situation is other than what it is.

The patient's spirits can be lifted substantially and appropriately if family and friends concentrate on what can make the remainder of the patient's life meaningful. Some topics that should be raised are practical in nature. Specifically, if patients have not previously filled out wills or living wills, they should be asked to specify their wishes about the distribution of their property and their preferred course of medical treatment. Even though Jewish law forbids morose talk of death around a seriously ill patient for fear of undermining the patient's hope for recovery, it permits and even requires that relatives or friends ensure that the patient has written a will and even allows saying the final prayer of confession before death (*tziduk hadin*). One should also be sure that the patient has made funeral and burial arrangements. To preserve the patient's will to live and to fight the disease, Jewish law mandates that one tell the patient that writing a will, making plans for burial, and saying the confessional prayer are being done just in case the patient does not recover, but that many people who have done these things have subsequently recovered.[46]

Beyond these practical topics, visitors will buoy patients' spirits by treating them as adults, respecting them enough to engage in conversation about the same adult topics that previously interested them—and even some that they had not previously explored. One of the most enlightening experiences of my early rabbinic career was teaching a series of classes on Jewish theology to residents of a Jewish nursing home. The group consisted entirely of college graduates. Even though none of them had ever studied Jewish theology before, they had specifically asked for these classes because they were sick of playing Bingo. They had been intellectually active at earlier stages of their lives, and their physical illnesses now did not significantly change their intellectual interests or even their mental capacity—except that I had to speak just a little more slowly than I usually do. The students even read assignments in preparation for the class from specially prepared sheets with enlarged print. I wish my younger students were always as well prepared! Visitors do not normally discuss Jewish theology, but this example will, I hope, indicate just how seriously I mean to make the point that conversations with patients should be challenging and should cover a wide variety of topics.

The very normalcy of such discussions communicates that the illness has not diminished the visitor's respect for the patient's intelligence and humanity, and that the remainder of one's life can still be filled with meaningful conversation.

The Jewish tradition has also provided another mechanism to make the lives of terminal patients meaningful. That is the *ethical will.* In times past, ethical wills were written, but now they can be taped or even videotaped. Patients who know that they have a task to accomplish in leaving their children and especially their grandchildren a record of their experiences, values, thoughts, dreams, and hopes will redouble their efforts to live as long as they can so that they can complete this important project.[47]

Moreover, some families can, in the last stages of the patient's life, heal troubling elements of relationships that they were not able to resolve earlier. The limited term of life remaining for the patient becomes patently clear in such a setting, and that often motivates all concerned to be more forthcoming in their relationships with family and friends than they had been previously. In positive relationships, the time spent together in a beloved's last days can be the last gift that children give their parents or that spouses give each other. Even though life at this stage may be physically painful, it may be emotionally some of the most significant time the person has lived.[48]

Indeed, the U.S. courts that dealt with assisted suicide addressed what is fundamentally the wrong question. We should not be asking whether one may aid another in dying; rather, we should explore what prompts people to seek to die in the first place, and then we should remove those motivations through proper pain medication and through attentive care. Those are the most appropriate responses to requests for assisted death.

Medical hopelessness need not and should not amount to psychological hopelessness. People asking for help in dying to overcome the loneliness and the futility of their lives should not be offered aid in dying, but rather assistance in making life meaningful.

5. Moral: In refusing to allow people to "shuffle off this mortal coil"[49] when and how they wish, we are taking upon ourselves the moral responsibility of imposing our will on them, and why should a society based on individual liberty do that? This last concern, in fact, is precisely the basis of the Ninth Circuit's decision affirming the legality of assisted suicide.

The liberty argument is not nearly as cogent in Jewish thought as it is in American ideology and law, for Jews are born with duties rather than rights. Even in the American context, though, the government must protect the most vulnerable populations, and the dying are surely among them. Similarly, the Torah's demand, "Do not stand idly by the blood of your brother," was interpreted by the Rabbis as a duty to come to the aid of those at risk.[50]

As indicated above, permitting assisted suicide may at first *look* like an affirmation of the patient's liberty, but it soon transforms into a duty to die. Protecting individuals' liberty is more effectively achieved by making assisted suicide a socially unacceptable option so that individuals need not defend their desire to continue living. The current ban on assisted suicide inevitably infringes on the liberty to gain assistance in dying, but that is a reasonable price to pay in order to preserve the liberty of far more people to continue living without having to justify their choice.

Moreover, until now, we have assumed the morally pure situation, where the patient is in pain or in increasing states of degradation (as in Alzheimer's patients), with prospects for only further deterioration, and where the aide is acting out of the sole motive of helping the patient fulfill his or her wishes (stated now or previously) to end life under such circumstances. Real situations, however, are almost never that simple. With regard to the patient, one must ask the hard questions of whether the request to die is a response to a lack of social support, as we have discussed, or a state of psychological depression that can be treated medically, or the patient's worry that further medical care will seriously deplete the estate to be left to the heirs. With regard to the aide, one must ask whether he or she stands to benefit from the end of the person's life, either monetarily or simply by the freedom from taking care of this person any longer. Assisted suicide, in other words, rarely occurs in the morally pure atmosphere usually assumed in arguments about its moral appropriateness, and as soon as one exposes the less noble motives often involved, it seems considerably less honorable.

Another moral issue arises in these cases. As the Ninth and Second Appellate Courts maintained, modern medical advances have made the line between active and passive euthanasia increasingly hard to define. That does not mean, however, that it has disappeared. The distinction between them constitutes the very real moral difference between helping someone live and die in a natural way, on the one hand, and homicide, on the other. Moral sensitivity is precisely the ability to make distinctions, including some hard distinctions.[51] We have an important moral interest in discerning that line, however difficult it may be to see at times, because nothing less than our character as moral people is at stake.

These theological, social, economic, medical, psychological, and moral factors reinforce the ban embedded in Jewish law on suicide and on assisting a suicide. They also demand that we take a much more active role in ensuring that the dying are not abandoned to physical pain or to social ostracism, that we instead make the mitzvah of *bikur ḥolim* a critical part of our mission as Jews. This is especially important as Jews, along with others, become statistically older, for more and more of us in the time to come will need such care. In attending to the sick, we must assure that their physical needs are met and that their ending time in life is as psychologically, emotionally, and religiously meaningful as possible. Our compassion, in other words, must be expressed in these demanding ways rather than in acquiescing to a request for assistance in dying, for ultimately the Jewish tradition calls upon us to recognize God's rights of ownership of our bodies and God's exclusive right to take our lives in God's good time.

D. Conclusion

A Jew may not commit suicide, ask others to help in committing suicide, or assist in the suicide of someone else. Withholding or withdrawing machines or medications from a terminally ill patient, however, does not constitute suicide and is permitted. In my view, but not in Rabbi Reisner's, one may also withhold or withdraw artificial nutrition and hydration from such a patient, for that, too, falls outside the prohibitions of suicide and assisted suicide.

Notes

1. As we shall discuss below, the economic realities behind these arguments are real, but they argue not for assisted suicide, but for much greater utilization of hospice care.
2. *Compassion in Dying v. State of Washington* 79 F.3d 790 (9th Cir. 1996); *Quill v. Vacco* 80 F.3d 716 (2d Cir. 1996). (A subsequent petition for the Ninth Circuit to rehear the case *en banc* was denied: 85 F.3d 1440 [9th Cir. 1996].) The

Ninth Circuit also invoked the Supreme Court's past decisions on abortion in interpreting the Fourteenth Amendment's liberty clause to protect a person's right to make his or her own health care decisions. Thus, Judge Stephen Reinhardt, writing for an 8–3 majority, stated, "By permitting the individual to exercise the right to choose, we are following the constitutional mandate to take such decisions out of the hands of government, both state and federal, and to put them where they rightly belong, in the hands of the people."

3. See, for example, Exod. 19:5; Deut. 10:14; Ps. 24:1. See also Gen. 14:19, 22 (where the Hebrew word for "Creator" [*koneh*] also means "Possessor," and where "heaven and earth" is a merism for those and everything in between) and Ps. 104:24, where the same word is used with the same meaning. The following verses have the same theme, although not quite as explicitly or as expansively: Exod. 20:11; Lev. 25:23, 42, 55; Deut. 4:35, 39; 32:6.
4. Bathing, for example, is a commandment according to Hillel: *Leviticus Rabbah* 34:3. Maimonides summarizes and codifies the rules requiring proper care of the body in *M.T., Laws of Ethics* (*De'ot*), chaps. 3–5. He spells out there in remarkable clarity that the purpose of these positive duties to maintain health is not to feel good and live a long life, but rather to have a healthy body so that one can then serve God.
5. The prohibition against injuring oneself is stated in M. *Bava Kamma* 8:6 (90b); cf. *M.T., Laws of Injury and Damage* 5:1. Tannaitic sources recorded in the Talmud (B. *Bava Kamma* 91b) state divided opinions as to whether individuals may inflict nonfatal wounds on themselves. The later sources generally agree that people are not allowed to injure themselves, although some restrict the prohibition against self-injury to cases in which wounds are produced (*Ḥemdat Yisra'el,* commandment 310), and some think that the prohibition is not a violation of Gen. 9:5 or Deut. 4:9 (interpreted as a command to maintain one's health) but is instead rabbinic (*Leḥem Mishneh* on *M.T., De'ot* 3:1). In any case, people who injure themselves are not punished specifically for doing that, but they may be punished at the hands of Heaven (T. *Bava Kamma* 9:11), and rabbinic courts may inflict disciplinary flogging (*makat mardut*) for injuring oneself (*M.T., Laws of Murder* 11:5; *S.A., Ḥ.M.* 420:31; 427:10)—understandable, but more than a bit ironic! See "*Ḥovel,*" *Encyclopedia Talmudit* 12:681f. (Hebrew).

   The prohibition against suicide is not recorded in the Talmud itself. The post-talmudic tractate *Semaḥot* (*Eivel Rabati*) 2:1–5 serves as the basis for most of later Jewish law on suicide, together with *Genesis Rabbah* 34:13, which bases the prohibition on Gen. 9:5. Cf. *M.T., Laws of Murder* 2:3; *Laws of Courts* (*Sanhedrin*) 18:6; *S.A., Y.D.* 345:1ff. See *Encyclopaedia Judaica* 15:489–91, s.v. "Suicide."
6. B. *Sanhedrin* 74a.
7. B. *Avodah Zarah* 18a; *S.A., Y.D.* 339:1 (with gloss).
8. 2 Sam. 17:23. See Irving J. Rosenbaum, *The Holocaust and Halakhah* (New

York: Ktav, 1976), 36 and 162 n. 21, for a discussion of the origins of this maxim. Burying suicides outside the cemetery: *M.T., Laws of Mourning* 1:11; *S.A., Y.D.* 345:1—or at its edge: responsum 763 of Rabbi Solomon ben Abraham Adret (the "Rashba," c. 1235–c. 1310).

9. B. *Gittin* 57b.
10. B. *Sanhedrin* 74a–74b. Cf. *M.T., Laws of the Foundations of the Torah*, chap. 5; *S.A., Y.D.* 157:1.
11. E.g., Tosafot on B. *Avodah Zarah* 18a, s.v. *ve'al yeḥabeil atzmo;* Tosafot on B. *Gittin* 57b, s.v. *vekafetzu.*
12. *Kol Bo al Aveilut,* 319, sec. 50; Yeḥiel M. Tuchinski, *Gesher Haḥayim* (Jerusalem: Solomon, 1947, 1960), 1:271–73; Isaac Klein, *A Guide to Jewish Religious Practice* (New York: Jewish Theological Seminary of America, 1979), 282–83 (but note the mistake in citing the passage from *Gesher Haḥayim:* it should be 1:271–73, as noted above, not 1:71–73, as printed there). This may be based on an earlier source—namely, *Besamim Rosh* no. 345—claiming to be the opinion of the much-respected Rabbenu Asher (the "Rosh," c. 1250–1327), who there permits full Jewish burial of people who commit suicide "because of a multiplicity of troubles, worries, pain, or utter poverty." That source, even if accepted as authentically the opinion of Rabbenu Asher, does not permit committing suicide, and neither do the later Jewish authorities cited above; they only permit normal Jewish burial after the fact.
13. See Rosenbaum, *The Holocaust and Halakhah,* 35–40.
14. While it is distinctly uncomfortable to second-guess a rabbi ruling in those dire circumstances, one must also note, as Rabbi Aaron Mackler has pointed out to me, that Rabbi Oshry's decision is, in the end, one rabbi's ruling, and since it extends permission to commit suicide to cases beyond the well-established exceptions of martyrdom, it may simply be an erroneous ruling. I would prefer to deny its relevance as a precedent on the basis of the important distinctions between his case and ours—namely, that the man in his case faced the prospect of endangering the lives of others through no fault of his own, while the cases we are discussing include no such factor.
15. The prohibition of putting a stumbling block before the blind: Lev. 19:14. The rabbinic extension of that prohibition to apply not only to the physically blind, but to the morally blind as well: B. *Pesaḥim* 22b; B. *Mo'ed Katan* 5a, 17a; B. *Bava Metzia* 75b; etc. (The principle is also applied to prohibit intentionally giving bad advice to people [see *Sifra* on this verse] and to those who are theologically blind in that they might be tempted to worship idols [B. *Nedarim* 42b].)
16. If the aide additionally persuaded the person to commit suicide, the aide may be considered an "inciter" (*masit*). One who incites another person to worship idols is subject to death by stoning (Deut. 13:7; M. *Sanhedrin* 7:4, 10). In the case of other sins, the defendant can invoke the talmudic principle (B. *Bava Kamma* 56a), *divrei harav vedivrei hatalmid mi shom'in?* ("When the words of

the Master and the words of the student [conflict], to whom does one listen?)—the Master here being God and the student a human being. According to the Talmud (B. *Sanhedrin* 29a), those who incite other Jews to engage in idolatry cannot avail themselves of this defense because with regard to that offense, the Torah (Deut. 13:9) says, "Show him no pity or compassion, and do not shield him." Thus, although inducing someone to commit any other sin—such as suicide—is certainly not laudable behavior, it is not culpable in law because each of us is responsible for knowing right from wrong and for resisting lures to do the wrong.

17. "Strengthening one to commit a sin": B. *Nedarim* 22a; B. *Gittin* 61a. "Helping one to commit a sin": B. *Avodah Zarah* 55b. I would like to thank Rabbi Ben Zion Bergman for alerting me to this point.
18. See B. *Bava Batra* 22a, and see Tosafot there.
19. B. *Bava Kamma* 56a, which refers to, among other such cases, the one in B. *Bava Kamma* 47b concerning the person who places poison before a neighbor's animal.
20. M. *Bava Kamma* 8:7 (92a); *M.T., Laws of Injury and Damage* 5:11; *S.A., Ḥ.M.* 421:12.
21. For a sampling of varying religious approaches to assisted death, including my own more extensive treatment of Jewish perspectives on this issue, see *Must We Suffer Our Way to Death? Cultural and Theological Perspectives on Death by Choice,* ed. Ronald P. Hamel and Edwin R. Dubose (Dallas: Southern Methodist University Press, 1996).
22. M. *Avot* 2:16; B. *Berakhot* 4a; B. *Eruvin* 19a; B. *Ta'anit* 11a; B. *Kiddushin* 39b; *Genesis Rabbah* 33:1; *Yalkut Ecclesiastes* 978. Among later Jewish philosophers, Saadia is the first to affirm this doctrine (*Book of Opinions and Beliefs,* bks. 4, 5), while Maimonides rejects it (*Guide for the Perplexed,* pt. 3, chaps. 16–23).
23. B. *Berakhot* 5b. I would like to thank Rabbi Baruch Frydman-Kohl for suggesting the use of this source here.
24. See Elliot N. Dorff, "A Jewish Approach to End-Stage Medical Care," *Conservative Judaism* 43, no. 3 (spring 1991): 3–51, esp. 17–19 and 34–39 [chaps. 18–20 of this vol.; esp. pp. 314–16 and 348–54].
25. Avram Israel Reisner, "A Halakhic Ethic of Care for the Terminally Ill," *Conservative Judaism* 43, no. 3 (spring 1991): 52–89 [chaps. 16–17 of this vol.]; and, especially, Avram Israel Reisner, "*Mai Beinaihu*?" ibid., 90–91 [chap. 15 of this vol.].

    In Rabbi Reisner's view, I would imagine, if the physician knowingly administers enough morphine to kill a person, the physician would be liable for murder, even though his or her primary intent was to reduce pain. For me, in contrast, the primary intent of the physician to reduce pain makes such a case not one of injury, much less murder, but rather one of permissible benefit.

Therefore, the physician would not be liable for violating even the prohibition against indirect injury but would instead be carrying out his or her mandate to heal.

This case must be distinguished from acquiescing to a patient's request to die, even when the death is requested for the express reason of relieving pain. To kill oneself, or to ask others to help in doing so, is forbidden in Jewish law, so if that is the intent, it is illegitimate. In practice, this difference in motive may translate into the amount of medication administered. Because within a given range of dosages of morphine, doctors never know whether a given patient will die or not, these cases never fall into the talmudic category of *pesik reisheih ve'al yamut* ("Can you cut off the chicken's head and it will not die?" [B. *Shabbat* 75a; see Rashi on this principle on B. *Sukkah* 33b]), for within that range, the result is never inevitable. Therefore, doctors' attempt to relieve pain is legitimate, in my view, even if they fear that the amount they need to use in the last stages of life may be crossing the line into a fatal dosage for a given patient, for they are still within the range where they do not know that for certain. On the other hand, to administer a dosage that beyond all reasonable doubt will kill the person is to commit murder, even when the stated intent of the physician is to relieve pain and even if the patient requests it. (I want to thank Rabbi Gordon Tucker for calling my attention to the need to make this distinction clearly.)

26. See, for example, Moshe Halevi Spero, *Judaism and Psychology: Halakhic Perspectives* (New York: Ktav, 1980). I would like to thank Rabbi Mayer Rabinowitz for raising the question discussed in this paragraph.

27. As Rabbi Aaron Mackler has pointed out to me, the fact that American states do not criminalize suicide may be a function of the medicalization of suicide in our time rather than recognition of a legal right. That is, instead of sending to prison those who attempt suicide, we sedate them, treat them for depression, and restrain them if necessary. That does not mean that suicide is a legal right, for if it were, we would not try to prevent people from taking their own lives.

    The Ninth Circuit, though, has interpreted suicide, and therefore also assisting in suicide, as a legal privilege embedded in the Fourteenth Amendment's guarantee of liberty. Presumably, then, the only reason for trying to prevent people from committing suicide is that we doubt that they have the mental competence required by law to make that decision.

28. See n. 3 above.

29. This includes even inanimate property that "belongs" to us, for God is the ultimate owner. This is the law of *ba'al tashḥit,* the prohibition of destroying the world when human need does not require that. Cf. Deut. 20:19–20; B. *Bava Kamma* 8:6, 7; B. *Bava Kamma* 92a, 93a; *M.T., Laws of Murder* 1:4, where Maimonides specifically invokes this theological basis for the law

against suicide; *M.T., Laws of Injury and Damage* 5:5; *Sefer Haḥinukh,* commandment 529; *S.A., Ḥ.M.* 420:1, 31. See Barry D. Cytron and Earl Schwartz, *When Life Is in the Balance: Life and Death Decisions in Light of the Jewish Tradition,* 2d ed. (New York: United Synagogue of Conservative Judaism, 1994).

30. As Rabbi Myron Geller pointed out to me, one could conclude the exact opposite—namely, that since God inflicted the patient's illness, aiding the person in committing suicide would be merely assisting God in bringing about what is presumably God's intended goal. While that is logical, it is not the line of reasoning that the Jewish tradition has followed. On the contrary, Jewish law, as noted above, has consistently denied people the right to commit suicide or to assist others in that path. See note 35 below.
31. Yeḥiel M. Tuchinski, *Gesher Haḥayim* 1:269–70 [Hebrew; this is my translation]. He adds there that the person who commits suicide "is like one who flees to a place where the hand of the government will catch him and can bring him back to this place with additional punishment also for his escape"—an understandable metaphor in his theology, but one that unfortunately makes life a prison sentence.
32. I say this even though one Reform writer has maintained the contrary, claiming that contemporary Jews overwhelmingly believe that their bodies are their own and thus refuse to abide by medical directives based on God's ownership of our bodies. See Matthew (Menachem) Maibaum, "A 'Progressive' Jewish Medical Ethics: Notes for an Agenda," *Journal of Reform Judaism* 33, no. 3 (summer 1986): 27–33.
33. B. *Berakhot* 58b; *M.T., Laws of Blessings* 10:12. For an excellent account of these laws and the theology and practice surrounding them, see Carl Astor, . . . *Who Makes People Different: Jewish Perspectives on the Disabled* (New York: United Synagogue of America, 1985).
34. *M.T., Laws of Ethics* (*Hilkhot De'ot*) 3:3; see also 4:1.
35. The argument that assisting a suicide would be to further God's purpose in making the person sick in the first place is specifically rejected by Rashi and by Tosafot. Commenting on the Talmud's statement (B. *Bava Kamma* 85a) that Exod. 21:19 (*verapo yerapei*) serves as permission for physicians to heal, Rashi (s.v. *nitnah reshut larofe'im lerapot*) says, "And we do *not* say that the Merciful One struck [the patient] and he [the physician illegitimately] heals." Tosafot there (s.v. *shenitnah reshut larofei lerapot*) points out that one can derive authorization for the physician to heal from just the first of the words in the phrase in Exod. 21:19, *verapo yerapei,* so why does the Torah state the verb "to heal" in two different forms? Because if it were only stated once, Tosafot suggests, one might think that the physician may heal only those maladies inflicted by human beings but not those inflicted by God; the double presence of the verb in the biblical verse indicates that the physician has permission to heal even illnesses inflicted by God.

36. This is the law of *pikuaḥ nefesh,* saving a life, whether one's own or someone else's; see B. *Sanhedrin* 74a and B. *Yoma* 85b, and see nn. 3–6 above and the text for those notes. In American law, by contrast, until recently, when "Good Samaritan laws" were passed by many states, you could actually be sued if you tried to save a person in good faith and some injury resulted, and to this day no American law requires that you go out of your way to save a life. This is, in my view, American individualism at its worst. Along the same lines, while aiding a suicide is against the law in most states, committing suicide itself is not a violation of the law, another manifestation of American individualism. (Most life-insurance policies, though, become null and void if the insured commits suicide.)
37. See my short essay "Moral Distinctions," *Sh'ma: A Journal of Jewish Responsibility* 21, no. 401 (16 Nov. 1990): 6–8.
38. See Terrence Monmaney, "How We Die May Be Behind Assisted Suicide Debate," *Los Angeles Times,* 8 Jan. 1997, A1, A9.
39. For a fascinating comparative study of how the same diseases are treated differently in the United States, Great Britain, France, and Germany as a reflection of their national cultures, see Lynn Payer, *Medicine and Culture* (New York: Henry Holt, 1988).
40. On the other hand, in cases in which patients are not seeking to die and choose to endure some pain in order to be able to remain conscious, that request must be honored. It is permissible, in my view, to use whatever amount of medication is necessary to alleviate pain, but it is not required to relieve pain at the cost of consciousness if the patient chooses instead to remain conscious with some degree of pain.
41. This paragraph is based on Monmaney, "How We Die," A1, A9.
42. B. *Nedarim* 39b–40a.
43. B. *Nedarim* 39b–40a.
44. B. *Berakhot* 6a; 7b–8a; J. *Berakhot* 5:1; cf. *M.T., Laws of Prayer* 8:1.
45. Basil F. Herring quotes and discusses those sources in his *Jewish Ethics and Halakhah for Our Time* (New York: Ktav, 1984), chap. 2, entitled "Truth and the Dying Patient" (47–66).
46. *S.A., Y.D.* 335:7; 338:1.
47. For some poignant examples of ethical wills, including many modern ones, see Jack Riemer and Nathaniel Stampfer, eds., *Ethical Wills: A Modern Jewish Treasury* (New York: Schocken, 1983). For suggestions for preparing an ethical will, see Jack Riemer and Nathaniel Stampfer, eds., *So that your values live on—Ethical Wills and how to prepare them* (Woodstock, Vt.: Jewish Lights Publishing, 1991).
48. See Elisabeth Kübler-Ross, *Death Is of Vital Importance* (Barrytown, N.Y.: Station Hill Press, 1995), for some striking examples of how meaningful and reconciling the last stages of life and death itself can be. I would like to thank my friend and colleague, Rabbi Elie Spitz, for alerting me to this book.

49. The poetic expression comes from Shakespeare, *Hamlet,* 3.1.67.
50. Lev. 19:16; B. *Sanhedrin* 73a.
51. Just as bad as recognizing no distinctions is creating sweeping, unexceptionable categories rather than discerning the fine lines that characterize real moral life. See my response to J. David Bleich in my article “Moral Distinctions,” 6–8.

IV. RESPONSIBILITIES FOR THE HEALTH NEEDS OF OTHERS

H. ORGAN TRANSPLANTATION AND AUTOPSY

Introduction

Respect for the body of a person who has died, *kevod hameit,* is a powerful Jewish value. Respect for the dead body expresses not only respect for the memory of the individual who has died, but also respect for God, in whose image all persons are created. The tradition understands this value to entail specific prohibitions against disfiguring a dead body, deriving benefit from a dead body, and delaying burial.

This complex of values and normative rules raises problems for autopsy and organ transplantation. At the same time, the values of healing and, especially, the saving of life (*pikuaḥ nefesh*), can be even more powerful. These values, too, express respect for persons and reverence for God. Accordingly, the papers in this section allow and, in fact, encourage, autopsy and organ donation and transplantation in appropriate cases.

In the responsum "Autopsy," Rabbi Isaac Klein surveys classical sources on the general value of respect for the dead as well as responsa from the eighteenth century addressing the specific issue of autopsy. Klein concludes that autopsies can be acceptable "where there is an obvious help to other people," and would, in fact, be encouraged as a mitzvah when an autopsy could help to save life. While this paper was written decades before the others in the book, in 1958, it remains valuable both for its specific discussion of autopsy and for its concise articulation of issues that are central in organ transplantation as well.

Rabbi Joseph H. Prouser endorses and builds on Klein's position in "*Ḥesed* or *Ḥiyuv*?: The Obligation to Preserve Life and the Question of Postmortem Organ Donation." Prouser argues that donating organs from a dead body for purposes of lifesaving transplantation is not only a permissible and meritorious expression of compassion (*ḥesed*), but is, in fact, an obligation (*ḥiyuv*) of Jewish law. He presents classical statements of the responsibility to save life in general, and halakhic discussions of organ transplantation in particular. He considers as well the current need for organs in countries such as the United States, the effectiveness of transplantation, and emotional and psychological issues. Prouser concludes that individuals planning in anticipation of their own death, as well as relatives who have the power to donate organs after a loved one has died, are halakhically required to consent to the donation.

The final selection in this section reproduces the "Organ and Tissue Donation" pamphlet, with a donor card, developed and approved by the Committee on Jewish Law and Standards.

CHAPTER 27

Autopsy*

Isaac Klein

She'eilah (Question):

Is autopsy permitted according to halakhah?

Teshuvah (Response):

There is a whole literature around this question because it involves a number of problems posed by developments in the medical field. It involves the use of bodies for dissection in medical schools. It involves the transplanting of tissues from a deceased into a living body as well as postmortem examinations performed to study a disease with the purpose of furthering medical knowledge (i.e., to ascertain the exact manifestations of the disease from which the deceased died with a view to more efficient treatment of other cases of the same disease), or for juridical purposes (i.e., when there is suspicion of crime, to ascertain from the condition of the body, particularly the internal organs, whether death was due to natural causes).

The first recorded instance of this question in the form of a formal responsum comes to us from Ezekiel Landau (1713–93).[1] It treats a specific case of a man who was operated on in London for gallstones and died. The doctors wanted permission for an autopsy in order to improve techniques for future cases. The answer of Landau in the *Noda bi-Yehudah* is:

*Approved by the Rabbinical Assembly Committee on Jewish Law and Standards, 1958.

> The principle that even a possibility [not a certainty—I. K.] of saving a life waives all biblical commandments except in three cases applies only when such a possibility is concretely before us, as, for instance, a person who is sick with that same ailment. In our case, however, there is no patient whose treatment calls for this knowledge. It is only that people want to learn this skill in case of a future possibility that a patient will come before us who will need this treatment. For such a slight apprehension we do not nullify a biblical commandment or even a rabbinic prohibition.

What is this biblical commandment that Rabbi Ezekiel Landau speaks about? The Rabbis saw in the following biblical prescription an injunction for the reverent treatment of the body or the prohibition of *nivul hameit* (dishonoring the dead):

> And if a man have committed a sin worthy of death, and he be put to death, and thou hang him on a tree, his body shall not remain all night upon the tree, but thou shalt surely bury him the same day.[2]

In the Talmud, there are a number of places where the prohibition against *nivul hameit* is implied. These are the most explicit passages:

> It once happened at Bene-Berak that a person sold his father's estate and died. The members of the family thereupon protested that he was a minor at the time of his death. They came to Rabbi Akiba and asked whether the body might be exhumed. He replied to them: You are not permitted to dishonor him [*lenavelo*].[3]

> Whence do we learn the principle that we follow the majority? Said Rav Kahana: I learn it from the case of one who commits murder, for which the Torah prescribes the penalty of death. Why don't we suspect that the person murdered might have been *treif* (i.e., but rather assume that he was physically normal like most people)? Should you say that we examine the body in order to ascertain whether it has a blemish that would make the man *treif*? That would mean dishonoring the body (by dissection, which is forbidden).[4]

Upon these statements in the Talmud, the Rabbis have based their objection to any disfiguring of the body of the deceased.

Rabbi Moses Sofer (Ḥatam Sofer, 1763–1839) comes to the same conclusion[5] as Rabbi Ezekiel Landau. To those who would want to permit dissections on the grounds of *pikuaḥ nefesh* (saving of lives), which supersedes all prohibitions, he says that this applies only where there is a person with the same disease present who would benefit from an autopsy on a person who died from this disease.

It is obvious that in spite of the great halakhic prestige and competence of these two authorities, the matter could not rest there. With the pressure from medical schools that wanted bodies for dissection as well as the urgency of physicians who had special cases, the question came up again and again. In a number of European medical schools, it became an issue upon which depended whether Jewish candidates would be accepted into medical schools. In a number of Jewish communities, as a result, the policy was adopted to permit such dissections.[6]

In America, the request to permit autopsies came from the Denver Hospital, in order to study tuberculosis.[7] Rabbi Eliezer Meir Prail and Dr. Bernard Revel reaffirm the position of the previous authorities. With much scholarship and *pilpul,* they come to the same conclusion. There is only one dissenting voice that sounds a new note, from Rabbi Yehudah Leib Levin of Detroit: "However, in order not to shut the door to medical progress, and Scripture says, 'Her ways are ways of pleasantness,' I am inclined to think if a patient has, while alive, consented fully and with a legal validation, then it is permissible to dissect him."[8] The general opinion, however, is expressed forcefully by Rabbi Prail:

> With this we started and with this we end, that it is forbidden to dissect the dead bodies of Jews for the purpose of learning the nature of the disease even if there are sick people present who need this, because the cure is not clearly known. And even when the cure is clear, nevertheless, according to Rashi and Meiri, it is forbidden, since one is not permitted to save himself by causing a loss to others. . . . If because of the autopsy the body of the dead will be kept overnight, there is the additional transgression of *halanat hameit,* keeping the dead overnight. It is certainly forbidden for a physician who is a *kohein* to do the autopsy because there is the *isur* of *tum'at kohein,* the interdict against the defilement of a *kohein.*[9]

This, of course, goes beyond the decisions of the Ḥatam Sofer, who permits an autopsy when there are sick people present who could benefit by it. Furthermore, the distinction of Rabbi Prail between a sure cure and one that is not sure is surprising. How can one know the cure before trying it?[10] Rabbi Prail has softened his hard decision only in one instance:

> Accordingly, it is possible to say that if the patients and their relatives waive their privilege of the reverence due to dead bodies and consent to the performance of an autopsy, it is permitted. It is only when it is done against their wishes that it is forbidden.[11]

Rabbi Prail adds an explanation in parentheses that the position of the Ḥatam Sofer that one is forbidden to sell his body to a physician in order to be dissected after his death is explained on the basis of the *isur hana'ah,* the interdiction against deriving any benefit from a dead body. If he does not take money for it, this cannot apply. Evidently, Rabbi Prail is himself surprised at this liberal attitude and immediately adds: "However, even in this fashion it is forbidden to do so because of dishonoring the dead, for if this person pays no attention to his own honor he certainly does not pay honor to his Maker as the Ḥatam Sofer mentioned."[12]

The question is approached in an entirely different vein by Rabbi Chayim Hirshenson. He devotes a chapter to it in his celebrated work *Malki Bakodesh.*[13] It is actually a refutation of the strict view of Rabbis Prail and Revel. While the latter simply rehashed the responsa of the *Noda bi-Yehudah* and the Ḥatam Sofer, Rabbi Hirshenson goes back to the sources. First, he defines what we mean by *nivul hameit.* We usually interpret it as mutilation. That in itself, however, is not *nivul.* The term applies to an act inflicted upon the dead that will dishonor the living and also do dishonor to the soul of the deceased rather than to his body. The term *bizyon hameit* can thus apply only to cases in which that was the intention. Where these things are done *likhvod hameit* [for the honor of the dead], there is no *nivul.* Thus, the Talmud says:

> If he kept him overnight for the sake of his honor, to procure him a coffin or a shroud, he does not transgress thereby. . . . When did the Merciful One say, his body shall not remain all night upon the tree—only in a case similar to the hanged, where

> it involves disgrace. Nothing that is done for the honor of the living involves dishonor to the dead.[14]

Rabbi Hirshenson concludes that in cases in which physicians are seeking a cure for a disease and they think that through an autopsy they might find its cause and bring help to humanity, in general, and to those sick who are waiting for a cure, in particular, an autopsy should be permitted.

However, this does not apply to the use of bodies for dissection in medical schools. There, Rabbi Hirshenson maintains that there is no *kevod haḥayim* [honor of the living] or *tzorekh haḥayim* [need of the living] inasmuch as there are [bodies of] condemned criminals that are available, and their use for dissection is permitted.

Rabbi Ben Zion Uziel, the late chief rabbi of the Sephardic community of Israel, went even further than Rabbi Hirshenson. From two talmudic sources, he proves that where even *pikuaḥ nefesh* or loss of money is involved, there is no *isur nivul hameit*. It is only a dishonor to the dead when an act is committed for that purpose. Autopsy, therefore, when the body is dissected either to learn medicine or to heal other people, is perfectly permissible. To the objection of the Ḥatam Sofer that *pikuaḥ nefesh* is only where one with such a disease is present, Rabbi Uziel answers that there must be other people with that disease even if they are not present and concludes that both autopsies and dissections made for purposes of study are permitted. However, this applies only when there is no compensation to the person while alive or to his heirs for the use of his body. That would certainly be *bizyon hameit*.

There are two qualifications that Rabbi Uziel adds: one, after the body has been cut up, all the remains should be given proper burial; two, all this is *lehalakhah velo lema'aseh* [as a theoretical discussion]. For the practical decision, the question will have to be presented to the chief rabbinate.

Evidently, the question was not long in coming. When the Hadassah University Hospital was established, it entered into a formal agreement with the chief rabbinate, which reads, in part:

> Concordat entered between the chief rabbinate of Israel and the Hadassah University Hospital.
>
> 1. The chief rabbinate does not interfere with autopsies in the following categories:

a. Autopsies according to the requirements of law (to ascertain foul play).

b. Cases in which the physician, because of lack of knowledge, cannot ascribe to any disease the cause of death without surgical operation (autopsy). Permission for such autopsy to be given on condition that a certificate, according to the attached form, will certify that there is no possibility whatsoever to establish a cause of death without autopsy. This certificate shall be given and signed by the three doctors after a consultation among themselves: (1) the doctor in whose ward the patient died, or, in his absence, the resident of the hospital; (2) the director of the hospital, or, in his absence, his substitute; (3) the director of the institute for anatomy and histologic pathology, or, in his absence, his substitute.

c. Autopsy to save a life. In this category is included only such cases in which an autopsy may be of help to a patient at that time in the hospital or outside it.

d. In cases of hereditary diseases when there is a necessity to guide the family in its care. In these cases of experimentation, there shall be a consultation with the rabbinate.

2. In addition to the certificate of the three doctors, the hospital shall have a chart, in accordance with the attached form, that shall show under which category the autopsy was made on the deceased. In those cases where secrecy is not deemed necessary, the disease shall be recorded. The hospital administration shall provide a copy to the *ḥevra kadisha* (Ritual Burial Society) and a copy to the Religious Council of the Jerusalem Communities, the Knesset Israel.

3. The hospital administration shall endeavor to submit a copy to the *ḥevra kadisha* or to notify them by telephone about the outcome of the autopsy as early as possible before the funeral.

4. The hospital administration takes upon itself to carry out the autopsy in a way befitting the honor of the deceased.

5. The organs that shall be removed from the body for medical inspection, either microscopic or otherwise, that shall be deemed necessary by the Institute of Anatomy and Histological

> Pathology to ascertain the cause of death, shall remain in the Institute as long as necessary. At the conclusion of the investigation, the organs shall be turned over to the *ḥevra kadisha* for burial, and the hospital is to bear the expense of burial.

This concordat mentions only autopsies, but not the use of bodies in medical schools.

The question of whether a person can will his body to be used for the purpose of grafting parts of it into a living person in order to effect certain cures involves the same principles as does the question of autopsy and the transplanting of an eye. (The transplanting of an eye has been permitted by various rabbinic bodies.) The objection in those cases stems from two principles: *nivul hameit* (disgracing the dead body); and *isur hana'ah min hameit* (the interdict against deriving any benefit from the dead body).

The consensus of opinion is that if there is *pikuaḥ nefesh,* the *isur nivul hameit* does not apply. We can summarize it in the words of Rabbi Uziel: "It is reasonable that we call *nivul* only when done to dishonor the dead or where it is of no help to others."[15]

The question of *isur hana'ah* does not apply here. There is the talmudic law "One may cure himself with everything except three things."[16] The *isur hana'ah* would refer only to making a business out if it—i.e., to sell oneself for that purpose.[17] The question of *kevurah* (burial) has already been covered in the concordat between the chief rabbinate and the Hadassah University Hospital. We should add that the care insisted upon in the case of the organs applies to the blood, too. That, too, needs *kevurah*.

There is, however, the question of a person who wills his body so that each part of it can be used for transplantation. This would eliminate burial altogether. There is the question of law, and there is the question of sentiment and the entire procedure that centers on *kevurah*.

According to the Talmud, burial is a biblical commandment. "Rabbi Yoḥanan said in the name of Rabbi Simon ben Yoḥai: Where is there an indication in the Torah that burial is obligatory? In the verse, Thou shalt surely bury him."[18]

The Talmud also takes into consideration the feelings of the family and the sentiments of the person now dead. Thus, if an insult to the family results therefrom, his request is not to be considered. The Talmud does not come to any decision. Later *posekim* [decisors] have taken the line that *bizayon* is decisive.

> The students asked: Is burial in order to avert disgrace (Tosafot: "to the family") or as a means of atonement? What is the practical difference? If one said, "I do not wish to be buried." If the reason for burial is to avert disgrace to the family, he has no right to make such a request; if it is for atonement, then he has in effect declared, "I do not desire atonement."[19]

Today, we should follow the same line of reasoning. Since the use of parts of the body is permissible and the only question is the elimination of *kevurah,* we should take into consideration the feelings of the next of kin. If they give their consent to such a bequest, we should honor it. I would like to add an interesting comment [by Rabbi Yehudah Leib Graubart]:

> In a country where the Jews enjoy freedom, if the rabbis should refuse to allow the Jewish dead to be used for medical study, their action will result in *ḥilul hashem,* for it will be said that the Jews are not interested in saving lives; there is reason to permit it.[20]

A similar opinion is to be found in *She'eilot Uteshuvot Atzei Zeitim,* that where there is a *ḥashash nezek leyisra'el,* we should permit it.[21]

With this kind of reasoning, which is to be commended for its realism, we can permit all these uses of the bodies of the deceased where there is an obvious help to other people and where the general public considers such uses as *pikuaḥ nefesh.* If medical science claims that these may save lives, then we should add that in such cases, it is not only permitted but is actually a mitzvah. There should always, however, be a respectful attitude to the human body, and *kevurah* should be piously performed wherever feasible.[22]

Notes

1. *She'eilot Uteshuvot Noda bi-Yehudah Tinyana, Y.D.* no. 210.
2. Deut. 21:22–23.
3. B. *Bava Batra* 154a.
4. B. *Ḥullin* 11b.
5. *She'eilot Uteshuvot Ḥatam Sofer, Y.D.* no. 336.
6. *Universal Jewish Encyclopedia,* s.v. "Autopsy."
7. *Yagdil Torah* 1 (5676–77): 3.

8. Ibid., 112.
9. *Yagdil Torah* 8:57. Prail's answer is also reprinted in his collection of responsa, *She'eilot Uteshuvot Sefer Hama'or,* nos. 37–41.
10. See strictures of Rabbi Natan Nateh Hurewitz, *Yagdil Torah* 8:87.
11. *Yagdil Torah* 8:29.
12. See also *Sefer Hama'or,* 179.
13. *She'eilot Uteshuvot Malki Bakodesh,* pt. 3, no. 152.
14. B. *Sanhedrin* 47a.
15. *She'eilot Uteshuvot Mishpetei Uziel,* v. 1, *Y.D.* no. 28, p. 209.
16. B. *Pesaḥim* 43a.
17. See responsum, *Rabbinical Council of America Proceedings* (1948), 50.
18. B. *Sanhedrin* 46b.
19. Ibid.
20. *She'eilot Uteshuvot Ḥavalim Bane'imim,* pt. 3, no. 64.
21. *She'eilot Uteshuvot Atzei Zeitim, Y.D.* no. 60.
22. Additional resources utilized by the author include: *She'eilot Uteshuvot Benei Tziyon Y.D.* no. 170; *She'eilot Uteshuvot Maharam Shick Y.D.* no. 347; *She'eilot Uteshuvot Minḥat Eliezer,* pt. 4, no. 24; *She'eilot Uteshuvot Melamed Leho'il,* pt. 2, no. 108; *She'eilot Uteshuvot Or Hamei'ir,* Rabbi J. M. Shapiro, no. 24; Hirsh L. Gordon, "Autopsies according to Jewish Religious Law," *The Hebrew Physician* 1 (1937); Dr. Aaron Kottler, "Jewish Attitude to Autopsy," *N.Y. State Journal of Medicine* (1 May 1957).

CHAPTER 28

Ḥesed or Ḥiyuv? The Obligation to Preserve Life and the Question of Postmortem Organ Donation*

Joseph H. Prouser

She'eilah (Question):

What is the halakhic status of postmortem organ and tissue donation?

Teshuvah (Response):

A. Preservation of Human Life as Obligatory

The inestimable value of human life is a cardinal principle of Jewish law. "Human life is not a good to be preserved as a condition of other values but an absolute, basic, and precious good in its own right. The obligation to preserve life is commensurately all-encompassing."[1] This obligation includes not only self-preservation, but the duty to save the life of one's fellow human being, should he or she be in mortal danger. The Torah's commandment *lo ta'amod al dam rei'ekha*, "You shall not stand idly by the blood of your neighbor" (Lev. 19:16) provides the halakhic basis for this obligation.

In addition, the Talmud (*Sanhedrin* 73a) reformulates this prohibition (*mitzvat lo ta'aseh*) into a positive, prescriptive obligation (*mitzvat*

*Approved by the Rabbinical Assembly Committee on Jewish Law and Standards, Dec. 1995.

aseih), by relating the duty to intervene in life-threatening situations to the commandment (Deut. 22:1) regarding restoration of lost property, *hashavat aveidah*. "Every individual, insofar as he is able, is obligated to restore the health of a fellow man no less than he is obligated to restore his property."[2]

B. Who Is Obligated?

In codifying this mitzvah, Maimonides emphasizes how broadly its obligation devolves:

כל היכול להציל ולא הציל עובר על לא תעמוד על דם רעך

> Anyone who is able to save a life, but fails to do so, violates "You shall not stand idly by the blood of your neighbor."[3]

In describing the analogous duty to save the life of one being pursued by an assailant (*rodeif*), Maimonides leaves no room for exemption: *kol yisra'el metzuvin lehatzil,* "All Israel are commanded to take lifesaving action."[4] Indeed, not even the inability personally to save the life in peril relieves one of this obligation:

לא תעמוד על דם רעך - לא תעמוד על עצמך משמע אלא חזור על כל צדדין שלא יאבד דם רעך

> "You shall not stand idly by the blood of your neighbor" means "You shall not rely on yourself, alone." Rather you must turn to all available resources so that your neighbor's blood will not be lost.[5]

C. Precedence of the Obligation

It is abundantly clear that the mandate to preserve life—*pikuaḥ nefesh*—takes precedence over other religious obligations and considerations. (The prohibitions against murder, sexual immorality, and idolatry are, under normal[6] circumstances, the only exceptions—*yeihareig ve'al ya'avor.*)[7] Former British chief rabbi Immanuel Jakobovits articulates this principle in no uncertain terms:

> It is obligatory to disregard laws conflicting with the immediate claims of life, and . . . it is sinful to observe laws which are in suspense on account of danger to life or health. . . . [I]t is not only permitted but imperative to disregard laws in conflict with life or health.[8]

Thus, the seriously ill are required to eat on Yom Kippur. Similarly, it is forbidden to circumcise a sick or weakened infant if this would further compromise his health. The circumcision must be delayed, for *ein lekha davar she'omeid bifnei pikuaḥ nefesh,* "preservation of life overrides all other considerations."[9] This principle has many applications in regard to the laws of Shabbat. The requirement to preserve life at the expense of Sabbath observance is unambiguous:

> **מי שיש לו חולי של סכנה מצוה לחלל עליו את השבת והזריז הרי זה משובח והשואל הרי זה שופך דמים**
>
> It is commanded that we violate the Sabbath for anyone dangerously ill. One who is zealous (and eagerly violates the Sabbath in such a case) is praiseworthy; one who (delays in order to) ask (questions about the Law) is guilty of shedding blood.[10]

A noteworthy expression of this zeal is the recommendation (directed at Israeli society) in *Sefer Shemirat Shabbat Kehilkhatah* that when it becomes necessary to drive an ambulance on the Sabbath, it is preferable that Sabbath-observant Jews do the driving.[11]

D. Primary Objections to Postmortem Procedures

To be sure, postmortem donation of human tissue is not without halakhic difficulties. The halakhic objections[12] to this practice include the prohibitions against *nivul hameit* (disgracing the dead body, as by disfigurement), *hana'ah min hameit* (deriving benefit from a dead body), and *halanat hameit* (delaying burial). All three of these concerns, collectively termed *kevod hameit,* the dignity of the dead, are addressed in a responsum by former Israeli chief rabbi Isser Yehuda Unterman. As to the first two issues, Rabbi Unterman rules succinctly:

> **השאלה היא אם מותר מצד הדין לעשות נתוח בבשר אדם מת ולהעביר ממנו בשר . . . שיתקשר אח״כ באופן אורגני כחלק מן החי . . . ופשוט בעיני הדבר שיש בהם משום פקוח נפש לא קמבעי לן שאסורי התורה חמורים נדחים מפני פקוח נפש, ולכן הנתוחים שעושים להצלת נפש ודאי מותרים**
>
> Regarding the question of whether the Law permits surgical removal of tissue from a dead body . . . subsequently to be transplanted as an organic part of the living . . . I find the matter to be simple. Since these procedures constitute preservation of life, there is no difficulty. After all, weighty Torah prohibitions are set aside for the preservation of life. Hence, such surgical procedures conducted to save a life are absolutely permitted.[13]

Rabbi Efrayim Oshry rules with similar clarity:

> **היכא דשייך ענין של פקוח נפש לא חיישינן לניוול המת**
>
> "Where saving a life is involved, we are not concerned with the desecration of the dead."[14]

So, too, Rabbi Theodore Friedman: *pikuaḥ nefesh gadol mikevod hameit,* "Greater is saving a life than the dignity of the dead [*kevod hameit*]."[15]

As to the question of burial, Rabbi Unterman discusses only the particular organs or tissue being transplanted. In this regard, he considers transplanted tissue to be restored to life and thus not requiring burial with the donor's remains. The question of whether the donor's transplanted tissue will eventually be buried together with the recipient is not compelling, just as the requirement that blood be buried[16] poses no obstacle to blood donation.

Rabbi Unterman does not discuss the issue of delaying burial to facilitate postmortem procedures. Since, however, such delay is neither typical nor necessary,[17] we should not consider it an impediment. In those few, rare cases in which burial is delayed, we should rely on Rabbi Unterman's general approach: preservation of life takes precedence, and the prohibition of *halanat hameit* is likewise suspended. *Ein lekha davar she'omeid bifnei pikuaḥ nefesh,* "preservation of life overrides all other considerations."

While organ and tissue transplantation is a relatively new halakhic quandary, the related question of autopsy has a longer general and halakhic history.[18] "Many medical practitioners regard autopsy as essential to maintaining high standards of medical knowledge, hospital care, and community health."[19] The trend toward permitting autopsy under the rubric of *pikuaḥ nefesh,* however, has generally been conditioned by the stipulation that a specific beneficiary of information gained through the procedure be identified (*ḥole nimtza lefanenu*).[20] That is, theoretical medical knowledge alone does not constitute *pikuaḥ nefesh.* A demonstrable need for information required to avert immediate danger to a specific human life is necessary to render autopsy permissible. In the absence of such a need, autopsy remains prohibited. Indeed, Rabbi Unterman suggests organ donation as a desirable recourse when civil authorities mandate autopsies that would otherwise be halakhically objectionable:

> **היכי שחתכוהו בלאו הכי עפ"י דרישת החוק לצורך חקירה משפטית וכדומה אפשר שאין זה ניוול אם נשתמשו בחלק מחותך לרפואה**
>
> In cases where an autopsy (one otherwise not in conformity with Jewish Law) is performed in accordance with the demands of civil law, as part of a criminal investigation or the like, it may no longer be considered a desecration [*nivul*] if excised tissue is used for healing.[21]

So long as highly sophisticated, computerized, international organ-registration networks readily identify prospective organ recipients, the requirement of *ḥole nimtza lefanenu* is, in the case of organ donation, ipso facto satisfied. So immediate and specific is the need for organs that a prospective recipient typically "wears a pocket pager, waiting for a call saying that a new heart is available."[22] (As Rabbi Unterman indicates, however, fulfillment of this condition remains considerably more difficult to establish in regard to autopsy, the benefits of which are generally far less direct and immediate. Autopsy thus remains prohibited unless it is deemed necessary for saving the life of a *ḥole nimtza lefanenu.*)

E. Dimensions of the Need

The halakhic mandate to preserve life by consenting to postmortem tissue donation takes on compelling urgency by virtue of the massive need for tissue transplants. As of April 1995, there were 39,735 people on the waiting list of the United Network for Organ Sharing.[23] "Every thirty minutes, someone is added to this national waiting list. More than 500 patients on the national waiting list are children."[24] Due directly to the shortage of willing donors, "thousands continue to die each year because of a shortage of donated organs and tissues."[25] According to one estimate, seven people die each day for lack of available organs.[26]

The lifesaving impact of organ donation reaches far beyond the sizable number of potential recipients. "Faced with a dire lack of organs from cadavers, transplant surgeons are looking with increasing interest at living donors"[27]—in particular, close relatives of recipients. A recent, unsuccessful transplant attempt dramatizes this dangerous, emerging trend: "In a desperate attempt to save the life of a 9-year-old Minnesota girl whose lungs had failed, doctors first transplanted part of her father's lung, and when that was not enough, tried to transplant part of her mother's lung. . . . While still on the operating table, the girl, Alyssa Plum, died."[28]

Prospective living donors, as well as recipients, are thus needlessly placed at mortal risk by the shortage of cadaver organs. "Parents want to donate even when doctors are unwilling to do the operation because they think it would be futile or that there is too much risk for the donor."[29] This unacceptable risk led Dr. Thomas Starzl, the renowned surgeon who pioneered liver transplants,[30] to announce that he would no longer perform transplants from living donors. In 1987, he explained his decision:

> The death of a single well-motivated and completely healthy living donor almost stops the clock worldwide. The most compelling argument against living donation is that it is not completely safe for the donor.[31]

Nevertheless, medical reliance on living donors continues to mount. In August 1995, the *New England Journal of Medicine*[32] reported "increasing numbers of persons donating kidneys to their spouses." Citing evidence that "the survival rates of these kidneys are higher than those of cadaveric kidneys," the article concludes that "spouses are an important source of living-donor kidney grafts." Such a trend in the field of transplantation places tremendous pressure on relatives of prospective organ recipients to imperil themselves by serving as donors. In 1994 alone, 2,980 kidney transplants were performed using living donors.[33]

The *NEJM* article provides separate statistical data for kidney donation by husbands to wives based on whether the wife had ever been pregnant. The success rate for transplantation into women who had previously been pregnant is 76 percent, as opposed to 87 percent for women who had never been pregnant.[34] It must be assumed that among the former are a significant number of mothers with young children. Spousal donation in such cases means that both parents (donor and recipient)—and, therefore, their children's well-being—are placed at mortal risk. Yet an accompanying editorial asserts that there is "no ethical objection to using emotionally related (that, is, spousal) donors[!]."[35]

Even a minute risk to the living is a significant halakhic datum. Rabbi Jakobovits thus rules that "while the gift of blood constitutes a religious obligation, it cannot be enforced, since it may entail some risk for the donor."[36] Similarly, he views higher-risk living donation of organs "as acts of supreme charity but not as an obligation."[37] Risk to life, statistically insignificant or profound, constitutes a mitigating factor that renders living donation commendable but optional. This risk is, by definition, completely absent in postmortem donation. With the absence of risk as a mitigating factor, postmortem organ donation is, logically, rendered obligatory.

Indeed, the risk to prospective living donors makes the need for cadaver organs—and the halakhic mandate for donation—all the more urgent. It should be noted that, in addition to altruistic relatives acting as living donors, the shortage of cadaver organs has also led to "a recognized market in human body parts."[38] That is, individuals are hired to donate organs that are redundant (a kidney), "nonessential" (corneas), or regenerative (sections of livers).[39] While almost universally illegal, trade in human organs, like the "long-shot" attempts of relatives to save the lives of loved ones through living donation, demonstrates the desperate situation caused by the lack of available cadaver organs, and the personal desperation of prospective recipients.

F. Who Can Donate?

It should be stressed that mandating consent for postmortem organ donation does not mean that all, or even most, compliant individuals will actually serve as donors. However, any individual donor may well be uniquely qualified to save the life of a prospective recipient. About two million deaths are recorded annually in the United States. "Primary donors are between the ages of fifteen and sixty-five. They are in good health but have died suddenly, possibly through accidents and are declared brain-dead. . . . An estimated 20,000 to 25,000 brain deaths occur in the United States each year."[40] This select group of potential donors is further narrowed, as any particular organ transplant requires compatible tissue obtained from a "good genetic match," to minimize chances of natural organ rejection. Six pairs of genes are examined to determine matching human lymphocyte antigens (HLA proteins). The closer the match, the higher the prospects for a successful transplant.[41] Only an identical twin guarantees a perfect match. The smaller the pool of donors, the less likely it is to find a suitable cadaver organ for transplantation.

G. Secondary Objections to Obligation

An objection raised by some authorities[42] posits that while *pikuaḥ nefesh* may indeed be a privilege for the dead, it cannot properly be ruled an obligation. The dead are not bound by Jewish law (*ḥofshi mikol hamitzvot*)![43] This suggestion is mere semantics. The consent required for organ donation is given prior to one's death, or by surviving, responsible relatives. The deceased is the means by which *pikuaḥ nefesh* is achieved. The act of consent while alive (or the consent of survivors) constitutes the fulfillment of the mitzvah itself.

It is curious indeed, with the consistent historical penchant for unambivalent zeal in matters of *pikuaḥ nefesh,* that the mandatory status of postmortem organ donation has not previously been widely asserted. Various reasons for this apparent pattern of omission can be discerned. The first is that the technology of transplantation is still quite young. In the early 1940s, "Sir Peter Medawar (Oxford, England) described the rejection phenomenon, for which he won the Nobel

Prize. This discovery laid the foundation for the modern era of transplantation."[44] This era came into fruition[45] only in the late 1940s, precisely the time that Rabbi Unterman was composing his responsa on this topic. The first successful kidney transplant did not take place until 1954, two years after the publication of Rabbi Unterman's *Shevet mi-Yehudah*. Liver and lung transplants were first performed in 1963, and then only with limited success. The first recipient of a liver died within three weeks. The first successful heart transplant was performed in South Africa by Dr. Christiaan Barnard in 1967, and provoked years of debate and controversy. Successful lung transplants are an extremely recent achievement.

Thus, those responsa and rabbinic pronouncements issued early in the still-short history of transplantation could not assert with confidence that the procedures were, in fact, lifesaving.[46] The first attempts at each new procedure met with only limited success. Immunosuppressive therapy—the technology whereby natural rejection of "foreign" organs is medically and chemically combated—is still being perfected. However, this developing technology already accounts for "a near doubling in the numbers of heart, kidney and liver transplants performed. These advances also have increased the survival rates of kidney transplant recipients over age sixty by as much as 10 percent."[47]

Only with time and experience do transplant operations become sufficiently dependable to constitute clear *pikuaḥ nefesh*.[48] Kidney transplants currently enjoy an 80 to 90 percent success rate, heart transplants a success rate of 80 to 90 percent, and liver transplants 65 to 70 percent. Combined heart-lung transplants have a success rate of approximately 70 percent.[49] Success implies restoration of the recipient's quality of life and normal life expectancy. "Postmortem donor kidney transplantation function of more than twenty years is well documented."[50]

Similarly, before the advent of sophisticated, coordinated, and computerized national and international organ registries, mandating donation would have been premature. Recipients were more difficult to locate and identify. The requirement of *ḥole nimtza lefanenu* (a specific recipient) could not always be fulfilled early on in transplant history. This, as discussed above, is no longer commonly the case. The United Network for Organ Sharing (UNOS), a government-sanctioned organ registry, has replaced the less efficient methods for identifying recipients of earlier decades.

H. Determination of Death

Finally, there was a greater reluctance in the early years of the transplant era to mandate (indeed, to allow) donation because of fears regarding determination of the donor's death. Using brain death as a medical, much less halakhic, determinant of death dates only to the twenty-second World Medical Assembly, held in 1968.[51] Brain death is defined as "permanent functional death of the centers in the brain that control the breathing, pupillary, and other vital reflexes."[52] Rabbinic proponents of such a definition of death, that is, the total cessation of brain and brain-stem activity, as indicated (among other diagnostic methods) by an isoelectric or "flat" electroencephalogram (EEG), include Rabbis Seymour Siegel *z"l*,[53] Elliot Dorff,[54] Avram Reisner,[55] and David Golinkin[56] (all of the Rabbinical Assembly), Rabbi Moshe Tendler,[57] a preeminent Orthodox authority on Jewish medical ethics, as well as the chief rabbinate of Israel.

> All rabbinic authorities agree that the classic definition of death in Judaism is the absence of spontaneous respiration in a patient with no other signs of life. . . . Brain death is a criterion for confirming death in a patient who already has irreversible absence of spontaneous respiration.[58]

It should be noted that the determination of brain death is often made while the deceased appears to be breathing and to have a pulse, because of the use of a mechanical respirator. Where brain death is determined, these misleading data in no way constitute life. Quite to the contrary, "it might be forbidden to continue artificial means of 'life' in these conditions, since it would, in fact, be *halanat hameit,* a delay in burying a dead person."[59] Writing in 1975, Rabbi Jakobovits pointedly discusses the implications of this issue:

> The question of defining the moment of death with precision has . . . been rendered both more difficult and more critically acute by . . . the demand for viable cadaver organs for transplant purposes. The lapse of only a few minutes may spell the difference between success and failure in such operations; on the other hand, the premature removal of organs from the dying may hasten death and constitute murder.[60]

Greater familiarity with the practice of transplantation, as well as a broader medical and rabbinic literature on determination of death and brain death, has largely eliminated this concern. Prevalent premodern fears of "false death" are no longer compelling. The final moments of the donor's life are safeguarded by requirements that two physicians certify death, and that these physicians not be involved in the transplant procedure.[61]

I. Kevod Hameit: The Dignity of the Dead

Perhaps the most decisive factor in rabbinic reluctance to mandate postmortem organ donation, however, has simply been "the widespread aversion to any interference with the dead among most Jews."[62] In general, this "aversion" reflects entirely appropriate devotion to a venerable religious principle, and should be commended.

> Man is created in the image of God, and thus possesses dignity and value. . . . An indignity inflicted on man is a profanation of the name of God. The body that housed the soul is sanctified by Judaism. . . . Sanctity adheres to the body even after the soul has left. The care and consideration and respect that are bestowed upon the living must be accorded the dead as they are attended, prepared, and escorted to their final abode on earth.[63]

Kevod hameit—the dignity of the dead—is a weighty and cherished religious imperative. This is indicated by the designation given those charged with these religious tasks: *ḥevra kadisha,* the "Holy Society."

> If the body is honored to the extent that it is in Judaism, even in death . . . one can easily understand how many Jews would hesitate to mutilate it—or allow one's own body to be mutilated—even when it is for the noble purpose of helping to save someone else's life.[64]

It is precisely a sensitivity to such well-intentioned sentiments that characterizes Rabbi Unterman's call "to influence relatives and to persuade them to consent" (*lehashpia al hakerovim uleshadelam sheyaskimu*) to organ and tissue donation.[65] Framing this teaching in terms of persuasion rather than coercion does not imply that this life-saving action is elective. Are not rabbis frequently engaged in educational endeavors and persuasive techniques aimed at generating compliance with clear halakhic obligations? Persuading a Jew, for example to comply with the laws of Shabbat does not suggest that this observance is optional. Indeed, Rabbi Unterman's call for persuasive outreach reflects his recognition of the obligatory nature of *pikuaḥ nefesh*. So, too, Rabbi David Golinkin:

> **לא זו בלבד שמותר ליהודי לצוות את איבריו להשתלה לאחר מותו אלא מצוה עליו לעשות כן כדי להציל נפש אחת או נפשות רבות**
>
> It is not merely permissible for a Jew to bequeath his organs for transplantation following his death; it is a mitzvah for him to do so, in order to save one life, or several lives.[66]

Rabbi Tendler similarly states that "if one is in the position to donate an organ to save another's life, it's obligatory to do so."[67] The most sacred institutions and practices of Judaism may—indeed, must—be suspended for the purpose of saving lives. Does it not stand to reason that understandable but strictly subjective aversion and aesthetic objections to postmortem organ donation likewise must be set aside?

As to the similar conflict between personal rights and the halakhic obligation to preserve life, the general observation of renowned Israeli jurist Haim Cohn is instructive: "Jewish Law, as a system of law, knows no explicit rights. . . . It is no accident that Jewish Law concentrates on duties and has no room for rights. It is the performance of duties by which God is served."[68]

Rabbi Unterman similarly considers individual liberties, to the extent that they have any halakhic status, to be included among those values set aside for *pikuaḥ nefesh*.[69] We affirm that *ein lekha davar she'omeid bifnei pikuaḥ nefesh*, "preservation of life overrides all other considerations." We ought not, as our final act, glorify personal preference at the expense of other human beings' lives.

J. Emotional and Psychological Considerations

Rabbi Unterman's early call for educational outreach in regard to fulfilling the mitzvah of *pikuaḥ nefesh* through organ donation was predicated not only on halakhic principle, but on the spiritual significance of such an act. His metaphysical speculation also reflects a concern with the emotional impact of organ donation on the bereaved. Rabbi Unterman thus offers reassurance to donors' families.

> זכות גדולה לו וקורת רוח לנשמתו שנעשית מצוה גדולה כזו בגופו, ואין לזלזל בחשבון כזה
>
> It is a great merit to the deceased, and gratifying to his soul, that so great a mitzvah is fulfilled with his body. One must not underestimate this consideration.[70]

It is essential that one undertaking the persuasive outreach advocated by Rabbi Unterman follow his example in sensitively placing organ donation into a constructive context. Referring to lifesaving transplant procedures as the "harvesting" of organs, for example, evokes a sense of violence and disregard for the deceased, as indicated by a grieving father: "I'm a farmer and I know what harvest means. When we harvest corn, we tear the corn from the stalk—it just gets trampled under the tires and then thrown away. Nobody is going to harvest my boy."[71]

"Recover" or "retrieve" are more appropriate terms to describe the donation process. It is similarly imperative that a ventilator not be referred to as "life support," as this implies that the patient is not yet dead. (The ventilator is used following brain death to maintain circulation of oxygenated blood to viable organs.) Referring to the deceased by name (rather than as "the donor") "shows respect and sensitivity for the family's grief over the loss of their loved one."[72]

Dr. Calvin Stiller, chief of the Multi-Organ Transplant Service at University Hospital in London, Ontario, provides an inviting perspective on the transplant procedure:

> When the decision to transplant is made, the donor and the recipient are taken to the operating room. The donor's body is treated with profound respect, because we are watching one of the most extraordinary acts that a human being can accomplish. The surgical theatre is hushed and reverence for life prevails as the donor organ is removed and taken carefully to the sick, partially destroyed body of the recipient. The sick organ is removed to make way for the new healthy organ. We watch in silence as the retrieval of life from the donor occurs and the restoration of

> life in the recipient begins. We watch as the skin begins to clear, the body chemistry begins to improve and the brain gradually quickens as the new organ functions and restores life.[73]

Those contemplating organ donation should also be made aware that "studies have found that donation of the organs and/or tissue of a loved one who has died helps to shorten the time needed by members of a bereaved family to recover from their loss."[74] Serving as an organ donor thus not only saves lives, but also provides comfort and healing to one's own loved ones, "a blessedness made more remarkable and unexpected precisely because of its association with an experience of such abysmal despair and suffering. . . . It doesn't remove the pain or loss, but it allows something good to be salvaged from an otherwise horrible occurrence."[75] The emotionally therapeutic impact of organ donation is illustrated by the experience of a family who mourned the death of an eighteen-year-old killed in a motorcycle accident:

> We were so proud of Walter. Even in death his quiet, unassuming generosity was still alive. On the day of the funeral, a friend of ours on the police force called to let us know that the heart recipient was doing very well, and was setting records for recovery. This gave our whole family a lot of faith for getting through that day.[76]

In addition to the "redemptive comfort"[77] inherent in the act of giving, donor families identify further emotional benefits of organ donation. These include the sense that donors "will never be forgotten" by those whose lives they save. Relatives of donors also report a sense of "extended family" and "community" with other donors and recipients: "The giving and receiving of life is the peculiar essence of family, and the gift of life that is tissue and organ donation has extended my family in a very real sense."[78]

The adverse affect on the bereaved who are denied the opportunity to facilitate lifesaving organ donations can also be profound. Donation may be precluded if the cause of death is unknown. Potential donors may also be disqualified for various medical reasons: malignancies, transmissible disease, hemophilia, autoimmune diseases, rheumatoid arthritis, and so on.[79] Often, however, missed opportunities are due to the timidity of hospital personnel in approaching families for consent. A Canadian woman whose husband suffered a fatal brain aneurysm anticipated the opportunity to facilitate organ donation with a measure of solace. Her husband had, on principle, registered as an organ donor. By the time she was informed of his death, however—some ninety minutes thereafter—his organs were no longer viable.

> A wave of grief swept over her. Grief exceeding that of loss. It was now laced with anger. Her husband had been denied an opportunity to carry out his last wish. Judy left the hospital filled with rage. She, too, had been denied. The grieving process was now doubly bitter for her.[80]

Jewish mourners, called upon to grant consent for the use of a loved one's organs in a transplant procedure are, by definition, *onenim*. This stage of mourning, *aninut,* comprises the period between death and burial. "*Aninut* represents the spontaneous human reaction to death. . . . Man responds to his defeat at the hands of death with total resignation and with all-consuming, masochistic, self-devastating black despair."[81]

It is little wonder that many individuals at this stage of grief are not naturally inclined to seek out opportunities for organ donation. Understandably, an *onein* is emotionally ill-equipped to act selflessly and magnanimously for the preservation of human life. It is precisely the *onein* who is least prepared to "carry the human-moral load"[82] by opting for organ donation. For this reason, many bereaved families tragically miss a unique opportunity for an act of religious significance and personal therapeutic value. Such was the case of a mother mourning her twelve-year-old son:

> Anguish and grief at a time like that is such that all rational acts and thoughts are cast to the side. . . . Time eventually restores you to reality and thoughts of what you could have done before and after the tragic loss. . . . I wish that some or all of Jason's organs and eyes could have been used to help people less fortunate than himself. . . . If only I could look at another human and know that my son lives on in them and that they have had another chance at life because of Jason.[83]

Consenting to organ donation provides an effective source of comfort and emotional healing. Mandating organ donation thus doubly exemplifies human sensitivity. It brings physical healing to the deathly ill. It also brings emotional healing to the bereaved, while relieving them of an emotional burden that they are temporarily unable to bear.

K. Specific Procedures

1. Vital organs and corneas. Procedures that replace vital organs are the most obviously lifesaving in nature. These include transplantation of the heart, lung, liver, pancreas, kidney, as well as the rarer[84] joint heart-lung transplant. A single cadaveric donor can facilitate transplants in multiple recipients, saving several lives simultaneously. "The use of eyes removed from the dead, including their bequest for eye banks, for corneal transplants has also generally been permitted. In the view of the majority, the restoration or preservation of eyesight is to be regarded as a lifesaving act."[85]

As early as 1953, Rabbi Theodore Friedman, "with the approval of a majority of the [R.A. Law] committee," ruled corneal transplants permissible, stating that "it should readily be granted that blindness should be deemed a case of *pikuaḥ nefesh.*"[86]

While one might infer from the existence of eye banks that the requirement of *ḥole nimtza lefanenu* is not satisfied, this is not the case. Transplantation is performed three to seven days after donation.[87] Furthermore, over 90 percent of all such procedures successfully restore the recipient's vision.[88] With 43,743 corneal transplants in 1994, this represents the most common and the most successful transplant procedure being practiced,[89] "despite a continual shortage of donors."[90] To the extent that restoration of eyesight can be construed as preservation of life, corneas may thus be accorded the halakhic status of vital organs for the purpose of postmortem donation.

As with other anatomical gifts, one should specify that consent is given for transplantation only. As Rabbi Jakobovits stresses, "the disused part of the eye after the cornea has been removed should not be disposed of except by burial."[91]

2. Skin. The use of tissue from cadaveric donors for skin grafting presents a different set of considerations. According to Dr. Richard Kagan[92] of the Shriner's Burn Institute of Cincinnati, who is chairman of the American Association of Tissue Banks' Skin Council, the most urgent need for skin grafting is in the treatment of severe burn victims. While some surgeons prefer to use skin within three days of death, this is not always possible. Skin is frozen in a cryostat and retained by skin banks until a need arises. Because of the nature of their injuries, there can be no waiting list for burn victims. The need is sudden and immediate.

The preferred method in treating burn victims is "autograft," the transfer of healthy tissue from elsewhere on the victim's own body. In cases of extensive burning, a "homograft," the transfer of skin from a human donor, can be used only as a temporary measure. Skin is typically retrieved from relatively flat surfaces such as the back, thighs, and hips—not from the neck or face. "The grafted skin greatly enhances the surgeon's ability to handle a burn wound and to prevent infection," but must be considered "life-enhancing, not lifesaving." Skin used in a homograft eventually falls off the wound "like a scab." Where autograft is impossible, homograft is "the tool of first choice." Synthetic "skin" can serve the same purpose but represents "a very distant second choice."

Cadaveric skin thus represents a preferred mode of treatment, not an indispensable or vital medical resource. Skin homografts cannot properly be classified as transplantation, because of the temporary nature of such procedures. Thanks to the availability of other treatment options, any shortage of donor skin cannot accurately be described as life-threatening. Indeed, the death of severe burn victims is increasingly linked not to burns, but to pneumonia resulting from smoke inhalation. Donated skin, while frozen, has a limited "shelf life." Although the donor can specify that skin not be used for research, tissue that exceeds this period simply cannot be used for grafting.

In light of these considerations, no obligation to make an anatomical gift of skin can be inferred from the prohibition of *lo ta'amod al dam rei'ekha,* "You shall not stand idly by the blood of your neighbor." Such donations, however, should, if used for healing, be considered entirely permissible[93] acts of profound charity and kindness: *ḥesed.*

L. Conclusion

Given the increasing sophistication and success of transplant technology and the increased confidence regarding determination of death,[94] the postmortem donation of vital organs and tissue incontrovertibly constitutes *pikuaḥ nefesh,* which overrides all other considerations. The demand for organs far outweighs the supply, creating thousands of desperate, specific, life-threatening situations.

We must therefore conclude that consent must be granted when requested by doctors or hospitals for use in lifesaving transplantation procedures.[95] This obligation can also be fulfilled by personally registering as a donor by, for example, properly completing a donor card to be carried on one's person,[96] and by informing family members of one's intention in this matter. It is most advisable to provide family members with written documentation of one's donor status, possibly as part of a more general "living will."[97]

The preservation of human life is obligatory, not optional. Since all conflicting halakhic duties are suspended, and specific, readily identifiable human lives are at stake, withholding consent for postmortem organ and tissue donation when needed for lifesaving transplant procedures is prohibited by Jewish law. It violates the Torah's prohibition of *lo ta'amod al dam rei'ekha,* as well as the prescriptive obligation to preserve human life.[98] This applies to the individual in anticipation of his or her own death, as well as to health care proxies or "next of kin"[99] whenever they are legally empowered to make such decisions[100] on behalf of the deceased. The identity, and certainly the religious status, of the recipient are irrelevant. Lifesaving action is obligatory "even if the donor never knows who the beneficiary will be."[101]

"The act of saving the life of another by donating an organ after death seems to me the best and most practical demonstration of faith."[102] A bereaved family member who grants consent for organ donation acts as an agent and as a partner of the deceased in observance of the mitzvah of *pikuaḥ nefesh.* By so doing, he or she renders only profound and genuine honor to the deceased, while simultaneously bringing comfort to those who mourn. "There can be no greater *kevod hameit* than to bring healing to the living."[103]

Vehasho'eil shofekh damim—one who delays is guilty of shedding blood.[104] When needed for lifesaving transplantation, withholding consent for postmortem tissue donation must be considered forbidden.

כי נר מצוה ותורה אור ודרך חיים תוכחות מוסר

Notes

1. Rabbi J. David Bleich, *Contemporary Halakhic Problems* (New York: Ktav, 1977), 93.

2. Ibid., 95.
3. Maimonides, *Hilkhot Rotzeaḥ Ushmirat Nefesh* 1:14.
4. Ibid., 1:6.
5. *Sanhedrin* 73a, Rashi ad loc.
6. During a period of religious persecution, however, the law is more stringent, extending the requirement of martyrdom even to minor religious practices. See *Y.D.* 137:1.
7. *Sanhedrin* 74a; *Yoma* 82a.
8. Rabbi Immanuel Jakobovits, *Jewish Medical Ethics* (New York: Bloch, 1975), 50.
9. *Yoma* 82a; similarly, *sakanat nefashot doḥah et hakol, Y.D.* 263:1.
10. *O.Ḥ.* 328:2.
11. Rabbi J. I. Neuwirth, *Shemirat Shabbat Kehilkhatah* (Hebrew), 541.
12. See Rabbi Isaac Klein's responsum on autopsies, *Responsa and Halakhic Studies* (New York: Ktav, 1975), 40 [chap. 27, p. 443 of this vol.].
13. Rabbi I. Y. Unterman, *Shevet mi-Yehudah* (Mossad Harav Kook, 1983), 54. See also 368 for identical ruling based on *Noda bi-Yehudah* and *Maharam Shik* rulings on autopsies.
14. Rabbi Efrayim Oshry, *She'eilot Uteshuvot Mima'amakim* 2:10. English trans. from "Performing a Caesarean Section on a Dead Woman," in *Responsa from the Holocaust,* trans. Y. Leiman (New York: Judaica, 1983), 72. Rabbi Oshry authorized a cesarean section on a woman whose murder he witnessed, even though it was uncertain that the baby was still alive.
15. *Proceedings of the Rabbinical Assembly* 17 (1953): 44.
16. On the requirement that blood be buried, see "A Guide for the Chevra Kadisha," in Rabbi Maurice Lamm, *The Jewish Way in Death and Mourning* (New York: Jonathan David, 1969, 1979), 244.
17. "The Circle of Life: Organ and Tissue Donation," American Council on Transplantation (Alexandria, Va.: n.d.).
18. In *The Body as Property* (New York: Viking Press, 1981), Russell Scott calls autopsies "the oldest medical activities that use bodies" (29). Skilled dissection of human bodies can be traced to antiquity, as discriminating removal of organs was necessary for embalming, which was commonplace in ancient Egypt (see Gen. 50:2–3, 26). Western civil regulation of autopsies can be traced at least to 1504, when the Town Council of Edinburgh granted a charter for postmortem procedures to the British Guild of Surgeons and Barbers (Scott, 5).
19. Scott, 15.
20. This principle was recognized as early as the talmudic period. *Ḥullin* 11b discusses the permissibility of an autopsy to determine whether a murder victim was a *tereifah*—already suffering from a fatal wound or condition, in which case no death penalty was imposed. The prohibition of *nivul hameit* was suspended, as the findings of the autopsy might save the life of the convicted murderer! The earliest clear application of this principle in the responsa literature is in Rabbi Ezekiel Landau's *Noda bi-Yehudah* (*Mahadura Tinyana, Y.D.* 310), in

which he stipulates that autopsy is permissible only if a patient in the same hospital is suffering from the same condition and there would thus be an immediate, lifesaving benefit from the procedure. Rishon L'Tzion Ben Zion Mordecai Uziel ruled more leniently, extending the principle of *pikuaḥ nefesh* to general advances in medical knowledge. The Knesset passed the Law of Anatomy and Pathology in 1953, based on an agreement with the chief rabbinate, although there were later attempts to restore the more stringent guidelines of the *Noda bi-Yehudah*. Rabbi Isaac Klein concludes his responsum on the question of autopsy thus: "If medical science claims that these may save lives . . . it is not only permitted but it is actually a mitzvah."

21. Unterman, 60.
22. Calvin Stiller, M.D., *Lifegifts: The Real Story of Organ Transplants* (Toronto: Stoddart, 1990), 57.
23. UNOS newsletter, Apr. 1995. UNOS manages the National Organ Procurement and Transplant Network (OPTN).
24. "30 Facts about Organ Donation and Transplantation," The National Kidney Foundation (Alexandra, Va.: n.d.), 2.
25. "History of Transplantation and Organ Donation," Hartford Transplant Center (Hartford, Conn.: n.d.), 4.
26. Susan Reed, "Toward Remedying the Organ Shortage," *Technology Review* (Jan. 94): 38.
27. Gina Kolata, "Lungs from Parents Fail to Save Girl, 9, and Doctors Assess Ethics," *New York Times*, 20 May 1991, A-11.
28. Ibid.
29. Ibid., quoting pediatrician/ethicist Dr. John Lantos.
30. Scott, 20.
31. Christine Gorman, "Matchmaker, Find Me a Match," *Time*, 7 June 1991, 61.
32. Paul Terasaki et al., "High Survival Rates of Kidney Transplants from Spousal and Living Unrelated Donors," *New England Journal of Medicine* 333, no. 6 (10 Aug. 1995): 333–36.
33. UNOS newsletter, Apr. 1995.
34. Terasaki et al.
35. Jean-Paul Soulillou, M.D., "Kidney Transplantation from Spousal Donors," *New England Journal of Medicine* 333, no. 6 (10 Aug. 1995): 379–80.
36. Jakobovits, 285.
37. Ibid., 291. Rabbi Jakobovits here draws a distinction between *mitzvah* and *ḥova*. His allusion to "charity" is instructive: charity is a religious "obligation" that "cannot be enforced" at every juncture. One may, to a great extent, determine those occasions on which one will and will not give charity. In the same manner, according to Rabbi Jakobovits's argument, one may elect whether or not to preserve another's life at one's own risk. Every such act of *pikuaḥ nefesh* is a *mitzvah* (fulfillment of a "religious obligation"); not every such opportunity for *pikuaḥ nefesh*, however, is a *ḥova* (mandatory).

38. Scott, 3.
39. See Scott, chap. 1.
40. "30 Facts."
41. See Paul Terasaki, "Getting the Most Mileage from Donated Hearts," *Annals of Thoracic Surgery,* no. 2 (Febr. 1990): 177–78; Verdi J. DiSesa, M.D. et al., "HLA Histocompatibility Affects Cardiac Transplant Rejection and May Provide One Basis for Donor Allocation," ibid., 220–24.
42. See, for example, Rabbi Yekutiel Greenwald, *Kol Bo al Aveilut* (Jerusalem and New York: Feldheim, 1947), 46.
43. See, for example, *Shabbat* 151b, *Niddah* 61b.
44. "History of Transplantation and Organ Donation," 3.
45. Historical synopsis based on Scott, 19ff.
46. See Rabbi Moshe Tendler, *Medical Ethics,* 5th ed. (New York: Federation of Jewish Philanthropies, 1975), 50.
47. "30 Facts," 3.
48. In fact, confidence of long-term success should not be a prerequisite to mandating organ donation; see *O.Ḥ.* 329:4. See also *Shemirat Shabbat Kehilkhatah,* 430, par. 2. However, organ transplants were, early in their history, considered a calculated risk that might actually result in shortening the life of the recipient. At such a juncture, the permissibility of such procedures would still be at issue; mandating donation would certainly have been premature.
49. "Questions about Organ Donation" and "Fact Sheet, Organ/Tissue Donation and Transplantation," Hartford Transplant Center (Hartford, Conn.: n.d.).
50. "30 Facts," 3.
51. Scott, 158–59.
52. The Bantam Medical Dictionary (New York: Bantam Books, 1990), s.v. "Death," 112.
53. Siegel, "Updating the Criteria of Death," *Conservative Judaism* 30, no. 2 (winter 1976).
54. "A Jewish Approach to End-Stage Medical Care," ibid., 43, no. 3 (spring 1991) [chaps. 18–20 of this vol.]; Rabbi Dorff writes of brain death: "If the patient meets the criteria for neurological death, we can, on good authority, consider the person dead within the terms of Jewish law" [chap. 20, p. 351 of this vol.].
55. "A Halakhic Ethic of Care for the Terminally Ill," ibid. [chaps. 16–17 of this vol.].
56. *Responsa of the Va'ad Hahalakhah* of the Rabbinical Assembly of Israel, 5:119–24 (Hebrew).
57. See, for example, "Communications," *Tradition* 28, no. 3 (spring 1994): 94–96. In this letter, written together with ethicist Dr. Fred Rosner, Rabbi Tendler also asserts acceptance of the brain-death criterion by his late father-in-law, Rabbi Moshe Feinstein, until his death the "dean" of American Orthodox halakhic decisors (*posekim*).

58. Ibid., 96. For the primary source on cessation of spontaneous respiration as determinant of death, see *Yoma* 85a.
59. Siegel, 28, citing Rabbi David Novak.
60. Jakobovits, 277.
61. See, for example, Connecticut Anatomical Gift Act, Section 7(b).
62. Jakobovits, 279.
63. Lamm, "A Guide for the Chevra Kadisha."
64. Rabbi Elliot Dorff, "Choosing Life: Aspects of Judaism Affecting Organ Transplantation," a paper prepared for the Park Ridge Center in Chicago [published in *Organ Transplantation: Meanings and Realities,* ed. Stuart J. Youngner, Renée C. Fox, and Laurence J. O'Connell (Madison: University of Wisconsin Press, 1996), 168–93].
65. Unterman, 368.
66. See n. 56 above. Rabbi Golinkin's responsum carries the unanimous assent of the *Va'ad Hahalakhah*. The English précis in the same volume renders this passage as follows: "It is a mitzvah to donate organs after death."
67. Quoted in "Religious Views on Organ Donation and Transplantation," in *American Council on Transplantation Promotional Kit* (Alexandria, Va.: 1989), 21. Rabbi Tendler adds: "It is given that the donor must be brain-dead."
68. Justice Haim Cohn, "The Right to Die in Jewish Law," lecture delivered at the Jewish Theological Seminary, 10 Apr. 1984. For a more extensive treatment of this subject, see Cohn's *Human Rights in Jewish Law* (New York: Ktav, Institute of Jewish Affairs, 1984), 17–19.
69. Unterman, 61. Rabbi Bleich, citing Rabbi Tucazinsky, states: "It is an established verity that, from the point of view of Judaism, man has no proprietary rights to his body" (see Bleich, 126). See also Rabbi Moshe Feinstein, *Iggerot Moshe, Y.D.*, pt. 3, no. 140; and Abraham S. Abraham, M.D., "Euthanasia," in *Medicine and Jewish Law,* ed. Fred Rosner, M.D. (Northvale, N.J.: Jason Aronson, 1990), 124.
70. Unterman, 60.
71. Stiller, 56.
72. Franki Chabalewski, R.N., and M. K. Gaedeke Norris, R.N., "The Gift of Life: Talking to Families about Organ and Tissue Donation," *American Journal of Nursing* (June 1994): 28–30.
73. Stiller, 57–58.
74. "30 Facts," 5.
75. Peter G. Sandstrom, M.D., "What Helps When It Hurts: It Is More Blessed to Give than to Receive," *For Those Who Give and Grieve* (spring 1995): 3–8. This publication is a quarterly newsletter for donor families, published by the National Kidney Foundation. Dr. Sandstrom's wife of twenty-six years served as an organ donor, having been declared brain-dead following a cerebral hemorrhage.
76. Bonnie Langeveld, quoted in Stiller, *Lifegifts,* 94.

77. Sandstrom.
78. Ibid.
79. "Guidelines for Tissue Donation," Northeast Organ Procurement Organization and Tissue Bank (Hartford, Conn.: n.d.).
80. Ibid., 91.
81. Rabbi J. B. Soloveitchik, quoted by Rabbi Jack Reimer, *Jewish Reflections on Death* (New York: Schocken, 1975), 76.
82. Ibid.
83. Stiller, 14.
84. According to UNOS, sixty-nine such procedures were performed in 1994, as compared with 11,108 kidney transplants.
85. Jakobovits, 285.
86. *Proceedings of the Rabbinical Assembly* 17 (1953): 42.
87. "Questions and Answers about Eye Donation and Corneal Transplantation," Eye Bank Association of America (Washington, D.C.: n.d.).
88. Ibid.
89. Ibid.
90. "Transplant Gives Gift of Sight," *Connsight* (newsletter of the Connecticut Eye Bank & Visual Research Foundation) (Jan. 1995): 1.
91. Jakobovits, 286.
92. This characterization of skin grafting and skin banks, as well as all otherwise unattributed quotations in this section, are based on a telephone interview with Dr. Kagan, 18 Dec. 1995.
93. See, for example, Rabbi David Golinkin, *Responsa of the Va'ad Hahalakhah* of the Rabbinical Assembly of Israel, 5:122 (Hebrew); Rabbi Greenwald (45–56) asserts that the prohibition of *hana'ah min hameit* does not apply to skin grafts.
94. While the medical and ethical issues relating to determination of death are increasingly complex, the former rabbinic concern regarding "false death" is no longer compelling.
95. According to the National Kidney Foundation, "most states have passed 'required request' laws, which make it mandatory for the hospital to offer the family the option of donating their deceased loved one's organs and tissues" ("Understanding the Organ Procurement Process").
96. Connecticut's 1988 Anatomical Gift Act ruled that "an anatomical gift not revoked by the donor before death is irrevocable and shall not require consent or concurrence of any person after the death of the donor" [Section 2(h)].
97. See the Rabbinical Assembly's "Jewish Medical Directives for Health Care," ed. Rabbi Aaron L. Mackler and based on papers of Rabbis Elliot Dorff and Avram Reisner [chap. 23 of this vol.]. Through this document, one can indicate the "desire that when I die, any or all of my vital organs and other body parts be donated for the purpose of transplantation. The rest of my remains should

then be buried in a Jewish cemetery in accordance with Jewish law and custom." The document is distributed by United Synagogue Book Service, 155 Fifth Ave., New York, NY 10010.

98. See *Sanhedrin* 73a and Deut. 22:1.
99. A typical system of precedence, as in Connecticut's Anatomical Gift Act: spouse, adult son or daughter, parent, adult sibling, grandparent, guardian [Section 3(a)].
100. Civil law limits the right of a family member to consent to donation, as when "the person proposing to make an anatomical gift knows of a refusal or contrary indications by the decedent." So, too, medical facilities are restricted from accepting organ or tissue donations "if the donee knows of the decedent's refusal or contrary indications." [Connecticut Anatomical Gift Act, Sections 3(a) and 6(c), 1988; based on Uniform Anatomical Gift Act (UAGA), U.S. 1987; see Stiller, Appendix E. According to UNOS and the Department of Health and Human Services, Division of Organ Transplantation, similar provisions have been in force in all fifty states since 1968. For a state-by-state analysis of variations and revisions to the UAGA, see D. Sipes and L. J. McGaw, "UNOS & Uniform Anatomical Gift Act Revisions," *Nephrology News and Issues* (June 1989)]. So, too, the Human Tissue Gift Act of 1986 [Ontario, Canada; similar legislation has been adopted in all Canadian provinces and territories]: "No person shall act upon a consent given under this section if he has reason to believe that it was subsequently withdrawn . . . [or] if he has reason to believe that the person who died or whose death is imminent would have objected thereto" [Stiller, Appendix D]. Such refusal, however, is itself in violation of Jewish law. Under ordinary circumstances, an instruction to violate Jewish law, even by a parent, must be disregarded (see Lev. 19:3, Rashi ad loc., citing *Bava Metzia* 32a; *Y.D.* 240:15). Since such disregard would violate the law of the land, one is, rather, duty-bound to urge revocation of such refusal prior to death, explaining both the extent of the need and the religious imperative. It should be noted, however, that mere "failure to make an anatomical gift . . . is not an objection to the making of an anatomical gift" [Section 3(e)]. Similarly, "A gift to give (or a refusal to give) certain particular parts is not to be taken as a refusal to give other parts. Thus the next of kin may feel free to give additional anatomical gifts" [see Sipes/McGaw, 21; citing Revised UAGA, sections 2(j) and 2(k)].
101. Rabbi Moshe Tendler. See n. 67 above.
102. Stiller, 166–67.
103. Rabbi Isaac Klein, *A Guide to Jewish Religious Practice* (New York: Jewish Theological Seminary, 1979), 275.
104. It is likewise incumbent upon individual rabbis and rabbinic organizations to educate the Jewish community as to the seriousness of this religious obligation.

See, for example, "Resolution on Organ and Tissue Donation," *Proceedings of the Rabbinical Assembly* 52 (1990): 279.

והנשאל הרי זה מגונה שהיה לו לדרוש ברבים

A rabbi whose spiritual charges delay lifesaving action out of ignorance of the Law is disgraced, for he has been remiss in not addressing the matter publicly. (*O.Ḥ.* 328:2, *Magen Avraham* ad loc.)

CHAPTER 29

Organ and Tissue Donation Card*

Joseph H. Prouser, Editor

"There is no greater *kevod hameit* (honor to the deceased) than to bring healing to the living."

Rabbi Isaac Klein

Organ and Tissue Donation

A Project of the Rabbinical Assembly and the United Synagogue of Conservative Judaism

The Need

- Over 42,000 people are waiting for organ transplants.
- Of this number, over 1,400 are children.
- Many thousands more need donated tissues.
- About 25% of these patients will die because an organ will not be available for them.
- Typically, 8 or more such patients die each day.

The Success

Most organ transplants are very successful, either saving lives or greatly improving the quality of life for the recipients.

*Approved by the Rabbinical Assembly Committee on Jewish Law and Standards, Mar. 1996. This document was published by the Rabbinical Assembly in 1996.

One-year success rates range from 70% for livers and lungs, to over 90% for kidneys.

Many of these recipients have had functioning transplants for over 20 years.

Success rates continually improve as better methods to control rejection are identified.

The Process

1. Collect information about donation and transplantation.

2. Familiarize yourself with the Jewish obligation to preserve life.

3. Talk to your family about your decision.

4. Sign the attached donor card in the presence of two witnesses.

5. Carry the signed card in your purse or wallet, with your identification. Include your donor status in any more comprehensive advance medical directives.

Other Information to Help You Decide

The body of an organ and/or tissue donor is always treated with care and respect.

There is no charge to the donor or to his or her family for donation.

Organ and tissue donation will not delay funeral arrangements.

Studies show that organ donation helps to shorten the time needed by members of a bereaved family to recover from their loss.

The traditional Jewish belief in resurrection in no way precludes organ donation.

The Rabbinical Assembly Committee on Jewish Law and Standards has ruled that one is obligated to permit postmortem transplantation of his or her organs in lifesaving medical procedures and that withholding consent for such organ donation is contrary to Jewish law.

The Donor Card

Please detach and give this portion of the card to your family. You may wish to provide copies of this document to various family members.

This is to inform you that I want to be an organ and tissue donor if the occasion ever arises. Please see that my wishes are carried out by informing attending medical personnel that I am a donor. In so doing, you will be acting as my partner and agent in the mitzvah of *pikuaḥ nefesh,* saving lives.

In keeping with the Jewish belief that the human body is God's creation and is thus to be accorded sanctity even after death, please see that all appropriate steps are taken on my behalf to maintain *kevod hameit* (honor to the deceased). As soon as needed organs or tissues are retrieved in accordance with my instructions, see that the rest of my remains are buried in a Jewish cemetery, in accordance with Jewish law and custom.

Thank you.
Signature ______________________________
Date ______________________________
The Rabbinical Assembly, (212) 280-6000

In keeping with the moral and religious teaching of Jewish law, and in an effort to help others, I hereby make this anatomical gift, if medically acceptable, to take effect upon my death. FOR PURPOSES OF TRANSPLANTATION ONLY, I donate:

____a) Any needed organs or tissues
____b) Only the following organs or tissues
(specify which organs or tissues): ______________________
Limitations or special wishes, if any: ______________________
____

Signature of donor: ______________________________
Birth date: ______________________________
City & state where signed: ______________________________
Date ______________________________
Witness: ______________________________
Witness: ______________________________
Must be signed by donor and two witnesses in the presence of each other

---

Additional Reflections

"You shall not stand idly by the blood of your neighbor."
Leviticus 19:16

"Anyone who is able to save a life, but fails to do so, violates this mitzvah."
Maimonides

"It is not merely permissible for a Jew to bequeath his organs for transplantation following his death; it is a mitzvah for him to do so, in order to save one life, or several lives."
Rabbi David Golinkin
Law Committee Chairman, Rabbinical Assembly of Israel;
Dean, Seminary of Jewish Studies, Jerusalem

"The overriding principles of honoring the dead (*kevod hameit*) and saving lives (*pikuaḥ nefesh*) work in tandem. That is, saving a person's life is so sacred a value in Judaism that if a person's organ can be used to save someone else's life, it is actually an honor to the deceased."
Rabbi Elliot N. Dorff
Rector, University of Judaism

"The preservation of human life is obligatory, not optional. Since all conflicting halakhic duties are suspended and human lives are at stake . . . consent must be granted for postmortem organ donation when requested by doctors or hospitals for use in lifesaving transplantation procedures. . . . This applies to the individual in anticipation of his or her own death, as well as to health care proxies or next of kin whenever they are legally empowered to make such decisions on behalf of the deceased."
Rabbi Joseph H. Prouser,
"*Ḥesed* or *Ḥiyuv*?: The Obligation to Preserve Life and the Question of Postmortem Organ Donation," responsum adopted by the Rabbinical Assembly Committee on Jewish Law and Standards [chapter 28 of this volume]

The Rabbinical Assembly, founded in 1901, is the international association of Conservative rabbis. The Assembly actively promotes the cause of Conservative Judaism and works unceasingly to benefit *Kelal Yisra'el;* publishes learned texts, prayer books, and works of Jewish interest; and administers the work of the Committee on Jewish Law and Standards for the Conservative movement.

The Rabbinical Assembly
3080 Broadway
New York, NY 10027
Tel. (212) 280-6000
Fax (212) 749-9166
E-mail: rabassembly@jtsa.edu

I. NEW CHALLENGES

Introduction

The papers in this section address a variety of contemporary challenges in bioethics. A paper by Rabbis Elliot N. Dorff and Aaron L. Mackler, "Responsibilities for the Provision of Health Care," begins by analyzing the limited halakhic precedents that directly address the provision of health care, as well as the more extensive discussion that the tradition provides on analogous issues of responding to the human needs of poverty and the urgent plight of one being held captive. The authors proceed to examine the extent of the responsibilities of patients and families, health care providers, and the community to assure provision of care. They argue that individuals have the responsibility to care for their own health, and the primary responsibility to pay (directly or through insurance) for needed health care. Physicians and other health care professionals have a significant responsibility to make health care available to those who cannot afford standard fees, but at the same time may generally expect to receive compensation and to be able to earn a living. The community bears ultimate responsibility to assure provision of health care that is truly needed (not necessarily all desired, or even all beneficial, care). In contemporary nations such as the United States, this responsibility rests primarily with the national society, including both government and the private sector.

"Curiouser and Curiouser," by Rabbi Avram I. Reisner, concerns the genetic engineering of nonhuman life. He considers whether such genetic engineering is acceptable in itself, and whether the transplantation into a plant or an animal of genes deriving from an animal that is not kosher would render the product not kosher as well. Reisner concludes that genetic engineering as currently practiced is acceptable, and would not render the product not kosher. Questions of possible ecological threat arising from genetic engineering, as well as future hybrids that would radically challenge the current identification of species, are identified as meriting future consideration.

The final paper, by Rabbi Seymour Siegel, addresses the issue of smoking. Siegel considers traditional precedents that mandate the preservation of health and prohibit endangering one's health or assuming excessive risk. In light of contemporary scientific knowledge, "Jewish ethics and Jewish law would prohibit the use of cigarettes."

CHAPTER 30

Responsibilities for the Provision of Health Care*

Elliot N. Dorff and Aaron L. Mackler

She'eilah (Question):

1. To what extent are individual patients and their family members responsible for providing health care?
2. To what extent are physicians and other health care providers responsible for providing health care?
3. What is the extent of the community's responsibilities to provide health care? In contemporary countries such as the United States and Canada, to what extent are these responsibilities of the Jewish community? Of the general society?

Teshuvah (Response):

Providing health care in modern nations is a great and growing challenge. While health care in centuries past was both largely ineffective and inexpensive, in our time medicine can do remarkable things to save and enhance our lives, but all at a considerable cost. How shall we apportion that cost, and how should societies decide what to provide each citizen in the first place?

The provision of health care touches on values and responsibilities that are central to the Jewish tradition. Moreover, in the Jewish under-

*Approved by the Rabbinical Assembly Committee on Jewish Law and Standards, Sept. 1998.

standing, health care involves issues of justice and communal obligation relevant to all societies. While classical Jewish sources presume a context in which medicine was less expensive and less complicated than it is now, the Jewish tradition nevertheless offers important guidance for individual patients, family members, and health care providers in our day.

While traditional sources less directly address the responsibilities of societies in the provision of health care, halakhic guidance on these issues is needed as well. The Jewish tradition understands the provision of needed health care to involve issues of justice and communal obligation that are relevant for all societies. Jews who are citizens of democracies accordingly have at least some degree of responsibility to concern themselves with the justice and well-being of these national societies, including the just and beneficent distribution of health care.

This paper presents three related *teshuvot* on the responsibilities of individuals, health care providers, and communities for the provision of health care. These are preceded by an overview of Jewish understandings of medical care and human needs that will be relied on by each *teshuvah*. The *teshuvot* will provide limited but important guidance from our halakhic tradition. One limit relates to the need for prudential judgment, as well as compassion, in applying these guidelines to complex real-life situations. Another limit reflects the scope of the paper. Additional questions, which might profitably be addressed in future papers (by us or others) include: more specific guidelines for when better care should be chosen (by patients, health care providers, or society) despite increased cost; the role of rabbis as patient advocates in settings such as managed care; asset shifting to family members in order to become eligible for Medicaid; the right of physicians to strike; the priority to be accorded to research relative to current patient care; triage and the allocation of limited resources (such as organs for transplantation); and the selling of organs. Additional issues continue to develop. Despite these limitations, guidance from the tradition is both possible and important.

I. Traditional Views on Health Care and Human Needs

A. The Duty to Provide Medical Care

1. The theological and legal bases for medical intervention. Until the discovery of penicillin in 1938, physicians could do little to cure disease.

Preventive medicine was better developed, although not uniformly practiced, but curative medicine was largely ineffective. At the time when physicians could not do much to heal a sick patient, their services were easily attainable and relatively cheap. When the Talmud says, "The best of physicians should go to hell,"[1] it reflects the fact that patients seldom were cured by physicians, even though doctors held out that hope.

With the advent of antibiotics, other new drug therapies, and new diagnostic and surgical techniques, however, there has been an immense increase in the demand for medical care precisely as it has become much more expensive. This raises not only the "micro" questions of how physicians and patients should treat a given person's disease, but also the "macro" questions of how we, as a society, should arrange for the medical care to be distributed. On both levels, the ultimate question is the Kantian one: no one has a duty to do what humanly cannot be done, but once we gain the ability to do *x*, the moral question arises as to whether we should. On the macro level, this becomes the question of how much medical care should be provided to everyone in society as part of our collective duty to care for one another.

According to Jewish law, we have the clear duty to try to heal, and this duty devolves upon both the physician and the society. This, theologically, is somewhat surprising. After all, since God announces in the Bible that He will inflict illness for sin and, conversely, that He is our healer,[2] one might think that medicine is an improper human intervention in God's decision to inflict illness.

The Rabbis were aware of this line of reasoning, but they counteracted it by pointing out that God Himself authorizes us to heal. In fact, they maintain, God requires us to heal. They found that authorization and that imperative in various biblical verses, including Exodus 21:19–20, according to which an assailant must ensure that his victim is "thoroughly healed," and Deuteronomy 22:2 ("And you shall restore the lost property to him"). The Talmud understands the Exodus verse as giving "permission for the physician to cure." On the basis of an extra letter in the Hebrew text of the Deuteronomy passage, the Talmud declares that that verse includes the obligation to restore another person's body as well as his property, and hence, there is an obligation to come to the aid of someone in a life-threatening situation. On the basis of Leviticus 19:16 ("Nor shall you stand idly by the blood of your fellow"), the Talmud expands the obligation to provide medical aid to encompass expenditure of financial resources for this purpose.[3]

In addition to these halakhic grounds for providing health care, there is an important theological underpinning. God is to be our model whom we are to imitate. As the Talmud (*Sotah* 14a) teaches:

> "Follow the Lord your God" (Deut. 13:5). What does this mean? Is it possible for a mortal to follow God's presence? The verse means to teach us that we should follow the attributes of the Holy One, praised be He. As He clothes the naked, you should clothe the naked. The Bible teaches that the Holy One visited the sick; you should visit the sick.

We praise God in the *Amidah:* "You support the falling, heal the ailing, free the fettered."[4] Accordingly, we are called upon to help others and provide health care to those in need.

While each Jew must come to the aid of a person in distress, and while the assailant has the direct duty to cure his victim, Jewish law recognized the expertise involved in medical care and thus here, as in similar cases, the layman may hire the expert to carry out his obligations. Experts, in turn, have special obligations because of their expertise. Thus, Joseph Karo (1488–1575) says: "The Torah gave permission to the physician to heal; moreover, this is a religious precept and is included in the category of saving life, and if the physician withholds his services, it is considered as shedding blood."[5]

That the community shares in this responsibility together with the physician becomes clear from several sources. So, for example, the Talmud describes ten services that a city must provide to make it fit for a Jewish scholar to live there, and the services of a physician is one of them:

> A scholar [of Torah] should not reside in a city where [any of] the following ten things is missing: (1) a court of justice that [has the power to] impose flagellation and decree monetary penalties; (2) a *tzedakah* [charity] fund collected by [at least] two people and distributed by [at least] three; (3) a synagogue; (4) public baths; (5) a privy; (6) one who performs circumcisions [a *moheil*]; (7) a physician; (8) a scribe [who also functions as a notary]; (9) a [kosher] butcher; and (10) a schoolmaster. Rabbi Akiba is quoted as including also several kinds of fruit [in the list] because they are beneficial to one's eyesight.[6]

Since each Jewish community needed a rabbi to interpret Jewish law and to teach the tradition, this list of requirements for having a rabbi effectively makes it every Jewish community's responsibility to furnish medical services. In the Middle Ages, Naḥmanides (1194–1270) offers an additional rationale for this communal duty, basing it on the commandment in the Torah, "You shall love your neighbor as yourself," and reasoning that just as you would want medical care when you need it, so you need to provide it for others when they need it.[7]

2. *Prevention in preference to cure.* Illness is debilitating. In addition to any physical pain involved, sickness brings with it the frustration of not being able to pursue our normal tasks in life. We feel shaken in our sense of physical and psychological integrity, our sense of safety and security, and, indeed, in our sense of ourselves.

Illness is also degrading. When sick, we feel diminished as human beings. As much as we need to divorce ourselves from a common American evaluation of people in terms of their skills and accomplishments, recognizing instead the inherent value in every human being, when sick we inevitably feel that the divine aspect of power has been reduced in us. It also can be humiliating to have to be dependent on others for help in doing the everyday tasks of living. One feels like an infant.

These characteristics of illness make it preferable to prevent it rather than to cure it once it strikes. There are, of course, pragmatic considerations as well. It is still true today that "an ounce of prevention is worth a pound of cure," and sometimes, as is currently the case with regard to AIDS, we cannot cure a disease at all, but we can prevent it. Historically, this was true for most diseases, for doctors were not able to cure very many, but their knowledge of preventive techniques was in some ways quite sophisticated. The fact that in practice, we can prevent disease more easily and more economically than we can cure it, though, is not the whole of the story; we must also prefer prevention to cure to ward off the debilitating and degrading aspects of disease.

B. Precedents and Analogies for the Provision of Health Care: Poverty and the Redemption of Captives

Halakhic sources are clear that members of the community are obligated to perform the mitzvah of *bikur ḥolim,* visiting the sick. Even if our ancestors did not have many medications to cure diseases, they knew better than we that cure depends crucially upon the patient's will to live. Disease is inherently isolating and degrading. Those who visit the sick and engage them in adult conversations therefore contribute immeasurably to their recovery. This is especially crucial in our own time, when patients with serious illnesses are often treated not in the familiar surroundings of home, but rather in the strange, antiseptic environment of the hospital. Our communal responsibility for health care demands our time and caring. In addition to conversation and prayer—attending to the spiritual needs of the sick individual—visitors are expected to care for the tangible needs of the patient as well.[8]

Some authorities also articulate a general expectation that the community as a whole will contribute to the healing of ill individuals.[9] Traditional sources, though, have relatively little discussion of the extent of this responsibility. This is not surprising, as both the effectiveness and costs of medical treatments were much more limited in past centuries than they are today. Traditional sources, however, have more extensive discussion of the extent of the community's responsibility to provide for individuals in other contexts, of which two are especially relevant to health care: *tzedakah,* support for the poor; and *pidyon shevuyim,* redeeming captives.[10]

1. *Poverty legislation (tzedakah).* Halakhah understands the responsibility of *tzedakah* (lit., "justice") to entail enforceable obligations for the community and its members. Codifying traditions going back to the Talmud, the *Shulḥan Arukh* states that "each individual is obligated to give *tzedakah.* . . . If one gives less than is appropriate, the courts may administer lashes until he gives according to the assessment, and the courts may go to his property in his presence and take the amount that it is appropriate for him to give."[11]

Halakhic authorities seek to specify the minimum levels of support required by *tzedakah* from the perspectives of both giver and recipient. The general rule is that one pay a tenth of one's income (including acquired capital) for *tzedakah.* Giving one-fifth represents "choice" fulfillment of the obligation, and one should give "according to the needs of the poor," even above one-fifth of one's income, if one can afford to do so. Many authorities add that one must give at least one-fifth when one can afford to do so without difficulty and there is pressing need, and one must give whatever is required in cases immediately involving the saving of life. In other cases, giving more than one-fifth is generally seen as commendable, but not obligatory.[12]

The limits on the redistribution of resources required by *tzedakah* depend most importantly on the needs of the poor. The exact determination of needs is debatable, but a broad consensus does emerge from the tradition, centered on the idea of lack, or that which is missing. The Talmud sets parameters in its exegesis of Deut. 15:8: "You shall surely open your hand to him, and shall surely lend him sufficient for his need/lack, according as he needs/lacks" (*dei maḥsoro asher yeḥsar lo*). The Talmud cites an earlier baraita: " 'Sufficient for his lack'—you are commanded to support him, and you are not commanded to enrich him; 'according as he lacks'—even a horse on which to ride, and a servant to run in front of him."[13] As Maimonides paraphrases the guideline, "according to that which is lacking for the poor person, you are commanded to give him. . . . You are commanded to fill in for his lack, but you are not commanded to enrich him."[14] Note that *tzedakah,* and by implication, the distribution of health care, only requires meeting the needs of all members of society, not providing anything that would be of benefit. At the same time, as the second half of the baraita suggests, we must be prepared to construe these needs broadly.

The general standard against which lacks are evaluated is largely implicit. Traditional sources, however, provide a list of paradigmatic cases:

> If it is appropriate to give him bread, they give him bread; if dough, they give him dough; . . . if to feed him, they feed him. If he is not married and wants to take a wife, they enable him to marry; they rent a house for him, and provide a bed and furnishings.[15]

A woman who wishes to be married is similarly provided with a dowry. Clothing and other basic needs are implicit. Moses Isserles notes that the provision of such needs is primarily the responsibility of the community.[16] The basic requirement of *tzedakah* is thus to provide food, clothing, and shelter, and with these the opportunity for family life.[17] Yet even the meeting of other needs may be obligatory, as the baraita's discussion of providing a horse at least rhetorically reminds us.[18]

Extrapolating from these general requirements would require the provision of a "decent minimum" of health care, sufficient to meet the needs of each member of the community. Such needs could generally be interpreted in a fairly basic and objective way, though special needs of individuals may in some cases be considered as well.

2. *Redemption from captivity (pidyon shevuyim).* The redemption of captives, those captured by slave traders or unjustly held as prisoners, provides a precedent even more closely analogous to at least some types of medical care. This category of acute needs is seen to take precedence even over general obligations of *tzedakah*. Funds collected or allocated for any other purpose may be diverted to securing the release of captives when necessary. Maimonides, for example, states that "the redemption of captives takes precedence over the support of the poor, and there is no greater obligatory precept than the redemption of captives." He offers the explanation that "a captive falls in the category of the hungry and the thirsty and the naked, and stands in danger of his life."[19] Health care shares these characteristics that justify the priority accorded to *pidyon shevuyim:* both concern individuals who are suffering and may be in immediate danger. Further, both categories entail special needs that vary greatly among individuals. Jewish law and ethics understand the community to have a fundamental obligation to save lives whenever possible, diverting funds from other projects as required.[20]

II. Patients and Family Members

She'eilah 1:

To what extent are individual patients and their family members responsible for providing health care?

Teshuvah:

Individuals bear some of the responsibility for maintaining their health. This begins with taking steps to prevent illness in the first place. While curative medicine in past centuries was not well developed, our ancestors knew a great deal about preventive medicine. Thus, Maimonides, for example, asserts a positive obligation "to avoid anything that is injurious to the body, and to conduct oneself in ways that promote health." He already states the importance of proper diet, exercise, hygiene, and sleep. Conversely, he repeats the Talmud's prohibition of abusing our bodies through unhealthy habits.[21] In carrying out our primary duty to provide for our own health care, we in our time need to pay heed to those ancient prescriptions for keeping ourselves healthy so that we can carry out our God-given mission to help others and to fix the world.

When one needs the aid of health care professionals, the individual must bear at least some of the financial burden. Thus, the *Shulḥan Arukh* rules: "If someone is taken captive and he has property but does not want to redeem himself, we redeem him [with the money that his property will bring] against his will."[22] While this source speaks of redemption from captivity and not health care, the duty to redeem captives is based on the danger to their lives in captivity. As argued above, this rule about financing a person's freedom is thus a reasonable source for determining whether an individual has a financial responsibility for one's own health care as well, and the ruling makes it clear that one does.

In traditional Jewish sources, these requirements are described as the duties of a man toward his own health care, but a man's responsibility to pay for the health care of his wife is even clearer, for among the obligations that a man assumes in marriage is the medical care of his wife.[23] Similarly, for her redemption, the *Shulḥan Arukh* rules: "If a man and his wife are in captivity, his wife takes precedence over him. The court invades his property to redeem her. Even if he stands and shouts, 'Do not redeem her from my property!' we do not listen to him."[24] Thus, a man has a clear duty to provide medical care for his wife, especially—but not exclusively—when her life is threatened in captivity or, presumably, in some other way.

He has the same duty vis-à-vis his children and other relatives if they cannot care for themselves. Once again, the precedent for this comes from the laws of redemption from captivity:

> A father must redeem his son if the father has money but the son does not. Gloss: And the same is true for one relative redeeming another, the closer relative comes first, for all of them may not enrich themselves and thrust the [redemption of] their relatives on the community.[25]

In our own, more egalitarian, society, these sources would presumably mean that spouses of either gender have responsibility for the health care of each other and of their children. In carrying out that responsibility, one may not preserve the family fortune and make the Jewish community or government pay for one's own health care or that of one's spouse or children, except to the extent that the government itself makes provision for all sick, elderly citizens in programs such as Medicare without restrictions as to a person's income or estate. Absent such provisions in the law, one must provide for one's own health care and for that of one's relatives. One might do that by using one's own assets or through buying a health insurance policy, either privately or through one's employment. One may only, according to these sources, call on public aid when and if one qualifies for aid to the poor through programs such as Medicaid.[26]

Patients who have no resources to pay for health care may accept public assistance to procure it. In fact, they must do so, for to refuse needed care is to endanger their lives, which is, for Jewish law, tantamount to committing suicide. Still, the *Shulḥan Arukh* strongly condemns those who use public funds for their health care when they do not need to do so, and it appreciates those who postpone calling upon the public purse for as long as possible:

> Anyone who does not need to take from the *tzedakah* fund and deceives the community and takes will not die until he does indeed need *tzedakah* from others. And whoever needs to take such that he cannot live unless he takes—for example, an elderly person or a sick person or a suffering person—but he forces himself not to take is like one who sheds blood [namely, his own], and he is liable for his own life, and his pain is only the product of sin and transgression. But anyone who needs to take [*tzedakah*] but puts himself instead into a position of pain and pushes off the time [when he takes *tzedakah*] and lives a life of pain so that he will not burden the community will not die until he sustains others, and about him Scripture says, "Blessed is the man who trusts in God."[27]

Conversely, unless a given drug or medical procedure is so scarce that the government has put limits on who may obtain it even with their own money, individual patients who have the money to afford something that the government or their private plan does not provide may decide to use it to pay for the drug or procedure privately. Thus, the *Shulḥan Arukh*, following earlier formulations of Jewish law, puts a limit on the amount of money a community may spend on redeeming any given captive in order to depress the market in captives and ultimately to deter kidnapping altogether. But even though that is a distinct social good, a given individual is free to spend as much of his own funds as he wishes to redeem himself or his relative: "We do not redeem captives for more than their worth out of considerations of fixing the world, so that the enemies will not dedicate themselves to take them captive. An individual, however, may redeem himself for as much as he would like."[28] This is unfair in one sense, but it is only the unfairness built into any capitalistic system, and Jewish sources do not require that Jews use socialism as their form of government or their rule for distributing and charging goods. In the provision of health care, as in other areas, the Jewish tradition does not enforce a ceiling limiting the resources that one may spend for one's own benefit; rather, it seeks to establish a floor that, as a minimum, assures at least the basic needs for all.

Conclusion to she'eilah 1. Individuals and family members have the responsibility to care for their own health, and the primary responsibility to pay (directly or through insurance) for health care needed by themselves or by family members. When they cannot do so, they may and should avail themselves of publicly funded programs to acquire the health care they need. In any case, one should seek to prevent illness rather than wait to cure an illness that has already occurred.

III. Physicians and Other Health Care Personnel

She'eilah 2:

To what extent are physicians and other health care providers responsible for providing health care?

Teshuvah:

The same general principles would apply to the societal obligation for provision of health care. To begin with the physician: halakhic sources, as noted above, discuss in general terms the mandate for the individual physician to heal and for the individual patient to seek healing.[29] While physicians have definite obligations toward their patients, they generally may expect to receive appropriate fees.

Nonetheless, Jewish medical writers through the ages have urged physicians to treat the poor without charge. The Talmud commends as an ideal the practice of Abba, the therapeutic bloodletter. He had his patients deposit their payments in a box so that those who could afford to pay could pay, and those who could not afford to do so could receive treatment without embarrassment. In some cases, he would give a needy patient money for sustenance during recuperation.[30] In the nineteenth century, Rabbi Eleazar Fleckeles ruled that free care of the poor was not only a virtue to be expected from a benevolent physician, but a halakhic obligation enforceable by a (religious) court.[31] While there are limits on the extent of such obligation in contemporary societies, as discussed below, the strong expectation that physicians will provide health care that is needed is clear.

While traditional sources focus on the responsibility of providing health care for the needy, in our own day these questions no longer affect the poor alone. Most people simply do not have (and cannot borrow) enough money to pay for some of the new procedures. The size of the problem makes even conscientious and morally sensitive physicians think that any individual effort on their part to resolve this issue is useless. Moreover, the costs that they themselves assumed in gaining a medical education must somehow be repaid—to say nothing of malpractice insurance, overhead for their offices and for the hospitals in which they practice, staff, and the like. The question of paying for medical care in our society therefore becomes a critical issue.

Traditional Jewish communities that expected physicians to treat those in need without pay customarily offered tax benefits and other privileges in return. In some cases, the community would directly hire physicians to provide for the treatment of the poor and others. While unpaid treatment of the poor was the norm, the Portuguese-Jewish community in Hamburg in 1666 declined the offer of a physician to treat the poor with no charge, on grounds that "it is not fitting to engage someone without salary; for the payment will force the doctor to be [o]n time when called in by a patient."[32] Along the same lines, the Talmud asserts that a physician who heals for nothing is worth nothing.[33]

Still, the example of Abba, the bleeder, and the stipulation in the *Shulḥan Arukh* that withholding medical care is akin to murdering someone both establish that in Jewish law, physicians have a primary duty to provide medical care. This would make systems of managed care, which discourage doctors from providing needed and effective care, Jewishly illegitimate, or at least suspect. Capitation, for instance, gives doctors a sum of money for each patient per year regardless of the amount of care they provide; that makes it economically disadvantageous to doctors to treat patients extensively, for the more time they spend with a patient, the less they earn per patient. Such a system can only be reconciled with the fundamental Jewish duty of physicians to care for their patients if there is some way to offset the economic pressure that mitigates against treatment so as to guarantee that doctors will nevertheless provide good care. Modifications of the physicians' professional code of ethics or government regulation may be part of what is needed to spell out accepted standards of care, and—however the standards are established and announced—capitation would inevitably require more frequent peer review than now occurs. If such measures proved unsuccessful in counterbalancing the economic pressures of capitation so as to guarantee a reasonable level of care, Jewish principles would forbid capitation as a violation of the duty to provide needed medical care.[34]

In addition, the underlying duty of physicians to provide care means that they bear at least some responsibility for making health care available to those who cannot afford their normal fees. This would impose on doctors the obligation to do some work at reduced rates or for free. Like other people, though, they have a right to earn a living, so the community and the individual patient must also share a portion of the financial burden.

In times past, all medical procedures were administered by two types of personnel, the physician and the surgeon. It is only in recent times that other health care professions have arisen as separate entities. Thus, classical Jewish sources do not speak about nurses, physician assistants, health care technicians, social workers concentrating in health care, and so on. One would expect, though, that the sources discussed above governing physicians would apply, *mutatis mutandis,* to other health care personnel as well. That is, such personnel, on this analysis, would have the positive obligation to provide some *pro bono* and emergency services, but that obligation would be limited so that they could earn a fair living. The remainder of the cost must be provided by the community and by the individual patient.

Conclusion to she'eilah 2. Physicians and other health care professionals must treat patients in case of emergency, and they have some responsibility more generally to make health care available to those who cannot afford their normal fees. At the same time, health care professionals legitimately may expect compensation for their efforts and expenses, and should be able to earn a living.

IV. The Community

She'eilah 3:

What is the extent of the community's responsibilities to provide health care? In contemporary countries such as the United States and Canada, to what extent are these responsibilities of the Jewish community? Of the general society?

Teshuvah:

A. Responsibilities

As communities have grown larger and the provision of health care more expensive, the role of the community in assuring provision of needed care has become more central.[35] While accepting Fleckeles' nineteenth-century ruling on the individual physician's obligation to provide care, the contemporary authority, Rabbi Eliezer Yehudah Waldenberg, notes problems in enforcement even within a traditional Jewish community today. The logical basis for the ruling, he observes, is that when an individual cannot afford to pay for medical care, the court, on behalf of the community, acquires the obligation for that person's healing. Because the court has responsibility for the health care of that individual, it has the power to force the physician to treat the individual. The community's responsibility for the care of that person logically falls on the physician more than on anyone else, because of the physician's special knowledge and ability.[36]

Waldenberg asserts that while a virtuous physician is expected to provide charitable free care for the poor, this can only be enforced as a legal responsibility in a community that has just one physician. In contemporary communities with more than one physician, possibilities for meeting the community's obligation to assure provision of health care include appropriating money from the general welfare (*tzedakah*) fund, conducting a special financial appeal, and equitably apportioning cases to all physicians for treatment on a *pro bono* basis. The most praiseworthy option, however, is to establish a special fund for the payment of physician fees for treatment of the poor.[37]

The central point of Waldenberg's analysis is consistent with the tradition's understanding of the importance of health care, and the general guidance provided by discussion of *tzedakah* and *pidyon shevuyim*. If an individual cannot afford to pay for needed health care, the obligation to provide for that care devolves on the community as a whole. The community may legitimately choose any of a variety of ways to meet this responsibility, so long as the responsibility is met in every case of need. While it is commendable for a physician to treat the poor without charge, and while a virtuous physician will do so routinely as part of his or her practice and always when an emergency arises, such treatment represents a halakhic obligation and requirement of justice only when the community has fairly designated the physician as responsible for fulfilling the community's obligation. Preferred ways to meet this communal responsibility for the care of the poor include a societal health-payment program, perhaps analogous to Medicare or national health insurance, or direct government provision of medical care.

The standard for the amount of care to be assured is that of need. Patients are not entitled to, and society is not obligated to provide, all care that is desired, all care that might offer some benefit, or all care that anyone else in the society receives. The community is obligated, however, to assure access to all care that is needed by a patient to lead a reasonably full life.[38] While identifying "needed" treatments will change with developing medical practice and vary among individual cases, in general it would be treatment that would be effective in sustaining life, curing disease, restoring health, or improving function.[39]

Two areas of health care require special mention. First, in distribution of health care, as in other areas, halakhah would understand health and health care to include mental as well as physical health.[40] Second, the community's responsibilities to provide health care are not limited to curative care; they include preventive care as well.[41] In the societies of times past, the preventive medical care that was available was relatively limited in cost, so the need to allocate significant resources for such care did not seem to have arisen. In our own time, the provision of some preventive care, such as vaccination and prenatal care, is mandatory on two grounds. First, since prevention is often less expensive than cure, and since society is ultimately obligated to provide all curative care needed, communities should provide significant preventive care as a cost-effective way to meet that duty.[42] Second, since prevention avoids the degradation of illness, communities must provide preventive care for theological and humanitarian consideration as well.

B. Limits

There are some limits. The responsibility to provide for the redemption of captives may also be limited when the captive is responsible for his own predicament, though only in the most extreme cases. The *Shulḥan*

Arukh considers the case of one who sells himself into captivity, or is held prisoner as a result of defaulting on a loan. The community must pay to free the captive if this is the first or second time that he has brought about his own captivity, but the community need not make such payments after the third such occurrence. In case of immediate threat to the captive's life, though, even the captive responsible for his own captivity must be rescued.[43] By analogy, those who make choices (in lifestyle or health care) that turn out to be unfortunate or irresponsible thereby attenuate their claims to the community's support, but do not forfeit all such claims. Individuals who do not purchase health insurance when they are able to do so fail to live up to their responsibilities. Still, they remain persons of infinite value, created in God's image. The community must continue to provide some care even for those responsible for their own misfortune, in this or other ways, especially in cases involving threats to life. Formulating an equitable public policy within these parameters is a complex challenge. Possible alternatives include universal national health insurance, and requirements for individuals to purchase catastrophic health insurance coverage.

A more general limitation is noted on the financial extent of the obligation to redeem captives. "One does not redeem captives for more than their monetary worth" as slaves. This provision dates back to the Mishnah, and the Talmud debates whether such a limit could be justified as protecting the community from onerous burdens or as "improving the world" (*tikun olam*) by avoiding incentives for future hostage taking. The *Shulḥan Arukh,* following Maimonides and other codifiers, accepts only the latter justification.[44] Resources to help an individual with exceptional needs may be limited to generally accepted levels when this limitation is necessary to avoid endangering others. By analogy, it could be argued that a community's paying for extremely expensive experimental treatments, such as an artificial heart, might significantly weaken the health care system as a whole, thereby depriving future patients of needed care. In such cases, a community may be justified in limiting expenditures to the range reasonably expected by most patients.

Moreover, the community must use its resources wisely. The Talmud lists ten services that a community must provide (as noted above), and in our own day, there are undoubtedly others that the non-Jewish government took care of in talmudic and medieval times but that are vital to any society—services such as defense, civil peace, and roads and bridges. The community must balance its commitments to health care against its responsibility to provide other services, whether those on the Talmud's list of ten or others that arise and are deemed necessary, and it must ensure that those who receive public assistance for their health care deserve that assistance.

Such limits should not be invoked too quickly, however. Very few interventions require such extraordinary expenditures that their provision would not only be burdensome for society, but would endanger the health care system. More basically, possible limits to intervention must always be weighed against the value of human life and healing, and the injunction that a physician who fails to provide needed care is considered as one who sheds blood. In the case of redemption of captives (*pidyon shevuyim*), some authorities state that even excessive ransoms may (or must) be paid in cases of immediate danger to a hostage, despite the importance of saving future lives.[45]

Similarly, although the talmudic consideration of a limit on payments for the redemption of captives in order to avoid an onerous burden on the community has been accorded little weight by halakhic authorities, it might be argued that modern medical technology has revived the need for consideration of such limits on societal obligations, at least in extreme cases involving very expensive and questionably effective procedures. The relevance of such limits to contemporary nations such as the United States requires further consideration and empirical research. Given the relative affluence of such countries, though, much more could be done for the poorest and most disadvantaged without approaching the above limits on minimal obligations. In particular, these societies do not face the absolute poverty that would force them to allow otherwise preventable deaths by failing to provide adequate health care (or by failing to provide adequate food, clothing, or shelter). While there is some room for consideration of limits on expenditures, the strong presumption of the Jewish tradition is for provision of the resources necessary to preserve and save life.[46]

C. Responsibilities of the Jewish and General Communities

The community has a responsibility to provide needed health care to all its members. But what counts as a community—the United States as a whole? a synagogue? a metropolitan area's general or Jewish population? And, however we define "community," what are the obligations to those outside the community?

Jewish sources do not provide an unambiguous position. Our own best reading of them is that all members of the community and, in fact, all humans have equal intrinsic value before God.[47] From this point of view, one relates to each person as a being of value whom one must respect. Yet one additionally stands in a variety of special relationships with some persons, such as family members and fellow citizens. These special relationships of care and commitment entail particular responsibilities in varying degrees. For example, it may be appropriate for citizens of the United States to accord some degree of priority to fellow citizens over the needy in other nations or even over those living in the United States illegally.

Consistent with this view, halakhic sources picture the individual's responsibilities as radiating in concentric circles, with responsibility most acute for those to whom one stands in closest relation. Accordingly, if an individual's resources to meet the needs of others are limited, priority should be given to members of one's household before others, and to inhabitants of one's own city before those of other cities. While greatest resources should be devoted to those with whom one stands in closest relationship, however, one must offer some degree of support to those who are more distant as well.[48]

Some degree of responsibility would extend to those beyond the community. Throughout most of Jewish history, Jews have formed independent or semiautonomous communities; only in recent centuries have Jews been equal citizens in societies of nation-states. For most classical sources, then, the "community" refers to the Jewish community. Even from this vantage point, classical sources call on Jews to support the needy outside the Jewish community along with needy Jews, "for the sake of the paths of peace."[49]

In our own day, Jewish federation councils coordinate the fund-raising activities of the Jewish community, so the federation may be seen as the communal agency that, according to the sources, should be responsible for providing for health care. Federations, however, do not have the taxing or police powers of pre-Enlightenment Jewish communities, so federations are not completely parallel to the communal authorities of the past. In any case, the cost of health care today is far beyond the resources of federations to supply. Such costs are more appropriately borne by insurance companies and governments, as is indeed the case.

The real question is whether federations should provide some support for Jewish hospitals as an expression of the Jewish communal duty to provide health care. Jewish communities in the early decades of the twentieth century sponsored hospitals to provide places where Jewish doctors could work, because they were barred from practicing in many non-Jewish hospitals. When that form of anti-Semitism diminished in mid-century, Jewish federations continued to sponsor hospitals in order to provide kosher food and other Jewish amenities to Jewish patients, and also as the Jewish contribution to the general community's health care. In our day, the cost of health care is far beyond the resources of the Jewish community, and there are many other important claims on the Jewish community's resources in the areas of Jewish education and social services. Individual federations will need to judge whether any of the former grounds for Jewish support of hospitals still hold or whether there are new reasons for the Jewish community to support health care and, if so, how those resources should be balanced against other needs of the community. In any case, because the federation is not the full equivalent of the communal governing authorities of the past, and because unmet health care costs far exceed those of the past, Jewish law would not require federations to support hospitals or other forms of health care, leaving it to the judgment of the federation to balance this communal activity against the others that would benefit the community. Ultimate responsibility for the meeting of health care needs is that of the nation's government and health care system as a whole.

According to the Jewish model of *tzedakah* and its application to the distribution of health care, the community has concrete responsibilities to provide all needed health care to all within the community. Responsibilities to those outside the community are less strictly enforceable, but still significant. By implication, national communities would have an obligation to provide all needed health care to those within the community: to all citizens without question, probably to all residing legally in the country, and perhaps even to those in the country illegally. After all, as Rabbi Eugene Borowitz observes, the Bible's creation story, depicting all of humanity as descendants of a common ancestor, suggests that "all human beings have familial obligations to one another."[50]

One basic issue in current discussions of the allocation of health care resources is whether contemporary nations are the types of communities that have obligations toward their members. Especially in the United States, the distribution of health care is often debated as if providing access to health care were a matter of charity and benevolence.

Even on these grounds, it would seem that enlightened self-interest would provide a compelling reason for affording universal access to needed health care. A vision of the nation as a community would make a stronger claim. The Jewish position developed above would make a claim yet stronger, based upon our duty to pursue justice and to love and care for our neighbor and, indeed, the stranger.

Specific claims of halakhah are not binding on secular nations, of course. Jewish understandings of justice should not (and could not) be imposed monolithically, but should contribute to a national dialogue in which diverse philosophical, religious, and other views would be represented. In the Jewish understanding developed in this paper, securing access to all health care that is needed represents a matter of foundational justice. And whatever the differences between traditional Jewish societies and contemporary countries such as the United States and Canada, all societies are appropriately responsible for the achievement of foundational justice. Jews who are citizens of democratic societies have at least some degree of responsibility to support general institutions that will assure the provision of needed care, through lobbying, social action, and other means.

From the time of the Bible, Judaism has understood social justice as both morally obligatory and crucial to national security. And since that time, Jews have been urged to seek the peace and well-being (*shalom*) of the nations in which they live.[51] If such counsel was given even for the Babylonia of Jeremiah's time, the responsibility of Jewish citizens of contemporary nations, in which Jews are full and free citizens, to lobby for sufficient health care for all citizens (and possibly all residents) is much stronger.[52]

Conclusions to she'eilah 3. Jewish law requires that people be provided with needed health care, at least a "decent minimum" that preserves life and meets other basic needs, including some amount of preventive care. The responsibility to assure this provision is shared among individuals and families, physicians and other health care providers, and the community.

The community bears ultimate responsibility to assure provision of needed health care for individuals who cannot afford it, as a matter of justice as well as a specific halakhic obligation. The "community" that bears that responsibility in our day is the national society, through its government, health care institutions, insurance companies, and private enterprise. Jewish citizens should support (by lobbying and other means) general societal institutions that will fulfill this responsibility. The Jewish community, though its federations, synagogues, and other institutions, must assess whether and to what extent it should support hospitals and other forms of health care. It should balance that purpose against its commitment to other important Jewish needs, such as Jewish education and social services, in light of contemporary patterns of funding health care.

The guarantee of provision of needed health care does not extend to all treatment that is desired, or even all that might provide some benefit. Even needed treatment might be limited when it is so extraordinarily expensive that its provision would deprive other patients of needed care. Still, possible limits to interventions must be weighed against the value of human life and healing, and the injunction that a physician who fails to provide needed health care is considered as one who sheds blood.

Summary of Conclusions

1. Jewish law requires that people be provided with needed health care, at least a "decent minimum" that preserves life and meets other basic needs, including some amount of preventive care. The responsibility to assure this provision is shared among individuals and families, physicians and other health care providers, and the community.

2. Individuals and family members have the responsibility to care for their own health, and the primary responsibility to pay (directly or through insurance) for health care needed by themselves or by family members. When they cannot do so, they may and should avail themselves of publicly funded programs to acquire the health care they need. In any case, one should seek to prevent illness rather than wait to cure an illness that has already occurred.

3. Physicians and other health care professionals must treat patients in case of emergency, and they have some responsibility more generally to make health care available to those who cannot afford their normal fees. At the same time, health care professionals legitimately may expect compensation for their efforts and expenses, and should be able to earn a living.

4. The community bears ultimate responsibility to assure provision of needed health care for individuals who cannot afford it, as a matter

of justice as well as a specific halakhic obligation. The "community" that bears that responsibility in our day is the national society, through its government, health care institutions, insurance companies, and private enterprise. Jewish citizens should support (by lobbying and other means) general societal institutions that will fulfill this responsibility. The Jewish community, though its federations, synagogues, and other institutions, must assess whether and to what extent it should support hospitals and other forms of health care. It should balance that purpose against its commitment to other important Jewish needs, such as Jewish education and social services, in light of contemporary patterns of funding health care.

5. The guarantee of provision of needed health care does not extend to all treatment that is desired, or even all that might provide some benefit. Even needed treatment might be limited when it is so extraordinarily expensive that its provision would deprive other patients of needed care. Still, possible limits to interventions must be weighed against the value of human life and healing, and the injunction that a physician who fails to provide needed health care is considered as one who sheds blood.

Notes

1. M. *Kiddushin* 4:14 (82b). Exactly why "the best of physicians should go to hell" is disputed. Rashi suggests several reasons: (1) being unafraid of illness, they do not appropriately adjust the diet of the sick and feed them instead food for healthy people; (2) again, because they do not fear illness and sometimes cure it, they are haughty before the Almighty; (3) their treatment is sometimes fatal; and, (4) on the other hand, by refusing treatment to the poor, they may indirectly cause their death. Hanokh Albeck, in his commentary to the Mishnah ([Tel Aviv: Dvir, 1958], 3:330), suggests that it is because they are not careful in their craft and thus cause sick people to die (similar to Rashi's first and third explanations combined). Philip Blackman suggests in his commentary to the Mishnah ([New York: Judaica Press, 1963], 3:484 n. 27) that the subject of this curse is not doctors per se, but "one who pretends to be a specialist and in consequence brings disaster to his patients." The Soncino translation and commentary to the Talmud ([London: Soncino, 1936], Nashim, 4:423 n. 9, citing the *Jewish Chronicle*) says that "it is probable that it is not directed against healing as such, but against the 'advanced' views held by physicians in those days."
2. God inflicts illness for sin: Lev. 26:16; Deut. 28:22, 59–60. God as our healer: e.g., Exod. 15:26; Deut. 32:39; Isa. 19:22, 57:18–19; Jer. 30:17, 33:6; Hos. 6:1; Ps. 103:2–3, 107:20; Job 5:18.
3. B. *Bava Kamma* 85a; B. *Sanhedrin* 73a.

4. Translations from *Siddur Sim Shalom,* ed. Jules Harlow (New York: Rabbinical Assembly and United Synagogue of America, 1985), 19, 107.
5. Joseph Karo, *S.A., Y.D.* 336:1.
6. B. *Sanhedrin* 17b.
7. Naḥmanides, *Kitvei Haramban,* ed. Bernard Chavel (Jerusalem: Mossad Harav Kook, 1963), 2:43 (Hebrew). The verse from the Torah: Lev. 19:18.
8. *S.A., Y.D.* 335; Immanuel Jakobovits, *Jewish Medical Ethics,* 2d ed. (New York: Bloch, 1975), 106–9. In addition, *S.A., Y.D.* 249:16, indicates that the financial needs of the sick have at least equal claim on communal resources as other requirements of *tzedakah,* and may have special priority.
9. See n. 7.
10. These issues are further discussed in Aaron L. Mackler, "Judaism, Justice, and Access to Health Care," *Kennedy Institute of Ethics Journal* 1 (1991): 143–61.
11. *S.A., Y.D.* 248:1. The obligation of *tzedakah* in Judaism is binding, analogous to the duty to pay income taxes in the United States.
12. *S.A., Y.D.* 249:1. See Cyril Domb, *Maaser Kesafim* (Jerusalem: Feldheim/Association of Orthodox Jewish Scientists, 1980), 34–38.
13. B. *Ketubbot* 67b.
14. Moses Maimonides, *M.T., Laws of Gifts to the Poor* 7:3.
15. *S.A., Y.D.* 250:1.
16. Ibid.
17. The provision of universal education is a separate communal obligation. See *S.A., Y.D.* 245:7, 249:16; *Encyclopaedia Judaica,* s.v. "Education."
18. The Talmud, and subsequently codes, understand the "lack" of a horse as relative to the previous condition of a once wealthy recipient. Following this paradigm, special needs might be understood in terms of the previous status of an individual, current psychological needs, or expectations or felt needs. While this paper follows a relatively conservative interpretation of focusing on objective needs and a basic level of support, the provision of a horse serves as a rhetorical injunction to be sensitive to special needs of individuals, at least in exceptional cases.
19. *M.T., Laws of Gifts to the Poor* 8:10. See similarly *S.A., Y.D.* 252:1.
20. *S.A., Y.D.* 252:4; B. *Gittin* 45a. The standard case in the tradition is that in which payments for the captive's release are necessary and will be effective in securing the captive's freedom. Accordingly, the analogy would apply to medical care that is both necessary and effective.
21. *M.T., Laws of Ethics (De'ot),* 4:1ff.
22. *S.A., Y.D.* 252:11.
23. M. *Ketubbot* 4:9; *S.A., E.H.* 79.
24. *S.A., Y.D.* 252:10, *E.H.* 78. This is ultimately based on the Mishnah's insistence that a man redeem his wife from captivity before being able to divorce her; cf. M. *Ketubbot* 4:9.
25. *S.A., Y.D.* 252:12.

26. The individual also has a duty to contribute to the medical care of others. Although this generally is not spelled out in just those words, it is a clear implication of the understanding of the community's obligations seen above. Traditional sources obligate individuals to contribute to the needs of others through *tzedakah* and *pidyon shevuyim*. Moreover, the Rabbis, as we have seen, see the absence of health care as shedding blood. Since the physician alone cannot be expected to bear the costs of health care for those who cannot afford it, this duty devolves upon the community, and the costs of health care for the poor become part of the *tzedakah* that one must give, a strict and enforceable obligation. See the discussion above in section I; *M.T., Laws of Gifts to the Poor* 7:10; *S.A., Y.D.* 248:2. At the same time, there are limits on this obligation. The *S.A.*, and the Jewish tradition in general, acknowledge limits on the obligation to provide for the needs of others, at least in exceptional cases. In the most extreme case, one does not have to endanger one's own life in order to save the life of another. As seen above, each individual is generally not obligated to pay more than 10 or 20 percent of income toward the provision of the needs of the poor. While the obligation to provide all resources necessary to save lives generally supersedes all such limits, halakhic sources can envision cases in which not all lives can be saved, and offer various sets of priorities to consider in such extreme cases. *S.A., Y.D.* 252:5–12; see Shlomo Dichowsky, "Rescue and Treatment: Halakhic Scales of Priority" (Hebrew), *Dine Israel* 7 (1976): 45–66; Martin Golding, "Preventive vs. Curative Medicine," *Journal of Medicine and Philosophy* 8 (1983): 276–79; Fred Rosner, *Modern Medicine and Jewish Ethics,* 2d ed. (Hoboken, N.J.: Ktav, 1991), 375–90.
27. *S.A., Y.D.* 255:2.
28. *S.A., Y.D.* 252:4.
29. See above, section I; *S.A., Y.D.* 336; Rosner, 5–19; J. David Bleich, "The Obligation to Heal in the Judaic Tradition: A Comparative Analysis," in *Jewish Bioethics,* ed. Fred Rosner and J. David Bleich (New York: Sanhedrin Press, 1979), 1–44.
30. B. *Ta'anit* 21b.
31. Eleazar Fleckeles, *Teshuvah Me'ahavah* (Prague, 1820), 70, on *S.A., Y.D.* 336.
32. Jakobovits, 224–28.
33. B. *Bava Kamma* 85a.
34. In the United States, a number of states have passed laws restricting financial incentives to physicians. For example, Texas prohibits financial incentives that serve as inducements to limit medically necessary care (Tracy E. Miller, "Managed Care Regulation: In the Laboratory of the States," *Journal of the American Medical Association* 278 [1997]: 1104). According to the Council on Ethical and Judicial Affairs of the American Medical Association, "Financial incentives are permissible only if they promote the cost-effective delivery of health care and not the withholding of medically necessary care." Furthermore, "regardless of any allocation guidelines or gatekeeper directives, physicians must advocate for

any care they believe will materially benefit their patients ("Ethical Issues in Managed Care," *Journal of the American Medical Association* 273 [1995]: 334–35). Before affiliating with a managed care plan, an individual physician has the responsibility to ascertain the implications for his or her being able to provide appropriate patient care (as Haavi Morreim, a secular ethicist who is generally sympathetic to managed care, notes [*Balancing Act: The New Medical Ethics of Medicine's New Economics* (Washington, D.C.: Georgetown University Press, 1995), 121–23]). A physician should be willing to make at least some degree of financial sacrifice in order to better care for patients. In some cases, some degree of compromise from the ideal might be required for a physician to be able to practice in a given area. Precise resolution of such dilemmas is beyond the scope of this paper. Note, though, that for the Council on Ethical and Judicial Affairs of the American Medical Association, "Physicians should not participate in any plan that encourages or requires care at or below minimum professional standards" ("Ethical Issues in Managed Care," 334–35).

35. Indeed, by the sixteenth century, Isserles noted that the central locus for the provision of *tzedakah* had shifted from individuals to the community (*S.A., Y.D.* 250:1).
36. Eliezer Yehudah Waldenberg, *Tzitz Eliezer* 5. *Ramat Raḥel* (Jerusalem, 1985), responsum no. 24, p. 31.
37. Ibid., 31–32.
38. Traditional Jewish sources find concepts analogous to "need" relatively unproblematic and devote little attention to specifying the levels of food, shelter, or medical care required by justice. The generally implicit standard of the codes at least roughly corresponds with the concept of "natural function" or "species-typical functioning," developed by Christopher Boorse and utilized by Norman Daniels in discussing allocation of health care (Daniels, *Just Health Care* [New York: Cambridge University Press, 1985], esp. 26–32).
39. Possible limits on the degree to which a particular society can afford to provide such care as balanced against its other obligations are discussed below.
40. Elliot N. Dorff, "The Jewish Tradition," in *Caring and Curing: Health and Medicine in the Western Religious Traditions,* ed. Ronald L. Numbers and Darrel W. Amundsen (New York: Macmillan, 1986), 23–25; David M. Feldman, *Health and Medicine in the Jewish Tradition* (New York: Crossroad, 1986), 49; citing: B. *Yoma* 82a; Naḥmanides, *Torat Ha'adam;* Israel Meir Mizrahi, Responsa *Peri Ha'aretz, Y.D.* no. 2; Mordekhai Winkler, Responsa *Levushei Mordekhai, Ḥ.M.* no. 39; Responsa *Minḥat Yitzḥak,* vol. 1, no. 115; *Iggerot Moshe, E.H.* no. 65.
41. See Golding, "Preventive vs. Curative Medicine," 269–86.
42. Louise Russell and others, however, note that the relative cost-effectiveness of preventive and curative care varies greatly, and that many preventive measures cannot be justified solely on the basis of cost-effectiveness. While preventing one person's disease is generally less expensive than curing disease that has occurred,

large numbers of patients may need to be screened and treated for each case of disease prevented. Studies have found that screening for cervical cancer among low-income elderly women who had not been screened in many years can save money, for example, but that routinely screening women every year instead of every two years costs $1.8 million for each year of life saved, far more than many curative interventions (Louise B. Russell, "The Role of Prevention in Health Reform," *New England Journal of Medicine* 329 [1993]: 352–54). See also Russell's "Some of the Tough Decisions Required by a National Health Plan," *Science* 246 (1989): 892–96; *Is Prevention Better than Cure?* (Washington, D.C.: Brookings Institution, 1986), 110; David M. Eddy, "Cost-Effectiveness Analysis: Is It Up to the Task?" *Journal of the American Medical Association* 267 (1992): 3346–47. The extent of preventive care that should be considered appropriate or "needed" is an issue of ongoing debate in bioethics and health policy. Paul Menzel (*Medical Costs, Moral Choices* [New Haven: Yale University Press, 1983], 83), for example, argues that even granting that "people need to avoid suffering or dying does not mean that they need all the things which reduce the chances of suffering or dying." At the same time, even preventive measures that increase health care expenses may be warranted because they prevent suffering and support human dignity, as discussed in the text.

43. *S.A., Y.D.* 252:6.
44. B. *Gittin* 45a; *S.A., Y.D.* 252:4.
45. See above, and *S.A., Y.D.* 252:4; 336.
46. While full evaluation of arguments for rationing is beyond the scope of this paper, rationing that denies needed health care is a last resort, and at best premature, given the lack of serious efforts to provide needed health care or to limit that which is unneeded.
47. See Louis Finkelstein, "Human Equality in the Jewish Tradition," in *Aspects of Human Equality,* ed. Lyman Bryson et al. (New York: Harper and Brothers, 1956), 179–205. Finkelstein argues that all humans are equal in that they may serve and have obligations to God, and that all may have a share in the world to come.
48. This priority may be found in *M.T., Laws of Gifts to the Poor* 7:13; *S.A., Y.D.* 251:3. While these texts are unclear about whether there are exceptions to this order, Rabbi Yeḥiel Michal Halevi Epstein argues that this order of priority is not absolute (*Arukh Hashulḥan, Y.D.* 251:4).
49. M. *Gittin* 5:8; B. *Gittin* 61a; *M.T., Laws of Idolatry* 10:5, *Laws of Gifts to the Poor* 7:7. The tradition sees Jews as having special responsibilities to support those within the community, but these responsibilities extend to others in the broader human community as well.
50. Eugene B. Borowitz, *Exploring Jewish Ethics* (Detroit: Wayne State University Press, 1990), 99. See also M. *Sanhedrin* 4:5; Simon Greenberg, *A Jewish Philosophy and Pattern of Life* (New York: Jewish Theological Seminary of America, 1981), esp. 219–21.

51. Jer. 29:7.
52. As Abraham Joshua Heschel wrote in another context: "In regard to the cruelties committed in the name of a free society, some are guilty, while all are responsible. I did not feel guilty as an individual American . . . , but I feel deeply responsible. 'Thou shalt not stand idly by the blood of thy neighbor' (Leviticus 19:15). This is not a recommendation but an imperative, a supreme commandment" (*Moral Grandeur and Spiritual Audacity,* ed. Susannah Heschel [New York: Farrar, Straus and Giroux, 1996], 225).

CHAPTER 31

Curiouser and Curiouser: Genetic Engineering of Nonhuman Life*

Avram I. Reisner

She'eilah (Question):

Modern science has succeeded in circumventing the natural process of sexual reproduction by learning how to manipulate and engineer the DNA that is at the heart of all biological cells—what was formally known as recombinant DNA technology. Increasingly, the market seeks to introduce genetically altered strains of common food items. If a genetic sequence is adapted from an unkosher species and implanted in a new strain of a kosher foodstuff—for example, if a gene for swine growth hormone is introduced into a potato to induce larger growth, or if a gene from an insect is introduced into a tomato plant in order to give it unusual qualities of pest resistance—is that new strain rendered unkosher?

Teshuvah (Response):

At the outset, it is desirable to indicate what I *do not* deal with in this responsum. Much good might be derived medically from this ability to alter flawed genes to eliminate malformations and overcome disease. There is little question that that should be permitted under our broad conception of healing—but this responsum does not concern itself with such human genetic engineering. Even the bioengineering of

*Approved by the Rabbinical Assembly Committee on Jewish Law and Standards, Dec. 1997.

plants and animals can be turned to medical uses. Thus, the ability to create transgenic animals that bear or lack traits that mimic human diseases has enormous potential for research.[1] Since the products are not for consumption, however, these are not the subject of this responsum. Or again, research has been undertaken with an eye toward developing products in plants and animals by genetic alteration, which products will then be available to treat human disease. Thus, pigs have been altered to produce proteins that are active in humans, and such pigs can be used as a resource for large-scale production of medically necessary proteins that are in short supply. Similar uses as factories for the production of pharmaceuticals have been proposed for plants.[2] Here, human consumption is precisely the intent behind the genetic alteration. In all these cases, however, Judaism's emphasis on healing individuals who are sick is likely to override any combination of concerns that might otherwise affect the technique. Whereas some consideration of the above cases is in order, these are not properly my concern here.

The concern here is that, absent health considerations, many genetic alterations are proposed for purely commercial reasons. Thus, the majority of tests for specific traits of transgenic crops in industrialized countries prior to 1992 were for resistance to herbicides, so that it might be possible to treat a field with a substance to kill other growth and leave the crop plant unaffected. Similarly, most of the other traits tested were for insect and disease resistance, altered ripening qualities, and other such matters important to the farmer and marketer, but morally neutral.[3] It is in such cases that the question of the kashrut of the resulting hybrid is relevant.

A. The Kashrut Issue

Superficially, the primary potential problem with such a hybrid is the problem of the admixture of a nonkosher product with a kosher product. With regard to admixtures, the primary rule is that they are forbidden *benotein ta'am*—when they impart a flavor to the resultant product. This is estimated, as a matter of law, at one part in sixty, such that a lesser admixture is permitted, a greater admixture forbidden. Several caveats are affixed to this basic ruling. First, the ruling is taken as applicable only in accidental admixtures. Thus, intentionally mixing less than one part in sixty of a nonkosher product in one's preparation bars the use of the resultant product altogether. Here, there is an open debate as to whether an admixture of a nonkosher product prepared intentionally by a non-Jew is to be treated at law as an intentional admixture, hence nonkosher, or as an unintentional admixture, since the non-Jew was permitted to prepare the food in that way, and the Jew first addresses the question only after it already was completed, as he does with an accidental admixture. Further, an exception is made for nonkosher ingredients that serve as stabilizers and flavoring agents that are deemed to have a perceptible effect even in tiny proportions, thereby rendering the final product unkosher.[4]

Were it the case that the rules of admixture should, in fact, be applied here, then it would be appropriate to consider whether a genetic alteration using a gene from a nonkosher source renders the resultant product nonkosher or whether it does not. The added gene (a) is always much less than one part in sixty,[5] but (b) it is intentionally administered, albeit largely by non-Jews, and (c) it has a perceptible effect—for it changes the attributes of the animal or vegetable in some way, otherwise it would not be desirable—but most often an invisible effect. However, these commonsense criteria prove to be altogether immaterial. And the reason is contained within the essential nature of these very criteria.

Halakhah had to distinguish between what is counted and what is nullified, what is perceptible and what is not. In the matter of stabilizers and flavoring agents, it needed to determine in every case whether the standard rules of nullification or the specialized rules for "perceptible substances" should apply. In so doing, Jewish law in the modern period has settled on the rule of thumb that microscopic items, not visible to the naked eye, are discounted altogether in determining Jewish law. This ruling was made by R. Yeḥiel Michal Halevi Epstein in his work *Arukh Hashulḥan, Yoreh De'ah* 84:36, published in the 1890s, and is generally accepted. As he rightly points out, were we to consider microscopic life forms, we would be unable to drink the water or breathe the air.[6] It is for this reason, among others, that the major kashrut agencies have permitted the use of genetically engineered chymosin (microbial rennet) in the production of cheese, wherein a microbe is induced to produce an enzyme generally found only in animal stomachs and that enzyme is then used to curdle milk. Similarly, here, genetic transfer happens at a submicroscopic level that the halakhah is hard-pressed to consider.[7]

Several other considerations similarly conspire to nullify any kashrut concerns here. Transfer of material from a nonkosher animal at the genetic level would not constitute prohibited "eating" under the laws of foods. It has already been determined that eating must include "oral stimulation," and that absent that, no blessings are required. Similarly, most authorities rule that gastric tube feeding would not constitute a transgression of the restrictions of Yom Kippur. This insight serves as the basis variously for permitting transfusion, though the eating of blood is prohibited, and of permitting the use in a Jewish patient of a porcine heart valve. Indeed, all Jewish law on transplantation begins with the assumption that to receive a transplant is not, at heart, a prohibited act of cannibalism. Rather, the principle is clearly enunciated by R. Yehuda Unterman, the former chief rabbi of Israel, in his responsum that opened the path to all subsequent considerations of transplantation in Jewish law, that an organ that is implanted in a body and flourishes by connection to that body's functions becomes a part of the host in all respects.[8] Thus, the rules of kashrut, the rules of admixtures, simply fail to address the nature of transgenic creations. Absent a reason to declare the new product unkosher, it would appear to be fit for consumption.

B. The Kilayim Question

The more relevant question is that of *kilayim*, or biblically prohibited mixing across species lines. Are transgenic creations to be prohibited as extensions of the biblical rule of *kilayim*? The question is a somewhat vexed one, because the biblical laws of *kilayim* are unclear as to their reason and scope. Several different forms of *kilayim* are recorded. It is prohibited to mix seed of different agricultural species, called *kil'ei zera'im* (Lev. 19:19); it is also prohibited to plant different species adjacent to one another in the same field, called *kil'ei hakerem* (Deut. 22:9). It is prohibited to crossbreed animals or to graft plants, together the class of *harkavah* (Lev. 19:19); or simply to yoke an ox and donkey, or any other two species, together to the plow (Deut. 22:10). It is even prohibited to interweave specifically wool and linen, *sha'atneiz* (Lev. 19:19 and Deut. 22:11). But at no time is any reason presented. The tradition faced a problem in analyzing these rules precisely because it needed first to give them a context and an explanation.

A context is, in fact, suggested by the text of Lev. 19:19. In full, the verse reads:

את חקתי תשמרו בהמתך לא תרביע כלאים שדך לא תזרע כלאים ובגד כלאים שעטנז לא יעלה עליך

> You shall observe my laws. You shall not mate your cattle with a different kind; you shall not sow your field with two kinds of seed; you shall not put on cloth from a mixture of two kinds of material.

The introductory phrase begs an explanation. One is offered by Samuel in reflecting on the (minority!) tannaitic opinion that *kilayim* (crossbreeding but not interweaving) is among the laws applicable to Gentiles (*mitzvot benei noaḥ*):

מנא הני מילי אמר שמואל דאמר קרא את חקתי תשמרו חוקים שחקקתי לך כבר בהמתך לא תרביע כלאים שדך לא תזרע כלאים מה בהמתך בהרבעה אף שדך בהרכבה

> Whence this assertion? Said Samuel—Scripture says: "You shall observe my laws"—the laws I have already enacted for you: "You shall not mate your cattle with a different kind" and "You shall not sow your field with two kinds of seed." Just as this refers to crossbreeding of your cattle, so it refers to hybridization of your field [i.e., your produce].[9]

This position appears to be that of the Sifra, *Kedoshim* 4:17, cited in Yerushalmi, *Kilayim* 1:7:

מניין שאין מרכיבין .... תלמוד לו׳ את חקותי תשמורו

> Whence (the ruling) that we do not hybridize? . . . The teaching is: "You shall observe my laws,"

as it is interpreted by R. Yonah and R. 'Lezer in the name of Rav Kahana to apply even to Adam. In that light, an elaboration of this reason is offered there, "Why? Because 'of every kind' [Gen. 1:21] is written about them." But R. Yosi interprets this text from Sifra, in the name of R. Hila, in line with the majority opinion that holds that *kilayim* is only prohibited to Jews as of Sinai. Either way, transgenic creations might be prohibited as *kilayim,* a fundamental rebellion against the species created by God in the beginning.

Ramban (Naḥmanides) takes that tack in his commentary on *kilayim* on the relevant passages in *Kedoshim* (Leviticus 19). "The reason for *kilayim* is that God created species in the world . . . and gave them the ability to procreate in order that said species should continue forever, [that is,] for as long as God wishes for the world to continue. . . . Whoever intermingles two species changes and denies the Creation, as if he thought that God did not complete the work of His world as much as necessary, and he wishes to aid in the creation of the world, to add creatures to it." And he adds another observation, that in nature "the species of animals do not crossbreed, and even [with regard to] close relatives in nature, those that may be born to them . . . are infertile. We see that as far as this is concerned, the act of crossbreeding species is a repugnant and futile act." Indeed, in the modern day, Mary Douglas has seconded Ramban's appreciation, arguing that the very rules of kashrut are intended to reflect a pure speciation of the universe, with natural creatures that cross the lines of the classes that the Torah perceives being declared unkosher on that account.[10] Thus, in the growing secular debate about transgenic plants and animals, Ramban is prominently quoted by the Alliance for Bio-Integrity, an organization that seeks to form an interfaith lobby against transgenic foods, or for their labeling. The organization writes, "Genetic engineering rejects the idea that man must defer to a higher power, and its underlying theology has no room for a purposeful Creator whose plan must be respected."[11] To repeat the question: Are transgenic creations to be prohibited as extensions of the biblical rule of *kilayim*? This reasoning would appear to argue strongly that they should be.

The above is based, as we said, on a particular interpretation of the reasons behind the commandment of *kilayim,* which are nowhere stated explicitly. There is another way to explain the leading words at the beginning of the cited verse in Leviticus. It is possible to understand that the rules of *kilayim* as stated are without cognitive reason—that the acceptance of the divine commandment, in this case, is to be taken on faith. Indeed, the very word *ḥukah* (law), which appears prominently in that verse, is taken to refer to divine decrees without stated reason.[12] In this light, Rashi's comment to this verse takes on legal significance. To wit:

את חקתי תשמרו - ואלו הן בהמתך לא תרביע כלאים וגו', חקים אלו גזרות מלך שאין טעם לדבר

> "You shall observe my laws"—and these are they: "You shall not mate your cattle with a different kind" etc. These laws are decrees of the sovereign that have no reason.

Such a classification has clear and clearly relevant ramifications. What is taken as a decree of the written word is taken to be specific and precise, limited exactly as written. As Rashi notes on the second mishnah on *Menaḥot* 27a, reflecting the reasoning of the Gemara there: *ketiv ḥukah . . . veḥukah ikuva*—"The Torah writes 'decree'—and a 'decree' is limiting." Throughout rabbinic literature, a *ḥidush*—an unprecedented turn in the Torah's decrees—may not be extended, for to extend it would be hubris when the very intent and meaning is unclear. By this interpretation, then, only the specific examples in the biblical text are prohibited as *kilayim,* that is, crossbreeding and hybridization through natural means, and any extension we seek to make to transgenic species arrived at through means unimaginable to the Bible may not be valid.[13]

C. The Law of Kilayim

An assessment of the settled law of *kilayim* as codified leads me to conclude that the Rabbis chose the more lenient approach with regard to the laws of *kilayim.* In the first instance, the midrash *ḥukim sheḥikakti lekha kevar,* "the laws I have already enacted for you," is tailor-made for the conclusion that Ramban comes to about the laws of *kilayim,* that *kilayim* is in contravention of God's creation, wherefore *kilayim* should be forbidden to humankind. Indeed, it was brought with regard to a minority position that the law of *kilayim* applies to Adam. But the majority rules that only Israel is prohibited *kilayim,* and offers the barely modified version of the midrash *ḥukim sheḥakakti be'olami,* "the laws I have enacted in my world," as referring to the laws given at Sinai to Israel alone.[14] Only if we favor Rashi's interpretation does it make any sense to permit *kilayim* to Gentiles while forbidding it to Israelites.[15] This leniency is suggested in *Shulḥan Arukh, Yoreh De'ah* 297:4, by the prohibition of allowing non-Jews to crossbreed an animal owned by a Jew, implying, of course, that to do so with his own animal would be permitted.

But the law is more liberal still. In his comments to Rambam, *Hilkhot Kilayim* 1:6, Radbaz offers the following:

> **ומותר לומר לנכרי להרביע בהמתו של הנכרי ולהרכיב אילנו של הנכרי אע״ג דאומר לו אני אקנה אח״כ**
>
> It is permissible to tell a Gentile to crossbreed the cattle of the Gentile or to hybridize the tree of the Gentile, even though he says to him that he will buy [the product] subsequently.

No attempt is made or suggested to reduce the incidence of Jews suborning *kilayim*. In a third point, the law's leniency is also evident. *Shulḥan Arukh, Yoreh De'ah* 297:5 reads:

> **מי שעבר והרכיב בהמתו כלאים הרי הנולד מהם מותר בהנאה ואם היה מין טהורה עם מין טהורה מותר באכילה**
>
> If one transgressed and crossbred one's animal, the offspring is permissible for use, and if the species were both pure [kosher], it is permissible to eat it.

A similar rule is enunciated concerning hybridization of plants in 295:7:

> **אסור לקיים המורכב כלאים אבל הפרי היוצא ממנו מותר ואפילו לזה שעבר והרכיבו. ומותר ליקח ענף מהמורכב ולנטעו במקום אחר**
>
> It is forbidden to maintain *kilayim,* but the fruit produced thereby is permitted even to the one who transgressed and produced the hybrid. It is permitted to take a branch from the hybrid and plant it elsewhere.[16]

Elsewhere in Jewish tradition, a fine is levied against willful transgressors to prevent them from disregarding the law.[17] The principle of *ein ḥotei niskar*—that the transgressor should not be rewarded—is well established. But here, no such defensive fine is contemplated. On the contrary, the use of the product of the hybridization is affirmatively permitted. In fact, many hybrids are presently on the market, hybrids of different strains of the same type of plant, which would not be *kilayim,* as well as those of separate species, which would be considered *kilayim,* the product of agricultural and animal husbandry techniques honed before the advent of genetic engineering. No such product is banned. Indeed, this is not even a modern leniency, having its earliest source in the Tosefta.[18]

In the most direct application to our issue, the great twentieth-century sage R. Avraham Karelitz, known as the Ḥazon Ish, reports the ruling that *kilayim* is to be forbidden exclusively where there is genital contact, but that "there is no prohibition placing the seed of one species into another."[19] If artificial insemination does not cross the boundaries of *kilayim,* even though it introduces the entire genome of one species into another, certainly the transfer of a few genes by genetic-engineering techniques far removed from natural sexual contact cannot be seen as prohibited.

D. A Caveat

The Union of Concerned Scientists, the Alliance for Bio-Integrity, and others raise serious concerns of the potential damage to the earth's ecosystems through genetic engineering run amok.[20] They raise concerns that a damaging genetically engineered strain will be unleashed into the world's ecosystems and prove unstoppable. This type of concern animated the Michael Crichton thriller *The Andromeda Strain* and its successors. The scientific community has always responded that such a scenario is unlikely, its track record is exemplary, and that it had put into place careful research protocols to lessen the likelihood of any such mishap. But candor requires admitting that no safeguards are foolproof and that not all potential damage will prove predictable. A case in point was that of a strain of seaweed, engineered two decades ago in Germany for its looks, that was widely distributed to various aquariums. In a renovation, the Oceanographic Museum in Monaco emptied its tanks some fifteen years ago. Now that strain of seaweed is propagating out of control in sections of the Mediterranean, crowding out and killing most other plants and animals in the regions it controls. Moreover, it is resistant to all attempts that have been made to kill it or to halt its advance.[21]

Potentially, this concern is of halakhic import. There are clear rulings that prohibit experimental medical procedures under the rubric of *venishmartem me'od lenafshoteikhem,* "You shall be exceedingly careful" (Deut. 4:15). But there are equally clear permissions granted when the danger is remote and the benefit great.[22] Some would prohibit smoking,[23] but the majority clearly do not. Skiing and bungee jumping could both be prohibited on this basis. Clearly, we permit risk taking when the danger has not risen to the level of our concern. The relevant question is whether concern here is in order. Thus, it could reasonably be argued that the current AIDS epidemic was facilitated by the ease of international air travel, but we would not consider the distant concern of some unknown virus sufficient to prohibit air travel. Despite the current case of the rampant seaweed, where potential strategies of control are also being discussed, the harm proposed appears to me to be too fanciful and unspecific to elicit our halakhic prohibition of any and all genetic engineering. Specific cases, should they come to our attention, may merit further consideration. At the very least, our secular legislatures must consider any potential risk to human health and establish appropriate regulations as a matter of public policy.

Thus, the Alliance for Bio-Integrity further argues, in the alternative, for clear labeling laws that will require producers to indicate if a product has been genetically engineered. While implementation of such rules is not required by this responsum, and while the technical difficulties in enforcing such a standard are significant, there is sufficient minority warrant for a halakhic position that would prohibit said products as *kilayim*. Labeling rules would permit those who seek the *ḥumra* (the added restriction) to do so.[24]

Beyond my concern for these matters, there is a point at which, it seems to me, the *ḥumra* might be cogent, and the pull of Ramban's concern for Creation's integrity may yet require our consideration. While we have permitted genetic engineering to produce desirable traits within the foods we consume, there is a point at which the product of genetic engineering is less like a hybrid and more like a differing creature. Imagine, if you will, producing a small winged lamb that does indeed fly. The aerodynamic problem, of course, is primary, but heavier things than aircraft can fly, and even this is not beyond our imaginings. Is such a creature to be treated as permitted? Can such genetic mixing be allowed?

The arguments, herein, present a prima facie case to answer these questions in the affirmative. But my heart wishes to answer in the negative. Why? There seems to be a qualitative difference between traits that, while they may be tested for, are expressed invisibly within an apparently unchanged creature and those gross characteristics that make up our traditional taxonomic observations. Thus, for instance, the Torah's very kashrut criteria are of gross features such as split hooves, scales, or number of legs (Leviticus 11). Rambam seeks to codify just such a distinction when he writes, in *Hilkhot Kilayim* 3:5, *ein holekhim bekhil'ayim ela aḥar mar'it ha'ayin,* "With regard to [the laws of] *kilayim,* one follows appearances." This dovetails rather well with the concept that we discovered concerning kashrut that halakhah disregards the microscopic, that which is invisible. Yet small genetic changes can effect large-scale, visible results. Among the early experiments with genetic engineering was an experiment transplanting the illuminating mechanism of a firefly into a plant, producing a luminescent plant. Is that to be treated as permissible, a human-induced mutation not unlike the mutations that occur naturally, or has the species line been crossed? The burden of this paper is *lehakeil* (lenient) and would permit even such a genetically engineered plant. Still, when we are able to change not a single trait, but much of the genome of a creature—to create, as it were, a creature of our own devising—then we must ask, is that the point at which we must stop?

There is an odd tannaitic text that reflects both sides of this question. On *Pesaḥim* 54a, we find the following:

> **רבי יוסי אומר: שני דברים עלו במחשבה ליבראות בערב שבת ולא נבראו עד מוצאי שבת, ובמוצאי שבת נתן הקדוש ברוך הוא דיעה באדם הראשון מעין דוגמא של מעלה, והביא שני אבנים וטחנן זו בזו ויצא מהן אור. והביא שתי בהמות והרכיב זו בזו ויצא מהן פרד. רבן שמעון בן גמליאל אומר :פרד בימי ענה היה . . . . דורשי חמורות היו אומרים: ענה פסול היה, לפיכך הביא פסול לעולם**

> R. Yosi says: Two things were planned for Creation on Friday but were not created until Saturday night. On Saturday night, the Holy One (praised be He) granted Adam wisdom similar to that in heaven, and He took two stones and ground them against each other and created fire, and He took two animals and mated them and created a mule. Rabban Shimon ben Gamaliel says: The mule was [created] in the days of Ana. . . . The allegorical interpreters would say: Ana was impure, so he created an impurity.

Shimon ben Gamaliel and the allegorical interpreters clearly understood that *kilayim* was an aberration. Yosi, however, argued that *kilayim* was a piece of divine wisdom.[25] Yet *kilayim,* shown by God to Adam, was nevertheless forbidden to Jews. Are we ready to take on "the wisdom of heaven"?

Josephus—not a halakhic authority, to be sure, but an early interpreter of rabbinic traditions—was aware of the potential of crossbreeding to denigrate the respect in which we hold Creation, and ultimately humankind. In *Antiquities* 4:8:20, he speculated on the ultimate reason behind the prohibition:

> Nature does not rejoice in the union of things that are not in their own nature alike. You are not to permit beasts of different kinds together, for there is reason to fear that this unnatural abuse may extend from beasts of different kinds to men . . . by imitation whereof any degree of subversion may creep into the constitution.

It is excessive to emplace barriers against manipulation of the human species at the point of genetic manipulation of protein expression. It may not be excessive to emplace such barriers at manipulation of the very characteristics by which species are identified. I reserve final judgment in this area.

E. Conclusions

The kashrut laws of prohibited admixtures do not apply to the submicroscopic manipulation of genetic material. The laws of *kilayim,* which might apply, show an extraordinary tendency toward leniency. "Natural" *kilayim* products, though the fruit of an illicit operation of *kilayim,* have nonetheless been permitted as early as the Tosefta, and the rationale tying the laws of *kilayim* to the Creation, while often tempting exegetes, has not become the dominant law. Of genetically engineered foodstuffs, it should be minimally said that even if genetic engineering is to be prohibited, the products thereof are permissible.

Of the process of genetic engineering itself, moreover, I think there is ample reason to permit it even to the Jew. (1) The process of genetic engineering bears only a very minimal resemblance to the sexual and grafting processes that the Torah bans. If, indeed, we are enjoined to treat the Torah's ban as a *ḥok*—a ukase—and not to expand its parameters beyond the parameters given, then it seems that no extension to genetic techniques is warranted. (2) Although the question was formulated to focus on commercial use of genetic engineering, a fuller review of those very commercial considerations would find that most commercial considerations have a ramification that could be lifesaving. Thus, for instance, increased pest resistance, though useful to the food conglomerates in terms of their efficiency, will also prove useful in the endeavor to feed the world's starving population. Already such reports are mixed in among the early results of genetic engineering.[26] Nothing appears more crassly commercial than engineering for greater shelf life, but this, too, can facilitate the distribution of foodstuffs to the needy. Given the law's tendency to limit the scope of the prohibition of *kilayim,* this would appear to be sufficient reason to permit genetic engineering to continue. (3) On the matter of gross changes in the characteristics by which species are recognized, it remains necessary to engage in further study and consideration.

Notes

1. Bernard D. Davis, ed., *The Genetic Revolution* (Baltimore: Johns Hopkins University Press, 1991), 122–23; S. Donnelley, C. R. McCarthy, and R. Singleton, Jr., "The Brave New World of Animal Biotechnology," a special supplement, *The Hastings Center Report* 24, no. 1 (Jan.–Feb. 1994).
2. Donnelley, McCarthy, and Singleton, ibid.; J. Rissler and M. Mellon, "Perils Amidst the Promise: Ecological Risks of Transgenic Crops in a Global Market" (Cambridge, Mass.: Union of Concerned Scientists, Dec. 1993): 6.
3. Rissler and Mellon, ibid., 9. On the matter of the moral neutrality of these considerations, see below.
4. Joseph Karo, *S.A., Y.D.* 98ff. On the matter of non-Jewish commercial preparations manufactured intentionally for public (non-Jewish) use, the CJLS has gone on record with the more stringent ruling in its responsum by R. Elliot N. Dorff, "The Use of All Wines" (1985). But many of the national kashrut agencies apparently rely on the lenient opinion; see *Kashrus* magazine, no. 44 (Mar.–Apr. 1989): 54–56. Indeed, that position was cited by R. Max Arzt in his 1940 responsum on eating fish outside of the home. It is cited as the normative position by R. Eliezer Wolff in his book *Keeping Kosher in a Nonkosher World* (New York: E. Wolff, 1989), no. 100.
5. In natural crossbreeding, if one of the animals was nonkosher the offspring would be nonkosher; see *S.A.* 297:5. However, in such a case 50 percent of the DNA would be from the unkosher animal. Not so, here.
6. A similar response by R. Moshe Feinstein, *Iggerot Moshe, Y.D.* 3, 120:5 with regard to measurement, considers that the law cannot possibly demand microscopic exactness, since microscopes were not available to our ancestors. Reference to this standard without attribution, among other points, is made, as well, by the late-twentieth-century Jerusalem sage R. Shlomo Zalman Auerbach in his

responsum, *Minḥat Shelomo,* 87, about transient sparks that may be invisible to the naked eye. Dr. Fred Rosner makes reference to this ruling, without source, in "Genetic Engineering and Judaism," in *Jewish Bioethics,* ed. J. David Bleich and Fred Rosner (New York: Sanhedrin, 1979), 417. This nullification of microscopic agents is true only of those agents that are by their nature invisible to the naked eye, and not to ingredients that are visible in the form in which they are used, but become imperceptible to the consumer, being dissolved or integrated into the final product.

7. See M. M. Chaudry and J. M. Regenstein, "Implications of Biotechnology and Genetic Engineering for Kosher and Halal Foods," *Trends in Food Science & Technology* (May 1994): 165–68.
8. See *Sha'arei Teshuvah* to *S.A., O.Ḥ.* 197:8 and R. Eliezer Waldenberg, *Tzitz Eliezer* 10, no. 25, p. 21. R. Isser Yehuda Unterman's famous responsum is in his volume *Shevet mi-Yehudah* (vol. 1, 1:21). See also the interesting example provided by R. J. J. Greenwald, cited in Rosner, *Jewish Bioethics,* 363. Steven Druker of the Alliance for Bio-Integrity (see n. 11 below) argues that since a genetic transfer, unlike an admixture, is dynamic, it will grow over time and become significant, wherefore it should not be nullified, as a gelling agent (*ma'amid*) is not null. The concept is itself significant, for some halakhists do argue that, despite earlier nullification (*bitul*), if more of the original forbidden substance was added, bringing the total volume of the forbidden substance over the one-in-sixty limit, that the previously nullified material is rekindled (*ḥozer venei'or*) and is no longer null. This position is clearly taken by Moses Isserles, *Y.D.* 99:6, and, while opinions to the contrary are brought by Shabtai Hakohen (Shakh), 21, there, he concludes, "My (more lenient) view is nullified against theirs." Counter to this argument is precisely the understanding that once a gene is incorporated into an organism, its products are not foreign products at all, thus adding mass to the alien, forbidden matter, but they are to be treated as a part of that organism itself.
9. The tannaitic position is recorded in a baraita on *Sanhedrin* 56a–b. Samuel's commentary is there, on 60a. This and many of the other rabbinic texts cited here were first called to my attention by the introduction to Yehuda Felik's work on the first chapter of M. *Kilayim,* "Mixed Sowing, Breeding, and Grafting" (Heb.).
10. Mary Douglas, *Purity and Danger* (London: Routledge and Kegan Paul, 1966), 53–57.
11. The Alliance for Bio-Integrity, P.O. Box 2927, Iowa City, IA 52244 (www.biointegrity.org).
12. The classic example of a *ḥukah*—a decree without reason—is the red heifer. The Torah begins its description of the red heifer with the words *zot ḥukat hatorah,* "These are the laws of the Torah" (Num. 19:2). The midrash notes that this rule appears internally contradictory, for in performing the very purification rite, the

priest becomes impure. It sees the very unreasonableness of the rite as an occasion for doubts. It responds unambiguously,

אמר הקדוש ברוך הוא חקה חקקתי גזרה גזרתי אי אתה רשאי לעבור על גזרתי

Said the Holy One [praised be He]: I have enacted a rule, decreed a decree. You may not transgress my decree! (*Bemidbar Rabbah* 19:1, 5).

It relates the well-known story in which a Gentile asks Rabban Yoḥanan ben Zakkai if the red-heifer ceremony isn't just hocus-pocus. Rabban Yoḥanan ben Zakkai answers that it is just like an exorcism, an answer that satisfies the Gentile but perplexes his students. They seek a better answer, and he tells them,

חייכם לא המת מטמא ולא המים מטהרין

By your life! A corpse does not cause impurity and water does not purify!

He then cites the above (*Bemidbar Rabbah* 19:8). Indeed, the term *ḥukah* is specifically used to mean "without reason" in 19:6: "The Holy One [praised be He] said to Moses: I will reveal the reason for the [red] heifer to you. But to others—it is a *ḥukah*—a decree."

13. R. Abraham Karelitz writes, in *Hilkhot Kilayim* no. 1:

אי לאו דומיא דבהמתך, אין לנו לבדות מעצמנו איסור הרכבה

If it is not similar to [crossbreeding] your cattle, we may not create on our own a prohibition of hybridization.

Maimonides, in the *Guide for the Perplexed* (*Moreh Nevukhim* 3:49), presents a different reason altogether for the prohibition of *kilayim*. He understands the laws against animal crossbreeding as a function of the rules against aberrant sexual relations and the laws against hybridization as a function of the rules against idolatry and idolatrous fertility rites. Maimonides' positions in this regard are not normative, the *Guide* is not a halakhic work, and, at any rate, his positions are also subject to some of the comments that will follow.

14. See Bavli 60a and Yerushalmi *Kilayim* cited, and Tosafot and *Ritba* ad loc. Despite its familiarity, the rule of the seven Noahide commandments does not appear in *S.A.* It can be found in Maimonides, *Hilkhot Melakhim,* chap. 9. Having codified the seven, Rambam writes in 10:6 that these are also traditionally prohibited for non-Jews. See the comments of *Kesef Mishneh* and *Leḥem Mishneh* ad loc. *Mishneh Lamelekh* satisfies himself by pointing out that in *Hilkhot Kilayim* 1:6, Maimonides himself seems to accept that a Gentile may crossbreed his own livestock, and that position is accepted without question by both *Kesef Mishneh* and Radbaz. This is the dominant ruling; see *Shakh* to *Y.D.* 297:3. See also S. Lieberman, *Tosefta Kifshutah, Kilayim,* 619.

15. Indeed, particularly if Ramban is correct that speciation is inherent in the very acts of Creation, then Rashi would be correct, as well, that such a dichotomy is logically untenable. It is a dichotomy that can occasion doubts, and if we hold it nonetheless, that is because we hold it to be a decree without reason, whose limits are opaque to us, therefore a decree that we cannot extend.
16. See also Rambam, *Hilkhot Kilayim* 1:7 and Radbaz, there.
17. The classic case concerns items cooked illicitly on Shabbat. In T. *Shabbat* 2:15, as reported widely, R. Meir, R. Yehudah, and R. Yoḥanan Hasandlar all agree that one who intentionally cooks on Shabbat is forbidden to eat that food on Shabbat. They differ about whether it is permissible to eat it after Shabbat and whether it is permitted for another to eat it. Much diversity attends the proper interpretation, but all agree that a fine is called for. Even were one only to transgress the rabbinic prohibition by instructing a Gentile to transgress the Sabbath for you, one may not benefit until enough time has elapsed after Shabbat that it could have been prepared afterward. *S.A., O.Ḥ.* 318:1 and 307:20. A closer case, that of castration, sees a similar fine. R. Joshua Falk tries to justify that distinction; see *Drisha* to *Tur, Y.D.* 297, the latter half, on the last line of p. 243a, beginning *vekhatav zal hanolad mi-kil'ayim.*
18. S. Lieberman, T. *Kilayim* 2:15 and *Tosefta Kifshutah,* there.
19. R. Avraham Karelitz (Ḥazon Ish), *Kilayim* 2:16.
20. Rissler and Mellon, "Perils Amidst the Promise"; "Genetically Engineered Food: Why It Is Wrong," the Alliance for Bio-Integrity (see n. 11 above); "Views Differ Sharply over Benefits, Risks of Agricultural Biotechnology," *Chemical and Engineering News* (21 Aug. 1995).
21. Marlise Simons, "A Delicate Pacific Seaweed Is Now a Monster of the Deep," *New York Times,* 16 Aug. 1997. As this was being prepared for publication, a new report surfaced of a natural algal bloom doing similar damage off the coast of Florida. Explicitly comparing the situations, the reporter, Janet Raloff, writes, "Unlike its rogue cousin ... overtaking the Mediterranean ... this alga is a native species" ("Algal Bloom is Smothering Florida Coast," *Science News* 157 [10 June 2000], 373). Ecological damage is not solely the province of genetically engineered species.
22. This issue comes up, *inter alia,* in R. David Bleich's discussion of plastic surgery, *Contemporary Halakhic Problems I* (Ktav: New York, 1977), 119–23, and "Hazardous Medical Procedures," in *Contemporary Halakhic Problems II* (Ktav: New York, 1983), 80–84. A section is dedicated to the question in Rosner, *Jewish Bioethics,* 377–97.
23. Such was the position of R. Seymour Siegel in a responsum, "Smoking: A Jewish Perspective," which was never acted upon by the CJLS but has been prepared for inclusion in an upcoming volume of the committee proceedings [this paper appears as chap. 32 of this vol.]. Such has been reported, of late, in the name of former Israeli Sephardic chief rabbi Ovadia Yosef.

24. This concern has recently had significant support in the cover article by Paul B. Thompson, "Food Biotechnology's Challenge to Cultural Integrity and Individual Consent," *The Hastings Center Report* 27, no. 4 (July–Aug. 1997): 34–38.
25. The medieval sage Maharal miPrague (Judah Loew ben Bezalel) is cited by R. Michael Broyde in the *Journal of Halacha and Contemporary Society* no. 34, p. 64, from a source in Be'er HaGolah (Jerusalem 5731): 38–39, thus: "The creativity of people is greater than nature. When God created in the six days of Creation the laws of nature, the simple and the complex, and finished creating the world, there remained additional power to create anew, just like people can create new animal species through interspecies breeding. . . . People bring to fruition things that are not found in nature; nonetheless, since these are activities that occur through nature, it is as if it entered the world to be created."
26. "Higher content of essential amino acids may aid in fight against malnutrition," reports the Weizmann Institute in its newsletter. Clipping without date, 1994.

CHAPTER 32

Smoking: A Jewish Perspective*

Seymour Siegel

She'eilah (Question):

May an observant Conservative Jew continue to smoke cigarettes, in view of the fact that "cigarette smoking is dangerous to your health"?

Teshuvah (Response):

"The Surgeon General Has Determined that Cigarette Smoking Is Dangerous to Your Health." This sentence confronts us wherever we go. It is prominently displayed on all cigarette advertisements. It is printed on every package of cigarettes. It is repeated on radio and television. Nevertheless, the smoking of cigarettes continues in the United States and abroad.

Judaism expresses attitudes and values that are relevant to the question of cigarette smoking. There are definite directives about substances that are "dangerous to your health."

A. The Preservation of Health Is a Mitzvah

It is important, first, to explain the biblical attitude toward the mainte-

*This paper was written by the late Rabbi Seymour Siegel, Ralph Simon Professor of Ethics and Theology, the Jewish Theological Seminary of America. It was not discussed or voted upon by the Committee on Jewish Law and Standards and is not an official opinion of the Committee on Jewish Law and Standards. However, Rabbi Siegel was the chairman of the CJLS for many years, and this paper in the form of a responsum is included in this volume as a tribute to his memory.

nance of our own health. The basic attitude is expressed in Deuteronomy 4:15: "Take good care of your lives." This reflects the understanding basic to all biblical faiths, that life is a gift, a privilege given to us by the Creator. This means that we are bidden to guard, preserve, and enhance our lives and the lives of others. To neglect our health, to willfully do something that can harm us, is not only to court disaster for ourselves but is also an affront to the One who gave us life. Therefore, the preservation of health is a mitzvah.

This idea is expressed most concisely by Moses Maimonides (1135–1204), who is considered one of history's greatest physicians. Maimonides is accepted as one of Judaism's greatest scholars. Maimonides' legal code [the *Mishneh Torah*] is [also] called *Yad Haḥazakah* (the strong hand). In the section entitled "Murder and the Guarding of Life," he writes:

> It is a positive commandment to remove any stumbling block that constitutes a danger and to be on guard against it. The sages have prohibited many things because they endanger one's life. If one disregards any of them and says, "I am only endangering myself, what business do others have with me?" or "I don't care [if they are dangerous,] I use them [that is, harmful things]," he can be subjected to disciplinary flogging.[1]

Maimonides reflects the Judaic ethos, which sees life as not being the exclusive possession of the individual. A person must avoid harm to self and must also avoid being a source of harm to others. One should not feel that if self-inflicted harm affects oneself, it is of no concern to the community. We are all part of one another. The community has a stake in the well-being of the community. Both the community and the individual have responsibilities to the Creator. Life is too precious to expose it deliberately to dangerous and harmful effects.

B. Danger to Life Is Stricter than a Prohibition

The Talmud states that a person is not permitted to wound himself.[2] The Rabbis derive this law from the biblical admonition that sees the Nazarite who voluntarily deprives himself of the legitimate goods of the world as a sinner. They reason that if a person who deprives himself of wine is considered in a bad light, certainly one who causes himself to suffer (by bodily harm) is culpable in God's eye.

Another classical writer, Rabbi Moses Isserles (1525–72), whose notes on the *Shulḥan Arukh* are seen as binding, writes:

> One should avoid all things that might lead to danger because a danger to life is stricter than a prohibition. One should be more concerned about a possible danger to life than about a possible prohibition. . . . And it is prohibited to rely on a miracle or to put one's life in danger.[3]

The concept that Rabbi Isserles expounds—"a danger to life is stricter than a prohibition. One should be more concerned about a possible danger to life than about a possible prohibition"—is of special importance. Judaism exhorts the Jew to be careful in avoiding anything that might be prohibited according to ancient Jewish prescription. Therefore, an observant Jewish person would make sure that he does not eat anything about which there would be the slightest suspicion that anything forbidden—for example, swine's flesh—might be in the food. Rabbi Isserles says that he should be even more careful about eating or taking into his body anything that might be dangerous. The application of this exhortation to the problem of cigarette smoking seems obvious.

C. Do Not Rely on Miracles

It is also interesting to note that Rabbi Isserles says: "In these matters, . . . it is prohibited to rely on a miracle." This means that an individual should not deceive himself into thinking that, although others are harmed, he might escape the consequences since he possesses special merit or because he is entitled to special divine providence. The sources are clear: avoid endangering your health; do not assume that God will help you avoid dangerous consequences. It is a divine commandment to preserve the health of your body and spirit.

These exhortations apply even when the risk appears to be minimal. This is illustrated in the following way. In ancient times, people were warned not to drink water that had been left uncovered for a period of time; the water might have become contaminated in some way. The Rabbis prohibited the drinking of "uncovered water." What if the risk is minimal? The Rabbis ruled: "If a jar was uncovered, even though nine persons drank of its contents without any fatal consequences, the tenth person is still forbidden to drink from it."

Even a minimal risk should not be taken. Life is too precious; health is too important; well-being is too vital to be risked.

D. Avoid Risk

The attitude of Judaism toward possible risk to health can be summed up:

1. Life is precious. It is given to us as a trust. We may therefore not do anything that would possibly impair our health, shorten our lives, or cause us harm or pain.
2. As we may not do this to ourselves, so may we not do harm to others. All human lives are precious in God's sight.
3. The responsibility to avoid danger to ourselves or to others applies even when it is not certain that harm will ensue. We are forbidden even to take the risk.
4. The harm is to be avoided even if the bad effects are not immediately evident, but will show up in the long run.

E. Conclusion

There is little difficulty in applying these principles to the question of smoking. Scientific evidence has now established beyond doubt that smoking, especially cigarette smoking, is injurious to our health. It is now evident, too, that the nonsmoker can be harmed when he has to suffer the smoke of those who use tobacco. The smoking habit is dirty, harmful, and antisocial. It would therefore follow that Jewish ethics and Jewish law would prohibit the use of cigarettes. Smoking should, at least, be discouraged in synagogues, in Jewish schools, and in Jewish gathering places. The rabbinate and community leaders should discourage smoking. This would help us live longer and healthier. In doing so, we would be fulfilling our responsibilities to God and man.

There is one aspect of this question that is of special interest. According to Jewish law, the observance of the Sabbath is of paramount importance. One of the Ten Commandments exhorts us to cease from labor every seventh day. The Rabbis have long and complicated discussions of what is "work." The kindling of fire and the extinction of fire is forbidden on the Sabbath. Thus, from sundown Friday to sundown Saturday, Jewish law forbids smoking. I have known many people who were heavy smokers who did not touch tobacco the entire Sabbath day. What is remarkable is that in most of these cases, all hunger for smoking ceases during the Sabbath day. It is only as the sun begins to wane and the end of the Sabbath day approaches that the yearning for tobacco returns. I myself experienced this phenomenon when I was a habitual smoker. As far as I know, scientists have not fully investigated the fact that religious prohibitions against smoking on the Sabbath seem to distract habitual smokers from their addiction. It means that determination and commitment can overcome the desire to smoke.

Surely, religious people seek to do God's will. When they accept the idea that it is forbidden to smoke on the Sabbath day, they are freed from the compulsion. We fervently hope that the considerations of the danger to health by smoking might become internalized so that those who now shorten their lives by smoking cigarettes will hear God's command and will stop smoking.[4]

Notes

1. *M.T., Hilkhot Rotzeaḥ* 11:4–5.
2. B. *Bava Kamma* 80a.
3. *Rema, Y.D.* 116:5.
4. Additional resources utilized by the author include: Moses Aberbach, "Smoking and Halacha," *Tradition* 10, no. 3 (spring 1969): 49–60; F. W. Birkenhead, *Kipling* (New York: Random House, 1978); J. Bleich, *Tradition* 10, no. 4 (spring 1977): 121–23; John Brooke, *King George III* (New York: McGraw-Hill, 1972); Reuben Bulka, "Smoking in Jewish Law," *Hadarom,* no. 48 (Nisan 5739).

For Further Reading

A. Conservative Jewish Authors

Cytron, Barry D., and Earl Schwartz. *When Life Is in the Balance: Life and Death Decisions in Light of the Jewish Tradition.* 2d ed. New York: United Synagogue of Conservative Judaism, National Youth Commission, 1994.

Dorff, Elliot N. *Matters of Life and Death: A Jewish Approach to Modern Medical Ethics.* Philadelphia: Jewish Publication Society, 1998.

Feldman, David M. *Birth Control in Jewish Law.* Rev. ed. Northvale, N.J.: Jason Aronson, 1998. (Earlier ed.: *Marital Relations, Birth Control, and Abortion in Jewish Law.* New York: Schocken, 1974.)

Feldman, David M. *Health and Medicine in the Jewish Tradition.* New York: Crossroad, 1986.

Gold, Michael. *And Hannah Wept: Infertility, Adoption, and the Jewish Couple.* Philadelphia: Jewish Publication Society, 1988.

Mackler, Aaron L. *Jewish and Roman Catholic Approaches to Bioethics.* Washington, D.C.: Georgetown University Press, forthcoming.

B. Other Jewish Works

Bleich, J. David. *Judaism and Healing*. New York: Ktav, 1981. Also, *Bioethical Dilemmas: A Jewish Perspective*. Ktav, 1998; *Contemporary Halakhic Problems*. Ktav, vols. 1 (1977), 2 (1983), 3 (1989), 4 (1995).

Dorff, Elliot N., and Louis E. Newman, eds. *Contemporary Jewish Ethics and Morality: A Reader*. New York: Oxford University Press, 1995.

Freedman, Benjamin. *Duty and Healing: Foundations of a Jewish Bioethic*. New York: Routledge, 1999.

Jacob, Walter, ed. *Questions and Reform Jewish Answers*. New York: Central Conference of American Rabbis, 1992. Also, *Contemporary American Reform Responsa* (1987); *American Reform Responsa* (1983).

Jakobovits, Immanuel. *Jewish Medical Ethics*. Rev. ed. New York: Bloch, 1975.

Meier, Levi, ed. *Jewish Values in Bioethics*. New York: Human Sciences Press, 1986.

Newman, Louis E. *Past Imperatives: Studies in the History and Theory of Jewish Ethics*. Albany: State University of New York Press, 1998.

Plaut, W. Gunther, and Mark Washofsky, eds. *Teshuvot for the Nineties: Reform Judaism's Answers for Today's Dilemmas*. New York: Central Conference of American Rabbis, 1997.

Rosner, Fred. *Modern Medicine and Jewish Ethics*. 2d ed. Hoboken, N.J.: Ktav, 1991.

Rosner, Fred, ed. *Pioneers in Jewish Medical Ethics*. Northvale, N.J.: Jason Aronson, 1997.

Steinberg, Avraham, ed. *Encyclopedia of Jewish Medical Ethics* [Hebrew]. 6 vols. Jerusalem: Schlesinger Institute, 1988-98.

Zohar, Noam J. *Alternatives in Jewish Bioethics.* Albany: State University of New York Press, 1997.

Zoloth, Laurie. *Health Care and the Ethics of Encounter: A Jewish Discussion of Social Justice.* Chapel Hill: University of North Carolina Press, 1999.

C. Selected General Works in Biomedical Ethics

American Fertility Society, Ethics Committee. "Ethical Considerations of Assisted Reproductive Technologies." *Fertility and Sterility* 62 (Nov. 1994, supp.): 1S–125S.

Arras, John D., and Bonnie Steinbock, eds. *Ethical Issues in Modern Medicine.* 5th ed. Mountain View, Calif.: Mayfield, 1999.

Beauchamp, Tom L., and James F. Childress. *Principles of Biomedical Ethics.* 4th ed. New York: Oxford University Press, 1994.

Beauchamp, Tom L., and LeRoy Walters, eds. *Contemporary Issues in Bioethics.* 5th ed. Belmont, Calif.: Wadsworth, 1999.

Kelly, David F. *Critical Care Ethics: Treatment Decisions in American Hospitals.* Kansas City: Sheed and Ward, 1991.

New York State Task Force on Life and the Law. *When Death Is Sought: Assisted Suicide and Euthanasia in the Medical Context.* New York: New York State Task Force on Life and the Law, 1994.

Reich, Warren T., ed. *Encyclopedia of Bioethics.* 2d ed. 5 vols. New York: Simon and Schuster Macmillan, 1995.

Numerous journals, including: *Cambridge Quarterly of Healthcare Ethics; Hastings Center Report; Journal of the American Medical Association; Journal of Clinical Ethics; Journal of Law, Medicine, and Ethics; Journal of Medicine and Philosophy; Kennedy Institute of Ethics Journal; New England Journal of Medicine.*

D. Selected Web Sites

Web addresses correct as of time of compilation

Louis Finkelstein Institute for Religious and Social Studies
www.jtsa.edu/research/finkel/

Judaism and Medicine on the Web, links compiled by the Albert Einstein Synagogue
www.shamash.org/shuls/einstein/medlinks.html

The Dr. Falk Schlesinger Institute for Medical-Halachic Research
www.szmc.org.il/machon/index.htm

The Institute for Jewish Medical Ethics
www.ijme.org

UAHC Committee on Bio-Ethics
www.shamash.org/reform/uahc/bioethic.html

National Library of Medicine, Internet Grateful Med to search bibliographical databases, including Bioethicsline and Medline
igm.nlm.nih.gov

National Reference Center for Bioethics Literature
bioethics.georgetown.edu (or www.georgetown.edu/research/nrcbl)

Center for Bioethics, University of Pennsylvania
www.med.upenn.edu/bioethics